D0316476

THE OFFICIAL TOURIST BOARDS GUIDE

New 42nd Edition

Star-Rated

ENGLAND'S QUALITY ASSESSED PLACES TO STAY

2017

★★★★★

www.visitor-guides.co.uk

Penelope, Viscountess Cobham
Chairman of VisitEngland

Have you ever having fancied tucking into a proper English breakfast in a real farmhouse, relaxing in a B&B overlooking the sea, or savouring afternoon tea in a quaint thatched cottage?

England is packed full of incredible experiences that you can't find anywhere else. Our stunning coastlines, vibrant cities, history, heritage and countryside, offer something for everyone.

From landmark scholarly anniversaries to major new attractions showcasing the best of British innovation, there is no shortage of new inspiration to holiday in England in 2017. Highlights include Hull, the UK's 2017 'city of culture,' preparing to join the city break hotspot list as it presents '365 days of transformative culture', with each season celebrating a different aspect of the city's place in the world.

2017 sees a number of literary celebrations including the 200th anniversary of the death of one of England's best loved and most acclaimed authors, Jane Austen with events planned across her home county of Somerset.

It is also the 50th anniversary of the death of Arthur Ransome, author of the *Swallows and Amazons* children's book series set in Suffolk, the 125th anniversary of the death of Alfred, Lord Tennyson of Lincolnshire and the 20th anniversary of the Harry Potter book series. The British Library will host a new exhibition dedicated to the magic of Harry Potter and in the home counties of these literary heroes there will be events taking place to commemorate their anniversaries.

A new heritage museum, Aerospace Bristol, is due to open in the summer of 2017 and will tell the story of England's South West world-class aerospace industry – past, present and future – bringing together nationally significant exhibits and hidden archive records for the first time.

Hot on the heels of the 'Year of the English Garden' and the 300th anniversary of 'Capability' Brown, comes a brand new event, the Royal Horticultural Society (RHS) Chatsworth Flower Show. The RHS is planning a show unlike any other with a focus on cutting edge design, inspired by gardeners and garden designers from the past as well as the talent, ideas and conceptual thinking of today's designers.

Taking place at 10 museums across the length of Hadrian's Wall, Hadrian's Cavalry will be a new, wall-wide exhibition celebrating the legendary Roman cavalry regiments that guarded Hadrian's Wall and projected the power of Imperial Rome 2000 years ago.

For holiday inspiration and ideas for things to do all year round find the best places to escape to in England at wwww.visitengland.com. We understand that quality is key when deciding where to stay and all the accommodation, be it B&B, hotel, self-catering or campsites in this guide have been independently assessed as part of the VisitEngland National Quality Assessment Scheme and wear their star-rating with honour. Whether you are planning a fun-fuelled family break, an action-packed adventure holiday, a romantic getaway, a city-break for culture vultures or a rural escape for country lovers, this guide is packed full of accommodation options to suit your taste and budget.

Contents

How to use this guide

This official tourist boards guide is packed with information from where to stay, to how to get there and what to see on arrival. In fact, this guide captures everything you need to know when exploring England.

Choose from a wide range of quality-assessed accommodation to suit all budgets and tastes. This guide contains an extensive listing of:
- Hotels and Bed and breakfast properties including guesthouses, farmhouses, inns, hostels, and campuses.
- Self-catering accommodation including boats, caravans, touring and camping. As well as holiday parks and holiday villages participating in the British Graded Holiday Park Scheme.

Each property has been visited annually by professional assessors, who apply nationally agreed standards, so that you can book with confidence knowing your accommodation has been checked and rated for quality.

Check out the places to visit in each region, from towns and cities to spectacular coast and countryside, plus historic homes, castles and great family attractions! Maps show accommodation locations, selected destinations and some of the National Cycle Networks.

For even more ideas go online at www.visitengland.com.

Regional tourism contacts and tourist information centres are listed – contact them for further information. You'll also find events, travel information, maps and useful indexes.

Accommodation entries explained

Each accommodation entry contains detailed information to help you decide if it is right for you. This has been provided by proprietors and our aim is to ensure that it is as objective and factual as possible.

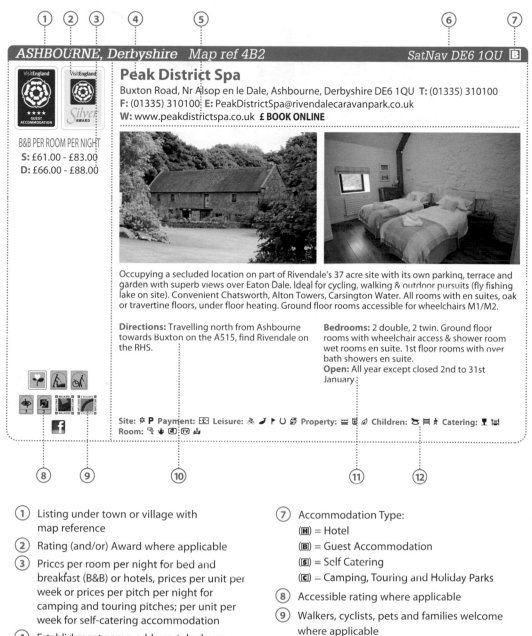

ASHBOURNE, Derbyshire   Map ref 4B2

SatNav DE6 1QU **B**

VisitEngland ★★★★ GUEST ACCOMMODATION

VisitEngland *Silver* AWARD

B&B PER ROOM PER NIGHT
S: £61.00 - £83.00
D: £66.00 - £88.00

Peak District Spa

Buxton Road, Nr Alsop en le Dale, Ashbourne, Derbyshire DE6 1QU **T:** (01335) 310100
F: (01335) 310100 **E:** PeakDistrictSpa@rivendalecaravanpark.co.uk
W: www.peakdistrictspa.co.uk **£ BOOK ONLINE**

Occupying a secluded location on part of Rivendale's 37 acre site with its own parking, terrace and garden with superb views over Eaton Dale. Ideal for cycling, walking & outdoor pursuits (fly fishing lake on site). Convenient Chatsworth, Alton Towers, Carsington Water. All rooms with en suites, oak or travertine floors, under floor heating. Ground floor rooms accessible for wheelchairs M1/M2.

Directions: Travelling north from Ashbourne towards Buxton on the A515, find Rivendale on the RHS.

Bedrooms: 2 double, 2 twin. Ground floor rooms with wheelchair access & shower room wet rooms en suite. 1st floor rooms with over bath showers en suite.
Open: All year except closed 2nd to 31st January.

Site: ❀ **P Payment:** 🔢 **Leisure:** ⚲ ♪ ⊦ ∪ ⅀ **Property:** 🛏 🔲 ⌀ **Children:** 👶 🛏 🕺 **Catering:** 🍷 🍽
Room: 🍵 ☕ 📻 📺 ✎

---

1. Listing under town or village with map reference
2. Rating (and/or) Award where applicable
3. Prices per room per night for bed and breakfast (B&B) or hotels, prices per unit per week or prices per pitch per night for camping and touring pitches; per unit per week for self-catering accommodation
4. Establishment name, address, telephone and email
5. Website information
6. Satellite navigation

7. Accommodation Type:
   - (**H**) = Hotel
   - (**B**) = Guest Accommodation
   - (**S**) = Self Catering
   - (**C**) = Camping, Touring and Holiday Parks
8. Accessible rating where applicable
9. Walkers, cyclists, pets and families welcome where applicable
10. Travel directions
11. Indicates when the establishment is open
12. At-a-glance facility symbols

5

Key to symbols

Information about many of
the accommodation services
and facilities is given in the
form of symbols.

Ⓢ Self Catering

Site Features

P   Private parking
✿   Garden

Booking & Payment Details

€   Euros accepted
💳   Visa/Mastercard/Switch accepted

Leisure Facilities

✎   Tennis court(s)
↘   Swimming pool – outdoor
↗   Swimming pool – indoor
●   Games room
∪   Riding/pony-trekking nearby
▸   Golf available (on site or nearby)
♪   Fishing nearby
🚲   Cycles for hire

Children

🏃   High chairs available
🛏   Cots available
🎠   Children welcome

Property Facilities

🗐   Linen provided
🗐   Linen for hire
🗐   Laundry facilities
🖥   Wi-Fi/Internet access
🐕   Dogs/pets accepted by arrangement
∥   Cleaning service

Unit Facilities

☎   Telephone
BBQ   Barbecue
∅   Real log/coal fires
📀   DVD player
📺   Satellite/cable/freeview TV
📺   Television
✂   Hairdryer
🖭   Washing machine
📟   Microwave cooker
🗄   Dishwasher
🗄   Freezer

Ⓒ Camping

Pitches/Units

🚐   Caravans (number of pitches and rates)
🚍   Motor caravans
     (number of pitches and rates)
🛆   Tents (number of pitches and rates)
🏠   Caravan holiday homes
     (number of pitches and rates)
🏚   Log cabins/lodges (number of units and rates)
🏠   Chalets/villas (number of units and rates)

Site Features

🅿   Parking next to pitch
🍺   Public house/Inn

Booking & Payment Details

☼   Booking recommended in summer
€   Euros accepted
💳   Visa/Mastercard/Switch accepted

Leisure Facilities

✎   Tennis court(s)
↘   Swimming pool – outdoor
↗   Swimming pool – indoor
●   Games room
∪   Riding/pony-trekking nearby
▸   Golf available (on site or nearby)
♪   Fishing nearby
🚲   Cycles for hire

Children

⚠   Childrens outdoor play area
🎠   Children welcome

Catering

🛒   Foodshop/Mobile foodshop
✗   Restaurant on site

Park Facilities

🚿   Showers available
📞   Public telephone
🗐   Laundry facilities
🖥   Wi-Fi/Internet access
♫   Regular evening entertainment
🐕   Dogs/Pets welcome by arrangement

Camping & Touring Facilities

⚡   Water/waste hook-up
🔌   Electrical hook-up points
🔥   Calor Gas/Camping Gaz purchase/
     exchange service
🚽   Chemical toilet disposal point

H *Hotels &*
B *Bed and Breakfast*

Site Features

- **P** Private parking
- ✳ Garden
- € Euros accepted
- 💳 Visa/Mastercard/Switch accepted

Leisure Facilities

- ⚇ Tennis court(s)
- ⚲ Swimming pool – outdoor
- ⚲ Swimming pool – indoor
- 𝄢 Sauna on site
- ⚕ Health/beauty facilities on site
- ⚡ Gym on site
- ⚙ Games room
- ⚘ Riding/pony-trekking nearby
- ⚑ Golf available (on site or nearby)
- ⚓ Fishing nearby
- 🚲 Cycles for hire nearby

Property Facilities

- ⚏ Real log/coal fires
- ⚏ Passenger lift
- ◐ Night porter
- ⚏ Lounge for residents' use
- ⚏ Laundry facilities
- ⚏ Wi-fi or internet access
- ⚏ Dogs/pets accepted by arrangement
- ⚏ Conference facilities
- ⊜ Air conditioning

Children

- ⚏ High chairs available
- ⚏ Cots available
- ⚏ Children welcome

Catering

- ⚏ Special diets available
- ⚏ Licenced (table or bar)
- (✗ Evening meals

Room Facilities

- 📀 DVD player
- 📺 Television
- ⚏ Satellite/cable/freeview TV
- ☎ Telephone
- ☕ Tea/coffee making in bedrooms
- ⚏ Hairdryer
- ⚏ Bedrooms on ground floor
- ⚏ Four-poster bed(s)
- ⚏ Smoking rooms available

Campus/Hostels

- ⚏ Cooking facilities available

Visitor Attraction Quality Scheme

 Participating attractions are visited by a professional assessor. High standards in welcome, hospitality, services, presentation; standards of the toilets, shop and café (where provided) must be achieved to receive this VisitEngland award.

Visitor Attraction Quality Scheme Accolades

- For top-scoring attractions where visitors can expect a really memorable visit.
- For 'going the extra mile', ensuring that visitors are really well looked after.
- For small, well-run attractions that deserve a special mention.
- For particularly innovative and effective interpretation or tour, telling the story to capture visitors' imaginations
- For attractions with cafés and restaurants that consistently exceed expectations.

 Pets Come Too - accommodation displaying this symbol offer a special welcome to pets. Please check for any restrictions before booking.

Businesses displaying this logo have undergone a rigorous verification process to ensure that they are sustainable (green). See page 20 for further information.

VisitEngland's Breakfast Award recognises hotels and B&Bs that offer a high quality choice of breakfast, service and hospitality that exceeds what would be expected at their star rating. Look out for the following symbol in the entry 🏆

National Accessible Scheme
The National Accessible Scheme includes standards for hearing and visual impairment as well as mobility impairment. See pages 10-11 for further information.

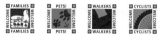

Welcome Schemes
Walkers, cyclists, families and pet owners are warmly welcomed where you see these signs. See page 8 for further information.

 Motorway Service Area Assessment Scheme
The star ratings cover a wide range of aspects of each operation including cleanliness, the quality and range of catering and also the quality of the physical aspects, as well as the service provided. See page 364 for further information.

A special welcome

To help make booking your accommodation easier, VisitEngland has four special Welcome schemes which accommodation in England can be assessed against. Owners participating in these schemes go the extra mile to welcome walkers, cyclists, families or pet owners to their accommodation and provide additional facilities and services to make your stay even more comfortable.

Families Welcome

If you are searching for the perfect family holiday, look out for the Families Welcome sign. The sign indicates that the proprietor offers additional facilities and services catering for a range of ages and family units. For families with young children, the accommodation will have special facilities such as cots and highchairs, storage for push-chairs and somewhere to heat baby food or milk. Where meals are provided, children's choices will be clearly indicated, with healthy options also available. They'll have information on local walks, attractions, activities or events suitable for children, as well as local child-friendly pubs and restaurants. However, not all accommodation is able to cater for all ages or combinations of family units, so do remember to check for any restrictions before confirming your booking.

Welcome Pets!

Do you want to travel with your faithful companion? To do so with ease make sure you look out for accommodation displaying the Welcome Pets! sign. Participants in this scheme go out of their way to meet the needs of guests bringing dogs, cats and/or small birds. In addition to providing water and food bowls, torches or nightlights, spare leads and pet washing facilities, they'll buy in pet food on request and offer toys, treats and bedding. They'll also have information on pet-friendly attractions, pubs, restaurants and recreation. Of course, not everyone is able to offer suitable facilities for every pet, so do check if there are any restrictions on the type, size and number of animals before you confirm your booking.

Walkers Welcome

If walking is your passion, seek out accommodation participating in the Walkers Welcome scheme. Facilities include a place for drying clothes and boots, maps and books for reference and a first-aid kit. Packed breakfasts and lunches are available on request in hotels and guesthouses, and you have the option to pre-order basic groceries in self-catering accommodation. On top of this, proprietors provide a wide range of information including public transport, weather forecasts, details of the nearest bank, all night chemists and local restaurants and nearby attractions.

Cyclists Welcome

Are you an explorer on two wheels? If so, seek out accommodation displaying the Cyclists Welcome symbol. Facilities at these properties include a lockable undercover area, a place to dry outdoor clothing and footwear, an evening meal if there are no eating facilities available within one mile and a packed breakfast or lunch on request. Information is also available on cycle hire, cycle repair shops, maps and books for reference, weather forecasts, details of the nearest bank, all night chemists and much much more.

National Accessible Scheme

Finding suitable accommodation is not always easy, especially if you have to seek out rooms with level entry or large print menus. Use the National Accessible Scheme to help you make your choice.

Additional help and guidance on accessible tourism can be obtained from the national charity Tourism for All:

Tourism for All

Tourism for All UK
7A Pixel Mill
44 Appleby Road
Kendal, Cumbria LA9 6ES

Information helpline
0845 124 9971
(lines open 9-5 Mon-Fri)
E info@tourismforall.org.uk
W www.tourismforall.org.uk

Proprietors of accommodation taking part in the National Accessible Scheme have gone out of their way to ensure a comfortable stay for guests with hearing, visual or mobility needs. These exceptional places are full of extra touches to make everyone's visit trouble-free, from handrails, ramps and step-free entrances (ideal for buggies too) to level-access showers and colour contrast in the bathrooms. Members of staff may have attended a disability awareness course and will know what assistance will really be appreciated.

Appropriate National Accessible Scheme symbols are included in the guide entries (shown opposite). If you have additional needs or specific requirements, we strongly recommend that you make sure these can be met by your chosen establishment before you confirm your reservation. The index at the back of the guide gives a list of accommodation that has received a National Accessible Scheme rating.

For more information on the NAS and tips and ideas on holiday travel in England go to: **www.visitengland.com/accessforall**

The criteria VisitEngland has adopted does not necessarily conform to British Standards or to Building Regulations. They reflect what the organisation understands to be acceptable to meet the practical needs of guests with mobility or sensory impairments and encourage the industry to increase access to all.

England

Mobility Impairment Symbols

 Older and less mobile guests
Typically suitable for a person with sufficient mobility to climb a flight of steps but who would benefit from fixtures and fittings to aid balance.

 Part-time wheelchair users
Typically suitable for a person with restricted walking ability and for those who may need to use a wheelchair some of the time and can negotiate a maximum of three steps.

 Independent wheelchair users
Typically suitable for a person who depends on the use of a wheelchair and transfers unaided to and from the wheelchair in a seated position. This person may be an independent traveller.

 Assisted wheelchair users
Typically suitable for a person who depends on the use of a wheelchair and needs assistance when transferring to and from the wheelchair in a seated position.

 Access Exceptional is awarded to establishments that meet the requirements of independent wheelchair users or assisted wheelchair users shown above and also fulfil more demanding requirements with reference to the British Standards BS8300.

Visual Impairment Symbols

 Typically provides key additional services and facilities to meet the needs of visually impaired guests.

 Typically provides a higher level of additional services and facilities to meet the needs of visually impaired guests.

Hearing Loss Symbols

Typically provides key additional services and facilities to meet the needs of guests with hearing loss.

Typically provides a higher level of additional services and facilities to meet the needs of guests with hearing loss.

Peace of Mind with Star Ratings

Many hotels, bed and breakfast, self-catering, camping and caravan parks in England are star rated by VisitEngland. We annually check that our standards are comparable with other British tourist boards to ensure that wherever you visit you receive the same facilities and services at any star rated accommodation.

The majority of the accommodation in this guide is annually checked by VisitEngland assessors and an on-site assessment is made every year. This means that when you see the Quality Rose marque promoting the star rating of the property, you can be confident that we've checked it out.

The national standards used to assess accommodation are based on VisitEngland research of consumer expectations. The independent assessors decide the type (classification) of accommodation, for example if it's a 'small hotel', 'campsite', 'bed and breakfast', 'boat accommodation' etc. and award star ratings based on the quality and standards of the service or equipment and accommodation offered, as well as, where appropriate, a further special quality award.

Our assessors consider every aspect of your stay when rating all classifications of accommodation. For bed & breakfast and hotels, the warmth of the welcome, the comfort of furnishings, the food quality, the cleanliness and the level of care offered are just some of the aspects considered. For self-catering and camping accommodation there are over fifty aspects considered, from landscaping and layout to maintenance, customer care and, most importantly, cleanliness.

The Quality Rose marque helps you decide where to stay, giving you peace of mind that the accommodation has been thoroughly checked out before you check in.

Accommodation Types

Always look at or ask for the classification of accommodation, each offers a very distinct experience.

The hotel designators you'll find in this guide are:

Hotel – minimum of 5 bedrooms, but more likely to have over 20.

Small Hotel – maximum of 20 bedrooms, usually more personally run.

Country House Hotel – set in ample grounds or gardens, in a rural or semi-rural location and an emphasis on peace and quiet.

Town House Hotel – maximum of 50 rooms in a city or town-centre location, high quality with distinctive and individual style, high ratio of staff to guests. Dinner may not be served but room service available. Might not have a dining room so breakfast may be served in bedroom.

Metro Hotel – can be any size and in a city or town centre location - offering full hotel services, but not dinner (although will be within easy walking distance of a range of places to eat).

Budget Hotel – part of a large, 'branded' hotel group offering clean and comfortable en suite facilities, many with 24-hour reservations. Budget hotels are not awarded individual star ratings.

Accredited Hotel – accredited hotels have been visited by VisitEngland assessors to check the standards of cleanliness and maintenance meet or exceed guests' expectations. This annual assessment does not include an overnight stay and no star ratings are awarded.

Looking for something a little different?

Within this guide you'll find some interesting alternatives to hotels. **Restaurants with Rooms** are just that – the restaurant is the main business and they will be licensed. **Hotel Boats** are generally narrow boats and are worked by a crew. They can be booked by individuals or groups and provide all the services of a hotel, including meals and refreshments.

Star ratings you can trust
Hotels are awarded a rating from 1 to 5 stars. All star ratings assure you of certain services which are:
- All rooms have an en suite or private bathroom
- Designated reception and staff available during day and evening (24 hrs in case of emergency)
- Licence to serve alcohol
- Access to hotel at all times for registered guests
- Dinner available at least five days a week (except Town House or Metro Hotels)
- All statutory obligations will be met, including Fire Safety

The bed and breakfast designators you'll find in this guide are:

Guest Accommodation – wide range of establishments from one-room bed and breakfast to larger properties, which may offer dinner and hold an alcohol licence.

Bed and Breakfast – accommodating generally for no more than six people, the owners of these establishments welcome you into their home as a special guest.

Guest House – generally comprising more than three rooms. Dinner may be available (if it is, it will need to be booked in advance). May possibly be licensed.

Farmhouse – bed and breakfast, and sometimes dinner, but always on a farm.

Inn – pubs with rooms, and many with restaurants as well.

Room Only – accommodation that either does not offer breakfast or, if it does, it will not be served (ie self-service or breakfast pack)

Hostel – safe, budget-priced, short-term accommodation for individuals and groups. The Hostel classification includes Group Hostel, Backpacker and Activity Accommodation (all of which are awarded star ratings).

Campus – accommodation provided by educational establishments, including university halls of residence and student village complexes. May be offered on a bed and breakfast or sometimes on a self-catering basis.

Star ratings you can trust

All bed and breakfast accommodation that is awarded a star rating (from 1 to 5 stars) will assure you of minimum standards, so you can be confident that you will find the basic services that you would expect, such as:

- A clear explanation of booking charges, services offered and cancellation terms.
- A full cooked breakfast or substantial continental breakfast.
- May offer en suite facilities, but also shared bathroom facilities.
- For a stay of more than one night, rooms cleaned and beds made daily.
- Printed advice on how to summon emergency assistance at night.
- All statutory obligations will be met, including Fire Safety.

To achieve higher star ratings, an increasing level of facilities and services are offered. For example, at 3-star, bed and breakfast must offer a guest bathroom which cannot be shared with the owners and bedrooms must have a washbasin if not en suite. At 4-star, 50% of bedrooms will be en suite or with private bathroom. At 5-star, all rooms must be en suite or with a private bathroom.

Star ratings are based on a combination of the range of facilities, the level of service offered and quality – if an establishment offers facilities required to achieve a certain star rating but does not achieve the quality score required for that rating, a lower star rating is awarded. Accommodation with limited facilities but high quality standards may be capped at a lower star rating, but may achieve a Silver or Gold Award.

The self-catering accommodations in this guide are:

A requirement of this category is to be self-contained and have a kitchen so you will always have the option of eating in. NB: this requirement only applies to self-catering accommodation rated 4 star and above and therefore is not applicable to every property listed in this guide.

Holiday Cottages, Houses and Lodges – from cosy country cottages, smart town-centre apartments, seaside villas, grand country houses for large family gatherings, and even quirky windmills, railway carriages and lighthouse conversions. Most take bookings by the week, generally from Friday to Saturdays, but as short breaks are increasing in popularity, accommodation providers often take bookings for shorter periods, particularly outside of the main season.

Holiday Cottage Agencies – these range from small local organisations to large Britain-wide operators. Some agencies organise their own assessments, but the majority use national tourist board quality standards and are gradually bringing all their properties into the star-rating scheme. Many agencies have also been assessed and accredited by VisitEngland to ensure they are well-run and provide excellent customer care. For full details of Holiday Cottage Agencies, see pages 366 to 369.

Boat Accommodation – quality-assessed boats in small and large fleets across England's waterways also offer accommodation. Narrowboats are purpose-built, traditionally decorated boats on canals and rivers and can sleep up to 12 people; Cruisers operate mainly on the Norfolk Broads and the Thames and can range from practical affordable craft, to modern, stylish boats with accessories such as dishwashers, DVD players and flat-screen TV's.

Approved Caravan – approved caravan holiday homes are let as individual self-catering units and can be located on farms or holiday parks. All the facilities, including a bathroom and toilet, are contained within the caravan and all main services are provided. There are no star ratings for these caravans, however, they are assessed annually to check they meet the minimum quality standards.

Alternative Accommodation – Self-catering accommodation with a twist. Alternative accommodation ranges from wigwams or tipis to shepherds' trailers, treehouses or camper vans. Usually located in rural environments this unique style of accommodation allows you to get back to nature. Most proprietors will take bookings for short breaks as well as longer holidays and all facilities are checked to ensure that they meet minimum quality standards, but many are surprisingly luxurious due to the rise in the term 'glamping' (glamorous camping).

All self-catering accommodation is awarded a rating from 1 to 5 stars (apart from Approved Caravans and Alternative Accommodation). All will meet the minimum standards shown below:

- Clear information prior to booking on all aspects of the accommodation including location, facilities, prices, deposit, policies on smoking, children, cancellation, etc.
- No shared facilities, with the exception of a laundry room in multi-unit sites.
- All appliances and furnishings will meet product safety standards for self-catering accommodation, particularly regarding fire safety.
- Clear information on emergency procedures, including who to contact.
- Contact details for the local doctor, dentist, chemist, etc.
- All statutory obligations will be met, including an annual gas safety check and public liability insurance.

The more stars, the higher the quality and the greater the range of facilities and services on offer. For example, a 3-star accommodation must offer bed linen (with or without additional charge) while at a 4-star, all advertised sleeping space will be in bedrooms (unless a studio) and beds will be made up on arrival.

Some self-catering establishments offer a choice of accommodation units that may have different star ratings. In this case, the entry in this guide indicates the star range available.

The camping accommodations in this guide are: Always look at or ask for the type of accommodation as each offers a very distinct experience. The parks you'll find in this guide are:

Camping Park – these sites only have pitches available for tents.

Touring Park – sites for your own caravan, motor home or tent.

Holiday Park – sites where you can hire a caravan holiday home for a short break or longer holiday, or even buy your own holiday home. Sites range from small, rural sites to larger parks with added extras, such as a swimming pool. Many of the above parks will offer a combination of these classifications.

Star ratings are based on a combination of the range of facilities, level of service offered and quality - if a park offers the facilities required to achieve a certain star rating but does not achieve the quality score required for that rating, a lower star rating is awarded.

A random check is made of a sample of accommodation provided for hire (caravans, chalets, etc) and the quality of the accommodation itself is included in the grading assessment.

The more stars, the higher the quality and the greater the range of facilities and level of service. For example, a 2-star park must be clean with good standards of maintenance and customer care, plus improved level of landscaping, lighting, maintenance and refuse disposal. May be less expensive than more highly rated parks. 5-star parks offer the highest level of customer care provided. All facilities will be maintained in pristine condition in attractive surroundings.

Holiday Villages – usually comprise of a variety of types of accommodation, with the majority in custom-built rooms, for example, chalets. The option to book on a bed and breakfast, or dinner, bed and breakfast basis is normally available. A range of facilities, entertainment and activities are also provided, which may, or may not, be included in the tariff. Holiday Villages must meet minimum requirements for provision and quality of facilities and services, including fixtures, fittings, furnishings, décor and any other extra facilities.

Forest Holiday Village – a holiday village situated in a forest setting with conservation and sustainable tourism being a key feature. Usually offering a variety of accommodation, often purpose built and with a range of entertainment, activities and facilities on site, free of charge or at extra cost.

Holiday Villages in England are assessed under a separate rating scheme (for details see www. qualityintourism.com).

Also included in this guide are Bunkhouses and Camping Barns – safe, budget-priced, short-term accommodation for individuals and groups.

Silver and Gold Awards

How can you find those special places to stay? VisitEngland's Gold and Silver Awards highlight excellence and are given to accommodation that offer the highest level of quality within their particular star rating. Those that, regardless of the range of facilities and services, achieve exceptional scores for quality. VisitEngland professional assessors make recommendations for Gold and Silver Awards during assessments.

High star ratings mean top quality in all areas and all the services expected of that classification. Lower star ratings with a Silver or Gold Award indicate more limited facilities or services but top quality. You may therefore find that a 2-star Gold Award hotel offering superior levels of quality may be more suited to your needs if, for example, enhanced services such as a concierge or 24-hour room service are not essential for your stay. For self-catering particular attention is paid to the bedrooms and bathrooms, kitchen, public areas and most importantly the cleanliness. For Camping, Touring and Holiday Parks they look for aspects of exceptional quality in all areas, in particular, cleanliness, facilities and reception.

For self-catering accommodation, Gold Awards are given to individual units on sites with multiple lettings, therefore you should check with the owner before booking if you wish to stay in the unit which has been given the Gold Award.

Sometimes a bed and breakfast establishment has exceptional bedrooms and bathrooms and offers guests a very special welcome, but cannot achieve a higher star rating because, for example, there are no en suite bedrooms. This is sometimes the case with period properties. Look out for accommodation with Gold or Silver Awards which recognise quality rather than specific facilities.

VisitEngland's unique Gold and Silver Awards are given in recognition of exceptional quality. A list of all Gold and Silver Award winning accommodation with a detailed entry in this guide is given on page 392.

The more stars, the higher the quality and the greater the range of facilities and level of service. The following refers to the Hotel scheme:

★★ Two-Star must provide

Dinner five nights a week (unless Metro hotel)

★★★ Three-Star must provide

All en suite bedrooms (i.e. no private bathrooms)
Telephones in all rooms
Room service during core hours
A permanently staffed reception

★★★★ Four-Star must provide

Enhanced guest services e.g. 24 hour room service, porterage, afternoon tea etc.
Superior bedrooms and bathrooms

★★★★★ Five-Star must provide

Some permanent suites
Enhanced services, such as concierge, valet parking etc.

Gold and Silver Awards

VisitEngland's unique Gold and Silver Awards are given in recognition of exceptional quality in self-catering, hotel and bed and breakfast accommodation.

VisitEngland professional assessors make recommendations for Gold and Silver Awards during assessments. They look for aspects of exceptional quality in all areas.

While star ratings are based on a combination of quality, the range of facilities and the level of service offered, Gold and Silver awards are based solely on quality. Therefore a 3 star accommodation with limited facilities but exceptional quality could still achieve the Gold Award status. Detailed entries for these properties are also included in the regional pages and can be found using the property index on page 407.

An index of Gold and Silver Award-winning properties with a detailed entry in this guide can be found at the back of the book.

Gold Award Self-Catering Accommodation
with entries in the regional pages

Woodthorpe Hall Country Cottages
Alford, Lincolnshire

Outchester & Ross Farm Cottages
Bamburgh, Northumberland

Riding Farm Cottages
Beamish, Tyne and Wear

Spindle Cottage Holidays
Binegar, Somerset

Rookery Farm Norfolk
Bodham, Norfolk

Over Brandelhow
Borrowdale, Cumbria

Mellwaters Barn
Bowes, Co Durham

Tamar Valley Cottages
Bude, Cornwall

Whalesborough Cottages & Spa
Bude, Cornwall

Wooda Farm Holiday Park
Bude, Cornwall

Lackford Lakes Barns
Bury St. Edmunds, Suffolk

Beech Croft Farm Caravan & Camping Park
Buxton, Derbyshire

Pyegreave Cottage
Buxton, Derbyshire

Highfield Farm Touring Park
Cambridge, Cambridgeshire

Brackenhill Tower & Jacobean Cottage
Carlisle, Cumbria

The Tranquil Otter
Carlisle, Cumbria

Riding House Farm Cottages
Castleton, Derbyshire

The Little Trout
Chesterfield, Derbyshire

Laneside
Chichester, Sussex

The Stables
Cirencester, Gloucestershire

Craster Tower Penthouse Apartment
Craster, Northumberland

Hodges
Crowborough, Sussex

Cofton Country Holidays
Dawlish, Devon

Medley Court - Hever Castle
Edenbridge, Kent

The Old Bakery
Enfield, Inner London

2 Westgate Barns
Fakenham, Norfolk

Hard Farm Barns
Field Dalling, Norfolk

Graywood Canvas Cottages
Heathfield, Sussex

Monnington House
Monnington on Wye
Hereford, Herefordshire

Woodford Bridge
Country Club
Holsworthy, Devon

Manor Farm
Holiday Barns
Holt, Norfolk

Ingleby Manor
Ingleby Greenhow,
North Yorkshire

Cressland
Kersey, Suffolk

White Heron Properties
Kington, Herefordshire

Cowldyke Farm
Kirkbymoorside,
North Yorkshire

Surprise View Cottage,
Field Barn Cottage &\n
Lowna Farmhouse
Kirkbymoorside,
North Yorkshire

Piccadilly Caravan
Park Ltd
Lacock, Wiltshire

The Apartments -
Chelsea & Marylebone
London SW3,
Inner London

Louth Barn
Louth, Lincolnshire

Castle House Lodgings
Ludlow, Shropshire

Sutton Court
Farm Cottages
Ludlow, Shropshire

The Silver Pear
Apartments
Ludlow, Shropshire

Home Farm
Holiday Cottages
Malton, North Yorkshire

Walnut Garth
Malton, North Yorkshire

Rhydd Barn
Malvern,
Worcestershire

Darwin Forest
Country Park
Matlock, Derbyshire

1 The Green
Melton Mowbray,
Leicestershire

Holme House Barn
Mitcheldean,
Gloucestershire

Forty Eight
The Penthouse
Newquay, Cornwall

Link House Farm
Holiday Cottages
Newton-by-the-Sea,
Northumberland

Sea Winds
Newton-by-the-Sea,
Northumberland

Woodview Cottages
Nottingham,
Nottinghamshire

Blackthorn Gate
Nunthorpe,
North Yorkshire

Peartree Cottage
Okehampton, Devon

Martin Lane Farm
Holiday Cottages
Ormskirk, Lancashire

Sunday & School
Cottages
Padstow, Cornwall

Hall Farm Kings Cliffe
Peterborough,
Northamptonshire

Kale Pot Cottage
Pickering, North Yorkshire

South Winchester
Lodges
Pitt, Hampshire

Rosehill Lodges
Porthtowan, Cornwall

Upton Grange
Holiday Cottages
Ringstead, Dorset

Buff's Old Barn
Saxmundham, Suffolk

Woodlands Holiday
Cottages
Sheringham, Norfolk

Solely Southwold
Southwold, Suffolk

Trethem Mill
Touring Park
St. Just in Roseland,
Cornwall

Broad Oak Cottages
Stow-on-the-Wold,
Gloucestershire

Long Cover Cottage
& The Coach House
Sutton, Worcestershire

Rochford Park
Cottages
Tenbury Wells,
Worcestershire

Long Barn Luxury
Holiday Cottages
Torquay, Devon

Hartsop Fold
Holiday Lodges
Ullswater, Cumbria

Hillcroft Holiday Park
Ullswater, Cumbria

Durdle Door
Holiday Cottages
Wareham, Dorset

Pear Tree Cottages
Wedmore, Somerset

Forest Lodge Farm
Whitby, North Yorkshire

Lemon Cottage
Whitby, North Yorkshire

Church Farm Barns
Wickmere, Norfolk

Park Cliffe Camping
& Caravan Estate
Windermere, Cumbria

The Blue Rooms
York, North Yorkshire

York Lakeside Lodges
York, North Yorkshire

Gold Award Hotels with entries in the regional pages

Barnsley House
Barnsley, Gloucestershire

Stanley House Hotel
& Spa
Blackburn, Lancashire

Clare House
Grange-over-Sands,
Cumbria

Chewton Glen
New Milton, Hampshire

Scafell Hotel
Rosthwaite,
Cumbria

Rye Lodge Hotel
Rye, Sussex

Calcot Manor Hotel
& Spa
Tetbury,
Gloucestershire

Silver Award Hotels with entries in the regional pages

Tickton Grange
Hotel & Restaurant
Beverley, East Yorkshire

The Crown Hotel
Blandford Forum,
Dorset

The Pier House Hotel
Charlestown,
Cornwall

Millstream Hotel
Chichester,
Sussex

Stoke by Nayland
Hotel, Golf & Spa
Colchester, Essex

The Coniston Hotel,
Country Estate & Spa
Skipton, North Yorkshire

Lensbury
Teddington, Outer
London

Gold Award Guest Accommodation
with entries in the regional pages

Abbey Guest House
Abingdon-on-Thames,
Oxfordshire

Marlborough House Guest House
Bath, Somerset

Fenham Farm Coastal Bed & Breakfast
Berwick-upon-Tweed,
Northumberland

Mitchell's of Chester Guest House
Chester, Cheshire

Cladda House B&B and Self Catering Apartments
Dartmouth, Devon

Hever Castle Luxury Bed & Breakfast
Edenbridge, Kent

Church Oast
Hernhill, Kent

Knole Farm
Okehampton, Devon

Colton House
Rugeley, Staffordshire

The Barn & Pinn Cottage Guest House
Sidmouth, Devon

The Close B&B
Stroud,
Gloucestershire

The Downs, Babbacombe
Torquay, Devon

Silver Award Guest Accommodation
with entries in the regional pages

Peak District Spa
Ashbourne, Derbyshire

Yorkshire Bridge Inn
Bamford, Derbyshire

Pulteney House
Bath, Somerset

Alannah House
Berwick-upon-Tweed,
Northumberland

4 Star Phildene Blackpool
Blackpool, Lancashire

Gurney Manor Mill
Bridgwater, Somerset

Broseley House
Broseley, Shropshire

4 Canon Lane
Chichester, Sussex

Castle View Guest House
Durham, Co Durham

Kiln Farm Guest House
Elmswell, Suffolk

The Baskerville
Henley-on-Thames,
Oxfordshire

Bosavern House
Lands' End, Cornwall

Temple Lodge Club Ltd
London W6,
Inner London

Goodenough Club
London WC1N,
Inner London

Beach House
Lymington,
Hampshire

The Limes
Maidstone, Kent

Hillborough House
Milton-under-
Wychwood,
Oxfordshire

Overcliff Lodge
Mundesley, Norfolk

Tredower Barton
St. Minver, Cornwall

Adelphi Guest House
Stratford-upon-Avon,
Warwickshire

Avonlea
Stratford-upon-Avon,
Warwickshire

Ness House
Teignmouth, Devon

The Gallery Bed & Breakfast
Thirsk, North Yorkshire

Spring Cottage B&B
Truro, Cornwall

Lulworth Cove Inn
Wareham, Dorset

Smugglers Inn
Weymouth, Dorset

1777 Bedrooms and Breakfast at The Albion
Wimborne, Dorset

Village Limits Country Pub, Restaurant & Motel
Woodhall Spa,
Lincolnshire

Rose Awards

VisitEngland's ROSE (Recognition Of Service Excellence) Awards recognise accommodation businesses who truly go the extra mile for their guests. Designed to showcase those establishments that provide the warmest of welcomes, the 100 annual recipients include accommodation businesses where the owners, managers and staff really know how to delight their customers, irrespective of their star rating, style or type of accommodation.

In its 2nd year, the 2016 winners were announced at the Independent Hotel Show on 18th October. The nominations are triggered following annual VisitEngland quality assessment visits, but other evidence, including online customer reviews are taken into account. The final judging panel also looks for innovation that sets the business apart. This includes facilities or services offered to make the customer's stay really special.

Rose Award Hotels

The Lamb Inn
Burford, Oxfordshire

Clare House
Grange-over-Sands, Cumbria

Park House Hotel
King's Lynn, Norfolk

Cleve Court Hotel
Paignton, Devon

Wentbridge House Hotel
Pontefract, West Yorkshire

Aviary Court
Redruth, Cornwall

Rose Award Guest Accommodation

West Acre House
Alnwick, Northumberland

Stone Green Farm
Ashford, Kent

Stane House
Bignor, West Sussex

Number One St Lukes
Blackpool, Lancashire

The Pembroke
Blackpool, Lancashire

Lower Meadows House
Boscastle, Cornwall

Brookside Guest House
Brixham, Devon

Griff House
Buxton, Derbyshire

Kalimera B&B
Cambridge, Cambridgeshire

Bridge Cottage B&B
Canterbury, Kent

Holly House
Cheltenham, Gloucestershire

Field Green Oast B&B
Cranbrook, Kent

The Beeches B&B
Dawlish, Devon

Alkham Court
Dover, Kent

Daisy Cottage B&B
Ely, Cambridgeshire

Rydon Farm
Exeter, Devon

Beechwood B&B
Halland, East Sussex

Friars Farm
Hatfield Heath, Hertfordshire

Lowe Farm B&B
Hereford, Herefordshire

Causeway House B&B
Hope Valley, Derbyshire

Somerset B&B
Ilminster, Somerset

Nundeeps
Isles of Scilly, Cornwall

Woodpecker Barn
Lamberhurst, Kent

Poole Farm B&B
Launceston, Devon

Clyde House
Leyburn, North Yorkshire

Creston Villa Guest House
Lincoln, Lincolnshire

Kandara Guest House
London, Greater London

Long Melford Swan
Long Melford, Suffolk

Sunny Cottage
Maidenhead, Berkshire

Pebble House
Mevagissey, Cornwall

South Lodge
Milton Keynes, Buckinghamshire

There are hundreds of "Green" places to stay and visit in England from small bed and breakfasts to large visitor attractions and activity holiday providers. Businesses displaying this logo have undergone a rigorous verification process to ensure that they are sustainable (green) and that a qualified assessor has visited the premises.

We have indicated the accommodation which has achieved a Green award... look out for the  symbol in the entry.

The Langbury
Minehead, Somerset

The Old School
Moreton in Marsh,
Gloucestershire

Tosson Tower Farm
Morpeth,
Northumberland

Heald Country House
Nantwich, Cheshire

Bridge House
Newark,
Nottinghamshire

The Thatched House
Nr Arundel, West Sussex

Cornerways
Guest House
Penzance, Cornwall

Fern Cottage B&B
Pucklechurch,
South Gloucestershire

Newdegate House
Saffron Walden, Essex

Leena's Guest House
Salisbury, Wiltshire

Malabar
Guest House
Seahouses,
Northumberland

Brooke House
Shanklin, Isle of Wight

Sueños Guesthouse
Southend on Sea,
Essex

The Elm Tree
Spilsby, Lincolnshire

The Tom Cobley
Tavern
Spreyton, Devon

The Olive Branch
St Ives, Cornwall

Roundhouse Barns
St Mawes, Cornwall

Colcharton Farm
Tavistock, Devon

The Minadab
Cottage
Teignmouth, Devon

Kingston House
Torquay, Devon

The 25 Boutique B&B
Torquay, Devon

Little Roseveth
Truro, Cornwall

Twiga House
Wareham, Dorset

The Warwick
Weymouth, Dorset

Eighteen97
Whitby, Yorkshire

The Old Chapel
Wigton, Cumbria

Browns of Holbeck
Worksop,
Nottinghamshire

Camelot House
Worthing, West Sussex

Barnabas House
Yelverton, Devon

Hazelwood Farm
B&B
York, North Yorkshire

Rose Award Self-Catering Accommodation

The Secret Cottage
Aldeburgh, Suffolk

Cheviot Holiday
Cottages
Alnwick,
Northumberland

River Reach
Alveston, Stratford-
upon-Avon,
Gloucestershire

Kits Coty Glamping
Aylesford, Kent

Hunting Hall
Berwick Upon Tweed,
Northumberland

The Bothy
Bradworthy, Nr. Bude,
Devon

The Barn
Brampton, Cumbria

Ebenezer Cottage
and The Sheilings
Burnham Market,
Norfolk

Wheeldon Trees Farm
Buxton, Derbyshire

Kipps Independent
Hostel
Canterbury, Kent

Packway Farm
Chediston, Suffolk

Reclaim Cottage
Colkirk, Norfolk

Grasmere Hostel
Grasmere, Cumbria

The Cart House
Hartland, Nr. Bideford,
Devon

Greetham Retreat
Holidays
Horncastle,
Lincolnshire

Primrose Cottage
Kersey, Suffolk

Meadowview Cottage
Launceston, Cornwall

Treworgey Cottages
Liskeard, Cornwall

Longhouse
Little Barugh,
Nr. Pickering, Yorkshire

Ralph Boyce House
Looe, Cornwall

Walnut House
Lowestoft, Suffolk

Butters Cottage
Mountfield,
East Sussex

Degembris Farmhouse
& Cottages
Newquay, Cornwall

Nethercourt Touring
Park
Ramsgate, Kent

Silver Trees Holiday
Park
Rugeley, Staffordshire

Oversteps House
Salcombe, Devon

Seafield Caravan
Park
Seahouses,
Northumberland

Torridge House
Cottages
Torrington, Devon

Lowarth Glamping
Wadebridge, Cornwall

Beacon View Barn
and Dale View Barn
Whitby, North
Yorkshire

Monkbridge Court
York, North Yorkshire

The Dovecote Barns
York, North Yorkshire

Wolds Edge
York, Yorkshire

VisitEngland Awards for Excellence

This year's VisitEngland Awards for Excellence 2016 ceremony took place on Tuesday 8 March at the Winter Gardens in Blackpool, where the top honours were awarded to the businesses that have demonstrated exceptional customer service, and given their visitors an unforgettable English holiday experience.

Below are just a few of the 2016 VisitEngland Awards for Excellence winners.

Self-Catering Holiday Provider of the Year
GOLD WINNER
Treworgey Cottages, Nr. Looe, Cornwall

Treworgey Cottages are set on a 150 acre farm overlooking the Looe River valley, and have been restored to high standards and retain the original charm of the Devon hamlet.

Features include log fires, beautiful bedrooms, excellent bathrooms, well equipped kitchens and pretty private gardens. Holly and her team work tirelessly in pursuit of excellence. The on-site farm brims with indoor and outdoor activities such as play areas, pony riding friendly animals and an outdoor heated pool with a view!

There are splendid country walks nearby, home cooked food delivered to the door, local produce available on-site and happy worn out children is guaranteed. A visit here makes for a perfect stay.

Self-Catering Holiday Provider of the Year
SILVER WINNER
**Wolds Edge Holiday Lodges & Snug Huts,
Bishop Wilton, York**

Wolds Edge Holiday Lodges offer a choice of comfortable, well-equipped self-catering lodges and two cosy shepherd's huts in a truly peaceful rural setting. Relax in your hot tub, pop to the excellent village pub for a hearty lunch, go walking on the nearby Wolds Way or hire a bike, or just stay in, pour a glass of bubbly and watch the bird box cam on your TV.

Self-Catering Holiday Provider of the Year
BRONZE WINNER
Whalesborough Cottages & Spa, Bude, Cornwall

With bright, contemporary accommodation complete with wood burning stoves, under floor heating and lovely open plan kitchens, Whalesborough Cottages & Spa is a luxurious getaway near to the beach. Its bright, contemporary accommodation comes complete with free use of state of the art spa facilities, indoor and outdoor heated pools, dedicated children's play areas, tennis courts and massage facilities.

Self-Catering Holiday Provider of the Year
HIGHLY COMMENDED
**The Dandelion Hideaway,
Market Bosworth, Leicestershire**

The Dandelion Hideaway offers thoughtfully designed cosy canvas cottages in a rural paradise, complete with roll top baths, wood fired stoves and oil lamps. There is also a whole farm to explore, with baby animals galore, goat milking, egg collecting and pony grooming. This is family glamping at its best.

The Dovecote Barns, York, North Yorkshire

The Dovecote Barns offers spacious and spotless self-catering accommodation in barns converted to a very high standard with spectacular kitchens, individually styled ensuite bedrooms, squashy sofas and attentive and committed management. There are also fresh eggs from the on-site hens to welcome you, along with a basket of homemade bread and lovely jams.

Holiday Park/Holiday Village of the Year
GOLD WINNER
Woodovis Park, Tavistock, Devon

Woodovis is a tranquil, family owned park in 14 acres of pleasant rural land near the historic market town of Tavistock.

Offering a range of accommodation from static holiday homes, glamping pods, camping and caravanning to a self-catering cottage, the park prides itself on high standards and excellent park facilities. Activities offered here include under-cover boules, circus skills, story-telling and archery, as well as water-walking in the indoor swimming pool. There's also a children's' play area and dog exercise area. Restored red phone box houses information and take-away maps of the many local walks which may be enjoyed on electric hire bikes. Special features include a twice weekly hog roast, visits from the weekly fish and chip van and the site-owned pub is just down the road.

Holiday Park/Holiday Village of the Year
SILVER WINNER
Darwin Forest Country Park, Matlock, Derbyshire

Darwin Forest Country Park is an excellent holiday park set within 47 acres of woodland paradise, featuring 110 luxuriously furnished timber lodges built by the park's sister company Pinelog and maintained to a very high standard. The premier Spa Lodges include outdoor hot tubs.

Holiday Park/Holiday Village of the Year
BRONZE WINNER
Poston Mill Park, Peterchurch, Herefordshire

Poston Mill Holiday Park is set in 25 acres of riverside farmland close to the cathedral city of Hereford, and promises peace and quiet, riverside walks and on site activities including a pitch and putt course, river fishing and a very popular pub and restaurant in a historic converted mill.

Holiday Park/Holiday Village of the Year
HIGHLY COMMENDED
Castlerigg Hall Caravan & Camping Park, Keswick, Cumbria

Castlerigg Hall Caravan & Camping Park is a well-maintained, family owned site with superb views and glorious sunsets overlooking Derwentwater, and provides facilities for touring and static caravans, 'pods' and camping. There is an onsite restaurant, a well-stocked campers' shop selling local products and, unusually, an art gallery complete with a coffee bar.

Padstow Touring Park, Padstow, Cornwall

Padstow Touring Park consists of 150 well-spaced and landscaped touring caravan and family camping pitches. Open all year, it provides the ideal base for touring this beautiful area of Cornwall. Bed & Breakfast/Guest Accommodation of the Year.

Holiday Park/Holiday Village of the Year
GOLD WINNER
Trevose Harbour House, St Ives, Cornwall

Trevose House is a high-end B&B located close to St Ives harbour, with seaside decor throughout and large and airy rooms with sea views.

The hosts, both graduates of the Lausanne Hotel School, are charming, hospitable and will happily offer local information and maps to explore nearby eateries or local art galleries. Breakfasts at Trevose are divine! Fresh and individually cooked, menus include full English and vegetarian options using locally sourced produce.

Fine linen and generous up-market toiletries are available in all rooms, along with a well-stocked fridge and a different indulgent bedside chocolate every day. The en suite Garden Room is particularly spacious and luxurious and well-worth the extra cost. Offering exemplary comfort in artistic surroundings, not to mention St Ives' finest collection of retro G-Plan and Ercol furniture you'd be spoilt for a reason not to visit Trevose.

Holiday Park/Holiday Village of the Year
SILVER WINNER
Low Mill Guesthouse, Bainbridge, North Yorkshire

Situated in a beautiful village in the Yorkshire Dales, Low Mill is set in a converted mill, complete with functioning water wheel and mill workings, and oozes character and provides perfect hospitality to its guests.

Holiday Park/Holiday Village of the Year
BRONZE WINNER
Pebble House Boutique Guest House, Mevagissey, Cornwall

Pebble House is the perfect place to escape from the kids, where guests are treated to a glass of bubbly on arrival and rooms with views to die for.

Holiday Park/Holiday Village of the Year
HIGHLY COMMENDED
Molland Manor House B&B, Canterbury, Kent

A historic and beautifully restored home from home, Molland Manor is set in tranquil grounds close to such attractions as Wingham Wildlife Park and Deal Castle.

St Cuthbert's House, Seahouses, Northumberland

St Cuthbert's Guest House is situated in an elegant converted 19th century chapel just a short walk from Seahouses harbour and within easy reach of the spectacular Northumbrian coast.

Large Hotel of the Year
GOLD WINNER
Rockliffe Hall Hotel, Golf & Spa, Darlington, County Durham

Rockliffe Hall is an impressive 60-roomed luxury golf and spa hotel, where beautifully presented accommodation is offered with traditional, but stylish Old Hall rooms.

The spa facilities and dining experience are truly memorable. With three restaurants to choose from, the Orangery stands out with its golden pillars and outstanding food impeccably served with theatrical flair. The newly created spa is one of the biggest in the country, offering professional treatments in elegant surroundings and including the indoor/outdoor Spa Garden for total relaxation.

Many of the bathrooms feature 'tile TVs' for added luxury, and with a staff of around 300 across the whole estate to attend to their every need, guests feel truly pampered.

Large Hotel of the Year
SILVER WINNER
Chewton Glen Hotel & Spa, New Forest, Hampshire

Celebrating its 50th year, Chewton Glen Hotel and Spa is a world renowned luxury resort that manages to be sumptuous and elegant, whilst retaining a friendly, relaxed atmosphere and where the staff are prepared to go that extra mile.

Large Hotel of the Year
BRONZE WINNER
South Lodge, an Exclusive Hotel, Horsham, West Sussex

South Lodge Hotel is a magnificent country house hotel set in 93 acres of woodland and parkland. Many of its rooms have wonderful views of the South Downs, and are kept to an exceptionally high standard. Unlike some large hotels, the staff are particularly well motivated, providing outstanding service. Special touches include anti-snoring pillows and self-decorate Christmas trees in the rooms.

Large Hotel of the Year
HIGHLY COMMENDED
Peckforton Castle, Chester, Cheshire

Housed in a truly magnificent Victorian castle set high up overlooking Cheshire, Peckforton Castle Hotel is everyone's vision of 'medieval' grandeur. Labyrinthine corridors and stone spiral staircases link the individually styled rooms - you might find yourself housed in a turret with fantastic views of the castle's wooded surroundings.

Salcombe Harbour Hotel & Spa, Salcombe, Devon

Described as 'a luxurious coastal spa', the Salcombe Harbour Hotel certainly takes full advantage of its superb location overlooking the water. Its balconies and terraces would seem particularly suited to wedding parties, birthday celebrations or a romantic weekend away. Staff will even scatter rose petals and arrange candles in the hotel's cinema when a proposal is in the offing.

Small Hotel of the Year
GOLD WINNER
Yorebridge House, Bainbridge, North Yorkshire

Set amongst breath taking scenery in the heart of Wensleydale, Yorebridge House is a five-star 'restaurant with rooms' in a historic Grade II listed former headmaster's house and school.
Set in five acres and flanked by two rivers, this winner of the Mills and Boon Most Romantic Venue Award 2015, offers 12 luxurious contemporary bedrooms, wonderful bathrooms and exemplary service in a relaxed atmosphere. With features such as private outdoor hot tubs for selected rooms, outstanding cuisine, sumptuous public rooms and a welcome as warm as the log fire, this is indeed a very special boutique hotel.

SILVER WINNER
Cross Lane House Hotel & Restaurant, Allerford, Exmoor National Park, Somerset

Cross Lane House is a small country guesthouse with the impeccable service and eye for detail that would make it the envy of any grand establishment. The hosts go to extraordinary lengths to make guests enjoy their stay, even down to washing their cars' windscreens before departure (unasked) and supplying goodie bags for the journey home. Customers' comments invariably include the word 'perfect'.

Small Hotel of the Year
BRONZE WINNER
Hell Bay Hotel, Bryher, Isles of Scilly

Hell Bay Hotel is a stylish seaside retreat in what is simply the best location in the islands with outdoor pool, friendly, attentive staff and excellent mostly locally sourced food from their delightful rustic little eatery. The renowned The Crabshack, adjoining the hotel, is open during the summer season for guests to enjoy the local seafood.

Small Hotel of the Year
HIGHLY COMMENDED
Kentisbury Grange, Barnstaple, North Devon

Kentisbury Grange, situated on the edge of Exmoor National Park, is a superbly refurbished Victorian manor house featuring beautifully furnished bedrooms and superb ensuite bathrooms. The Coach House by Michael Caines is a masterpiece of contemporary rustic design and serves beautifully presented innovative yet classic cuisine. In addition there are five two bed/two bath lodges set in the landscaped gardens which come with balcony hot tubs.

Tudor Farmhouse, Forest of Dean, Gloucestershire

This stylish and romantic retreat in the charming village of Clearwell boasts cosy rooms with fluffy towels and roll top baths. Tudor Farmhouse extends its warm hospitality to many returning guests who appreciate the winning combination of excellent service, beautifully presented food and a team that are prepared to go that extra mile.

To find a full list of the winners please visit www.visitenglandawards.org

Visit England Awards for Excellence: Silver Winner

Holiday Park/Holiday Village

Darwin Forest Country Park

Holidays at Darwin Forest are spent in luxury wooden lodges nestled in 47 acres of mixed woodland between Matlock and Bakewell in the stunning Derbyshire Peak District.

The range of accommodation is hard to beat, from a cosy Classic Lodge to an airy contemporary Vogue Lodge or Spa Lodge with its own discreetly sited outdoor hot tub. Pet friendly lodges cater specifically for dog lovers who want to take advantage of the woodland walks. All the lodges are bright and spacious and give access to a huge range of facilities inside the park.

There is plenty to keep guests entertained with the attractive woodland setting and its extensive cycle and hiking paths. Little ones will love the Little Monkeys indoor soft play area while older ones head for the Activity Den for the pool, table tennis, air-hockey or arcade games. Families of all ages will enjoy tennis and mini-golf and more interesting activities including archery, body zorbing and Water Walkerz and the Evolution Health & Fitness Centre gives guests a chance to rebalance their equilibrium.

Enjoy eating out at the Explorers Café or try the Foresters' Bar and Restaurant with its more expansive menu or order food-to-go and dine privately in your lodge or alfresco on the decking.

Whichever choice you make at Darwin Forest, you will feel restored by the picturesque setting and proximity to nature.

Tel: (01629) 732428
enquiries@darwinforest.co.uk
www.darwinforest.co.uk

Visit England Awards for Excellence: Silver Winner

Large Hotel of the Year

Chewton Glen Hotel & Spa

With a stunning location, tucked into the Southern edge of the 900,000 acre New Forest but only a 10 minute walk from the sea, Chewton Glen is a world-class hotel that combines a quintessentially English hotel experience with modern day luxury in a traditional setting.

This iconic hotel offers 70 luxurious bedrooms and suites, a first class spa and leisure and sporting facilities. The distinctive Treehouse suites have captured the imagination of guests and drawn global acclaim.

"The success of Chewton Glen has been built on passion", says Managing Director, Andrew Stembridge, "At the heart of everything we have done for the past 50 years, it is our belief that our guests come first."

An award-winning dining room using produce grown in the hotels Kitchen Garden provides a healthier style of cooking. An impressive 17m ozone-treated outdoor pool, state of the art gymnasium, tennis centre with indoor and outdoor courts, a par-3 golf course and driving range, clay pigeon shooting and croquet lawn keep guests entertained.

The interior design of the hotel combines sophisticated modern fabrics with traditional country house furniture and antiques in keeping with the building's 18th century origin. Each of the spacious bedrooms and suites is individually styled to provide the ultimate in luxury and comfort as befits a member of the prestigious Relais & Chateaux Group.

Tel: (01425) 282212
reservations@chewtonglen.com
www.chewtonglen.com

Visit England Awards for Excellence: Bronze Winner

Self-Catering Holiday Provider

Whalesborough Cottages & Spa

Combining luxury with a relaxed attitude to dogs is not an easy trick to pull off, but in doing so, Whalesborough Cottages have created a countryside haven just minutes from the holiday town of Bude and a 20 minute walk from the golden beaches of North Cornwall.

Find yourself with a choice of one of 20 eco-friendly cottages, luxuriously furnished in a fresh contemporary style for any number between 2 and 11 with free Wi-Fi set in 500 acres of secluded countryside.

For dog lovers, the cottages have fenced private gardens and your four legged friend will be greeted with a special Pooch Pack with all the essentials. For everyone, there are outdoor and indoor heated pools and on-site tennis courts. Guests find themselves close to a whole range of holiday activities from

cycling and walking the coast path, to surfing, sea kayaking, canoeing, bird watching and fishing.

If a peaceful escape or a special break is in order, the cottages have spa facilities including a gym, steam room, massage facilities, sauna and Jacuzzi. While families will enjoy the barn-style games room, sandpit, beach volley ball court, basketball hoop, table tennis and pool table.

Discover this secluded and peaceful patch of Cornwall and base yourself at Whalesborough Cottages for a secret place you will want to return again and again.

Tel: (01288) 361626
jproudfoot@whalesborough.plus.com
www.whalesborough.co.uk

Sustainable Tourism in England

More and more operators of accommodation, attractions and events in England are becoming aware of sustainable or "green" issues and are acting more responsibly in their businesses. But how can you be sure that businesses that 'say' they're green, really are?

Who certifies green businesses?

There are a number of green certification schemes that assess businesses for their green credentials. VisitEngland only promotes those that have been checked out to ensure they reach the high standards expected. The members of those schemes VisitEngland has validated are truly sustainable (green) businesses and appear amongst the pages of this guide with our heart-flower logo on their entry.

 Businesses displaying this logo have undergone a rigorous verification process to ensure that they are sustainable (green) and that a qualified assessor has visited the premises.

At the moment VisitEngland promotes the largest Green Tourism Scheme in the world - Green Tourism Programme.

Green Tourism Programme

Green Tourism is the market leading sustainable certification programme for the tourism sector in the UK and Internationally. From small bed and breakfasts to large visitor attractions and activity holiday providers. A Green Tourism Award means that a business works responsibly, ethically and sustainably, contributes to their community, is reducing their impact on the environment and aims to be accessible and inclusive to all visitors and staff.

With over 2,100 Green Tourism businesses all independently inspected graded Bronze, Silver or Gold they identify businesses that are really making a difference, so you can choose the greenest option with confidence.

How are these businesses being green?

Any business that has been certified 'green' will have implemented initiatives that contribute to reducing their negative environmental and social impacts whilst trying to enhance the economic and community benefits to their local area.

Many of these things may be behind the scenes such as energy efficient boilers, insulated lofts or grey water recycling, but there are many fun activities that you can expect to find too. For example, your green business should be able to advise you about traditional activities nearby, the best places to sample local food and buy craft products, or even help you to enjoy a 'car-free' day out.

David Bellamy *Conservation Award*

2016/17

GOLD

'**These well-deserved awards are a signpost to parks which are making real achievements in protecting our environment. Go there and experience wrap-around nature ... you could be amazed at what you find!' says Professor David Bellamy.**

585 gold, silver and bronze parks were named in the 2016/17 David Bellamy Conservation Awards, organised in conjunction with the British Holiday and Home Parks Association.

These parks are recognised for their commitment to conservation and the environment through their management of landscaping, recycling policies, waste management, the cultivation of flora and fauna and the creation of habitats designed to encourage a variety of wildlife onto the park. Links with the local community and the use of local materials are also important considerations.

Parks wishing to enter for a David Bellamy Conservation Award must complete a detailed questionnaire covering different aspects of their environmental policies, and describe what positive conservation steps they have taken. The park must also undergo an independent audit from a local wildlife or conservation body which is familiar with the area. Final assessments and the appropriate level of any award are then made personally by Professor Bellamy.

An index of award-winning parks featured in the regional pages of this guide can be found on page 386.

Don't Miss...

Eden Project

St. Austell, Cornwall PL24 2SG
(01726) 811911
www.edenproject.com
Explore your relationship with nature at the world famous Eden Project, packed with projects and exhibits about climate and the environment, regeneration, conservation and sustainable living. Be inspired by cutting-edge buildings, stunning year round garden displays, world-class sculpture and art, as well as fabulous music and arts events. See all the sights and immerse yourself in nature with a walk among the the treetops on the Rainforest Canopy Walk or a ride on the land train.

Paignton Zoo

Paignton, Devon TQ4 7EU
(01803) 697500
www.paigntonzoo.org.uk
One of Britain's top wildilfe attractions, Paignton Zoo has all the usual suspects with an impressive collection of lions, tigers, gorillas, orangutans, rhinos and giraffes. It is also home to some of the planet's rarest creatures and plants too. For a day jam-packed with family fun and adventure there's Monkey Heights, the crocodile swamp, an amphibian ark and a miniature train, as well as the hands-on interactve Discovery Centre.

Roman Bath

Bath, Somerset BA1 1LZ
(01225) 477785
www.romanbaths.co.uk
Bathe in the naturally hot spa water at the magnificent baths built by the romans, indulge in a gourmet getaway, or enjoy a romantic weekend exploring the wealth of historic architecture. You can find all of this in the beautiful city of Bath and attractions such as Longleat Safari Park and Stonehenge are all within easy reach too.

Sherborne Castle & Gardens

Sherborne, Dorset DT9 5NR
(01935) 812072
www.sherbornecastle.com
Built by Sir Walter Raleigh in c1594, the castle reflects various styles from the Elizabethan hall to the Victorian solarium, with splendid collections of art, furniture and porcelain. The grounds around the 50-acre lake were landscaped by 'Capability' Brown and the 30 acres of tranquil lakeside gardens are the perfect place to escape.

Stonehenge

Amesbury, Wiltshire SP4 7DE
(0370) 333 1181
www.english-heritage.org.uk/stonehenge
The Neolithic site of Stonehenge in Wiltshire is one of the most famous megalithic monuments in the world, the purpose of which is still largely only guessed at. This imposing archaeological site is often ascribed mystical or spiritual associations and receives thousands of visitors from all over the world each year.

South West

Cornwall & Isles of Scilly, Devon, Dorset, Gloucestershire, Somerset, Wiltshire

The South West is Britain's most popular holiday area, offering visitors an unrivalled combination of unspoilt countryside and coastline. Whether you choose the mellow stone villages of the Cotswolds in the North, Wiltshire with its crop circles and ancient monuments or the wild moorland, blue waters and golden sands of Devon and Cornwall, the beauty of this region and the welcome it offers visitors never fails to delight.

Gloucestershire

Wiltshire

Somerset

Devon

Dorset

Cornwall

Explore – South West

Cornwall

Blue seas and steeply wooded valleys, exotic gardens and Cornwall's industrial heritage draw visitors from far and wide. Pounding Atlantic waves attract surfers from all over the world to its beaches and make Cornwall a mecca for watersports of all kinds. The BBC's 'Poldark' has brought fans eager to relive the action in the series' real locations.

The majestic and largely untouched wilderness of Bodmin Moor is only one example of the rich natural environment that can be found here, with miles of walking paths criss-crossing the impressive landscape. This walkers paradise has something for everyone, with The Cornish Way - over 200 miles of inter-linking trails connecting Bude to Land's End – and the spectacular 300 mile long South West Coast Path National Trail with its beautiful views of secluded coves, sandy beaches and jaw-dropping cliffs.

West Cornwall's captivating light and landscape has intrigued and inspired artists since the early 19th century. St Ives is at the heart of today's vibrant art scene, with local arts and crafts galleries rubbing shoulders with international stars such as the Tate St Ives and the Barbara Hepworth Museum and Sculpture Garden.

Cornwall also has a diverse history reaching back to prehistoric, Celtic and medieval roots and there are a huge number of heritage attractions in this corner of the country. St Michael's Mount is an ancient island of myth and legend, Tintagel Castle overlooks the dramatic windswept Atlantic coast, while Grade I listed Port Eliot House & Gardens is a hidden gem nestling beside a secret estuary near Saltash.

Devon

Take a hike or a mountain bike and discover the rugged beauty of Exmoor, explore the drama of the craggy coastline, or catch a wave on some of the region's best surf beaches. North Devon is also rich in heritage with many stately homes and historic attractions including Hartland Abbey and the picturesque Clovelly village, where the steep pedestrianised cobbled main street, takes you to a beautiful deep-blue harbour.

Stunningly beautiful, Dartmoor is perhaps the most famous of Devon's National Parks and offers miles of purple, heather-clad moorland, rushing rivers and stone tors. Walk the length and breadth of the moor or cycle the Drake's Trail, where you'll come across wild ponies and plenty of moorland pubs, perfect for a well earned rest. Head east and discover the imposing Blackdown Hills 'Area of Outstanding Natural Beauty', stopping off in one of the area's picture-postcard villages for a delicious Devon Cream Tea.

Plymouth is famous for its seafaring heritage, with Plymouth Hoe as the backdrop for Sir Francis Drake's legendary game of bowls, as well as being one of the most beautiful natural harbours in the world. Climb Smeaton's Tower for the incredible views if you're feeling energetic, visit the world-famous Plymouth Gin Distillery at Sutton Harbour, or take the kids to the National Marine Aquarium for an afternoon of fishy fun.

Torquay, gateway to the English Riviera, boasts elegant Victorian villas, iconic palm trees, a sweeping sandy beach and a rich maritime history. Paignton offers great days out including its famous zoo, and the traditional fishing harbour of Brixham is awash with seafood restaurants, waterside pubs and cafés. This whole area is also home to a huge selection of beaches from small, romantic coves to larger, award-winning stretches. The Jurassic Coast is a UNESCO World Heritage Site which stretches for 95 miles along the Devon/Dorset coast, revealing 185 million years of geology and is a must for visitors to the South West.

Dorset

Stretching from historic Lyme Regis in the west to Christchurch in the east, and including a number of designated heritage areas, the whole Dorset coastline is a treasure trove of geology. Interesting landforms are plentiful - Durdle Door, Lulworth Cove, the Isle of Portland with the famous Portland Bill lighthouse and the shingle bank of Chesil Beach to name but a few. Weymouth and Portland are two of the best sailing locations in Europe and offer water sports galore, as well as pretty harbours. For traditional English seaside resorts visit Victorian Swanage, or Bournemouth with its fine sandy beach, perfect for families.

Inland, enchanting market towns, quaint villages and rolling countryside play host to delightful shops, museums, family attractions, historic houses and beautiful gardens such as the Sub-Tropical Gardens at Abbotsbury. Explore Dorset's natural beauty on foot or by bicycle at Stoborough Heath and Hartland Moor nature reserves.

Gloucestershire

The Cotswolds tranquil villages are recognised as the prettiest in the country and draw tourists from all over the world. The elegant spa town of Cheltenham makes a perfect base for exploring the area whether you come for the racing festival, the Cheltenham Gold Cup, its Festival of Music or simply for its Regency town houses and leafy squares.

Tewkesbury, famous for its fine half-timbered buildings, alleyways and 12th century Norman Abbey, is one of the best medieval townscapes in England. Enjoy a riverside stroll along the River Severn or a boat trip along the Avon. Grade I listed Sudeley Castle & Gardens, set against the dramatic backdrop of the Cotswolds, is well worth a visit and at the centre of the Severn Vale, Gloucester is a vibrant and multicultural city with an impressive cathedral. It combines historic architecture with numerous visitor attractions, quirky shops and mouth-watering tearooms, restaurants and pubs, and is only a stone's throw from the ancient woodlands of Forest of Dean.

Somerset & Bristol

The maritime city of Bristol is packed with historic attractions, exciting events and fabulous festivals. Cabot Circus offers first class shopping, while stylish restaurants and cafés on the Harbourside serve up locally produced food to tempt and delight. Out and about, Isambard Kingdom Brunel's Clifton Suspension Bridge and the Bristol Zoo Gardens are firm favourites.

Topped by the tower of the ruined 15th century church, Glastonbury Tor is the stuff of myth and legend, rising high above the Somerset Levels near the delightful town of Glastonbury. Believed to be the site of a Saxon fortress, it has breathtaking views reaching to Wells, the Mendips and the Bristol Channel in the North, Shepton Mallet and Wiltshire in the East, South to the Polden Hills and to the Quantocks and Exmoor in the West.

Wiltshire

Surrounded by stunning scenery and home to a magnificent Cathedral, a wealth of heritage and cultural, dining and shopping venues, the medieval city of Salisbury is the jewel in the crown of South West England's rural heartland.

Further afield you can find an abundance of quintessential English market towns and villages. Marlborough, famed for its charming high street and independent shops, is stylish and sophisticated with a cosmopolitan café culture, while Wilton, the ancient capital of Wessex, is home to Wilton House and a beautiful Italianate Church.

Visit – South West

Cornwall

Blue Reef Aquarium
Newquay, Cornwall TR7 1DU
(01637) 878134
www.bluereefaquarium.co.uk
Over 40 naturally themed habitats take you on a fantastic journey from Cornish waters to exotic seas.

Boardmasters
Trebelsue Farm, Watergate Bay, Cornwall TR8 4AN
www.boardmasters.co.uk
Europe's largest surf and music festival, takes place at Fistral Beach and Watergate Bay in early August.

Cornwall Film Festival
November, Cornwall
www.cornwallfilmfestival.com
A month long festival of fabulous films.

Crantock Bale Push
September, Crantock, nr Newquay
www.balepush.co.uk
Teams pushing giant hay bales around the village.

Lost Gardens of Heligan   ⚜
St. Austell, Cornwall PL26 6EN
(01726) 845100
www.heligan.com
An exploration through Victorian Productive Gardens & Pleasure Grounds, a sub-tropical Jungle and more.

Minack Theatre
Porthcurno, Cornwall TR19 6JU
(01736) 810181
www.minack.com
Cornwall's world famous Minack open-air theatre.

National Maritime Museum Cornwall
Falmouth, Cornwall TR11 3QY
(01326) 313388
www.nmmc.co.uk
Award-winning museum with something for everyone.

National Seal Sanctuary
Helston, Cornwall TR12 6UG
(01326) 221361
www.sealsanctuary.co.uk
With over 55 years experience the National Seal Sanctuary Cornwall rescues, rehabilitates and releases over 40 seal pups a year.

Newquay Fish Festival
September, Newquay, Cornwall
www.newquayfishfestival.co.uk
Three days celebrating delightful fresh local produce against the backdrop of one of the town's gems, it's 300 year old harbour.

Newquay Zoo
Newquay, Cornwall TR7 2LZ
(01637) 873342
www.newquayzoo.org.uk
Multi-award winning Zoo set in sub-tropical lakeside gardens and home to over 130 species of animals, there is lots to see and do at on a visit to the Zoo.

Royal Cornwall Show
June, Wadebridge, Cornwall, PL27 7JE
www.royalcornwallshow.org
The county's biggest annual event. A fascinating glimpse into rural life, enjoy 3 days of Cornish heritage, entertainment, displays and fairs.

St Michaels Mount
Marazion, Cornwall TR17 0HS
(01736) 710265
www.stmichaelsmount.co.uk
Explore the amazing island world and discover legend, myth and over a thousand years of incredible history.

Tate St Ives
St. Ives, Cornwall TR26 1TG
(01736) 796226
www.tate.org.uk/visit/tate-st-ives
An introduction to modern and contemporary art, including works from the Tate Collection.

Devon

The Agatha Christie Festival
September, Torquay, Devon
www.agathachristiefestival.co.uk
Celebrate the world's most famous crime writer, Dame Agatha Christie. A literary festival with a murder mystery twist!

Bicton Park Botanical Gardens
Budleigh Salterton, EX9 7BJ
(01395) 568465
www.bictongardens.co.uk
Magnificent gardens, streams, woodlands and features. Take a walk through the arboretum before a relaxing meal at the Orangery Restaurant.

Bournemouth Air Festival
August, Bournemouth, Devon
www.bournemouthair.co.uk
Free four-day seafront air show.

Brixham Pirate Festival
April, Brixham, Devon
www.brixhampirates.com
Brixham turns pirate with live music, games, re-enactments, skirmishes on the Golden Hind.

Clovelly Village
(01237) 431781
www.clovelly.co.uk
Most visitors consider Clovelly to be unique. Whatever your view, it is a world of difference not to be missed.

Crealy Great Adventure Theme Park
Sidmouth Road, Exeter, Devon EX5 1DR
(01395) 233200
www.crealy.co.uk/Devon
Enter the magical land of Cornwall's Crealy and hold on tight for a thrilling ride.

Custom House Visitor Centre
Exeter, Devon EX2 4AN
(01392) 271611
www.exeter.gov.uk/customhouse
Discover the history of Exeter in 15 minutes at the Quay House Visitor Centre on Exeter's Historic Quayside.

Dartmouth Castle
Dartmouth, Devon TQ6 0JN
(01803) 833588
www.english-heritage.org.uk/dartmouthcastle
For over six hundred years Dartmouth Castle has guarded the narrow entrance to the Dart Estuary and the busy, vibrant port of Dartmouth.

Dartmouth Steam Railway
Queens Park Station, Torbay Road, Paignton TQ4 6A
(01803) 555872
www.dartmouthrailriver.co.uk
Running Paignton along the spectacular Torbay coast and through the wooded slopes bordering the Dart estuary, with stunning scenery and seascapes.

Devon's Crealy Great Adventure Park
Exeter, Devon EX5 1DR
(01395) 233200
www.crealy.co.uk/Devon
This award-winning adventure park has over 60 rides and attractions for the whole family set in over 100 acres of glorious Devon countryside.

Escot Gardens, Maze & Forest Adventure
Ottery St. Mary, Devon EX11 1LU
(01404) 822188
www.wildwoodescot.org
Historical gardens and fantasy woodland surrounding the ancestral home of the Kennaway family.

Fishstock
September, Brixham, Devon
www.fishstockbrixham.co.uk
A one-day festival of seafood and entertainment held in Brixham.

Hartland Abbey & Gardens
(01237) 441496/234
www.hartlandabbey.com
Hartland Abbey is a family home full of history in a beautiful valley leading to a wild Atlantic cove.

Ilfracombe Aquarium
Ilfracombe, Devon EX34 9EQ
(01271) 864533
www.ilfracombeaquarium.co.uk
A fascinating journey of discovery into the aquatic life of North Devon.

Kents Cavern
Torquay TQ1 2JF
01803 215136
www.kents-cavern.co.uk
*Kents Cavern is one of Europe's top prehistory Stone
Age caves with an extensive labyrinth of spectacular
and easily accessible caverns open daily all year.*

Plymouth City Museum and Art Gallery
Devon PL4 8AJ
(01752) 304774
www.plymhearts.org/pcmag
*The museum presents a diverse range of
contemporary exhibitions, from photography to
textiles, modern art to natural history.*

Dorset

Athelhampton House and Gardens
Athelhampton, Puddletown, Dorchester DT2 7LG
(01305) 848363
www.athelhampton.co.uk
*One of the finest 15th century Houses in England
nestled in the heart of the picturesque Piddle Valley.*

Christchurch Food and Wine Festival
May, Christchurch, Dorset BH23 1AS
www.christchurchfoodfest.co.uk
*Celebrity chefs, over 100 trade stands, culinary treats,
cookery theatres and some eminent food critics.*

Corfe Castle Model Village and Gardens
Corfe Castle, Dorset BH20 5EZ
(01929) 481234
www.corfecastlemodelvillage.co.uk
*Detailed 1/20th scale model of Corfe Castle and
village before its destruction by Cromwell.*

Dorset County Museum
Dorchester, Dorset, DT1 1XA
(01305) 262735
www.dorsetcountymuseum.org
*Follow Dorset through time; visit the nostalgic
Victorian Gallery, walk on real Roman mosaic floors and
discover the dinosaurs that roamed the lands and seas.*

Dorset Knob Throwing Festival
April, Kingston, Maurward, Dorchester DT2 8PY
www.dorsetknobthrowing.com
World famous quirky festival.

Lulworth Castle & Park
Wareham, Dorset BH20 5QS
(01929) 400352
www.lulworth.com/visit/places-to-visit/castle-and-park
Enjoy historic buildings & stunning landscapes.

Lyme Regis Fossil Festival
April, Lyme Regis, Dorset
www.fossilfestival.co.uk
*A natural science and arts cultural extravaganza on
the UNESCO World Heritage Jurassic Coast.*

Portland Castle
Portland, Dorset DT5 1AZ
(01305) 820539
www.english-heritage.org.uk/visit/places/portland-castle
Coastal fort built by Henry VIII to defend Weymouth.

Sherborne Abbey Music Festival
April - May, Sherborne, Dorset
www.sherborneabbeyfestival.org
Five days of music.

Sturminster Newton Cheese Festival
September, Sturminster, Dorset
www.cheesefestival.co.uk
A celebration of the region's dairy heritage.

Swanage Regatta and Carnival
July - August, Swanage, Dorset
www.swanagecarnival.com
The South's premier carnival.

Bristol

Aerospace Bristol
Stoke Gifford, Patchway, Bristol BS34 7QH
(01179) 315315
www.aerospacebristol.org
*Showcasing the story of Bristol's world-class
aerospace industry. Due to open in Summer 2017.*

At-Bristol
Bristol BS1 5DB
(0117) 915 1000
www.at-bristol.org.uk
21st century science and technology centre.

Avon Valley Railway
Bristol BS30 6HD
(0117) 932 5538
www.avonvalleyrailway.org
Much more than your average steam train ride.
A whole new experience or a nostalgic memory.

The Bristol Hippodrome
Bristol, BS1 4UZ
(0844) 871 3012
www.atgtickets.com/venues/bristol-hippodrome
One of the country's top provincial theatres, staging
major West End and Broadway productions.

Bristol Zoo Gardens
Bristol BS8 3HA
(0117) 428 5300
www.bristolzoo.org.uk
Your passport for a day trip into an amazing world
of animals, exhibits and other attractions.

Brunel's SS Great Britain
Bristol BS1 6TY
(0117) 926 0680
www.ssgreatbritain.org
Award-winning attraction showing the world's first
great ocean liner and National Brunel Archive.

City Sightseeing The Bristol Tour
Central Bristol BS1 4AH
(0117) 403 1994
www.bristolinsight.co.uk
Open-top bus tours, with guides and headphones,
around the city of Bristol. Runs through the year.

Gloucestershire

Chavenage
Chavenage, Tetbury, Gloucestershire GL8 8XP
(01666) 502329
www.chavenage.com
Elizabethan Manor Chavenage House, a TV/
Film location is still a family home, offers unique
experiences, with history, ghosts and more.

Corinium Museum
Cirencester, Gloucestershire GL7 2BX
(01285) 655611
www.coriniummuseum.org
Discover the treasures of the Cotswolds as you
explore its history at this award-winning museum.

Forest Food Showcase
October, Forest of Dean, Gloucestershire GL16 7EL
www.forestshowcase.org
A celebration of the foods and fruits of the forest
with over 100 top local and artisan producers, a big
serving of stunning hot food, add a dash of real ale
and wine. A lovely foodie family day out.

Gloucester Cathedral
Gloucestershire GL1 2LX
(01452) 528095
www.gloucestercathedral.org.uk
A place of worship and an architectural gem. The
Cathedral offers a wealth of things to see and do from
climbing the tower to special family activities and events.

Gloucester Waterways Museum
Gloucester GL1 2EH
(01452) 318200
www.gloucesterwaterwaysmuseum.org.uk
Housed in a Victorian warehouse, this museum tells
the story of Gloucester's wonderful canals and rivers.

Hidcote Manor Garden
Chipping Campden, Gloucestershire GL55 6LR
(01386) 438333
www.nationaltrust.org.uk/hidcote
Rare trees and shrubs, outstanding herbaceous
borders and unusual plants from all over the world.

Painswick Rococo Garden
Painswick, Gloucestershire GL6 6TH
(01452) 813204
www.rococogarden.org.uk
A fascinating step back to a flamboyant and sensual
period of English Garden Design

Sudeley Castle Gardens and Exhibition
Winchcombe, Gloucestershire GL54 5JD
(01242) 602308
www.sudeleycastle.co.uk
Award-winning gardens surrounding Castle and
medieval ruins.

Westonbirt, The National Arboretum
Tetbury, Gloucestershire GL8 8QS
(0300) 067 4890
www.forestry.gov.uk/westonbirt
600 acres with one of the finest collections of trees.

Somerset

Bridgwater Arts Centre
Bridgwater, Somerset, TA6 3DD
(01278) 422700
www.bridgwaterartscentre.co.uk
Be entertained by one of the evening shows, relax in the cosy bar, or stroll through the local gallery.

Forde Abbey & Gardens
Chard, Somerset TA20 4LU
(01460) 220231
www.fordeabbey.co.uk
Founded 850 years ago, Forde Abbey was converted into a private house in c.1649.

Glastonbury Abbey
Somerset BA6 9EL
(01458) 832267
www.glastonburyabbey.com
Somewhere for all seasons! From snowdrops and daffodils in the Spring, to family trails and quizzes and Autumn colour on hundreds of trees.

Glastonbury Festival
June, Pilton, Somerset
www.glastonburyfestivals.co.uk
Known for its contemporary music, but also features dance, comedy, theatre, circus, cabaret and other arts.

Haynes International Motor Museum
Yeovil, Somerset BA22 7LH
(01963) 440804
www.haynesmotormuseum.co.uk
More than 400 vehicles displayed in stunning style, dating from 1886 to the present day.

The Jane Austen Centre
Bath, Somerset BA1 2NT
(01225) 443000
www.janeausten.co.uk
Celebrating Bath's most famous resident.

Number One Royal Crescent
Bath, Somerset BA1 2LR
(01225) 428126
www.no1royalcrescent.org.uk
Restored and authentically furnished town house shows fashionable life in 18th century Bath.

West Somerset Railway
Minehead, Somerset TA24 5BG
(01643) 704996
www.west-somerset-railway.co.uk
Longest independent steam railway in Britain.

Wiltshire

Bowood House and Gardens
Bowood, Calne, Wiltshire, SN11 0LZ
(01249) 812102
www.bowood.org/bowood-house-gardens
Stately home with formal grounds and woodlands created by master landscaper Capability Brown.

Longleat
Warminster, Wiltshire BA12 7NW
(01985) 844400
www.longleat.co.uk
A wealth of exciting attractions along with lots of special events to keep you and your family entertained.

Old Sarum
Salisbury, Wiltshire SP1 3SD
(01722) 335398
www.english-heritage.org.uk/oldsarum
The mighty Iron Age hill fort where the first cathedral stood and where our ancestors left their mark.

Salisbury Cathedral
Salisbury, Wiltshire SP1 2EJ
(01722) 555120
www.salisburycathedral.org.uk
Britain's finest 13th century cathedral with the tallest spire in Britain. Discover nearly 800 years of history, the world's best preserved Magna Carta (AD 1215).

Stourhead House and Garden
Warminster, Wiltshire BA12 6QF
(01747) 841152
www.nationaltrust.org.uk/stourhead
A breathtaking 18th century landscape garden with lakeside walks, grottoes and classical temples.

Wilton House
Wilton House, Wilton, Wiltshire SP2 0BJ
(01722) 746700
www.wiltonhouse.com
Wilton House has one of the finest art collections in Europe and is set in magnificent landscaped parkland featuring the Palladian Bridge.

Tourist Information Centres

When you arrive at your destination, visit the Tourist Information Centre for quality assured help with accommodation and information about local attractions and events, or email your request before you go.

Axminster	The Old Courthouse	01297 34386	axminstertic@btopenworld.com.com
Barnstaple	Museum of North Devon	01271 375000	info@staynorthdevon.co.uk
Bath	Abbey Chambers	0844 847 5256	tourism@bathtourism.co.uk
Bideford	Burton Art Gallery	01237 477676	bidefordtic@torridge.gov.uk
Blandford Forum	Riverside House	01258 454770	info@blandfordinformation.co.uk
Bodmin	Shire Hall	01208 76616	bodmintic@visit.org.uk
Bourton-on-the-Water	Victoria Street	01451 820211	info@visitbourton.com
Bradford on Avon	50 St. Margaret's Street	01225 865797	tic@bradfordonavon.co.uk
Braunton	The Bakehouse Centre	01271 816688	info@brauntontic.co.uk
Bridport	Bridport Town Hall,	01308 424901	bridport.tic@westdorset-weymouth.gov.uk
Bristol : Harbourside	E Shed	0906 711 2191	ticharbourside@destinationbristol.co.uk
Brixham	Hobb Nobs Gift Shop	01803 211 211	holiday@englishriviera.co.uk
Bude	Bude Visitor Centre	01288 354240	budetic@visitbude.info
Budleigh Salterton	Fore Street	01395 445275	info@visitbudleigh.com
Cartgate	South Somerset TIC	01935 829333	cartgate.tic@southsomerset.gov.uk
Chard	The Guildhall	01460 260051	chardtowncouncil@chard.gov.uk
Cheltenham	The Wilson	01242 522878	info@cheltenham.gov.uk
Chippenham	Hight Street	01249 665970	info@chippenham.gov.uk
Chipping Campden	The Old Police Station	01386 841206	info@campdenonline.org
Christchurch	49 High Street	01202 471780	enquiries@christchurchtourism.info
Cirencester	Corinium Museum	01285 654180	cirencestervic@slm-ltd.co.uk
Combe Martin	Seacot	01271 883319	mail@visitcombemartin.co.uk
Dartmouth	The Engine House	01803 834224	holidays@discoverdartmouth.com
Dawlish	The Lawn	01626 215665	dawtic@teignbridge.gov.uk
Dorchester	11 Antelope Walk	01305 267992	dorchester.tic@westdorset-weymouth.gov.uk
Exeter	Visitor Information Centre	01392 665700	tic@exeter.gov.uk
Exmouth	The Strand	01395 830550	
Fal River	11 Market Strand	01326 741194	evit@falriver.co.uk

Fowey	5 South Street	01726 833616	info@fowey.co.uk
Frome	Spalmer Street	01373 465757	info@frometowncouncil.gov.uk
Glastonbury	The Tribunal	01458 832954	info@glastonburytic.co.uk
Gloucester	28 Southgate Street	01452 396572	tourism@gloucester.gov.uk
Honiton	Dowell Street	01404 43716	honitontic@btconnect.com
Ilfracombe	The Seafront	01271 863001	info@visitilfracombe.co.uk
Ivybridge	The Watermark	01752 897035	info@ivybridgewatermark.co.uk
Launceston	The White Hart Arcade	01566 772321	info@launcestontic.co.uk
Looe	The Guildhall	01503 262072	looetic@btconnect.com
Lyme Regis	Guildhall Cottage	01297 442138	lymeregis.tic@westdorset-weymouth.gov.uk
Lynton	Town Hall	01598 752225	info@lyntourism.co.uk
Malmesbury	Town Hall	01666 823748	tic@malmesbury.gov.uk
Melksham	32 Church Street	01225 707424	info@visit-melksham.com
Mere	The Library, Barton Lane	01747 861211	
Minehead	19 The Avenue	01643 702624	minehead.visitor@hotmail.com
Modbury	2 Modbury Court	01548 830159	enquiries@modburytic.org.uk
Moreton-in-Marsh	High Street	01608 650881	moreton@cotswold.gov.uk
Newquay	Municipal Offices	01637 854020	newquay.tic@cornwall.gov.uk
Newton Abbot	6 Bridge House	01626 215667	natic@teignbridge.gov.uk
Ottery St Mary	10 Broad Street	01404 813964	info@otterytourism.org.uk
Padstow	Red Brick Building	01841 533449	info@padstowtic.co.uk
Penzance	Station Approach	01736 335530	westcornwall@nationaltrust.org.uk
Plymouth	Plymouth Mayflower Centre	01752 306330	barbicantic@plymouth.gov.uk
Poole	4 High Street	01202 262600	info@pooletourism.com
Salcombe	Market Street	01548 843927	info@salcombeinformation.co.uk
Salisbury	Fish Row	01722 342860	info@salisburycitycouncil.gov.uk
Scilly, Isles Of	Porthcressa Bank	01720 424031	tic@scilly.gov.uk
Seaton	The Underfleet	01297 21660	visit@seaton.gov.uk
Shaftesbury	8a Bell Street	01747 853514	tourism@shaftesburydorset.com
Shepton Mallet	70 High Street	01749 345258	enquiries@visitsheptonmallet.co.uk
Sherborne	3 Tilton Court	01935 815341	sherborne.tic@westdorset-weymouth.gov.uk
Sidmouth	Ham Lane	01395 516441	ticinfo@sidmouth.gov.uk
Somerset	Sedgemoor Services	01934 750833	somersetvisitorcentre@somerset.gov.uk
South Molton	1 East Street	01769 574122	enquiries@visitsouthmolton.co.uk
St Austell	Southbourne Road	01726 879 500	staustelltic@gmail.com
St Ives	The Guildhall	0905 252 2250	info@stivestic.org.uk
Street	Clarks Village	01458 447384	info@streettic.co.uk
Stroud	Subscription Rooms	01453 760960	tic@stroud.gov.uk
Swanage	The White House	01929 422885	mail@swanage.gov.uk
Swindon	Central Library	01793 466454	infocentre@swindon.gov.uk
Taunton	Market House	01823 340470	tauntontic@tauntondeane.gov.uk
Tavistock	The Archway	01822 612938	tavistocktic@westdevon.gov.uk
Tetbury	33 Church Street	01666 503552	tourism@tetbury.org
Tewkesbury	100 Church Street	01684 855040	tewkesburytic@tewkesbury.gov.uk
Tiverton	Tiverton Museum	01884 230878	tivertontic@tivertonmuseum.org.uk
Torquay	Vaughan Parade	01803 211 211	holiday@englishriviera.co.uk
Torrington	Castle Hill	01805 626140	info@great-torrington.com
Totnes	The Town Mill	01803 863168	enquire@totnesinformation.co.uk
Trowbridge	St. Stephen's Place	01225 765072	tic@trowbridge.gov.uk
Truro	Municipal Building	01872 274555	tic@truro.gov.uk
Wareham	Discover Purbeck	01929 552740	tic@purbeck-dc.gov.uk
Warminster	Central Car Park	01985 218548	visitwarminster@btconnect.com
Wellington	30 Fore Street	01823 663379	wellingtontic@tauntondeane.gov.uk
Wells	Wells Museum	01749 671770	visitwellsinfo@gmail.com
Weston-Super-Mare	Vic The Tropicana	01934 888877	vic@wsm-tc.gov.uk
Wimborne Minster	29 High Street	01202 886116	wimbornetic@eastdorset.gov.uk
Winchcombe	Town Hall	01242 602925	winchcombetic@tewkesbury.gov.uk
Woolacombe	The Esplanade	01271 870553	info@woolacombetourism.co.uk
Yeovil	Petters House	01935 462781	tourism@southsomerset.gov.uk

Regional Contacts and Information

For more information on accommodation, attractions, activities, events and holidays in South West England, contact one of the following regional or local tourism organisations. Their websites have a wealth of information and many produce free publications to help you get the most out of your visit.

www.visitsouthwest.co.uk
www.visitdevon.co.uk
www.visitcornwall.co.uk
www.visit-dorset.com
www.visitsomerset.co.uk
www.visitbristol.co.uk
www.visitbath.co.uk
www.southwestcoastpath.org.uk

Stay – South West

Entries appear alphabetically by town name in each county. A key to symbols appears on page 6

Trevarth Holiday Park

Blackwater, Truro TR4 8HR
T: (01872) 560266 **E:** trevarth@btconnect.com
W: www.trevarth.co.uk **£ BOOK ONLINE**

VisitEngland
HOLIDAY, TOURING & CAMPING PARK

🚐	(30)	£13.50-£22.00
🚐	(30)	£13.50-£22.00
🏕	(30)	£13.50-£22.00
🛖	(0)	
	(0)	
🏠	(20)	£200.00-£730.00

30 touring pitches

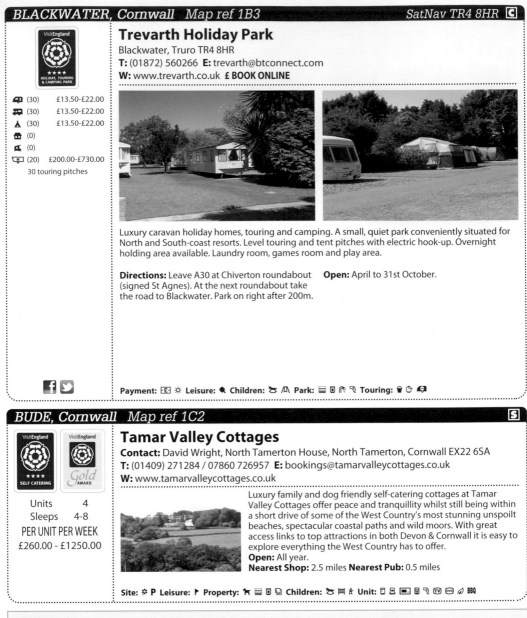

Luxury caravan holiday homes, touring and camping. A small, quiet park conveniently situated for North and South-coast resorts. Level touring and tent pitches with electric hook-up. Overnight holding area available. Laundry room, games room and play area.

Directions: Leave A30 at Chiverton roundabout (signed St Agnes). At the next roundabout take the road to Blackwater. Park on right after 200m.

Open: April to 31st October.

Payment: 💳 ☀ **Leisure:** 🔦 **Children:** 🛝 ⛰ **Park:** 🏢 🏠 🏨 🍴 **Touring:** 🚐 🌀 🚗

Tamar Valley Cottages

Contact: David Wright, North Tamerton House, North Tamerton, Cornwall EX22 6SA
T: (01409) 271284 / 07860 726957 **E:** bookings@tamarvalleycottages.co.uk
W: www.tamarvalleycottages.co.uk

VisitEngland
SELF CATERING

VisitEngland
Gold AWARD

Units	4
Sleeps	4-8

PER UNIT PER WEEK
£260.00 - £1250.00

Luxury family and dog friendly self-catering cottages at Tamar Valley Cottages offer peace and tranquillity whilst still being within a short drive of some of the West Country's most stunning unspoilt beaches, spectacular coastal paths and wild moors. With great access links to top attractions in both Devon & Cornwall it is easy to explore everything the West Country has to offer.
Open: All year.
Nearest Shop: 2.5 miles **Nearest Pub:** 0.5 miles

Site: ✿ P **Leisure:** ⌇ **Property:** 🐾 🏢 🏨 🍴 **Children:** 🛝 🛏 🚶 **Unit:** 🏢 🖥 📺 📀 🔊 BBQ

Book your accommodation online

Visit our websites for detailed information, up-to-date availability and to book your accommodation online. Includes over 20,000 places to stay, all of them star rated.

www.visitor-guides.co.uk

BUDE, *Cornwall* Map ref 1C2 — S

Units 20
Sleeps 2-10

PER UNIT PER WEEK
£450.00 - £3950.00

SPECIAL PROMOTIONS
Short breaks between
October and Easter.
Late availability and
offers on our website.

Whalesborough Cottages & Spa

Contact: James & Sharran Proudfoot, Owners, Whalesborough Farm,
Marhamchurch, Bude, Cornwall EX23 0JD **T:** (01288) 361626 / 07557 508641
F: (01288) 361317 **E:** jproudfoot@whalesborough.plus.com
W: www.whalesborough.co.uk **£ BOOK ONLINE**

VisitEngland
Awards for
Excellence 2016
BRONZE WINNER

Whalesborough luxury self catering cottages and spa, near Bude will appeal to visitors looking for contemporary, spacious holiday accommodation surrounded by the natural countryside of North Cornwall. Twenty 5 star gold award-winning cottages sleeping 2-10 people with indoor pool/spa, outdoor pool, tennis courts, indoor games barn and onsite café/bistro/shop. Walk/cycle from your cottage across the farm to the beach or down the Canal Towpath to Bude or use Whalesborough as a base to explore the rest of Cornwall and North Devon. Cottages all have private, enclosed gardens and are pet friendly too.

Open: All year.
Nearest Shop: 1 mile
Nearest Pub: 1 mile

Units: Most bedrooms have en suite facilities. 5 single storey cottages, all interiors professionally designed. Underfloor heating, woodburners. Enclosed gardens.

Site: ❊ P **Payment:** 💳 **Leisure:** ♪ ⚓ 🔍 ⚲ ⚲ ⚲ **Property:** ∥ 🐾 🖥 📖 🖥 **Children:** 🛝 🎱 🍴
Unit: 🗄 🗄 📺 🗄 🗄 📺 💿 ♨ BBQ

f

BUDE, *Cornwall* Map ref 1C2 — SatNav EX23 9HJ — C

🚐 (80) £20.00-£37.00
🚚 (60) £14.00-£37.00
⛺ (60) £14.00-£32.00
🏠 (55) £301.00-£1148.00
200 touring pitches

SPECIAL PROMOTIONS
See our website for
special offers.

Wooda Farm Holiday Park

Poughill, Bude, Cornwall EX23 9HJ
T: (01288) 352069 **E:** stay@wooda.co.uk
W: www.wooda.co.uk **£ BOOK ONLINE**

Stunning views over Bude Bay and countryside; 1.5 miles from safe, sandy beaches. Family-owned and run with excellent facilities for touring and camping and luxury holiday homes for hire. Activities include fishing, sports barn, tennis court, woodland walks and golf. An ideal base for touring the delights of Devon and Cornwall.

Directions: 1.5 miles from Bude, just outside the village of Poughill.

Open: April to October.

f ▾

Payment: 💳 **Leisure:** ♪ ⚓ ∪ 🔍 ⚲ **Property:** 🐾 🖥 🗄 📖 **Children:** 🛝 ⚠ **Catering:** ✕ 🍴

CHARLESTOWN, Cornwall   Map ref 1B3   SatNav PL25 3NJ [H]

★★★ HOTEL

Silver AWARD

B&B PER ROOM PER NIGHT
S: £80.00 - £100.00
D: £120.00 - £170.00

The Pier House Hotel

Harbour Front, Charlestown Road, St Austell, Cornwall PL25 3NJ **T:** (01726) 67955
F: (01726) 69246 **E:** pierhouse@btconnect.com
W: www.pierhousehotel.com

The Pier House Hotel is situated on the picturesque harbour of Charlestown with stunning views of the port and coastline of St Austell bay. Experience the ultimate luxury that you would expect from one of the premier hotels in Cornwall.
Directions: Please see our website for full directions.
Bedrooms: 7 single, 17 double, 3 twin, 3 family.
Open: All year except Christmas day.

Site: ✿ Payment: 🖃 Leisure: ♪ ▶ ♉ Property: ▦ ⛪ ◐ Children: ⚲ 🏚 ⚵ Catering: ⦿✕ ⛾ ⛾
Room: ♜ ⚶ ☎ ⊙ 📺 ⚱

CONSTANTINE BAY, Cornwall   Map ref 1B2   SatNav PL28 8JH

★★★★ SELF CATERING

B&B PER ROOM PER NIGHT
S: £73.50 - £115.00
D: £141.00 - £230.00
HB PER PERSON PER NIGHT
£98.00 - £139.50

SPECIAL PROMOTIONS
Prices vary throughout the seasons - please contact or visit website for further details.

Treglos Hotel

Constantine Bay, Padstow PL28 8JH **T:** (01841) 520727 **F:** (01841) 521163
E: stay@tregloshotel.com
W: www.tregloshotel.com **£ BOOK ONLINE**

This luxurious hotel on the North Cornish coast has 42 rooms and suites, many with dramatic views over Constantine Bay. Facilities include indoor pool, whirlpool, treatment rooms and award-winning restaurant. Treglos has its own golf course and self-catering apartments. Beaches and coastal paths are within a short stroll. Please contact for evening meal prices.

Directions: Please contact us for directions.

Bedrooms: 3 single, 23 double/twin, 10 family, 6 suite.
Open: February to November.

Site: ✿ P Payment: 🖃 Leisure: ♿ ♪ ▶ ♉ ♦ ⚵ ❖ Property: ⚘ ▦ ◫ ⛪ ◐ ∅ Children: ⚲ 🏚 ⚵
Catering: ⦿✕ ⛾ ⛾ Room: ♜ ⚶ ☎ 📺 ⊙ ⚱

EDMONTON, Cornwall *Map ref 1B2*

Units 2
Sleeps 1-4

PER UNIT PER WEEK
£200.00 - £600.00

SPECIAL PROMOTIONS
Weekend breaks £150 - £250. Please contact for details.

Quarrymans Cottages

Contact: Mr Huw Jenkins, 17 Granville Terrace, Mountain Ash CF45 4AL **T:** 07866 386611
E: jenkins@choicecornishcottages.com
W: www.choicecornishcottages.com **£ BOOK ONLINE**

These tastefully decorated, cosy cottages are situated overlooking the Camel Estuary. Originally the homes of 19th century slate quarrymen, they are positioned around a stone-flagged courtyard and adjacent to a traditional Cornish inn. Fifteen-minute drive from Padstow's pretty harbour and sandy beaches.

Open: All year.
Nearest Shop: 0.5 miles
Nearest Pub: 40 yards

Units: 2 bedrooms on 1st floor, 1 with double bed, 1 with twin beds.

Site: P **Leisure:** **Property:** **Children:** **Unit:**

FALMOUTH, Cornwall *Map ref 1B3*

Units 8
Sleeps 2-8

PER UNIT PER WEEK
£460.00 - £1425.00

SPECIAL PROMOTIONS
We offer short breaks with a minimum stay of three nights. Regular promotions are shown on our website throughout the year.

Mylor Harbourside Holidays

Contact: Mylor Yacht Harbour, Mylor Churchtown, Falmouth TR11 5UF **T:** (01326) 372121
E: enquiries@mylor.com
W: www.mylor.com/holidays **£ BOOK ONLINE**

Our luxury waterside retreats make for the perfect relaxing coastal getaway for couples, families and large groups, offering a variety of 2 storey cottages and single storey apartments. All however, share one thing in common - the stunning harbourside location.

Nestled into the heart of a traditional working harbour in Mylor, Cornwall, these beautiful cottages sit on the banks of the Fal River with views across the estuary and offer the ideal location for those who like to get out and explore the coastline, countryside and not forgetting some of the best sailing waters in the UK.

Open: All year.
Nearest Shop: 2 miles
Nearest Pub: On site in the Harbour

Units: We have a range of 1 and 2 storey properties all of which are fully furnished and equipped with modern fitted kitchens, some have en suite bathrooms.

Site: P **Property:** **Children:** **Unit:** BBQ

FOWEY, Cornwall *Map ref 1B3* *SatNav PL23 1JU* C

VisitEngland
HOLIDAY, TOURING & CAMPING PARK ★★★★

Penhale Caravan & Camping Park

Penhale Caravan & Camping Park, Penhale Farm, Fowey, Cornwall PL23 1JU
T: (01726) 833425 **F:** (01726) 833425 **E:** info@penhale-fowey.co.uk
W: www.penhale-fowey.co.uk **£ BOOK ONLINE**

(35)   £15.00-£30.00
(16)   £15.00-£30.00
(56)   £8.00-£30.00
(11)   £200.00-£650.00
56 touring pitches

Friendly, uncrowded family run park that overlooks unspoilt farmland and lovely views of the sea. In Area of Outstanding Natural Beauty close to sandy beaches, many scenic walks and the Eden Project. David Bellamy Award. Choice of caravans. Touring pitches, electric hook-ups, free showers. Overnight holding area available. **Directions:** From A30 west from Lostwithiel, on A390 turn left after 1 mile onto B3269, after 3 miles turn right onto A3082. **Open:** Easter or 1st April to End October.

Site: A P **Payment:** ☒ ☼ **Leisure:** ♪ ► ∪ ♦ **Children:** ☒ **Catering:** ☖ **Park:** ♞ ☲ ☵ ⟮ ⟑
Touring: ☂ ☺ ♨

HAYLE, Cornwall *Map ref 1B3* *SatNav TR27 5AW* C

VisitEngland
HOLIDAY, TOURING & CAMPING PARK ★★★★

Beachside Holiday Park

Phillack, Hayle, Cornwall TR27 5AW
T: (01736) 753080 **F:** (01736) 757252 **E:** reception@beachside.co.uk
W: www.beachside.co.uk **£ BOOK ONLINE**

(80)   £13.00-£44.00
(80)   £13.00-£44.00
(80)   £13.00-£44.00
(33)   £315.00-£1605.00
(80)   £265.00-£765.00
80 touring pitches

Beachside is a family holiday park, set amidst sand dunes right on the beach in the famous St Ives Bay. With a range of accommodation and touring pitches, our location is ideally situated in West Cornwall for a touring and beach holiday.

Directions: Travel west on A30 and turn off into Hayle. Turn right, following the sign to Phillack & Beachside. Our entrance is approximately 400m on right.

Open: Easter to End October.

f ♥

Site: ☞ A P **Payment:** ☒ ☼ **Leisure:** ♪ ∪ ♦ ⚘ **Children:** ☒ ⚠ **Catering:** ☖ **Park:** ♫ ☲ ☵ ⟮ ⟑
Touring: ☂ ♨

LANDS END, Cornwall *Map ref 1A3* *SatNav TR19 7RD* B

VisitEngland
GUEST HOUSE ★★★★

VisitEngland
Silver AWARD

B&B PER ROOM PER NIGHT
S: £40.00 - £50.00
D: £80.00 - £98.00

Bosavern House

Bosavern, St. Just, Lands End TR19 7RD **T:** (01736) 788301 **E:** info@bosavern.com
W: www.bosavern.com

17th century country house in attractive grounds. Centrally heated, comfortable accommodation. Most rooms have sea or moorland views. Home-cooking using local produce. Ideally situated for exploring West Cornwall. Ample parking. **Directions:** Take A3071 from Penzance towards St Just, turn left onto B3306 signed Lands End. Bosavern House is 0.5 mile on left. **Bedrooms:** 1 single, 3 double, 2 twin, 2 family. **Open:** All year except Christmas.

f

Site: ☼ P **Payment:** ☒ € **Leisure:** ⛳ ♪ ⚘ **Property:** ☲ ☵ **Children:** ☒ ☴ ☆ **Catering:** ♟ ☷
Room: ☖ ♨ TV ♨ ☵

LOOE, Cornwall Map ref 1C2   SatNav PL13 2DG [H]

Hannafore Point Hotel and Spa

Marine Drive, West Looe, Looe PL13 2DG T: (01503) 263273
E: stay@hannaforepointhotel.com
W: www.hannaforepointhotel.com

B&B PER ROOM PER NIGHT
S: £50.00 - £72.00
D: £100.00 - £154.00
HB PER PERSON PER NIGHT
£52.00 - £92.00

SPECIAL PROMOTIONS
Special-event packages. Extensive range of conference and business facilities. Weddings and special occasions. Christmas and New Year celebrations.

A warm welcome awaits you. Set in picturesque Cornish village with spectacular, panoramic sea views. Indulge in superb home-cooked food. Dining options include quality local produce and fresh fish. The terrace is a popular rendezvous for cream teas or cocktails. Spa pool, gym, sauna, steam and beauty therapies.

Directions: A38 from Plymouth, then A387 to Looe. Cross over stone bridge, turn 1st left (sign 'Hannafore') and uphill until overlooking bay.

Bedrooms: 4 single, 33 double.
Open: All year.

Site: ❀ Payment: ⊞ Leisure: ♿ ♪ ▶ ☋ ✳ ⚔ ♞ Property: ⚑ ☎ 🖼 🖪 ◐ Children: ☌ ▦ ⚲
Catering: ☮ 🍴 Room: 📺 🌢 ☏ ⌨ 📺 ♨ 🛁 ☕

MARAZION, Cornwall Map ref 1B3   [S]

Trevarthian Holiday Homes

Contact: Mr Sean Cattran, Trevarthian Holiday Homes, West End, Marazion TR17 0EG
T: (01736) 710100 F: (01736) 710111 E: info@trevarthian.co.uk
W: www.trevarthian.co.uk £ BOOK ONLINE

Units   16
Sleeps   1-5
PER UNIT PER WEEK
£240.00 - £910.00

Trevarthian Holiday Homes is a family business focussing on quality self-catering accommodation in the beautiful town of Marazion, Cornwall. All our properties are located opposite the large sandy beach and St Michael's Mount, a must-see for any visit to the South West, and within a five minute walk of the children's playground, village pubs, restaurants, galleries, shops and bus-stops. Accommodation ranges in size from single bedroom apartments to a three-bedroom cottage with a private garden. **Open:** All year.
Nearest Shop: 0.20 miles **Nearest Pub:** 0.20 miles

f ▶

Site: ❀ P Payment: ⊞ Leisure: ♿ ♪ ☋ Property: 🖼 🖪 🖳 Children: ☌ ▦ ⚲ Unit: 🖪 🖳 📺 ⌨ 📀 ⌀

NEWQUAY, Cornwall Map ref 1B2 S

Forty Eight The Penthouse

Contact: Peter Feltham, 12 Seacote, 6 Warren Edge Road, Bournemouth, Dorset BH6 4AU
T: 07729 926109 **E:** enquiries@thepenthousenewquay.co.uk
W: www.thepenthousenewquay.co.uk

Units 1
Sleeps 6

SPECIAL PROMOTIONS
Available on request.

Forty Eight is a recently refurbished luxury 3 bedroom apartment overlooking Fistral Beach. Spacious and light with a large open plan lounge, fully fitted modern kitchen and dining area with panoramic views of Fistral Beach and the Headland. This penthouse apartment is a 2 minute walk from the beach, 10 minute walk or 3 minute drive from Newquay town.

Forty Eight has a designated parking space and garage in a private gated complex in the quieter beachside area of Pentire. This apartment is suitable for families, couples and mixed singles aged 25 plus only. Prices available on the website.

Open: All year.

Units: Master bedroom with en suite. Family bathroom. Large private balcony spanning width of apartment. TV's & Chromecast in all bedrooms. Playstation.

Site: P Property: 🖥 📶 🛁 **Children:** 🐾 🍴 **Unit:** 🛏 🏢 📺 🎧 📻 TV 💿 📟

NEWQUAY, Cornwall Map ref 1B2 SatNav TR7 2NQ B

Harrington Guest House

25 Tolcarne Road, Newquay TR7 2NQ **T:** (01637) 873581
E: harringtonguesthouse@yahoo.com
W: www.harringtonguesthouse.com **£ BOOK ONLINE**

B&B PER ROOM PER NIGHT
S: £25.00 - £34.00
D: £46.00 - £58.00

The Harrington is a Bed & Breakfast with a central location situated within a short walk of all that Newquay resort has to offer. 5 mins walk from train station and local buses. Excellent value rooms with free Wi-Fi and free parking.
Bedrooms: En suite, flatscreen TV, tea and coffee facilities.
Open: All year except Christmas.

Site: P Payment: 💳 **Leisure:** 🎵 ▶ ⛳ **Property:** 🖥 🍴 **Children:** 🐾³ 🍴 **Catering:** 🍴 **Room:** 🍵 💧 TV

Riverside Holiday Park

Lane, Newquay, Cornwall TR8 4PE
T: (01637) 873617 **F:** (01637) 877051 **E:** info@riversideholidaypark.co.uk
W: www.riversideholidaypark.co.uk **£ BOOK ONLINE**

(65)	£19.50-£25.50
(4)	£330.00-£970.00
(1)	£330.00-£970.00
(12)	£245.00-£790.00
65 touring pitches	

SPECIAL PROMOTIONS

3 or 4 nights short stay up to the 14th July and from 2nd September.

Welcome to Riverside Holiday Park - Newquay, Cornwall. The park makes an excellent base for exploring the famous seaside resort – just two and half miles away – and the rest of Cornwall too. The park is family owned and run. It's well maintained and caters for families and couples only.

A warm welcome awaits at our reception and information desk which includes a small shop with basic everyday supplies. The park has sheltered, level touring pitches, luxury lodges and caravans. Covered, heated pool and bar.

Directions: Follow A392 for Newquay, at Quintrell Downs go straight over at roundabout, we are first left after Hendra Holiday Park.

Open: Easter to end of October.

Site: 🏠 **Payment:** 💷 ☼ **Leisure:** 🏊 ♪ ♪ ♪ ♪ **Children:** 🚲 ⛰ **Catering:** ✕ 🍴 **Park:** 🐕 🗑 📶 📶
Touring: 🚰 🚽 🚐

Sunday & School Cottages

Contact: Mrs Diane Hoe, Owner, Sunday Cottages, Lower Cottage, Preston-on-Stour, Stratford on Avon, Warwickshire CV37 8NG **T:** (01789) 450214 **E:** di@sundaycottage.co.uk
W: www.sundaycottage.co.uk

Units	2
Sleeps	2-6

PER UNIT PER WEEK

£525.00 - £1360.00

Two beautiful, peaceful and comfortable cottages in old Padstow, with super-fast broadband & off-road parking. Minutes' walk to harbour, shops, restaurants, beaches, coastal path, and stunning, unspoilt coastline! Both cottages make an ideal base for walkers.

School Cottage boasts a magical walled garden with summer house, BBQ and lovely old stone wood store, stocked with logs for the wood burner for our winter visits.

We accept children of 8 years and over. No pets allowed.
Availability can be checked on www.sundaycottage.co.uk

Open: All year except January.
Nearest Shop: 0.10 miles
Nearest Pub: 0.10 miles

Units: Sunday Cottage sleeps 4 in 2 bedrooms. School Cottage sleeps up to 6 in 3 bedrooms.

Site: ❋ P **Property:** ∥ ▤ 🗑 🗑 **Unit:** 🗑 🗑 🗑 🗑 📺 📀 🍽 BBQ 📞

PENZANCE, Cornwall Map ref 1B3   S

SELF CATERING

Units	1
Sleeps	1-2

PER UNIT PER WEEK
£210.00 - £420.00

SPECIAL PROMOTIONS
Short breaks can be booked at short notice outside of the high season months. Please phone for availability.

Broom Farm Cottage

Contact: Mrs June Markham, Broom Farm, Packet Lane, Rosudgeon, Near Marazion, Penzance TR20 9QD **T:** (01736) 763738 / 07876 088872
E: broomfarmcottage@yahoo.com

This single storey detached cottage, converted from a traditional stone barn, provides very comfortable accommodation for two people. It is the only letting unit on site, which makes it popular with guests, many returning year after year. A door through the carport leads to the patio and meadow, an ideal spot for relaxing on the swing seat, reading or just watching the sun go down. It is one mile to Prussia Cove and superb coastal walks, while footpaths and bridleways crisscross the surrounding Poldark countryside. The Lizard and the far west are both easily reached.

Open: All year round, including Christmas and New Year.
Nearest Shop: Shop / P.O are 400 yards away
Nearest Pub: Award-winning pub food 300 yards

Units: The bedroom has an en suite with bath/shower over with grab rails. Free storage heating keeps the cottage warm and cosy. All rooms are on same level.

Site: ✿ P **Leisure:** ▶ **Property:** 🐾 🖳 **Unit:** 🖥 🗦 📺 📀 BBQ

PENZANCE, Cornwall Map ref 1A3   SatNav TR20 9AU   C

HOLIDAY, TOURING & CAMPING PARK

🚐	(20)	£18.00-£26.00
🚏	(20)	£18.00-£26.00
⛺	(40)	£12.00-£26.00
🏠	(7)	£275.00-£600.00

40 touring pitches

Kenneggy Cove Holiday Park

Higher Kenneggy, Rosudgeon, Penzance, Cornwall TR20 9AU
T: (01736) 763453 **E:** enquiries@kenneggycove.co.uk
W: www.kenneggycove.co.uk

A tranquil park (no noise after 10pm), surrounded by glorious countryside in an Area of Outstanding Natural Beauty. Panoramic sea views. 12 minute walk to SW coastpath and secluded coves. Short footpath walks to Prussia Cove and a gastro-pub.
Directions: We are equidistant from Penzance and Helston off the A394 coast road (3m east of Marazion). At our blue sign, turn down the lane towards sea. We are near the end of the lane on the left.
Open: Mid May to end of September.

Site: 🅰️📶 **Payment:** € ☀ **Leisure:** ♿ ♪ ▶ ∪ **Children:** 🛝 ⛰ **Catering:** ✗ 🛒 **Park:** 🐾 🖳 📦 🐟 🗑
Touring: 💧 ⟳ 🚰

Book your accommodation online

Visit our websites for detailed information, up-to-date availability and to book your accommodation online. Includes over 20,000 places to stay, all of them star rated.

www.visitor-guides.co.uk

PORTHTOWAN, Cornwall Map ref 1B3

Rosehill Lodges

Contact: Mr John Barrow, Rosehill Lodges, Porthtowan, Cornwall TR4 8AR
T: (01209) 891920 **F:** (01209) 891935 **E:** reception@rosehilllodges.com
W: www.rosehilllodges.com **£ BOOK ONLINE**

| Units | 10 |
| Sleeps | 1-6 |

PER UNIT PER WEEK
£537.00 - £2296.00

SPECIAL PROMOTIONS
Weekend and mid-week breaks available. Open for Christmas and New Year. Low occupancy discounts available. Free superfast broadband over Wi-Fi. Free cots and highchairs. See website for special offers.

Five Star luxury Gold Award self-catering lodges right on the Cornish coast. Situated in the coastal village of Porthtowan just five minutes' walk to a sandy Blue Flag beach, bars and restaurants. Relax and leave your car behind. Each bespoke lodge features super-king size beds, log burners, your own personal hot tub spa and free superfast Wi-Fi. Go green with grass roofs and solar panels and dine al-fresco under glass covered decking whatever the weather. Each lodge has an external drench shower, ideal for washing down after a fun day on the beach. We look forward to giving you a warm welcome.

Open: All year.
Nearest Shop: 0.5 miles
Nearest Pub: 0.5 miles

Units: Bespoke luxury timber eco lodges, fully equipped and hand built locally with materials from sustainable sources. Luxury and green better together.

Site: ✿ P Payment: 💳 Leisure: 🚲 ⚓ ▶ ㋡ Property: ▭ 📱 📶 Children: 🐕 🛏 👶
Unit: 📺 💻 🔥 📶 📺 🖥 💿 BBQ 📞

REDRUTH, Cornwall Map ref 1B3

Tehidy Holiday Park

Contact: Richard and Julia Barnes, Owners, Tehidy Holiday Park, Harris Mill, Illogan, Nr Portreath, Redruth TR16 4JQ **T:** (01209) 216489 **F:** (01209) 213555
E: holiday@tehidy.co.uk **W:** www.tehidy.co.uk **£ BOOK ONLINE**

| Units | 26 |
| Sleeps | 1-6 |

PER UNIT PER WEEK
£270.00 - £820.00

SPECIAL PROMOTIONS
Special offers on our website. Short breaks are welcome outside the summer holiday period.

Nestled in a wooded valley, we are perfectly placed between St Ives and St Agnes giving easy access to the best that Cornwall has to offer. Regional Winners 2016 - for 4 years running and David Bellamy Gold Conservation Award 2017 - for 8 years running. Close to beautiful sandy beaches, gardens and cycle routes and much more.... We offer Cottages, holiday caravans, touring/camping and wigwam cabins, Woodland walks from site, play area and excellent facilities. We look forward to welcoming you to our beautiful, family run, setting for your next holiday in Cornwall.

Open: March to November.
Nearest Shop: On site and in the village
Nearest Pub: In the village

Units: Caravans and cottages have fully fitted kitchens and shower rooms with W/C.

Payment: 💳 Leisure: ▶ 🎣 Property: ▭ 📱 🏠 Children: 🐕

ST. AGNES, Cornwall Map ref 1B3 SatNav TR5 0PA B

VisitEngland ★★ GUEST ACCOMMODATION

B&B PER ROOM PER NIGHT
S: £30.00 - £60.00
D: £60.00 - £90.00

Penkerris

Penwinnick Road (B3277), St. Agnes TR5 0PA **T:** (01872) 552262 **E:** penkerris@gmail.com
W: www.penkerris.co.uk

Edwardian house with parking, lawned garden for relaxation and games, cosy lounge and delightful dining room serving real food. Close to dramatic cliff walks and iconic surfing beaches (nearest 1km). Beach hut available. Ideal location, central for all of Cornwall. Cyclist, walkers, families and pets all welcome.
Directions: From A30, big roundabout at Chiverton, 3 miles to village on B3277. Penkerris is just inside St Agnes village and 30mph sign and before the Museum. **Bedrooms:** 2 double, 2 twin, 2 family, 2 singles. **Open:** All year.

Site: P **Payment:** € **Leisure:** **Property:** **Children:** **Catering:** **Room:** TV

ST. AUSTELL, Cornwall Map ref 1B3 S

VisitEngland ★★★ SELF CATERING

Units 1
Sleeps 1-6
PER UNIT PER WEEK
£290.00 - £850.00

The Old Inn, Pentewan

Contact: Mr & Mrs Robert Haskins, 19 Ullswater Drive, Wetherby LS22 6YF
T: (01937) 580217 / 07802 819409 **E:** rjhaskins@gmail.com
W: www.inncornwall.com

Stone cottage near beach in quiet location, in area of outstanding beauty. Close to Mevagissey (2 miles), the Lost Gardens of Heligan (2 miles) and The Eden Project (7 miles). Once an alehouse for visiting sailors, now a modern 3-star self-catering unit. It retains its character with low beams, pictures and open fireplace. Pentewan has a pub, Post Office stores and restaurant. Country walks.
Open: All year. **Nearest Shop:** 500 yards **Nearest Pub:** 200 yards

FAMILIES WELCOME **Site:** P **Leisure:** **Property:** **Children:** **Unit:** TV BBQ

ST. COLUMB, Cornwall Map ref 1B2 S

VisitEngland ★★★ SELF CATERING

Units 1
Sleeps 1-4
PER UNIT PER WEEK
£225.00 - £525.00

Meadow Rise

Contact: Mrs Helen Grimsey, Proprietor, Cornish Holiday, 24 Valley Mead, Anna Valley, Andover SP11 7SB **T:** (01264) 335527 / 07881 623483 **E:** enquiries@cornishholiday.info
W: www.cornishholiday.info **£ BOOK ONLINE**

Cosy modern 2 bedroomed house in a quiet village location. An ideal base for all sightseeing and beach holidays. Padstow and Newquay less than 10 miles away.
Open: All year.
Nearest Shop: 0.30 miles
Nearest Pub: 0.5 miles

Site: P **Payment:** **Property:** **Children:** **Unit:** TV DVD BBQ

ST. IVES, Cornwall Map ref 1B3 S

VisitEngland ★★★★ SELF CATERING

Units 4
Sleeps 2-6
PER UNIT PER WEEK
£250.00 - £850.00

Trevalgan Holiday Farm

Contact: Mr Russell Osborne, Trevalgan Holiday Farm, Little Trevalgan, Trevalgan Farm, St Ives, Cornwall TR26 3BJ **T:** (01736) 796529 / 07921 450547 **E:** holidays@trevalgan.co.uk
W: www.trevalgan.co.uk **£ BOOK ONLINE**

Expect excellent accommodation, breathtaking scenery and a warm welcome on this family farm. Cottages are child-friendly, decorated, furnished and equipped to a very high standard. Why choose between a beach holiday and a countryside holiday when you can have both? With St Ives just a 5 minute drive our location is ideal for both families and couples to explore wonderful West Cornwall. **Open:** All year.
Nearest Shop: 1.5 miles **Nearest Pub:** 1.5 miles

Site: P **Leisure:** **Property:** **Children:** **Unit:** TV DVD

ST. JUST IN ROSELAND, Cornwall Map ref 1B3
SatNav TR2 5JF **C**

Trethem Mill Touring Park
St. Just in Roseland, Nr St Mawes, Truro, Cornwall TR2 5JF
T: (01872) 580504 **F:** (01872) 580968 **E:** reception@trethem.com
W: www.trethem.com

£20.00-£28.00
£20.00-£28.00
£20.00-£28.00
84 touring pitches

Multi award-winning 5 star luxury for touring caravans, motorhomes and tents. We're very proud to have been awarded the Enjoy England Gold Award for exceptional service and quality beyond the usual 5 star rating.
Directions: A3078 towards Tregony/St Mawes, over Tregony bridge. After 5 miles follow brown caravan and camping signs from Trewithian. Site 2 miles beyond on right-hand side.
Open: 1st April to 8th October.

Payment: 💷 ☀ **Leisure:** 🚴 🏊 ⛵ **Children:** 🐾 ⚠ **Catering:** 🍴 **Park:** 🏠 📺 🍴 🐾 **Touring:** 🚿 🔌 🚐

ST. MINVER, Cornwall Map ref 1B2
SatNav PL27 6RG **B**

Tredower Barton
St Minver, Wadebridge, Cornwall PL27 6RG **T:** (01208) 813501
E: dally.123@btinternet.com

B&B PER ROOM PER NIGHT
S: £40.00
D: £64.00 - £70.00

Tredower Barton is a farm bed and breakfast set in beautiful countryside near the North Cornish coast. A lovely garden/sun room with beautiful panoramic views available for guests' use. Delicious breakfast and relaxing stay guaranteed. Near to local attractions, Padstow, Port Isaac, Eden Project & Heligan Gardens only 45 minutes. Wi-Fi available.
Directions: 3 miles from Wadebridge on road B3314 to Port Issac.
Bedrooms: 1 twin, 1 family (can be used as family or double).
Open: Easter to October.

Site: ❀ **P Leisure:** 🚴 🎣 🏌 🎾 **Property:** 📺 🍴 **Children:** 🐾 🛏 🚸 **Room:** 🍴 ☕ 📺 🛏 🍴

TINTAGEL, Cornwall Map ref 1B2
S

Halgabron Mill Holiday Cottages
Contact: Robin Evans, Manager, The Keep, Halgabron Mill, St. Nectan's Glen, Tintagel, Cornwall PL34 0BB **T:** (01840) 779099 **E:** Robin@halgabronmill.co.uk
W: www.halgabronmill.co.uk

Units   4
Sleeps   2-5
PER UNIT PER WEEK
£267.00 - £979.00

Four well-equipped character stone cottages, with exposed beams and lead latticed windows, surround a former 18th century Water Mill. Situated in St. Nectan's Glen - a densely, wooded valley between Tintagel and Boscastle villages. Coastpath is 10 minute walk. Closest Beaches are a 10 minute walk or 5 minute drive.
Open: All year (Millstream Cottage Easter to Oct).
Nearest Shop: 1 mile
Nearest Pub: 1 mile

Site: ❀ **P Property:** 🏠 **Children:** 🛏 🚸 **Unit:** 🍴 🍴 📺 📺 📺 🎥 ⌀

TRURO, Cornwall Map ref 1B3
S

Pulla Farm Holidays
Contact: Mrs Mary Richards, Pulla Farm Holidays, Pulla Farm, Pulla Cross, Frogpool, Truro TR4 8SA **T:** (01872) 863143 **E:** info@pullafarmholidays.co.uk
W: www.pullafarmholidays.co.uk **£ BOOK ONLINE**

Units   1
Sleeps   2-4
PER UNIT PER WEEK
£240.00 - £485.00

Traditional accommodation with a warm welcome on a livestock farm between Truro and Falmouth. Ideal for touring, beaches, surfing, walking, cycling and National Trust properties and gardens. Welcome Pack. Cream Tea.
Open: All year.
Nearest Shop: 2 miles
Nearest Pub: 1 mile

Site: ❀ **P Payment:** 💷 **Leisure:** 🚴 🏊 🏌 🎾 **Property:** 📺 🏠 **Children:** 🐾 🛏 🚸 **Unit:** 🍴 📺 📺 🍴 📺 🎥 ⌀ BBQ

TRURO, Cornwall Map ref 1B3 SatNav TR2 4JA [B]

VisitEngland
★★★★
BED & BREAKFAST

VisitEngland
Silver AWARD

B&B PER ROOM PER NIGHT
S: £60.00 - £70.00
D: £75.00 - £80.00

Spring Cottage B&B
Probus, Truro, Cornwall TR2 4JA **T:** (01872) 520307 **E:** info@springcottage.co.uk
W: www.springcottage.co.uk **£ BOOK ONLINE**

Chris and David warmly welcome you to Spring Cottage, a quality B&B in a listed 17th century Cornish cottage, lovingly restored to provide stylish en suite accommodation. Truro five miles, Eden Project and Heligan within easy reach.
Bedrooms: En suite rooms with showers, TV, free Wi-Fi.
Open: All year except Christmas and New Year.

Site: ✿ **P Payment:** ⊞ **Property:** 🖵 **Room:** 📶 📺 📀

TRURO, Cornwall Map ref 1B3 [S]

VisitEngland
★★★★★
SELF CATERING

Units 46
Sleeps 2-7
PER UNIT PER WEEK
£495.00 - £2410.00

[f] [t]

The Valley
Contact: Reservations Team, Bissoe Road, Carnon Downs, Truro TR3 6LQ
T: (01872) 862194 **E:** info@the-valley.co.uk
W: www.thevalleycornwall.co.uk **£ BOOK ONLINE**

The Valley...Cornwall's hidden secret. Modern and tasteful self-catering accommodation with a personal service and great facilities. Pools, fitness suite, tennis, squash and stylish restaurant all situated in beautiful countryside.
Open: All year.
Nearest Shop: 0.5 miles
Nearest Pub: 0.5 miles

Site: ✿ **P Payment:** ⊞ **Leisure:** 🚲 ▶ 🔍 ⚲ ⚲ ⚲ **Property:** ⫽ 🐾 🖵 🖵 **Children:** 🧸 🏔 🚶 **Unit:** 🗍 🗍 🖵 📶 📺 📀

WATERGATE BAY, Cornwall Map ref 1B2 SatNav TR8 4AD [C]

VisitEngland
★★★★
HOLIDAY, TOURING & CAMPING PARK

🚐 (200) £11.50-£23.00
🚐 (200) £11.50-£23.00
⛺ (220) £11.50-£23.00
🏕 (2) £260.00-£730.00
200 touring pitches

SPECIAL PROMOTIONS
Outside of the dates 14th July to 28th August, book 7 nights or more and receive a 10% discount.

Watergate Bay Touring Park
Tregurrian, Newquay, Cornwall TR8 4AD
T: (01637) 860387 **F:** (08716) 617549 **E:** email@watergatebaytouringpark.co.uk
W: www.watergatebaytouringpark.co.uk

Half a mile from Watergate Bay's sand, surf and cliff walks. Rural Location in an 'Area of Outstanding Natural Beauty'. Personally run and supervised by resident owners. Heated indoor/outdoor pool, tennis courts, skate park, games room, shop/café, licensed clubroom, free entertainment including kids club and kids play area. Overnight holding area available. Free Mini-bus to Watergate Bay.

Directions: From A30 follow signs for Newquay then airport. After passing the airport, turn left onto the B3276. Park 0.5 miles on the right.

Open: 1st March to the 1st November.

Site: 🏕 **Payment:** ⊞ ☼ **Leisure:** 🎵 ∪ 🔍 ⚲ ⚲ ⚲ **Children:** 🧸 🏔 **Catering:** ✗ 🍴
Park: 🐾 🎵 🖵 🗍 📻 **Touring:** 🚰 🖵 ⚡ ♨

ST MARY'S, Isles of Scilly Map ref 1A3 S

VisitEngland ★★★★ SELF CATERING

Units 1
Sleeps 4-8
PER UNIT PER WEEK
£1600.00 - £1800.00

Trevean Holidays

Contact: Mrs Rosemary Sharman, Owner, Trevean, Robinswood Farm, Bere Regis, Wareham, Dorset BH20 7JJ **T:** (01929) 472181 / 07826 865776 **F:** (01929) 472182
E: info@treveanholidays.co.uk **W:** www.treveanholidays.co.uk

Trevean is a large, spacious granite town house, sleeps 8. Living accommodation on the top floor with views over the Harbour. It has 4 double bedrooms, 2 shower rooms, bathroom, heating, Sky, TV, Wi-Fi and Utility room. Close to shops, restaurants and off island boats. Ideal for the extended family to get together for a holiday to enjoy the beautiful islands. Beaches two minutes from front door.
Open: Easter to October and Christmas/New Year.
Nearest Shop: 1 minute **Nearest Pub:** 0.10 miles

Leisure: **Property:** **Children:** **Unit:**

BRAUNTON, Devon Map ref 1C1 SatNav EX33 1HG C

VisitEngland ★★★★ TOURING & CAMPING PARK

(60) £12.00-£34.00
(30) £12.00-£34.00
(90) £11.00-£34.00
180 touring pitches

Lobb Fields Caravan and Camping Park

Saunton Road, Braunton, Devon EX33 1HG
T: (01271) 812090 **E:** info@lobbfields.com
W: www.lobbfields.com **£ BOOK ONLINE**

South facing park with great views over the sea. On edge of Braunton, with Saunton beach only 1.5 miles away. Excellent bus service. Ideal for all holiday seaside activities. Surf board hire and snack bar on site. Seasonal pitches available.
Directions: From Barnstaple to Braunton on A361. Then follow B3231 for 1 mile towards Saunton. Lobb Fields is marked on the right of the road.
Open: 17th March to 29th October 2017.

Payment: **Leisure:** **Children:** **Park:** **Touring:**

BRIXHAM, Devon Map ref 1D2 SatNav TQ5 9AJ H

VisitEngland ★★★ HOTEL

B&B PER ROOM PER NIGHT
S: £50.00 - £94.00
D: £100.00 - £188.00
HB PER PERSON PER NIGHT
£58.00 - £110.00

SPECIAL PROMOTIONS
Special-event packages. Extensive range of conference and business facilities. Weddings and special occasions. Christmas and New Year celebrations.

Berry Head Hotel

Berry Head Road, Brixham TQ5 9AJ **T:** (01803) 853225 **F:** (01803) 882084
E: stay@berryheadhotel.com
W: www.berryheadhotel.com

Steeped in history, nestling on the water's edge in acres of outstanding natural beauty. Traditional hospitality, excellent, friendly and personal service with attention to detail. Comfortable accommodation, thoughtfully equipped. Imaginative menus, varied dining options, featuring quality local produce and fresh fish. Lounge, bars and terrace, indoor pool & spa, popular with locals and residents.

Directions: Enter Brixham, continue to harbour and around, up King Street for 1 mile to Berry Head.

Bedrooms: Combination of single, double, twin and family rooms.
Open: All year.

Site: **Payment:** € **Leisure:** **Property:** **Children:** **Catering:**
Room:

BRIXHAM, Devon   Map ref 1D2   S

Harbour Reach

Contact: Jenny Pocock, Owner, 23 Penn Lane, Brixham, Devon TQ5 9NR **T:** 07751 608021
E: enquiries@harbourreachholidays.co.uk
W: www.harbourreachholidays.co.uk

Units   2
Sleeps   1-11
PER UNIT PER WEEK
£230.00 - £600.00

The amazing views across the harbour, Torbay and out to sea, makes this a perfect holiday home at any time of year. Harbour Reach is excellently furnished and equipped and divided into a maisonette and flat which are let separately or jointly thereby sleeping 1 to 11. We are within 10 minutes' walk of the harbour side, town and South West coastal footpath. Short breaks available from October to March. **Open:** All year including Christmas & New Year. **Nearest Shop:** 500 metres **Nearest Pub:** 200 metres

Site: **P** Property: 🐾 🍴 🛏 🗑 📶 Children: 🧸 🛏 ⚡ Unit: 🛏 📺 🗑 🔌 📺 📀

CHAGFORD, Devon   Map ref 1C2   S

Swallows at Falkedon

Contact: Helen Ford, Owner, Falkedon, Spreyton, Devon EX17 5EF **T:** (01647) 231526 / 07768 342578 **E:** Helen@falkedon.net
W: www.swallowsholidaycottage.co.uk **£ BOOK ONLINE**

Units   1
Sleeps   1-2

PER UNIT PER WEEK
£200.00 - £500.00

SPECIAL PROMOTIONS
Short breaks available, bookings commence on Friday, other start days can be accommodated out of season and for short breaks.

Adjoining a beautiful Georgian farmhouse, this delightful 4 star apartment is situated just off a quiet country lane 1 mile from the pretty village of Spreyton with the famous Tom Cobley Tavern. Located in the center of Devon, close to Dartmoor National Park, 5 minutes from the A30 highway, Swallows at Falkedon is the perfect base to explore Devon and all it's attractions, National Trust properties, visit the North or South Devon coasts, the Cathedral city of Exeter. Full luxury bed linen and towels are provided together with a welcome hamper.

Open: All year.
Nearest Shop: 0.8 miles
Nearest Pub: 1 mile

Units: All on one level, large separate bathroom and bedroom, super king bed, can be a twin, state at booking. Separate lounge, kitchen/diner.

[f]

Site: **P** Payment: 💳 Leisure: 🏊 Property: 🛏 🗑 🖥 Children: 🛏 ⚡ Unit: 🛏 📺 🖥 🔌 📺 📀

Lulworth, Dorset ©Durdle Door Holiday Cottages

DARTMOUTH, *Devon*   Map ref 1D3

SatNav TQ6 9EF **B**

Cladda House B&B and Self Catering Apartments

88-90 Victoria Road, and Ford Valley (Our rear entrance car park), Dartmouth, Devon TQ6 9EF **T:** (01803) 835957 / 07967 060003 **E:** BandB@cladda-dartmouth.co.uk **W:** www.cladda-dartmouth.co.uk

B&B PER ROOM PER NIGHT
S: £78.00 - £93.00
D: £82.00 - £98.00

SPECIAL PROMOTIONS
Stay 7 Night's for the price of 6 - Contact us for Dartmouth Festivals - Candelit November 2016 - Christmas & New Year 2016 & for 2017 Music Festival May - Regatta Week August - Food Festival October.

Family run B&B in Dartmouth Town with 4 quality en suite super king, double, twin & standard double rooms and 2 self-contained 1 Bedroom (S/K or Twin) and Living Room (sofa bed) suites. The property is spacious for 2 or small families, walkers, golfers, etc.

We have our own FREE GUARANTEED on-site parking. A stroll to Dartmouth's Waterfront, restaurants, pubs, varied individual shops and galleries. Debit/Credit cards are accepted.

Directions: Description of getting to Dartmouth and detailed where to find us map of Dartmouth showing our on-site parking at back of Cladda House in Ford Valley sent with all of our booking confirmations.

Bedrooms: All rooms en suite, free Wi-Fi, flat screen colour TV/DVD, hair dryer, alarm clock/radio, quiet fridge & full hospitality tray.
Open: All year.

Site: ❄ **P Payment:** 💷 € **Leisure:** 🎣 ⚲ **Property:** 🐾 🖥 **Children:** 👶 ♨ ⛹ **Catering:** 🍽 **Room:** 🍵 🛁 📺 📀 ✦

f

DARTMOUTH, *Devon*   Map ref 1D3

S

The Old Bakehouse

Contact: Mrs Sylvia Ridalls, The Old Bakehouse, 7 Broadstone, Dartmouth TQ6 9NR
T: (01803) 834585 **F:** (01803) 834585 **E:** oldbakehousecottages@yahoo.com
W: www.oldbakehousedartmouth.co.uk

Units   4
Sleeps   2-6
PER UNIT PER WEEK
£315.00 - £685.00

Character cottages beams and old stone fireplaces, 2 minutes from historic town centre and river. Beach 15 minutes' drive. Free parking. Dogs free. Non smoking. Wi-Fi. Flat-screen TV/DVD with Freeview. Washing machines in all cottages and dishwashers in two. Spring, Autumn and Winter short breaks available. Reduced rates for OAPs 1st September to 30th June. Phone for Winter offers and more information. **Open:** All year.
Nearest Shop: 0.10 miles **Nearest Pub:** 0.10 miles

Site: P Payment: 💷 **Leisure:** 🎣 ⚲ **Property:** 🐾 🖥 🚭 🔥 **Children:** 👶 ♨ ⛹ **Unit:** 🛏 🖥 📶 📺 🍴 📀

DAWLISH, Devon   Map ref 1D2   **S**

Cofton Country Holidays

Contact: Starcross, Nr Dawlish, Exeter, Devon EX6 8RP **T:** (01626) 890111
F: (01626) 890160 **E:** info@coftonholidays.co.uk
W: www.coftonholidays.co.uk **£ BOOK ONLINE**

VisitEngland ★★★★ SELF CATERING

| Units | 17 |
| Sleeps | 4-6 |

PER UNIT PER WEEK
£395.00 - £1200.00

SPECIAL PROMOTIONS
Special offers and short breaks are available early and late season. Free coarse fishing on site between November and February. Latest offers available via our website.

WALKERS WELCOME   CYCLISTS WELCOME

Twelve cottages and five apartments, located either on our main holiday park or nearby on the Eastdon Estate. Cottages are converted from original farm buildings (some with hot tubs) and apartments are within the 18th century Georgian house. Enjoy views of the Exe Estuary and have acres of countryside to explore. Facilities on the park include swimming pools, indoor leisure complex, shop, takeaway, café & bar.

Open: All year.
Nearest Shop: 0.10 miles
Nearest Pub: 0.10 miles

Units: Each cottage is individual and comprises of 2 or 3 bedrooms sleeping a maximum of 6 people. Units are fully equipped including bed linen & towels.

Site: ✿ P **Payment:** 💷 **Leisure:** 🚲 🎵 ♨ 🎣 🎾 🏸 **Property:** 🛏 📺 🍽 **Children:** 🧸 🍼 🎠
Unit: 📱 🍳 📺 📻 📺 🎬 📀

DAWLISH, Devon   Map ref 1D2   *SatNav EX6 8RP*   **C**

Cofton Country Holidays

Starcross, Nr Dawlish, Devon EX6 8RP
T: (01626) 890111 **E:** info@coftonholidays.co.uk
W: www.coftonholidays.co.uk **£ BOOK ONLINE**

VisitEngland ★★★★ HOLIDAY, TOURING & CAMPING PARK   VisitEngland *Gold* AWARD

🚐 (450)	£17.50-£43.00
🚙 (450)	£17.50-£43.00
⛺ (450)	£17.50-£34.00
🏠 (17)	£395.00-£1060.00
🚐 (70)	£315.00-£960.00

450 touring pitches

SPECIAL PROMOTIONS
Save 25% on touring/ camping in winter, low, mid and high season for advance bookings of 5 or more nights.

A stunning setting surrounded by rolling meadows, mature woods, fishing lakes and just minutes from Dawlish Warren's Blue Flag beach. Superb countryside views. Hardstanding and super pitches available. Fantastic facilities in clean, tidy surroundings with indoor and outdoor swimming pools, play areas, restaurant, bars, park shop, take-away, woodland walks and games room complete with Bowling.

Directions: Leave M5 at junction 30, take A379 towards Dawlish. After passing through harbour village of Cockwood, park is on the left after half a mile.

Open: All year.

Site: 🏕 ✿ 🅰 P **Payment:** 💷 ☀ **Leisure:** 🎵 🏹 🎣 🎾 🏸 **Children:** 🧸 🎢 **Catering:** ✗ 🍴
Park: 🐕 🎵 🍽 📺 📱 🛒 🎣 **Touring:** 🚰 💧 🚿 ⛽

DAWLISH, Devon Map ref 1D2 SatNav EX7 0LX

Lady's Mile Touring and Camping Park

Exeter Road, Dawlish, Devon EX7 0LX
T: (01626) 863411 **F:** (01626) 888689 **E:** info@ladysmile.co.uk
W: www.ladysmile.co.uk **£ BOOK ONLINE**

VisitEngland ★★★★ HOLIDAY, TOURING & CAMPING PARK

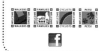

(480) £15.00
(200) £260.00-£1155.00

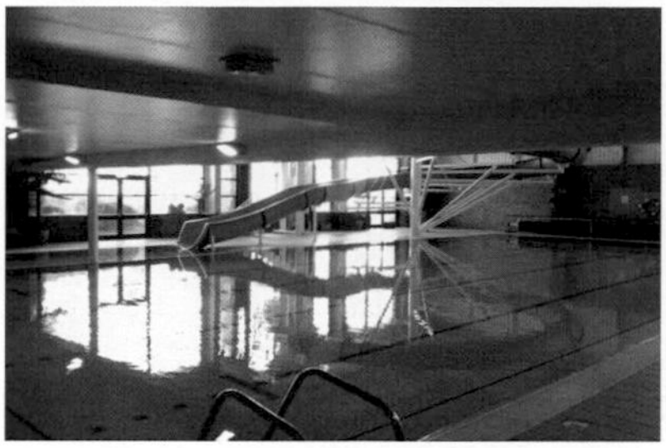

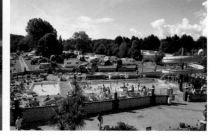

Lady's Mile is an award-winning, family run park designed to please everyone! With a fabulous range of indoor and outdoor sports and leisure facilities, you won't have to leave the site to enjoy a holiday full of family fun, come rain or shine! Please contact us for up to date prices.

Directions: Leave the M5 at Junction 30, take A379 to Dawlish, pass the Cockwood harbour for 2 miles over the Sainsburys roundabout and then take 2nd left.

Open: All year (except for the outdoor pool).

Site: **Payment:** **Leisure:** **Children:** **Catering:** **Park:**
Touring:

DAWLISH, Devon Map ref 1D2

Little Mermaid Cottage

Contact: The Barn House, 3 King Street, Dawlish, South Devon EX7 9LG **T:** (01626) 863881
E: sheilathomas@live.co.uk
W: www.littlemermaidcottage.com

VisitEngland ★★★ SELF CATERING

Units 1
Sleeps 2-6

PER UNIT PER WEEK
£345.00 - £605.00

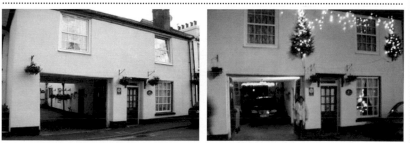

The Little Mermaid holiday Cottage is over 200 years old and will accommodate 6 people comfortably. It is situated by the town centre and is walking distance to the beach and train station. We have Wi-Fi and parking at the cottage.
Please see our website to view photos and price list.

Open: All year.
Nearest Shop: 5 mins walk
Nearest Pub: 5 mins walk

Units: Spacious lounge, dining room which has a double sofa bed, gallery kitchen which has washer/dryer, microwave, cooker and fridge freezer. Upstairs has a double room, twin room, bathroom and toilet.

Site: P **Property:** **Children:** **Unit:**

DAWLISH, Devon   Map ref 1D2

SatNav EX7 0ND C

VisitEngland
★★★★
HOLIDAY PARK

Oakcliff Holiday Park

Mount Pleasant Road, Dawlish Warren, Dawlish, Devon EX7 0ND
T: (01626) 863347 **F:** (01626) 888689 **E:** info@ladysmile.co.uk
W: www.oakcliff.co.uk **£ BOOK ONLINE**

(50)   £145.00-£1005.00

Oakcliff is an 8 acre park laid out in lawns and parkland around an elegant Georgian house, complete with a heated outdoor swimming pool and children's playground. Set in a prime location in Devon's premier holiday resort of Dawlish Warren, 600 yards from a Blue Flag beach and nature reserve. Away from the hustle and bustle, Oakcliff offers more peaceful surroundings with views across the estuary.

Directions: Leave M5 at junction 30, take A379 to Dawlish, continue past Cockwood harbour, pass Sainsburys roundabout, then take the 3rd left to Dawlish Warren for 3/4 mile.

Open: Accommodation: All year.
Pool: May to September.

WALKERS FAMILIES CYCLISTS
WALKERS FAMILIES CYCLISTS

f

Site: ⚑ **Payment:** 💷 **Leisure:** ↑ ⚘ **Children:** 🧒 🎠 **Park:** 🐕 📶

DAWLISH, Devon   Map ref 1D2

SatNav EX7 0PH C

VisitEngland
★★★★
HOLIDAY PARK

Welcome Family Holiday Park

Welcome Family Holiday Park, Warren Road, Dawlish Warren, Dawlish, Devon EX7 0PH
T: (03451) 656265 **E:** fun@welcomefamily.co.uk
W: www.welcomefamily.co.uk **£ BOOK ONLINE**

(60)   £390.00-£1290.00
(70)   £260.00-£870.00
(120) £225.00-£1065.00

Fantastic entertainment, terrific indoor fun–pools and a truly superb location just a short walk from a Blue Flag beach. These are just a few of the things that make 4* Welcome Family Holiday Park an ideal place for a fun packed, family seaside holiday. Accommodation is available to suit every taste and pocket and ranges from luxury lodges, to comfortable bungalows and cosy caravans.
Open: 1st April to 4th November 2017.

f t

Site: 🏕 **Payment:** 💷 ☀ **Leisure:** ↑ ⚘ ⚘ **Children:** 🧒 🎠 **Catering:** ✕ 🍴 **Park:** 🐕 🎵 📶 🖥 💳 📶

Sign up for our newsletter

Visit our website to sign up for our e-newsletter and receive regular information on events, articles, exclusive competitions and new publications.

www.visitor-guides.co.uk

[S]

Woodford Bridge Country Club

Contact: Milton Damerel, Nr Holsworthy, Devon EX22 7LL **T:** (0800) 358 6991
E: EuHotels@diamondresorts.com
W: www.DiamondResortsandHotels.com **£ BOOK ONLINE**

Units   103
Sleeps   1-6

PER UNIT PER WEEK
£270.00 - £1414.00

SPECIAL PROMOTIONS
Visit our website or call today for seasonal discounts and great savings.

A quiet haven in the heart of North Devon, this 15th century former coaching inn is 33 miles from Tintagel Castle, the rumoured birthplace of King Arthur. It has a pool, a gym and free parking on site. Woodford Bridge Country Club is a charming thatched building, with a variety of elegant rooms. Each spacious apartment offers an en suite bathroom, a TV with Freeview, and tea and coffee making facilities.

Guests can enjoy a drink in the bar and breakfast, lunch and dinner in the restaurant. Woodford Bridge has a library where guests can relax with a book in the peaceful garden.

Open: All year.
Nearest Shop: On Site
Nearest Pub: On Site

Units: A choice of Studio, one and two bedroom apartments available. All apartments boast a full kitchen, modern bathroom and Television with DVD player.

Site: ✿ P Payment: 💷 Leisure: ♪ ↑ ✾ Property: 🖥 🎱 Children: 🐎 🎮 ⚹ Unit: 💻 ❊ TV 📷 📞

[S]

Mary's Cottage

Contact: Susan West, Indicknowle Farm, Long Lane, Combe Martin, Ilfracombe, North Devon EX34 0PA **T:** (01271) 883980 **E:** mark.sue@indicknowle.plus.com
W: www.indicknowle.co.uk

Units   1
Sleeps   1-6

PER UNIT PER WEEK
£285.00 - £630.00

SPECIAL PROMOTIONS
Short breaks available. Also butchery, lambing and cider experiences out-of-season. Prices vary, based on the following percentages of the weekly rate; 3 nights 70%, 4 nights 80% and 5 nights 90%.

Adjoining a beautiful 18th century farmhouse, this delightful 4 star country cottage lies at the end of its own private lane. Indicknowle is a traditional family farm producing cider, lamb, pork and Ruby Red beef. Located in an area of outstanding natural beauty, close to Exmoor Park, it has easy access to the popular North Devon beaches and the South West Coastal Path.

Mary's Cottage is the perfect base for a beach, walking or touring holiday, Christmas or Easter break. We offer peace, tranquillity, relaxation and a taste of country life throughout the changing seasons of the farm year.

Open: All year.
Nearest Shop: 3 miles
Nearest Pub: 3 miles

Units: Bedrooms en suite with shower & WC. Downstairs cloakroom. Cot/baby bath available on request. Fitted kitchen. Centrally heated with log burner & Wi-Fi.

Site: ✿ P Property: 🖥 📷 🎱 Children: 🐎 🎮 ⚹ Unit: 💻 🖥 📷 ❊ TV 📷 🍴 BBQ

LYNMOUTH, Devon   Map ref 1C1   [S]

Clooneavin Holiday Apartments

Contact: Clooneavin Path, Lynmouth, Devon EX35 6EE **T:** (01598) 753334
E: relax@clooneavinholidays.co.uk
W: www.clooneavinholidays.co.uk

Units   7
Sleeps   2-6
PER UNIT PER WEEK
£290.00 - £510.00

Comfortable self-catering flats and bungalow on edge of Exmoor, with breathtaking views of river, harbour and bay. Close to all amenities.
Open: All year.
Nearest Shop: 1/2 mile
Nearest Pub: 1/2 mile

Site: ✿ P Leisure: ☆ ♪ ♪ ♂ Property: 🐕 🚭 🖶 🖳 Children: 🛏 🏃 ♿ Unit: 🖭 ♪ 📺

MORTEHOE, Devon   Map ref 1C1   SatNav EX34 7EG   [C]

AA
★★★★
TOURING & CAMPING PARK

North Morte Farm Caravan & Camping Park

North Morte Road, Mortehoe, Woolacombe EX34 7EG
T: (01271) 870381 **E:** info@northmortefarm.co.uk
W: www.northmortefarm.co.uk

🚐 (25)	£15.50-£25.00
🚍	£13.00-£25.00
⛺ (150)	£13.00-£20.00
🏠 (15)	£300.00-£725.00

25 touring pitches

Set in beautiful countryside overlooking Rockham Bay, close to village of Mortehoe and Woolacombe.
Directions: Take A361 from Barnstaple, turn left at Mullacott roundabout signed Mortehoe and Woolacombe, head for Mortehoe, turn right at Post Office, park 500m on left.
Open: April to October.

[f] [t]

Payment: 💷 ☼ Leisure: ♪ ♂ Children: 🛏 ⚠ Catering: 🍴 Park: 🐕 🚭 🖶 ♿ 🛁 Touring: ♀ ♂ 🔌 ♪

NEWTON ABBOT, Devon   Map ref 1D2   SatNav TQ12 6QT   [C]

VisitEngland
★★★★★
TOURING & CAMPING PARK

Twelve Oaks Farm Caravan Park

Teigngrace, Newton Abbot TQ12 6QT
T: (01626) 335015 **E:** info@twelveoaksfarm.co.uk
W: www.twelveoaksfarm.co.uk

🚐 (50)	£15.50-£24.00
🚍 (50)	£15.50-£24.00
⛺ (30)	£15.50-£24.00
🏠 (6)	£300.00-£1350.00

50 touring pitches

A working farm specialising in Charolais beef cattle. Friendly, personal service. Luxury showers and toilets, heated outdoor swimming pool. Coarse fishing. Good dog walks nearby. Children's play park. Wi-Fi Available. Loo of the Year Platinum 2016 Award.
Directions: Please come via the A38 south bound exit for Teigngrace straight through the village for two miles Twelve Oaks Farm on left.
Open: All year.

Payment: 💷 ☼ Leisure: ☆ ♪ ♂ ⚡ Children: 🛏 ⚠ Catering: 🍴 Park: 🐕 🚭 🖶 ♿ 🛁 Touring: ♀ ♂ 🔌 ♪

NORTH MOLTON, Devon   Map ref 1C1

SatNav EX36 3HQ **C**

Riverside Caravan and Camping Park

Marsh Lane, North Molton Road, South Molton, North Devon EX36 3HQ
T: (01769) 579269 **E:** relax@exmoorriverside.co.uk
W: www.exmoorriverside.co.uk

🚐 (42)	£15.00-£25.00
🚎 (42)	£15.00-£25.00
⛺ (40)	£10.00-£24.00
🏠 (2)	£210.00-£485.00
42 touring pitches	

SPECIAL PROMOTIONS
For special offers, please visit our website for full details.

4 Star Park set in 70 acres of landscaped parkland with lakes and rivers for fishing, new modern restaurant and bar, caravan storage and luxury statics for hire.

Directions: M5 turn off on junction 27 onto the A361 turn right when you see North Molton and riverside sign.

Open: All year.

Site: 🏕 Payment: 💷 ☼ Leisure: 🎣 ∪ Children: 🐕 ⛰ Catering: ✕ 🍴 Park: 🐎 🎵 📺 🎱 🛈 📷
Touring: 🚽 🕒 🔌 🔥

OKEHAMPTON, Devon   Map ref 1C2

SatNav EX20 4HA **B**

Knole Farm

Bridestowe, Okehampton, Devon EX20 4HA **T:** (01837) 861241 **F:** (01837) 861241
E: mavis.bickle@btconnect.com
W: www.knolefarm-dartmoor-holidays.co.uk

B&B PER ROOM PER NIGHT
S: £54.00 - £60.00
D: £38.00 - £40.00
EVENING MEAL PER PERSON
£18.00 - £20.00

Enjoy a scenic and restful break with us, taking in numerous activities and places to visit nearby. National Trust and Dartmoor is right on our doorstep. Come for a break you won't forget making lifelong memories. Free Wi-Fi.
Directions: Postcode EX20 4HA for Sat Nav - please see website for further directions or phone us.
Bedrooms: All spacious and en suite rooms.
Open: All year apart from Christmas.

Site: ❈ P Payment: 💷 Leisure: 🎿 🎣 ⏸ ∪ Property: 🐎 📺 🎱 🎿 Children: 🐕 🛏 🎒
Catering: (✕ 🍴 Room: 🍵 🛁 🍵 📺

OKEHAMPTON, Devon   Map ref 1C2

S

Peartree Cottage

Contact: Mrs Jacqueline Ellis, Owner, Howards Gorhuish, Northlew, Okehampton, Devon EX20 3BT **T:** (01837) 658750 **E:** jackie.ann.ellis@btinternet.com
W: www.peartreecottage-devon.co.uk

Units   1
Sleeps   4
PER UNIT PER WEEK
£350.00 - £935.00

Delightful Gold award-winning Peartree Cottage stands in the 2 acre grounds of Howards Gorhuish and overlooks a wild flower meadow and small copse. The cottage adjoins the owner's country house standing in a quiet rural position and is well-located to explore the attractions and stunning landscape the South West has to offer, especially Dartmoor and the spectacular North Devon coast. **Open:** All year. **Nearest Shop:** 2 miles **Nearest Pub:** 2 miles

Site: P Property: 🐎 📺 🎱 🖨 Children: 🐕 🛏 🎒 Unit: 🖨 🍽 💻 🖨 🍵 📺 📻 ♨ BBQ

Ladram Bay Holiday Park

Otterton, Budleigh Salterton, Devon EX9 7BX
T: (01395) 568398 **E:** info@ladrambay.co.uk
W: www.ladrambay.co.uk **£ BOOK ONLINE**

🚐 (65)	£15.00-£46.00
🚙 (65)	£15.00-£46.00
⛺ (35)	£15.00-£46.00
🏠 (500)	£129.00-£1895.00
160 touring pitches	

SPECIAL PROMOTIONS
Short breaks available,
Over 55's discount &
Seasonal pitches.

Nestled in the rolling Devon Hills overlooking the unspoilt Jurassic Coast, Ladram Bay is the Holiday Park in Devon that has something to offer everyone. Recently awarded 5 star statuses, you can be assured that your holiday is better than ever before!

With plenty of accommodation options ranging from tent & touring pitches, new glamping pods, holiday homes and luxury lodges all tastes and budgets are catered for. Enjoy our extensive range of facilities, perfect for the whole family including Swimming pool complex plus Pebbles Restaurant with delicious menu and stunning bay views.

Directions: M5 Junction 30, follow A376 to Clyst St Mary then A3052 to Newton Poppleford, then B3178 and follow signposts to Ladram Bay.

Open: 10th March to 31st October 2017.

Site: ❀ ⛺🅿 **Payment:** 💳 ☼ **Leisure:** ♪ ▶ ♣ ☂ **Children:** 🛝 ⛰ **Catering:** ✕ 🍴
Park: 🐾 🎵 🖥 🗑 🛒 ♟ **Touring:** 🚰 ♨ ⚡

Redcliffe Lodge Hotel

1 Marine Drive, Paignton TQ3 2NJ **T:** (01803) 551394 **F:** (01803) 551394
E: redcliffelodge@gmail.com
W: www.redcliffelodge.co.uk **£ BOOK ONLINE**

B&B PER ROOM PER NIGHT
S: £20.00 - £35.00
D: £40.00 - £70.00

HB PER PERSON PER NIGHT
£35.00 - £50.00

SPECIAL PROMOTIONS
2-4 year olds half-price when sharing with adults. Winter 2 night breaks, B&B and 3 course evening meal from £30pppn.

Redcliffe Lodge occupies one of Paignton's finest seafront positions, in its own grounds with a large, free car park. All rooms are en suite and comfortably furnished with modern facilities. Licensed bar. Panoramic views from both our sun lounge and dining room, where you will enjoy our high standard of cuisine.

Directions: Follow A3022 to Paignton seafront. The hotel is situated at the end of Marine Drive, on the right adjacent to Paignton Green.

Bedrooms: 2 single, 10 double, 3 twin, 2 family.
Open: All year.

Site: ❀ P **Payment:** 💳 € **Leisure:** ♿ ♪ ▶ ♺ **Property:** 🏠 🐾 🖥 🗑 🎵 ◐ **Children:** 🛝 🛏 🚼
Catering: ⦅✕ 🍷 🍽 **Room:** 🗝 ♨ 📺 🖥 📺 ☕

PLYMOUTH, Devon   Map ref 1C2
SatNav PL1 3BS **B**

VisitEngland
★★★★
GUEST
ACCOMMODATION

B&B PER ROOM PER NIGHT
S: £40.00 - £45.00
D: £60.00 - £65.00

Caraneal
12-14 Pier Street, West Hoe, Plymouth PL1 3BS **T:** (01752) 663589 **F:** (01752) 663589
E: caranealhotel@hotmail.com
W: www.caranealplymouth.co.uk **£ BOOK ONLINE**

Caraneal is a cosy family-run establishment near the famous Hoe and seafront and within easy walking distance of the city centre and the historic Barbican. Free Wi-Fi Available.
Directions: From A38 follow signs for City Centre, then the Hoe and Seafront. On seafront pass Plymouth Dome and turn right at the next mini-roundabout.
Bedrooms: 5 double, 2 twin.
Open: All year except Christmas and New Year.

Site: **P** Payment: £ Leisure: ✦ ♪ Property: ⊟ Children: ✕ ⊞ ☂ Catering: ⊞ Room: ✎

SALCOMBE, Devon   Map ref 1C3
SatNav TQ7 3DY **C**

VisitEngland
★★★
HOLIDAY, TOURING
& CAMPING PARK

🚐 (20)
🚙 (20)
⛺ (50)
🚐 (10)
70 touring pitches

Bolberry House Farm Caravan & Camping
Bolberry, Malborough, Kingsbridge TQ7 3DY
T: (01548) 561251 **E:** enquiries@bolberryparks.co.uk
W: www.bolberryparks.co.uk

Friendly family-run park between sailing paradise of Salcombe and Hope Cove (old fishing village). Peaceful, mostly level and good facilities. Children's play area. Good access to coastal footpaths. Sandy beaches nearby. Overnight holding area available. Please contact us for prices. **Directions:** A381 from Totnes, ringroad Kingsbridge to Salcombe. At Malborough sharp right through village, signs to Bolberry approx 1m. Do not follow Sat Nav from Totnes. **Open:** Easter to October.

Site: ⛺🅿 Payment: ☀ Leisure: ✦ ♪ ⊦ ∪ Children: ✕ ⚠ Catering: ⊞ BBQ Park: ⊨ ⊟ ⊟ ⊞ ⋔ ✎
Touring: ☎ 🚐

SALCOMBE, Devon   Map ref 1C3
SatNav TQ7 3BW **C**

VisitEngland
★★★★
TOURING &
CAMPING PARK

🚐 (25)   £15.00-£23.00
🚙 (40)   £15.00-£23.00
⛺ (50)   £14.00-£22.00
100 touring pitches

f

Higher Rew Touring Caravan & Camping
Higher Rew, Malborough, Kingsbridge, Devon TQ7 3BW
T: (01548) 842681 **E:** enquiries@higherrew.co.uk
W: www.higherrew.co.uk

Higher Rew is a family run park in an area of outstanding natural beauty close to the beautiful Salcombe Estuary. Three generations of the Squire family have, over many years, created a relaxed caravan and camping park for your enjoyment. We are annually inspected by the English Tourism Council, who have awarded our park four stars and have been featured in both the Lonely Planet and Rough Guides. Please contact or see website for 2017 rates.
Directions: Some Sat Navs give least suitable route for last 2 miles, please see website. **Open:** 31st March to 30th October.

Site: ⛺🅿 Leisure: ✦ ✎ Catering: ⊞ Park: ⊨ ⊟ ⊞ ⋔ Touring: ☎ 🚐

SEATON, Devon   Map ref 1D2
S

VisitEngland
★★★
SELF CATERING

Units   1
Sleeps   1-4
PER UNIT PER WEEK
£250.00 - £650.00

West Ridge Bungalow
Contact: Mrs Hildegard Fox, West Ridge Bungalow, Harepath Hill, Seaton EX12 2TA
T: (01297) 22398 **E:** fox@foxwestridge.co.uk
W: www.cottagesdirect.co.uk/3031758-1/west-ridge-bungalow-devon.aspx
£ BOOK ONLINE

Comfortably furnished bungalow on elevated ground in 1.5 acres of gardens. Beautiful, panoramic views of Axe Estuary and sea. Nearby - Beer, Branscombe, Lyme Regis, Sidmouth. Excellent walking, sailing, fishing, golf. 10% reduction for 2 persons only, throughout booking period.
Open: March to October.
Nearest Shop: 0.5 miles
Nearest Pub: 1 mile

Site: ✿ P Leisure: ✦ ♪ ⊦ ∪ Property: ⊨ ⊟ ⊟ Children: ✕ ⊞ ☂ Unit: ⊟ ⊟ ✎ TV ✎ DVD

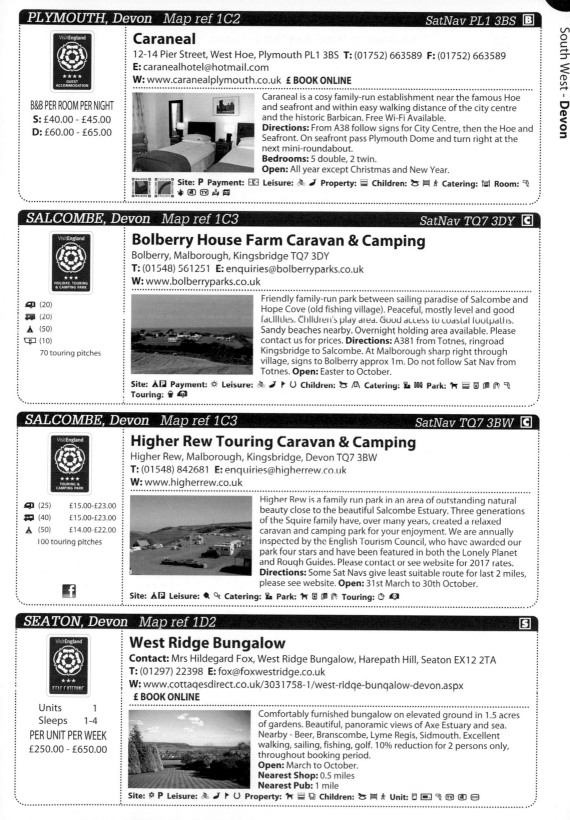

VisitEngland ★★★★ GUEST HOUSE

VisitEngland Gold AWARD

The Barn & Pinn Cottage Guest House

Bowd, Sidmouth, Devon EX10 0ND **T:** (01395) 513613
E: barnpinncottage@btinternet.com
W: www.thebarnandpinncottage.co.uk

B&B PER ROOM PER NIGHT
S: £48.00 - £55.00
D: £80.00 - £120.00
EVENING MEAL PER PERSON
£20.00 - £24.00

SPECIAL PROMOTIONS
3+ nights 1 for free, 2+
Nights & 7+ Nights
Special Rates please
see our website for
details.

Open over Christmas &
New Year.

Special occasions &
functions by
arrangement.

Please enquire.

This beautiful 15th century thatched cottage nestles within two acres of award-winning gardens, 5 minutes drive from Sidmouth. All en suite rooms have full central heating, Digital TV, and tea/coffee making facilities. Dinner available Thursday to Sunday. Good home cooking, varied menu, well stocked bar. Comfortable guest lounge, large private car park.

Directions: Located on A3052 12 miles from Exeter, 15 miles from Lyme Regis. Between Newton Poppleford and Sidford. 5 minutes from beach at Sidmouth using B3176.

Bedrooms: 1 single, 3 double, 1 kingsize, 2 luxury four posters with private garden, 2 twin. 1 holiday let as B&B or self catering. Family rooms possible.
Open: All year - See website for details.

Site: ❀ P **Payment:** 🖅 **Leisure:** 🎣 ♪ ▶ ∪ **Property:** ✝ **Children:** ☺ **Catering:** ♈ 🍽
Room: 🖥 🕯 📺 ⬚ 🛁

VisitEngland ★★★★★ HOLIDAY, TOURING & CAMPING PARK

Langstone Manor Holiday Park

Moortown, Tavistock, Devon PL19 9JZ
T: (01822) 613371 **F:** (01822) 613371 **E:** jane@langstonemanor.co.uk
W: www.langstonemanor.co.uk

🚐 (15)   £17.00-£20.00
🚏 (15)   £17.00-£20.00
⛺ (15)   £17.00-£20.00
🏠 (12)   £225.00-£599.00
45 touring pitches

Fantastic location with direct access onto moor, offering great walks straight from the park. Peaceful site with beautiful views of the surrounding moorland. Level pitches, some hardstanding with brand new five star facilities. Camping pods also available. The Langstone Bar provides evening meals. A warm welcome awaits!
Directions: Take the B3357 Princetown road from Tavistock. After approx. 1.5 miles, turn right at x-roads, go over cattle grid, up hill, left following signs. **Open:** 15th March to 15th November.

Site: 🏠 **Payment:** 🖅 ☼ **Leisure:** 🎣 ♪ ▶ ∪ ♣ **Children:** ☺ ⛰ **Catering:** ✗
Park: 🐕 🚮 🔌 🛒 🔥 **Touring:** ☗ 🕀 🚐 ♪

VisitEngland ★★★★ INN

VisitEngland *Silver* AWARD

B&B PER ROOM PER NIGHT
D: £100.00 - £150.00
EVENING MEAL PER PERSON
£15.00 - £25.00

Ness House

Ness Drive, Shaldon, Nr Teignmouth, Devon TQ14 0HP   **T:** (01626) 873480
E: nesshouse.shaldon@hall-woodhouse.co.uk
W: www.theness.co.uk   **£ BOOK ONLINE**

The Ness House is a Georgian property, built in 1810, on the outskirts of Shaldon village overlooking the Teign Estuary and only a stone's throw from the beach. The Smugglers Tunnel can be found 20 yards away, leading you down to the secluded Ness Beach, sheltered by the Ness Cliff. The ferry which runs between Teignmouth and Shaldon is also a 'must', when visiting the area.

Directions: Located on Marine Parade, take Ness Drive off the A379. There is a pay & display car park on the left just before you reach the Ness with plenty of spaces.

Bedrooms: 9 unique en suite rooms all finished to a luxurious, comfortable standard with flatscreen TV, bluetooth radio and tea & coffee making facilities.
Open: All year.

f

Site: ❀ Payment: 💷 Property: ⅄ 🛏 ⌀ Children: ➣ 🏠 ⚹ Catering: (✕ 🍴 Room: ⧍ 🖐 📺

VisitEngland ★★★★ SELF CATERING

Units   6
Sleeps   1-6

PER UNIT PER WEEK
£196.00 - £840.00

SPECIAL PROMOTIONS
We offer short and longer stays, free child place with two paying adults plus a discount for a two or more week stay.

Belgravia Holiday Apartments

Contact: Mrs Nadine Green, Owner, Belgravia Holiday Apartments, 31 Belgrave Road, Torquay, Devon TQ2 5HX   **T:** (01803) 293417   **E:** info@blha.co.uk
W: www.blha.co.uk   **£ BOOK ONLINE**

Welcome to Belgravia Holiday 4 star awarded self-catering apartments situated in the enviable number 1 position in the heart of the premier hotel area on Belgrave Road. Only 500 meters to the promenade and seafront, and only a few minutes' walk to Torquay town centre.

The English Riviera Centre with its pleasure pool and sports facilities is only 250 meters away, and we are also close to the Princess Theatre, restaurants and bars.

All apartments are kept to a high standard and we offer long or short stays fitting in with the needs of our guests.

Open: All year.
Nearest Shop: 0.01 miles
Nearest Pub: 0.01 miles

Units: All apartments have a fully fitted kitchen, central heating and spacious showers plus dining and sofa area.

f

Payment: 💷 Leisure: ♪ ⌇ Property: 🖥 🛏 🍴 Children: ➣ 🏠 ⚹ Unit: 🗄 📺 ⧍ 📺 📀

Best Western Livermead Cliff Hotel

Sea Front, Torquay TQ2 6RQ **T:** (01803) 299666 **F:** (01803) 294496
E: info@livermeadcliff.co.uk
W: www.livermeadcliff.co.uk **£ BOOK ONLINE**

B&B PER ROOM PER NIGHT
S: £35.00 - £110.00
D: £60.00 - £230.00
HB PER PERSON PER NIGHT
£40.00 - £140.00

Privately owned, 3 star Best Western hotel on the water's edge with direct access to the beach. Panoramic views, sea view lounge and en suite rooms, licensed bar and stunning new Riviera Terrace. Free parking. Free Wi-Fi. Ideally located for touring the South West of England.
Directions: Please contact us for directions.
Bedrooms: 13 single, 29 double, 14 twin, 8 family, 1 suite.
Open: All year.

Site: ✿ Payment: 💳 Leisure: ♿ ♪ ↾ ∪ Property: 🛈 🐕 🖃 🗑 ◐ Children: ⛄ 🛏 🎎 Catering: 🍽 🍴
Room: 🔌 ♨ ☎ 🎧 📺 📶 📠

Corbyn Head Hotel

Sea Front, Torquay, Devon TQ2 6RH **T:** (01803) 213611 **F:** (01803) 296152
E: info@corbynhead.com
W: www.corbynhead.com **£ BOOK ONLINE**

B&B PER ROOM PER NIGHT
S: £39.00 - £121.00
D: £69.00 - £250.00
EVENING MEAL PER PERSON
£23.50 - £29.50

[f] [t]

The Corbyn Head Hotel is one of Torquay's leading hotels with its seafront location. Most bedrooms enjoy stunning sea views, many have private balconies. Outdoor Swimming Pool. AA Rosetted Restaurant. Free Wi-Fi. Free on-site parking.
Directions: Torquay Seafront, turn right and follow signs for Cockington Village. Hotel on right.
Bedrooms: 3 single, 29 double, 10 twin, 3 family.
Open: All year.

Site: ✿ P Payment: 💳 Leisure: ♿ ♱ ⚲ ↾ Property: 🛈 🐕 🖃 🗑 🎎 ◐ Children: ⛄ 🛏 🎎
Catering: (✕ 🍽 🍴 Room: 🔌 ♨ ☎ 📺 📶

Livermead House Hotel

Torbay Road, Seafront, Torquay TQ2 6QJ **T:** (01803) 294361 **F:** (01803) 200758
E: info@livermead.com
W: www.livermead.com **£ BOOK ONLINE**

B&B PER ROOM PER NIGHT
S: £35.00 - £110.00
D: £60.00 - £230.00
HB PER PERSON PER NIGHT
£40.00 - £140.00

The Livermead House Hotel in Torquay, situated on the edge of the Cockington Valley was built in 1820 and is positioned on Torquay's sea front. The hotel offers breathtaking sea views, beautifully manicured lawns and exceptionally high standards of service and cuisine from award-winning Chef, Tony Hetherington.
Directions: Full directions and map available on our website.
Bedrooms: 7 single, 34 double, 25 twin, 1 family, all en suite.
Open: All year.

Site: ✿ Payment: 💳 Leisure: ♿ ♪ ↾ ∪ ⚲ ↾ Property: 🛈 🐕 🖃 🗑 ◐ Children: ⛄ 🛏 🎎 Catering: 🍽
🍴 Room: 🔌 ♨ ☎ 🎧 📺 📶 📠

TORQUAY, Devon   Map ref 1D2   S

Long Barn Luxury Holiday Cottages

Contact: Michael & Sandra Lane, Owners, Long Barn Luxury Holiday Cottages, Long Barn, North Whilborough, Newton Abbot, Torbay TQ12 5LP **T:** (01803) 875044 / 07946 378137
E: stay@longbarncottages.co.uk **W:** www.longbarncottages.co.uk **£ BOOK ONLINE**

Units 4
Sleeps 2-29

PER UNIT PER WEEK
£460.00 - £3650.00

SPECIAL PROMOTIONS
Short breaks available Autumn, Winter and Spring, 3/4/5 nights, subject to availability. View website for prices and availability.

Four Luxury 4* Gold Award Holiday Cottages in the tranquil Devon countryside sleeping 2, 6, 8 and 13 plus cots. Family friendly, each with its own garden as well as the outdoor play area with swings, climbing frames, trampoline and plenty of space for ball games. The cottages share a bookable indoor heated pool and an indoor play area catering for all the family with pool, table tennis and toys.

Open: All year.
Nearest Shop: 1.5 miles
Nearest Pub: 0.5 miles

Site: ❖ P Payment: 🖃 Leisure: ↾ ∪ ☍ ☌ Property: ▭ ⬚ ⬚ Children: ⛵ ⌁ ⚲
Unit: ⬚ ⬚ ⬚ ⬚ TV 🅰 DVD ⬚ BBQ

TORQUAY, Devon   Map ref 1D2   SatNav TQ1 3LN   B

The Downs, Babbacombe

Seafront, 41-43 Babbacombe Downs Road, Babbacombe, Torquay TQ1 3LN
T: (01803) 328543 **F:** (01803) 670557 **E:** enquiries@downshotel.co.uk
W: www.downshotel.co.uk **£ BOOK ONLINE**

B&B PER ROOM PER NIGHT
S: £69.00 - £84.00
D: £84.00 - £99.00
EVENING MEAL PER PERSON
£19.95

SPECIAL PROMOTIONS
Stay 3 or more nights & get 1 extra night free in January & February. Long Stay Discount for 7 nights or more when booked direct. We get preferential rates on green fees & theatre tickets. Call Kate now!

The Downs, Babbacombe in Torquay is family run with 12 en suite rooms, 8 with balconies & uninterrupted sea views over Lyme Bay. We have a Lounge Bar and Restaurant serving optional evening meals and are fully licensed. We have an elegant feel whilst maintaining a comfortable, relaxed atmosphere. Dogs & Children welcome.

WINNERS OF SOUTH DEVON TOURISM & HOSPITALITY AWARDS 2013 - B&B, GUEST HOUSE.

Directions: M5 South to Torquay A380, at Torquay Harbour take left at r/a to Babbacombe. On entering Babbacombe take right turn into Princes Street, left onto Babbacombe Downs Road, we are on the left.

Bedrooms: All bedrooms are fully en suite with simple yet stylish oak furniture and pocket sprung beds, luxurious toiletries & towels, in keeping with a 4*hotel.
Open: All year, Christmas breaks available.

Site: P Payment: 🖃 Leisure: ↾ Property: ↾ ▭ ⌂ Children: ⛵ ⌁ ⚲ Catering: ✕ ♟ 🍽
Room: ☍ ♨ ☏ TV

TORQUAY, Devon   Map ref 1D2 — SatNav TQ1 2LL [H]

HOTEL ★★★★
VisitEngland

The Osborne Hotel

Hesketh Crescent, Meadfoot Beach, Torquay TQ1 2LL **T:** (01803) 213311
F: (01803) 296788 **E:** enq@osborne-torquay.co.uk
W: www.osborne-torquay.co.uk **£ BOOK ONLINE**

B&B PER ROOM PER NIGHT
S: £75.00 - £105.00
D: £99.00 - £180.00
EVENING MEAL PER PERSON
£15.00 - £40.00

SPECIAL PROMOTIONS
Year round offers
available, see website
for details, or ring our
friendly reception
team.

The Osborne Hotel, known by the discerning as 'The Country House Hotel by the Sea', is the centrepiece of an elegant Regency crescent. Many rooms provide panoramic views across The Bay. The gourmet Langtry's Restaurant offers locally sourced, freshly prepared dishes, while The Terrace is open for al fresco dining during the summer months or just for a drink with a view.

Directions: From Torquay harbour, turn left at clocktower signposted Meadfoot Beach, turn right at traffic lights. Follow road straight ahead to the bottom of the hill.

Bedrooms: 1 single, 3 twin, 18 double, 2 superior, 6 junior suites and 2 family rooms, all with en suite, flat screen TV's, tea and coffee facilities.
Open: All year.

Site: ⚘ P **Payment:** 💳 **Leisure:** ♪ ⚑ ⚒ ⚔ ⚙ ⚲ ⚗ ⚘ **Property:** ⚑ 🖥 🗄 ◐ **Children:** 🛏 🎠 **Catering:** 🍽 🍴 **Room:** ⚒ ⬩ ☏ 📺

WOODBURY, Devon   Map ref 1D2 — SatNav EX5 1HA [C]

HOLIDAY, TOURING & CAMPING PARK ★★★★★
VisitEngland

Castle Brake Holiday Park

Castle Lane, Woodbury, Exeter EX5 1HA
T: (01395) 232431 **E:** reception@castlebrake.co.uk
W: www.castlebrake.co.uk

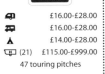

🚐	£16.00-£28.00
🚙	£16.00-£28.00
⛺	£14.00-£28.00
🏠 (21)	£115.00-£999.00
47 touring pitches	

Castle Brake is situated 1.5 miles from the village of Woodbury in the idyllic setting of Woodbury Common. It is a short drive to the Jurassic Coast beaches at Exmouth, Budleigh Salterton & Sidmouth or the city of Exeter.
Directions: From M5 Junction 30 follow A3052 to Halfway Inn. Turn right onto B3180. Turn right for Woodbury at the sign for Caravan Sites, 500 yards to Castle Brake.
Open: 10th March to 31st October 2017.

Site: 📷 **Payment:** 💳 ☀ **Leisure:** ⚲ ♪ ∪ ⚘ **Children:** 🛏 ⚠ **Catering:** 🛒 **Park:** 🐾 🖥 🗄 🏕 ☕ ⚘
Touring: ☎ ⟳ 🚐 ⚒

BLANDFORD FORUM, Dorset   Map ref 2B3 — [S]

SELF CATERING ★★★
VisitEngland

Dairy Cottage

Contact: Broadlea Farm, Sutton Waldron, Blandford Forum, Dorset DT11 8NS
T: (01747) 811330 **E:** j.s.asbury@btinternet.com

Units   1
Sleeps   4
PER UNIT PER WEEK
£325.00

Fully-equipped cottage amidst lovely countryside, south of Shaftesbury. Two bedrooms, sitting/dining room, separate kitchen and bathroom. Good base for visiting tourist attractions.
Open: All year.
Nearest Shop: 1.5 miles
Nearest Pub: 1.5 miles

Site: ⚘ P **Leisure:** ⚑ **Property:** 🖥 🗄 📠 📶 **Children:** 🛏 🎠 ⚠ **Unit:** 🗄 📺 🗄 ⚒ 📺 📀 ☏

BLANDFORD FORUM, Dorset Map ref 2B3 — SatNav DT11 9AD **C**

Inside Park

Fairmile Road, Blandford Forum DT11 9AD
T: (01258) 453719 **E:** mail@theinsidepark.co.uk
W: www.theinsidepark.co.uk **£ BOOK ONLINE**

VisitEngland
★★★★
TOURING &
CAMPING PARK

🚐 (90)	£14.00-£22.00
🚙 (10)	£14.00-£22.00
⛺ (25)	£14.00-£22.00
125 touring pitches	

Secluded park and woodland with facilities, built into 18th century stable and coach house. Ideal location for touring the county. 1.5 miles south west of Blandford on road to Winterborne Stickland. Country walks, cycling and wildlife.
Directions: Take Blandford St Mary exit at junction of A350/A354, proceed 1.5 miles SW of Blandford Forum on Fairmile Road. OS Ref: ST 864 052.
Open: April to October.

Payment: 📧 ☀ **Leisure:** 🚲 🎣 ∪ 🎯 **Children:** 🛝 ⛰ **Catering:** 🛒 **Park:** 🐕 🔥 📦 📷 **Touring:** 🚽 🚿 📶

BLANDFORD FORUM, Dorset Map ref 2B3 — SatNav DT11 7AJ **B**

The Crown Hotel

West Street, Blandford Forum, Dorset DT11 7AJ **T:** (01258) 456 626
E: crownhotel.reception@hall-woodhouse.co.uk
W: www.crownhotelblandford.co.uk **£ BOOK ONLINE**

VisitEngland
★★★★
INN

VisitEngland
Silver
AWARD

B&B PER ROOM PER NIGHT
D: £115.00 - £170.00
EVENING MEAL PER PERSON
£20.00 - £40.00

One of the oldest inns in Dorset, the Crown Hotel is set in the picturesque Georgian town of Blandford; a perfect example of traditional British hospitality. The beautifully panelled walls and carefully restored Oak floors make this the perfect place to explore the wonderful Georgian town of Blandford and the wider beauty of the Blackmore Vale.

Directions: Located on the edge of Blandford Forum opposite Morrisons on West Street.

Bedrooms: 27 unique en suite rooms all finished to a luxurious, comfortable standard with flatscreen TV, bluetooth radio and tea & coffee making facilities.
Open: All year.

Site: ❀ P **Payment:** 📧 **Property:** 🍷 🐕 🖅 🌀 ⌀ **Children:** 🛝 🍽 🧸 **Catering:** 🍴🍷 **Room:** 📶 🚿 📺

BOURNEMOUTH, Dorset Map ref 2B3 — SatNav BH1 3PF **B**

Balincourt

58 Christchurch Road, Bournemouth BH1 3PF **T:** (01202) 552962 **F:** (01202) 552962
E: reservations@balincourt.co.uk
W: www.balincourt.co.uk **£ BOOK ONLINE**

VisitEngland
★★★★★
BED & BREAKFAST

B&B PER ROOM PER NIGHT
S: £65.00 - £120.00
D: £85.00 - £130.00
EVENING MEAL PER PERSON
£23.00

Award-winning, elegant family-run Victorian guest accommodation. Prime location for attractions, seafront and town centre. Tastefully decorated en suite rooms. Warm and friendly service. Children minimum age 14 years. Evening meals by prior arrangement.
Directions: Please contact for directions.
Bedrooms: Special occasion flowers, chocolates, champagne available on request.
Open: All year.

Site: ❀ P **Payment:** 📧 **Leisure:** 🎣 ▶ 🔍 **Property:** 🖅 ♨ ⌀ **Catering:** 🍴🍷 🍽 **Room:** 📶 🚿 📺

BRIDPORT, Dorset *Map ref 2A3* [S]

VisitEngland
★★★★
SELF CATERING

Units   1
Sleeps   1-4

PER UNIT PER WEEK
£390.00 - £450.00

Mead Cottage, 17 Bramble Drive

Contact: Mrs Chrissie Fielder, Owner, Erin Lodge, Jigs Lane South, Warfield, Berkshire RG42 3DR **T:** (01344) 303370 / 07974 809736 **E:** mead.cottage@hotmail.co.uk

Situated within the heart of a World Heritage Conservation Area, offering some of best walking and coastal views in the country. Mead Cottage is a delightful, fully equipped modern mid terrace two (twin) bedroom cottage with secluded sunny garden and private car parking for 2 cars.

6 minutes stroll to coastal walks, sandy beach and lively harbour offering excellent fishing, boating and recreational activities. There are a variety of first class restaurants and pubs.
It's an ideal touring base.

Approximately 1 mile to the vibrant market town of Bridport and only 10 miles to Lyme Regis.

Open: April to mid-October.
Nearest Shop: 0.25 miles
Nearest Pub: 0.25 miles

Units: Lounge, kitchen with dining area, two twined bedded rooms with fitted wardrobe, bathroom with shower over bath, sunny garden, private car parking

Site: ❀ P Leisure: 🚴 ♪ ⼁ ∪ Property: 🖥 Unit: 🗋 ▣ 🗄 🍴 TV 🎧 DVD

BURTON BRADSTOCK, Dorset *Map ref 2A3* [S]

VisitEngland
3★ - 4★
SELF CATERING

Units   7
Sleeps   4-7

PER UNIT PER WEEK
£300.00 - £650.00

Cogden Cottages

Contact: Mrs Kim Connolly, Cogden Cottages, Old Coastguard Holiday Park, Coast Road, Bridport DT6 4RL **T:** (01308) 897223 / 07530 051517 **E:** oldcoastguard@hotmail.com
W: www.cogdencottages.co.uk **£ BOOK ONLINE**

Cogden Cottages is a former Victorian coastguard station with seven 2/3 bedroom cottages. Outstanding coastal views. All cottages have individual decking or patios. Free Wi-Fi, dishwasher, towels and linen.
Open: All year.
Nearest Shop: 0.80 miles
Nearest Pub: 0.80 miles

Site: ❀ P Payment: 💳 Leisure: 🚴 ♪ ⼁ ∪ Property: 🐾 ▤ 🗄 🖥 Children: 🍴 🛏 🧍 Unit: 🗋 🗄 ▣ 🗄 TV 🎧 DVD

CHRISTCHURCH, Dorset *Map ref 2B3* *SatNav BH23 8JE* [C]

VisitEngland
★★★
TOURING & CAMPING PARK

🚐 (60)   £18.50-£37.00
🚍 (60)   £18.50-£37.00
⛺ (14)   £18.50-£33.00
60 touring pitches

Harrow Wood Farm Caravan Park

Poplar Lane, Bransgore, Christchurch BH23 8JE
T: (01425) 672487 **F:** (01425) 672487 **E:** harrowwood@caravan-sites.co.uk
W: www.caravan-sites.co.uk

Quiet site bordered by woods and meadows.
Take A35 from Lyndhurst, turn right at Cat and Fiddle pub, site approximately 1.5 miles into Bransgore, first right after school. Sorry, No Dogs.
Directions: OS: N=97758 E= 19237
GPS: 50.7719 North 1.72872 West
Open: 1st March to 6th January.

f

Payment: 💳 ☀ Leisure: 🚴 ♪ ⼁ ∪ Children: 🍴 Park: ▤ 🗄 🅿 Touring: 🚿 ⊙ 🎧 ♪

EYPE, Dorset Map ref 1D2 *SatNav DT6 6AL* H

Eype's Mouth Country Hotel
Eype, Bridport, Dorset DT6 6AL **T:** (01308) 423300 **F:** (01308) 420033
E: info@eypesmouthhotel.co.uk
W: www.eypesmouthhotel.co.uk **£ BOOK ONLINE**

B&B PER ROOM PER NIGHT
S: £82.50 - £107.50
D: £112.50 - £132.50
EVENING MEAL PER PERSON
£28.00

Picturesque village of Eype, Bridport amidst downland and cliff tops of Heritage Coastline. Stunning sea views, lovely walking nearby, excellent hospitality, food and drink (bar meals are also available - see our website), in peaceful surroundings of family-run hotel. Overall a perfect place for relaxing. **Directions:** A35, Bridport bypass, take turning to Eype, also signed to service area, then 3rd right to beach. Hotel 0.5 miles down lane.
Bedrooms: 3 single, 12 double, 4 twin, 1 family. **Open:** All year.

Site: P Payment: Leisure: Property: Children: Catering: Room:

FOLKE, Dorset Map ref 2B3 S

Folke Manor Farm Cottages
Contact: Mr & Mrs John & Carol Perrett, Folke Manor Farm, Folke, Sherborne DT9 5HP
T: (01963) 210731 / 07929 139472 **E:** stay@folkemanorholidays.co.uk
W: www.folkemanorholidays.co.uk **£ BOOK ONLINE**

Units 4
Sleeps 40
PER UNIT PER WEEK
£420.00 - £1500.00

SPECIAL PROMOTIONS
Spring, Autumn and Winter Breaks. 3 nights minimum stay £295-£475 per cottage.

Folke Manor Farm Cottages are spacious barn conversions in a quiet part of the Blackmore Vale area of North Dorset. We are off the beaten track and set within the peaceful grounds of the farm, which has two large ponds and over looks the stunning countryside. There is a heated indoor swimming pool open all year round.

Open: All year.
Nearest Shop: 3 miles
Nearest Pub: 0.5 miles

Site: P Payment: Leisure: Property: Children: Unit:

LYME REGIS, Dorset Map ref 1D2 S

Cecilia's Cottage
Contact: Sammie Steepe, 11 Monmouth Street, Georges Square, Lyme Regis, Dorset DT7 3PX **T:** (01865) 297525 **E:** sammie@pennyandsinclair.co.uk
W: www.barkerevansproperties.com

Units 1
Sleeps 6
PER UNIT PER WEEK
£1300.00 - £1600.00

Beautiful, boutique hideaway for romantic couples or small families. Open plan lounge/dining room area with wood burning stove and dining table to seat 6. Master bedroom with en suite bathroom. Further double bedroom and twin bedroom. Large master bathroom with free standing bath and separate shower enclosure. Illuminated decked patio area. Parking for one car with permit in local car park. **Open:** All year.
Nearest Shop: 0.2km **Nearest Pub:** 0.1km

 Site: Payment: Property: Children: Unit:

S

Upton Grange Holiday Cottages

Contact: Mrs Kerrie Webster, Upton Farm, Ringstead, Dorchester, Dorset DT2 8NE
T: (01305) 853970 **E:** uptonfarmholiday@aol.com
W: www.uptongrangedorset.co.uk

Units   6
Sleeps   2-6

PER UNIT PER WEEK
£430.00 - £1350.00

SPECIAL PROMOTIONS
Short breaks available
from £175.00,
minimum 2
nights stay.

Cosseted in the centre of the tiny unspoilt hamlet of Upton, where the World Heritage Jurassic Coastline rejoices in the simplicity of nearby Ringstead Bay, the Tithe barn of Upton Farm stands majestic as it has done, in part, since 1579.

Having been sympathetically converted into a small number of holiday cottages, furnished and equipped to the most exacting standards, these unique properties are guaranteed to incite feelings of nostalgia. We accept all major credit and debit cards.

Open: All year.
Nearest Shop: 1 mile (approx)
Nearest Pub: 1 mile (approx)

Units: Some bedrooms feature 4 poster beds and log fires grace the lounges of the larger homes, our cottages can accommodate 2 - 6 persons.

Site: ✿ **Payment:** 💷 **Leisure:** 🚲 ♪ ▶ ♺ **Property:** 🖥 🏠 **Children:** 🐾 🛏 🏃
Unit: 📱 ▭ 🖥 ☕ 🍽 📺 🎧 💿 🔥 BBQ

f y

S

Durdle Door Holiday Cottages

Contact: Anne Pullin, West Lulworth, Wareham, Dorset BH20 5PU **T:** (01929) 400888
E: Durdle.door@lulworth.com
W: www.lulworth.com/stay

Units   6
Sleeps   2-6

Escape to the Jurassic Coast. Set in a truly inspirational location, high on the hill above the iconic rock arch of Durdle Door in Dorset, these collection of six beautifully restored, designed and ecologically built cottages occupy what was once a group of period farm buildings.

Sleeping 2-6, all six cottages share exclusive use of the fitness and recreation barn and in the summer months, the heated outdoor swimming pool. The cottages have contemporary open plan living spaces, are comfortably furnished and equipped to Visit England Four Star Gold Award Standard. Perfect for a weekend retreat for walking, coasteering and biking or for a family summer holiday.

Nearest Pub: East Lulworth, the Weld Arms & West Lulworth, the Cove Inn.

Units: Durdle Door Holiday Cottages on the Dorset coast at Durdle Door, are available for luxury holiday hire.

f

Site: ✿ **P** **Leisure:** ⚓ **Property:** 🖥 🏠 🏠

WAREHAM, Dorset *Map ref 2B3*   *SatNav BH20 5PU* **C**

Durdle Door Holiday Park

West Lulworth, Wareham BH20 5PU
T: (01929) 400200 **F:** (01929) 400260 **E:** durdle.door@lulworth.com
W: www.lulworth.com/stay **£ BOOK ONLINE**

🚐 (58)   £20.00-£52.00
🚙 (16)   £20.00-£52.00
🏠 (19)   £194.00-£851.00
58 touring pitches

SPECIAL PROMOTIONS
Please see website for
further details.

Wake up to big skies and sea air. Situated on the dramatic World Heritage Jurassic Coast and surrounded by glorious rolling Dorset countryside, Durdle Door Holiday Park is unique. Set within an 'Area of Outstanding Natural Beauty' on the Lulworth Estate, Durdle Door is a carefully managed Holiday Park popular with families, walkers and those who share a love of the natural environment. Offering direct access to the South West Coastal Path, unspoilt beaches, stunning landscapes and the famous 'Durdle Door', visitors can choose from a variety of accommodation options including fully serviced tourer pitches, camping pods, camping space and holiday homes.

Open February to October, Durdle Door Holiday Park is a great base for a holiday at any time of the year. Choose from three night weekend getaways, four day mid-week breaks or week-long holidays.

Directions: Please see website for details.   **Open:** 1st March to 31st October.

Site: 🏕 **Payment:** 💳 ☼ **Leisure:** ∪ **Children:** 🛝 🎠 **Catering:** ✗ 🍴 **Park:** 🐕 🎵 🖥 📺 🏢 📷
Touring: 🚿 🚻 💧 ♨

WAREHAM, Dorset *Map ref 2B3*   *SatNav BH20 5LR* **B**

Kingston Country Courtyard

Kingston, Nr Corfe Castle, Wareham, Dorset BH20 5LR **T:** (01929) 481066
F: (01929) 481256 **E:** relax@kingstoncountrycourtyard.com
W: www.kingstoncountrycourtyard.com **£ BOOK ONLINE**

B&B PER ROOM PER NIGHT
S: £40.00 - £60.00
D: £120.00 - £170.00
HB PER PERSON PER NIGHT
£60.00 - £70.00

Kingston Country Courtyard gives you a taste of authentic farmstead life in an 'Area of Outstanding Natural Beauty.' Tastefully converted outbuildings, high beamed ceilings, thick Purbeck stone walls. Bed and Breakfast or Self Catering apartments available. Some dog friendly rooms by arrangement. Views of the Castle from the garden. Limited Wi-Fi...enjoy an escape from the city!

Directions: From Wareham, take the A351 towards Swanage. On leaving the village of Corfe Castle, turn right on to the B3069 - signposted to Kingston, up the hill, round a sharp left bend, we are on the left.

Bedrooms: En suite, wet rooms or bathtubs. TVs, tea and coffee, kettles in rooms. No restaurant but group bookings over 30 catered for by prior arrangement.
Open: All year round except Christmas and New Year.

Site: ✿ P **Leisure:** 🚲 ♪ ▶ ∪ **Property:** 🍴 🐕 🖥 📺 ♿ **Children:** 🛝 🏊 🎯 **Catering:** 🍽 🍴
Room: 📶 ☕ 📺 📀 ✏ 🍴

For **key to symbols** see page 6   79

WAREHAM, Dorset Map ref 2B3 SatNav BH20 5RQ B

VisitEngland ★★★★ INN
VisitEngland Silver AWARD

B&B PER ROOM PER NIGHT
D: £110.00 - £140.00
EVENING MEAL PER PERSON
£15.00 - £25.00

Lulworth Cove Inn

Main Road, West Lulworth, Dorset BH20 5RQ **T:** (01929) 400333 **E:** lulworthcove.inn@hall-woodhouse.co.uk
W: www.lulworth-coveinn.co.uk **£ BOOK ONLINE**

Situated on the doorstep of Lulworth Cove, the Lulworth Cove Inn boasts stunning coastal views and scenic Jurassic footpaths. Only a few of minutes' drive from Durdle Door the Lulworth Cove Inn is an idyllic location for paradise seekers.

Directions: End of B3070, down Main Road, Lulworth Cove on the left at the end opposite Heritage Centre car park.

Bedrooms: 12 unique bedrooms all finished to a luxurious, comfortable standard with flatscreen TV, bluetooth radio and tea & coffee making facilities.
Open: All year.

Site: **Payment:** **Property:** **Children:** **Catering:** **Room:**

WEYMOUTH, Dorset Map ref 2B3 SatNav DT3 6HF B

VisitEngland ★★★★ INN
VisitEngland Silver AWARD

B&B PER ROOM PER NIGHT
D: £90.00 - £110.00
EVENING MEAL PER PERSON
£15.00 - £25.00

Smugglers Inn

Osmington Mills, Weymouth, Dorset DT3 6HF **T:** (01305) 833125
E: smugglersinn.weymouth@hall-woodhouse.co.uk
W: www.smugglersinnosmingtonmills.co.uk **£ BOOK ONLINE**

Nestled on the edge of the Jurassic coast, boasting stunning views and scenic footpaths, the Smugglers Inn is an idyllic location for those wishing to escape the hustle of everyday. Dating back to the 13th century, the Inn is known to have been the home of some of the most notorious smugglers of the age. In its present day, the Inn offers award-winning Badger cask ales and fresh dishes.

Directions: Located in Osmington Mills from A353 take Mills Road, follow to the end, car park on the right, Smugglers Inn on the left.

Bedrooms: Smuggler's Inn offers 4 en suite rooms with Wi-Fi access. All rates are per room, per night inc. breakfast and free car park pass.
Open: All year.

Site: **Payment:** **Property:** **Children:** **Catering:** **Room:**

WIMBORNE, Dorset   Map ref 2B3   SatNav BH21 1HR **B**

1777 Bedrooms and Breakfast at The Albion

1777, 19 High Street, The Square, Wimborne, Dorset BH21 1HR **T:** (01202) 884686
E: albion.wimborne@hall-woodhouse.co.uk
W: www.theolivebranchwimborne.co.uk **£ BOOK ONLINE**

B&B PER ROOM PER NIGHT
D: £100.00 - £170.00
EVENING MEAL PER PERSON
£20.00 - £40.00

1777 bedrooms & breakfast at The Albion is located in the heart of the historic market town of Wimborne Minster. The inn dates from the 17th century when it was the oldest of four coaching inns in the town – of which only two remain. Today the inn boasts 10 en suite bedrooms each designed around three themes from the Georgian era; Gentility, Mercantilism and The Sea.

Directions: Situated on the High Street in Wimborne just off The Square, the car park is located through the archway between Savilles and Thomas Cook.

Bedrooms: 10 unique en suite rooms all finished to a luxurious, comfortable standard with flatscreen TV, bluetooth radio and tea & coffee making facilities.
Open: All year.

Site: ✿ P **Payment:** 🖭 **Property:** ≕ **Children:** ᪶ **Catering:** (✕ ♟ **Room:** 🖭 🍴 TV ⚲ 🖾

BARNSLEY, Gloucestershire   Map ref 2B1   SatNav GL7 5EE **H**

Barnsley House

Barnsley, Cirencester GL7 5EE **T:** (01285) 740000 **E:** reception@barnsleyhouse.com
W: www.barnsleyhouse.com **£ BOOK ONLINE**

B&B PER ROOM PER NIGHT
S: £201.00 - £601.00
D: £219.00 - £619.00

Barnsley House is your very own country house set in extensive landscaped gardens, designed by Rosemary Verey, near Cirencester in Gloucestershire. The Hotel has a dedicated spa, private cinema and 18 large and luxurious bedrooms.
Directions: Centre of Barnsley, on the B4425 (Cirencester to Bibury and Burford road), 4 miles NE of Cirencester.
Open: All year.

Site: ✿ P **Payment:** 🖭 **Leisure:** ♨ ♪ ▶ ∪ ⚑ ⚲ **Property:** ⛛ 🐾 ≕ 🖥 ♨ ◑ ⌀ **Children:** ᪶14 ▦ ⚱
Catering: (✕ ♟ 🍴 **Room:** 🖭 🍴 ⚲ ⚱ TV 🖾 ⚲ 🖾

CHIPPING CAMPDEN, Gloucestershire   Map ref 2B1   **S**

Granary Cottage

Contact: Beverley Needham, Director, Back Lane, Mickleton, Chipping Campden, Gloucestershire GL55 6SJ **T:** (01386) 852462 **E:** campdencottages@icloud.com
W: www.campdencottages.co.uk **£ BOOK ONLINE**

Units   1
Sleeps   2
PER UNIT PER WEEK
£360.00 - £740.00

An interesting quirky 'upside down' cottage forming part of a Barn Conversion. Granary Cottage offers a well presented character accommodation with a pretty paved garden. Situated within a popular courtyard at the heart of the village. Close to the village amenities including the famous Pudding Club, two village shops and 2 pubs with restaurants. The Cottage has been completely refurbished to a very high standard whilst maintaining the character. Enclosed courtyard to the front of the Cottage.
Open: All year. **Nearest Shop:** 0.2 miles **Nearest Pub:** 0.2 miles

Site: ✿ P **Leisure:** ▶ ⚲ **Property:** 🐾 ≕ 🖥 🖾 **Unit:** 🖭 ▦ 🖥 ⚲ TV ⚲ 🖾 BBQ

CHIPPING CAMPDEN, Gloucestershire Map ref 2B1 [S]

VisitEngland ★★★★ SELF CATERING

Walnut Tree

Contact: Beverley Needham, Director, Barnhaven, Willersey Fields, Worcestershire WR11 7HF **T:** (01386) 852462 **E:** campdencottages@icloud.com
W: www.campdencottages.co.uk

Units	2
Sleeps	4

PER UNIT PER WEEK
£340.00 - £540.00

A honey coloured cotswold stone cottage, without doubt in the idyllic rural setting. Guests can relax in comfort, surrounded by the open countryside whilst still being within reach of tourist attractions, pubs and a village shop.
Open: All year.
Nearest Shop: 1.5 miles
Nearest Pub: 1.5 miles

Site: ✿ **P Payment:** ⊞ **Leisure:** ✦ ♪ ▶ ∪ ♦ ⤙ ⤙ ⤙ **Property:** ∥ ⱦ ▦ ⊡ ⊟ **Unit:** ⊟ ⊟ ▣ ⤙ ⤙ ⊡ ⊕ ⊘ BBQ ✆

CIRENCESTER, Gloucestershire Map ref 2B1   SatNav GL7 1LF [B]

VisitEngland ★★★★ GUEST ACCOMMODATION

Riverside House

Watermoor, Cirencester GL7 1LF **T:** (01285) 647642 **F:** (01285) 647615
E: riversidehouse@mitsubishi-cars.co.uk
W: www.riversidehouse.org.uk **£ BOOK ONLINE**

B&B PER ROOM PER NIGHT
S: £60.00 - £70.00
D: £75.00 - £85.00
EVENING MEAL PER PERSON
£10.00 - £18.00

SPECIAL PROMOTIONS
Special group discounts are available at weekends. Ideal for clubs and societies.

Recently refurbished bed and breakfast accommodation within walking distance of the historic market town of Cirencester. Riverside House makes an ideal base for exploring the Cotswolds with easy access to the M4/M5. Fully licensed restaurant open for evening meals Monday to Thursday. Built in the grounds of The Colt Car Company. Please be aware we do not have a lift.

Directions: Located just off A419 opposite the Tesco superstore.

Bedrooms: 15 double, 9 twin.
Open: All year.

Site: ✿ **P Payment:** ⊞ **Leisure:** ✦ ♪ ▶ ∪ **Property:** ▦ **Children:** ⤫ **Catering:** ♥ ⱦ
Room: ⤙ ⬩ ✆ ⊡ ⊡

CIRENCESTER, Gloucestershire Map ref 2B1 [S]

VisitEngland ★★★★★ SELF CATERING   VisitEngland Gold AWARD

The Stables

Contact: Rowena Paul, Forge House, Limes Road, Kemble, Cirencester, Gloucestershire GL7 6FS **T:** (01285) 771157 / 07787 258758 **F:** (01285) 771157
E: info@forgehousekemble.co.uk **W:** www.forgehousekemble.co.uk **£ BOOK ONLINE**

Units	1
Sleeps	1-8

PER UNIT PER WEEK
£595.00 - £1950.00

The Stables is a stunning recently converted barn conversion in a delightful courtyard across from the principal house. It has a 40ft beamed open plan living/dining room with contemporary log-burner perfect for celebrations or relaxing weekends away. It has a fully-equipped contemporary kitchen. Double patio doors open onto a seating area with teak garden furniture, the perfect place to relax. **Open:** All year.
Nearest Shop: Kemble Village Stores **Nearest Pub:** 0.5 miles

Site: ✿ **P Payment:** ⊞ **Property:** ▦ ⊡ **Children:** ⤫ ▦ ⱦ **Unit:** ⊟ ⊟ ▣ ⤙ ⤙ ⊡ ⊕ ⊘ BBQ

HOTEL BOAT

HB PER PERSON PER NIGHT
£130.00 - £199.00

SPECIAL PROMOTIONS
Complete package holidays with 3 Meals/day free tea/coffee, welcome drink, wine at dinner, outside tours, W-iFi and live entertainment. Special low prices in April and October. Singles welcome.

English Holiday Cruises

The Edward Elgar, Alexandra Quay, The Docks, Gloucester GL1 2LG **T:** (01452) 410411
F: (01452) 357959 **E:** sales@englishholidaycruises.co.uk
W: www.englishholidaycruises.co.uk **£ BOOK ONLINE**

For an unusual holiday in England, book a 'Rhine-style' complete package holiday with English Holiday Cruises in the Cotswolds Severn vale. Board their Hotel Boat Edward Elgar in Gloucester, unpack, relax and sail through glorious countryside to fascinating destinations steeped in history.

The meals are delicious and the crew really care! Why travel to the Rhine when 97% of guests recommend us?

Directions: Gloucester is easy to reach by car, train or coach from all parts of the UK. Passengers board MV Edward Elgar in the Historic Docks of Gloucester and secure parking is available nearby.

Bedrooms: 4-Star Hotel Boat standard. All cabins are cosy twin-bedded rooms, with a window, climate control, ample storage and en suite shower, basin and WC.
Open: 36 Cruise dates from 2-6 nights April to October.

 f

Payment: ⓔ **Property:** ⓔ 🍷 🛏 🖥 🎄 ◑ **Catering:** ⟨✕ 🍷 🍽 **Room:** 🦆 📞

SELF CATERING

Units   2
Sleeps   1-4

Hill Farm Cottages

Contact: Mrs Margaret McLellan, Hill Farm Cottages, Hill Farm, Upton Hill,
Upton St Leonards, Gloucester GL4 8DA **T:** (01452) 614081
E: hillfarmcottages@hotmail.co.uk

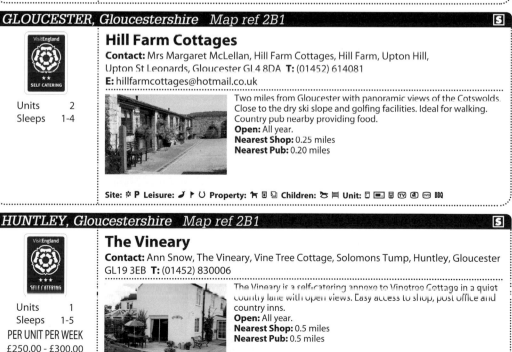

Two miles from Gloucester with panoramic views of the Cotswolds. Close to the dry ski slope and golfing facilities. Ideal for walking. Country pub nearby providing food.
Open: All year.
Nearest Shop: 0.25 miles
Nearest Pub: 0.20 miles

Site: ✿ P **Leisure:** ♪ ⴄ ♔ **Property:** 🐓 🖥 🔳 **Children:** ⌣ 🍽 **Unit:** 🛏 ▣ 🖥 📺 ④ 📀 BBQ

SELF CATERING

Units   1
Sleeps   1-5
PER UNIT PER WEEK
£250.00 - £300.00

The Vineary

Contact: Ann Snow, The Vineary, Vine Tree Cottage, Solomons Tump, Huntley, Gloucester GL19 3EB **T:** (01452) 830006

The Vineary is a self-catering annexe to Vinetree Cottage in a quiet country lane with open views. Easy access to shop, post office and country inns.
Open: All year.
Nearest Shop: 0.5 miles
Nearest Pub: 0.5 miles

Site: ✿ P **Leisure:** ♪ **Property:** 🔳 **Children:** ⌣ **Unit:** ▣ 🖥 📺 📀

MITCHELDEAN, Gloucestershire Map ref 2B1 [S]

Holme House Barn

Contact: Tim and Diana Bateman, Holme House, Jubilee Road, Mitcheldean, Gloucestershire GL17 0EE **T:** (01594) 543875 **E:** info@holmehousebarn.co.uk
W: www.holmehousebarn.co.uk **£ BOOK ONLINE**

Units   1
Sleeps   1-6

PER UNIT PER WEEK
£450.00 - £840.00

SPECIAL PROMOTIONS
Weekends and short midweek breaks available. Minimum stay 2 nights.

Holme House Barn is a luxury holiday cottage nestling in rural farmland, surrounded by fields and woodland. It is located 300 metres from a country lane and is only visible from Holme House itself.

Open: 2nd March to 30th September.
Nearest Shop: 1 mile
Nearest Pub: 1 mile

Units: Double, twin and bathroom on the ground floor. Open plan kitchen-diner and sitting room upstairs with a sofa bed, easy chairs and freeview TV.

Site: ✿ P Leisure: ◆ Property: 🐾 🖿 🖳 Children: ⚘ 🏠 ⚲ Unit: 🚪 🛏 🖥 📷 🍳 📺 🎧 📀 BBQ ☎

MORETON-IN-MARSH, Gloucestershire Map ref 2B1 [S]

Forget Me Not

Contact: Beverley Needham, Director, Campden Cottages Ltd, 10 Mount Pleasant, Blockley, Gloucestershire GL56 9BU **T:** (01386) 852462 **E:** campdencottages@icloud.com
W: www.campdencottages.co.uk **£ BOOK ONLINE**

Units   1
Sleeps   2
PER UNIT PER WEEK
£340.00 - £560.00

A popular, one bedroom cottage located in the centre of Blockley. Accessed from a footpath, its secluded location makes the cottage a most peaceful retreat. Forget Me Not Cottage provides all the charm and peace expected of a country home.
Open: All year.
Nearest Shop: 500 yards
Nearest Pub: 500 yards

Site: ✿ P Payment: 💳 Leisure: ⚴ ♪ ♡ ☘ Property: ∥ 🐾 🖿 🖳 Children: ⚘ 🏠 ⚲ Unit: 🚪 🛏 🖥 📺 🎧 📀 BBQ ☎

STOW-ON-THE-WOLD, Gloucestershire Map ref 2B1 [S]

Broad Oak Cottages

Contact: Mrs Mary Wilson, Owner, May Cottage, The Counting House, Oddington Road, Stow-on-the-Wold, Cheltenham GL54 1AL **T:** (01451) 830794 **F:** (01451) 830794
E: enquiries@maycottage.co.uk **W:** www.maycottage.co.uk **£ BOOK ONLINE**

Units   1
Sleeps   1-4
PER UNIT PER WEEK
£538.00 - £915.00

May Cottage is a luxury 5 Star/Gold Award, quiet 2 bedroom cottage all on one level and within a few minutes' walk of Stow Square. It includes a Master Suite with luxury bathroom, a conservatory and large sitting room opening onto a patio. Parking for 2 cars and private garden.
Open: All year.
Nearest Shop: 0.10 miles
Nearest Pub: 0.02 miles

Site: ✿ P Payment: € Leisure: ⚴ ♪ ♡ Property: 🖿 🖳 Children: ⚘ 🏠 ⚲ Unit: 🚪 🛏 🖥 📺 🎧 📀 BBQ ☎

STROUD, Gloucestershire   Map ref 2B1   SatNav GL6 9JE B

The Close B&B

The Close, Well Hill, Minchinhampton, Stroud, Gloucestershire GL6 9JE **T:** (01453) 883338
E: theclosebnb@gmail.com
W: www.theclosebnb.co.uk **£ BOOK ONLINE**

B&B PER ROOM PER NIGHT
S: £65.00 - £75.00
D: £85.00   £95.00

Historic Town House offering stylish and comfortable accommodation, the perfect place for a short break in the Cotswolds. Set in a charming small market town with shops and cafés nearby. Wonderful walking country with beautiful views.
Directions: 2nd house on the left, from the top of Well Hill.
Bedrooms: Spacious rooms with en suites, TVs and tea/coffee making facilities.
Open: Open February to December (closed January).

Site: ❀ P Payment: 💳 Leisure: ▶ ∪ Property: 🐾 🖵 🍽 ∅ Catering: 🍴 Room: 🕄 🌣 📺

TETBURY, Gloucestershire   Map ref 2B2   SatNav GL8 8YJ H

Calcot Manor Hotel & Spa

Tetbury, Gloucestershire GL8 8YJ **T:** (01666) 890391 **F:** (01666) 890394
E: reception@calcot.co
W: www.calcot.co **£ BOOK ONLINE**

B&B PER ROOM PER NIGHT
S: £194.00 - £524.00
D: £219.00 - £549.00

f 🐦

A charming Country House Hotel set in peaceful gardens, renowned for the excellence of its restaurant and the informality of its Gumstool Inn. Calcot has excellent facilities for children including family suites with bunk beds, baby listening facilities and an Ofsted-registered crèche. For adults there's the luxury of Calcot Spa, boasting seven treatment rooms, indoor pool and an outdoor hot tub by a blazing fire. **Directions:** 3 m West of Tetbury on A4135.
Bedrooms: 7 double, 15 twin, 12 family, 1 suite. **Open:** All year.

Site: ❀ Payment: 💳 Leisure: 🎱 ▶ 🎯 🏹 ⚲ 🎿 ⚲ Property: 🦮 🐾 🖵 🗗 🍽 ◐ ∅ Children: 🧸 🛏 🧍
Catering: 🕻 ✕ 🍽 🍴 Room: 🕄 🌣 🕻 📷 📺 🔌 🎛

TEWKESBURY, Gloucestershire   Map ref 2B1   S

9 Mill Bank

Contact: Bill & Dawn Hunt, Owners, 7 Mill Bank, Tewkesbury, Gloucestershire GL20 5SD
T: (01684) 276190 **F:** (01684) 276190 **E:** billhunt@9mb.co.uk
W: www.tewkesbury-cottage.co.uk

Units   1
Sleeps   1-3
PER UNIT PER WEEK
£395.00 - £510.00

A bijou, 16th century, riverside cottage in a delightful medieval town, bordering the Cotswolds. Outstanding location with open views across to the Malvern Hills. Nightly/weekend bookings available. "Peace, quiet and tranquility; it truly is a gem". Free Wi-Fi. See us on TripAdvisor.
Open: All year.
Nearest Shop: 0.1 miles
Nearest Pub: 0.1 miles

Payment: € Leisure: 🎱 🎿 ▶ ∪ Property: 🖵 🗗 🖵 Children: 🧸 🛏 🧍 Unit: 🖵 🕄 📺 🔌 📀
∅

WITHINGTON, Gloucestershire Map ref 2B1 S

SELF CATERING ★★★★

Ballingers Farmhouse Cottages

Contact: Ian & Judith Pollard, Ballingers Farmhouse Cottages, Withington, Cheltenham GL54 4BB **T:** (01242) 890335 **E:** pollardfam2005@btinternet.com
W: www.ballingersfarmhousecottages.co.uk **£ BOOK ONLINE**

Units	2
Sleeps	2

PER UNIT PER WEEK
£250.00 - £400.00

Delightful single storey cottages, converted from old farm buildings retaining many original features that tastefully combine old and new. Well furnished and equipped to ensure you enjoy your holiday. Set in a village location approximately 8 miles from Cheltenham and Cirencester. Ideal for exploring the Cotswolds and surrounding areas.
Open: All year.
Nearest Shop: 3 miles **Nearest Pub:** 0.5 miles

Site: ✿ P **Property:** 🐕 🖾 **Children:** 🍼 🎠 **Unit:** 📺 🖳 🍴 📺 🎧 📀 ⌀

WOOLSTONE, Gloucestershire Map ref 2B1 S

SELF CATERING ★★★★

Hill Farm Cottages

Contact: Mrs Diane Andrews, Owner, Woolstone Hill Farm, Woolstone GL52 9RG
T: (01242) 672803 / 07747 758503 **E:** woolstonehillfarm@hotmail.co.uk
W: www.thehillfarmcottage.co.uk **£ BOOK ONLINE**

Units	1
Sleeps	4

PER UNIT PER WEEK
£250.00 - £430.00

SPECIAL PROMOTIONS
Low season
£250-300 pw,
High season
£350-£430pw.

Delightful 3 bedroomed cottage set in a area of outstanding natural beauty overlooking the beautiful cotswold Valley towards Prescott hill climb. Customers have the privilege of using the hill for walks and can enjoy looking around the large working beef farm.

The cottage is situated 1 mile from the village of Gotherington which has a village shop, Post Office, and local pub. Ideally situated for exploring the Cotswolds and many picturesque towns and villages including Broadway, Chipping Campden, Stow-on-the-Wold and Moreton-in-Marsh. Cheltenham and its racecourse are just 4 miles away while Tewkesbury, Evesham, Stratford-upon-Avon are just a short drive away.

Open: All year.
Nearest Shop: 1 mile
Nearest Pub: 1 mile

Units: Fully equipped kitchen/dining room, Lounge with leather sofas, large TV & DVD, log effect gas fire. Ground floor single bedroom with en suite. Upstairs has two bedrooms and a fully fitted shower room.

Site: ✿ P **Leisure:** ♪ ∪ **Property:** 🖾 🖳 🖾 **Children:** 🍼5 **Unit:** 🖳 🖲 📺 🖳 🍴 📺 🎧 📀 BBQ

BATH, Somerset Map ref 2B2 SatNav BA1 2NQ B

GUEST ACCOMMODATION ★★★★ **Gold AWARD**

Marlborough House Guest House

1 Marlborough Lane, Bath BA1 2NQ **T:** (01225) 318175 **F:** (01225) 466127
E: mars@manque.dircon.co.uk
W: www.marlborough-house.net **£ BOOK ONLINE**

B&B PER ROOM PER NIGHT
S: £95.00 - £145.00
D: £95.00 - £155.00

Enchanting vegetarian townhouse in Bath's city centre, featuring elegant rooms, unique breakfast menu, and relaxing atmosphere. Close to theatre and excellent restaurants.
Directions: M4 junction 18 to Bath. A4 into city centre via Queen Square, take Charlotte Street exit, continue for 1 minute Marlborough Lane will be on your right.
Bedrooms: 2 double, 2 twin, 2 family.
Open: All year except Christmas.

Site: ✿ P **Payment:** 💷 € **Leisure:** 🎣 **Property:** ® 🖳 **Children:** 🍼 🎠 🏃 **Catering:** 🍽 🍴 **Room:** 🖳 ✆ 📺 🎧

Pulteney House

14 Pulteney Road, Bath BA2 4HA **T:** (01225) 460991 **F:** (01225) 460991
E: pulteneyhouse@gmail.com
W: www.pulteneyhotel.co.uk **£ BOOK ONLINE**

B&B PER ROOM PER NIGHT
S: £60.00 - £90.00
D: £85.00 - £160.00

SPECIAL PROMOTIONS
Reduced rates for stays
of 3 nights or more -
each booking assessed
individually.

Large, elegant, Victorian house in picturesque gardens. Large, private car park with CCTV. 5-10 minutes walk from city centre. An ideal base for exploring Bath and surrounding areas. All rooms (except one) are en suite. All have hairdryer, TV with Freeview/Sat, hospitality tray and radio/alarm clocks. Free Wi-Fi in all rooms.

Directions: Pulteney House is situated on A36, which runs through Bath. For more detailed directions please refer to our website.

Bedrooms: 2 singles, 8 doubles, 4 twins, 3 family. Twin rates inc. in double rates. Family rates £125 - £160.
Open: All year except Christmas.

Site: ✿ P Payment: 🖃 Property: 🖳 Children: 🍼 🎮 ⚹ Catering: 🍽 Room: 🍵 💧 📶 📺 ⚙ 🖨

The Bailbrook Lodge

35/37 London Road West BA1 7HZ **T:** (01225) 859090 **F:** (01225) 852299
E: bookings.bailbrook0411@siteminder.co.uk
W: www.bailbrooklodge.co.uk **£ BOOK ONLINE**

B&B PER ROOM PER NIGHT
S: £69.00
D: £95.00 - £150.00

SPECIAL PROMOTIONS
Please see website for
the current special
promotions.

A Grade II Listed country house with 14 rooms, excellently situated a mile and a half from the city centre, in a delightful, relaxing location with lovely lawns and gardens. We have 15 individually decorated and furnished bedrooms providing the utmost in comfort and charm to make your stay truly enjoyable. 5 of our 15 rooms include four-poster beds, the only boutique B&B or hotel in Bath offering this number of four-poster beds.
Car parking is free.

Directions: From the M4: come off at junction 18 and take A46, come off at Bath exit and at the roundabout turn left to Batheaston, hotel is immediately on the left.

Bedrooms: En suite, flat screen TV, quality teas and fresh ground coffee, biscuits, mineral water, cotton slippers.
Open: All year.

Site: ✿ P Payment: 🖃 Leisure: ⚑ Property: ⚑ 🖳 🏵 Children: 🍼 🎮 ⚹ Catering: 🍴 🍽
Room: 🍵 💧 📺 📀 🖨

BINEGAR, Somerset   Map ref 2B2 [S]

Spindle Cottage Holidays

Contact: Mrs Angela Bunting, Owner, Spindle Cottage, Binegar Green, Binegar, Near Radstock, Somerset BA3 4UE **T:** (01749) 840497 / 07837 782841
E: angela@spindlecottage.co.uk **W:** www.spindlecottage.co.uk **£ BOOK ONLINE**

| Units | 1 |
| Sleeps | 1-5 |

PER UNIT PER WEEK
£450.00 - £800.00

Fairytale 17th century cottage, quite magical, on Mendip Hills. Garden, summerhouse, gazebo and conservatory. Full of charm and delight. Lovely sitting room, low ceiling, oak beams. Woodburning stove. 3 bedrooms: double en suite, twin, single. Full of charm. Wells, Glastonbury, Bath, Cheddar, Wookey Hole within easy reach. Holiday of your dreams. 3 unique playhouses for young at heart. Unique. **Open:** All year.
Nearest Shop: 1 mile **Nearest Pub:** 0.5 miles

Site: ✿ P **Leisure:** ⌐ ⌐ ∪ **Property:** 🖵 🗄 🖳 **Children:** ⅚ ⋔ ⋔ **Unit:** ⬚ ⬚ ⬚ ⬚ ⬚ ⬚ ⬚ ⬚

BRIDGWATER, Somerset   Map ref 1D1   SatNav TA5 2HW [B]

Gurney Manor Mill

Gurney Street, Cannington, Bridgwater TA5 2HW **T:** (01278) 653582
E: gurneymill@yahoo.co.uk
W: www.gurneymill.co.uk

B&B PER ROOM PER NIGHT
S: £40.00 - £50.00
D: £70.00 - £80.00

Old watermill and barn conversion, alongside a stream with waterfall, pond and wildlife. Situated in picturesque village at gateway to Quantock Hills. Ideal location for touring the beautiful Historical West Country and South West.
Directions: Cannington (Bridgwater). Turn right into East St, turn right into Gurney St. Gurney Manor Mill is after Gurney Manor.
Bedrooms: 2 double, 1 twin, 1 family.
Open: All year.

Site: ✿ P **Payment:** 💷 **Leisure:** ⌐ ⌐ **Property:** 🐾 🖵 🗄 **Children:** ⅚ ⋔ ⋔ **Catering:** 🍴 **Room:** 🔌 ☕ 🖵 📺 🎀 🖨

BURNHAM-ON-SEA, Somerset   Map ref 1D1 [S]

Kings Lynn Holiday Apartments

Contact: Mrs V Young, 18 Oxford Street, Burnham-on-Sea, Somerset TA8 1LQ
T: (01278) 786666 **E:** mikevalyoung@btinternet.com

| Units | 2 |
| Sleeps | 2-4 |

PER UNIT PER WEEK
£220.00 - £435.00

Availability of either a two bedroom, ground floor apartment sleeping 2 plus 2 (bunk beds) or a one bedroom, first floor apartment sleeping 2 plus 2 (bed settee). Centrally located within sea side town of Burnham-on-Sea within easy walking distance of all amenities and sea front. Easy access to M5 motorway.
Open: All year.
Nearest Shop: 0.25 miles
Nearest Pub: 0.25 miles

Site: P **Property:** 🖵 🖳 **Children:** ⅚ **Unit:** ⬚ 🖵 🔌 📺 🖨

BURNHAM-ON-SEA, Somerset *Map ref 1D1* S

VisitEngland
★★★
SELF CATERING

Units 2
Sleeps 1-4

PER UNIT PER WEEK
£230.00 - £450.00

Stoddens Farm Cottages

Contact: Mrs Ruth Chambers, Owner, Stoddens Farm, 191 Stoddens Road, Burnham on Sea, Somerset TA8 2DE **T:** 07896 886051 **E:** info@stoddensfarmcottages.com **W:** www.stoddensfarmcottages.com **£ BOOK ONLINE**

Located in a Grade II listed barn conversion with plenty of character. Spacious and comfortable accommodation for up to 4 people in each of the 2 cottages. Large private gardens and stunning views over Somerset Levels.

Open: All year.
Nearest Shop: 0.5 miles
Nearest Pub: 0.5 miles

Units: One double and one twin bedroom in each cottage. Spacious open plan living area. Bath with electric shower over.

Site: ❀ P **Property:** ⊡ ▣ **Children:** ☎ ▥ ♠ **Unit:** ▣ ▣ TV ▣ BBQ

CHURCHINFORD, Somerset *Map ref 1D2* S

VisitEngland
★★★★
SELF CATERING

Units 2
Sleeps 2-6

PER UNIT PER WEEK
£150.00 - £650.00

SPECIAL PROMOTIONS
Late bookings available at discounted rate. Short breaks available upon request (2 nights minimum stay).

South Cleeve Bungalow

Contact: Mr J Manning, South Cleeve Bungalow, Churchinford, Nr Taunton, Somerset TA3 7PR **T:** (01823) 601378 / 07811 362740 **E:** enquiries@timbertopbungalows.co.uk **W:** www.timbertopbungalows.co.uk

Set in a quiet, rural location in 'An Area of Outstanding Natural Beauty' on the Devon/Somerset border. Within easy reach of National Trust houses, attractions, amenities and north and south coastlines. This fully equipped bungalow is set in its own large, secure lawn garden, which welcomes many wild and birdlife visitors, makes a superb holiday for all the family.
• Plenty of walks, fishing, golf and horse riding all close by.
• Managed by owners for over 20 years.
• Wi-Fi installed.
• Disabled friendly, wheelchair and ramp available.
• One well behaved pet welcome.
• Games room.

Open: All year.
Nearest Shop: 1 mile (Taunton 9 miles)
Nearest Pub: 1 mile

Units: Large, spacious bungalow set in a third of an acre of lawned garden, 2 double rooms (1 en suite) & 1 twin, lounge, kitchen/diner and conservatory.

Site: ❀ P **Leisure:** ♪ ▶ ∪ ♠ **Property:** ⌢ ▤ ▣ **Children:** ☎ ▥ ♠ **Unit:** ▣ ▣ ▣ ▣ ▧ TV ▣ ∅ BBQ

DUNSTER, Somerset Map ref 1D1

SatNav TA24 6SF [H]

★★★
HOTEL

B&B PER ROOM PER NIGHT
S: £65.00 - £90.00
D: £99.00 - £140.00
EVENING MEAL PER PERSON
£13.00 - £24.00

SPECIAL PROMOTIONS
Discounted rates for
longer stays
and midweek
bookings. Ring for
newsletter with
information on special
events. Group
bookings welcome.

Yarn Market Hotel
25-33 High Street, Dunster, Somerset TA24 6SF **T:** (01643) 821425 **F:** (01643) 821475
E: hotel@yarnmarkethotel.co.uk
W: www.yarnmarkethotel.co.uk **£ BOOK ONLINE**

Within Exmoor National Park, our hotel is ideal for walking, riding, fishing. Family-run with a friendly, relaxed atmosphere. All rooms en suite with colour TV. Four-poster and superior rooms available. Non-smoking. Home-cooked dishes to cater for all tastes. Group bookings welcomed. Conference facilities. Special Christmas and New Year breaks.

Directions: From M5 junction 25 follow signs for Exmoor/Minehead A358/A39. Dunster signed approx 0.5 miles from A39 on left. Hotel in village centre beside Yarn Market.

Bedrooms: 2 single, 12 double, 7 twin, 2 family.
Open: All year.

Site: ✿ Payment: 🔲 € Leisure: ♿ ♪ ↑ ↺ Property: ⚡ 🐕 🖥 🔲 🅟 Children: ⛱ 🎢 ⚲
Catering: (✗ 🍴 🍽 Room: 🔌 🌡 📺 📠

MINEHEAD, Somerset Map ref 1D1

[S]

★★★★
SELF CATERING

Units   1
Sleeps   2-4
PER UNIT PER WEEK
£295.00 - £630.00

Anchor Cottage
Contact: Wendy Steele, Owner, 11 Haven Close, Dunster, Somerset TA24 6RW
T: (01643) 821989 / 07702 985261 **E:** enquiries@anchorcottageminehead.co.uk
W: www.anchorcottageminehead.co.uk

Grade 2 listed 17th century fisherman's cottage in quiet location overlooking Minehead harbour. Refurbished to a very high standard whilst keeping loads of character. Well equipped with all home comforts. Double bedroom, twin bedroom with views. Patio above the rooftops. Beach opposite.
Open: All year.
Nearest Shop: 0.5 miles
Nearest Pub: 0.10 miles

Site: ✿ P Leisure: ♿ ♪ ↑ ↺ Property: 🐕 🖥 🔲 🅟 Children: ⛱ Unit: 🔲 🔲 💻 🖥 🔌 📺 ⏺ 📀 ⌀ ☎

Book your accommodation online

Visit our websites for detailed information, up-to-date availability and to book your accommodation online. Includes over 20,000 places to stay, all of them star rated.
www.visitor-guides.co.uk

PORLOCK, Somerset   Map ref 1D1   SatNav TA24 8HT **C**

Burrowhayes Farm Caravan & Camping Site & Riding Stables

West Luccombe, Porlock, Minehead TA24 8HT
T: (01643) 862463 **E:** info@burrowhayes.co.uk
W: www.burrowhayes.co.uk

🚐 (54)   £19.00-£26.00
🚚 (54)   £19.00-£26.00
🏕 (66)   £15.00-£21.50
🚐 (19)   £220.00-£490.00
139 touring pitches

Popular family site in delightful National Trust setting on Exmoor, just 2 miles from the Coast. Surrounding moors and woods provide a walker's paradise. Children can play and explore safely. Riding stables offer pony-trekking for all abilities. Heated shower block with disabled and baby-changing facilities, laundrette and pot wash.

Directions: From Minehead, A39 towards Porlock, 1st left after Allerford to Horner and West Luccombe, Burrowhayes is 0.25 miles along on right before hump-backed bridge.

Open: Mid-March to end of October.

Payment: 💳 ☼ **Leisure:** 🏃 🎣 ∪ **Catering:** 🍴 **Park:** 🐾 🚐 🅿 📱 📶 **Touring:** 🚰 🚽 🔌 ✈

PORLOCK, Somerset   Map ref 1D1   **S**

Green Chantry

Contact: Mrs Margaret Payton, Owner, Green Chantry, Home Farm, Burrowbridge, Bridgwater TA7 0RF **T:** (01823) 698330 / 07860 135848 **E:** maggie_payton@hotmail.com

Units   1
Sleeps   1-4
PER UNIT PER WEEK
£198.00 - £400.00

A charming Victorian cottage in a tranquil setting yet close to High Street with its range of shops, pubs and cafés and good local bus services. Good walking from cottage.
Open: All year.
Nearest Shop: 0.10 miles
Nearest Pub: 0.10 miles

Site: ✿ **Leisure:** 🏃 🎣 ∪ **Property:** 🐾 🖥 **Children:** 🍴 **Unit:** 🛏 📺 🔌 📶 📺 📀

PORLOCK, Somerset   Map ref 1D1   SatNav TA24 8ND **C**

Porlock Caravan Park

High Bank, Porlock, Somerset TA24 8ND
T: (01643) 862269 **F:** (01643) 862269 **E:** info@porlockcaravanpark.co.uk
W: www.porlockcaravanpark.co.uk **£ BOOK ONLINE**

🚐 (40)
🚚 (14)
🚐 (6)
40 touring pitches

Delightful, family run, award-winning park situated within walking distance of quaint village of Porlock. Luxury holiday homes for hire. Touring caravans, motor homes and tents welcome. Spotless facilities. Prices on Application.
Directions: A39 from Minehead, in Porlock village take B3225 to Porlock Weir, site signposted.
Open: March to October.

f **y**

Payment: 💳 ☼ **Leisure:** 🎣 ∪ **Park:** 🐾 🚐 🅿 📱 📶 **Touring:** 🚰 🚽 🔌

SOUTH PETHERTON, Somerset   Map ref 1D2   S

★★★★
SELF CATERING

| Units | 1 |
| Sleeps | 1-4 |

PER UNIT PER WEEK
£280.00 - £440.00

Tanwyn

Contact: Mr & Mrs Rodney & Ann Tanswell, Planhigyn, Penylan Road, St Brides Major, Vale of Glamorgan CF32 0SB **T:** (01656) 880524 / 07896 892448
E: rodney.tanswell@btinternet.com **W:** www.tanwyncottage.com

Tanwyn is a modernised hamstone cottage situated in a pleasant village with a pub and an award-winning restaurant. Ideally located for South coast, Exmoor, Cheddar, Bath, Wells, National Trust gardens etc. Large garden and orchard.
Open: All year except Christmas and New Year.
Nearest Shop: 1 mile
Nearest Pub: 0.25 miles

Site: ✿ P Property: 🖥 🔲 🍽 Children: 🛏10 Unit: 🔲 🔲 💻 🍴 🖥 📺 📀 📞

TAUNTON, Somerset   Map ref 1D1   SatNav TA3 5NW   C

★★★★
TOURING &
CAMPING PARK

🚐 (20)	£12.00-£16.00
🚚 (10)	£12.00-£16.00
⛺ (10)	£12.00-£16.00
🏠 (3)	£250.00-£300.00

30 touring pitches

Ashe Farm Caravan and Campsite

Ashe Farm Caravan and Campsite, Thornfalcon, Taunton TA3 5NW
T: (01823) 443764 **E:** info@ashefarm.co.uk
W: www.ashefarm.co.uk

Quiet farm site, lovely views, easy access. Central for touring. Easy reach coast and hills. Family run and informal.
Directions: Leave M5 at Junction 25, take A358 eastwards for 2.5 miles, turn right at Nags Head pub towards West Hatch. Site 0.25 miles on Right hand side.
Open: 1st April to 31st October.

Payment: ☀ Leisure: 🎣 ▶ ⛳ Children: 🛏 ⚠ Park: 🐕 🔲 🎖 Touring: 🚽 🔌

WEDMORE, Somerset   Map ref 1D1   S

VisitEngland ★★★★ SELF CATERING

VisitEngland *Gold* AWARD

| Units | 2 |
| Sleeps | 2-5 |

PER UNIT PER WEEK
£330.00 - £840.00

SPECIAL PROMOTIONS
Weekend breaks during low and mid season. 2 nights minimum stay.

Pear Tree Cottages

Contact: Mrs P Denbee, Pear Tree Farm, Stoughton Cross, Wedmore, Somerset BS28 4QR
T: (01934) 712243 **E:** info@peartree-cottages.co.uk
W: www.peartree-cottages.co.uk **£ BOOK ONLINE**

In the heart of the Somerset countryside are 2 luxury converted cottages with original features, on a working farm. A mecca for walkers, cyclists, nature lovers and golfers, they are also ideally situated for those who prefer exploring the villages, towns and cities of the area such as Wells, Cheddar, Bath, Bristol, Taunton and Glastonbury. Private south facing garden/patios.

Open: All year.
Nearest Shop: 1.5 miles
Nearest Pub: 0.5 miles

Units: The ground level luxury cottages are furnished to a high standard with under floor heating and woodburners. Bedrooms have own bath or shower rooms.

WALKERS

WALKERS

f

Site: ✿ P Leisure: 🎣 ▶ ⛳ Property: 🖥 🔲 🍽 Children: 🛏 🍽 ♿ Unit: 🔲 🔲 💻 🍴 🖥 📺 📀 ♨ BBQ

WESTON-SUPER-MARE, Somerset Map ref 1D1
SatNav BS22 9UJ **C**

Country View Holiday Park
29 Sand Road, Sand Bay, Weston-super-Mare BS22 9UJ
T: (01934) 627595 **E:** info@cvhp.co.uk
W: www.cvhp.co.uk

VisitEngland ★★★★ HOLIDAY, TOURING & CAMPING PARK

🚐 (90)
🚏 (90)
⛺ (30)
120 touring pitches

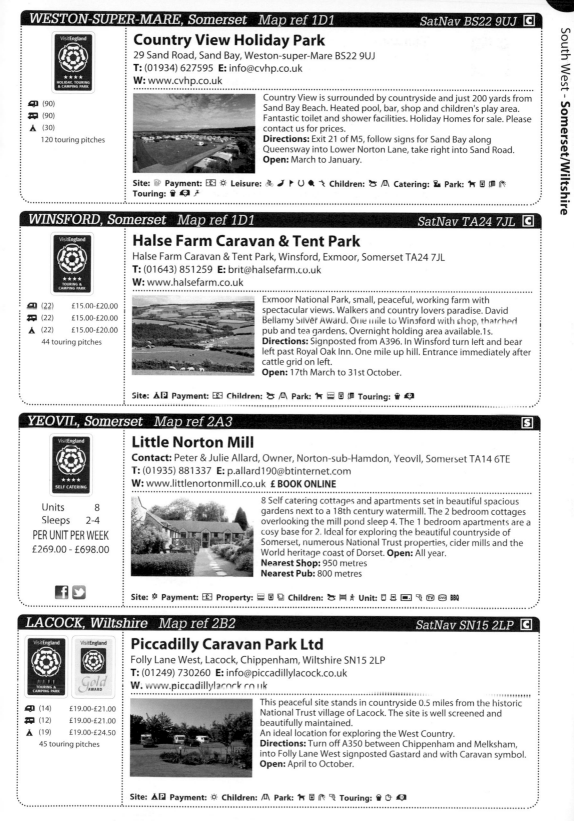

Country View is surrounded by countryside and just 200 yards from Sand Bay Beach. Heated pool, bar, shop and children's play area. Fantastic toilet and shower facilities. Holiday Homes for sale. Please contact us for prices.
Directions: Exit 21 of M5, follow signs for Sand Bay along Queensway into Lower Norton Lane, take right into Sand Road.
Open: March to January.

Site: ⛲ **Payment:** 🖼 ☼ **Leisure:** & ♪ ▶ ∪ ♣ ₹ **Children:** � ⚠ **Catering:** 🍴 **Park:** 🐕 🗑 📻 **Touring:** ☎ 🚐 ⚥

WINSFORD, Somerset Map ref 1D1
SatNav TA24 7JL **C**

Halse Farm Caravan & Tent Park
Halse Farm Caravan & Tent Park, Winsford, Exmoor, Somerset TA24 7JL
T: (01643) 851259 **E:** brit@halsefarm.co.uk
W: www.halsefarm.co.uk

VisitEngland ★★★★ TOURING & CAMPING PARK

🚐 (22) £15.00-£20.00
🚏 (22) £15.00-£20.00
⛺ (22) £15.00-£20.00
44 touring pitches

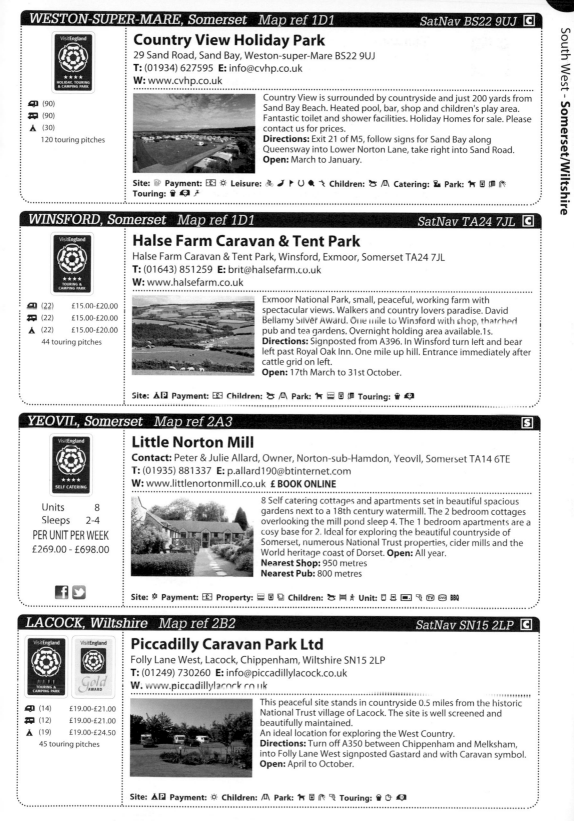

Exmoor National Park, small, peaceful, working farm with spectacular views. Walkers and country lovers paradise. David Bellamy Silver Award. One mile to Winsford with shop, thatched pub and tea gardens. Overnight holding area available.1s.
Directions: Signposted from A396. In Winsford turn left and bear left past Royal Oak Inn. One mile up hill. Entrance immediately after cattle grid on left.
Open: 17th March to 31st October.

Site: ⛺🅿 **Payment:** 🖼 **Children:** ⍺ ⚠ **Park:** 🐕 🗑 📻 **Touring:** ☎ 🚐

YEOVIL, Somerset Map ref 2A3
S

Little Norton Mill
Contact: Peter & Julie Allard, Owner, Norton-sub-Hamdon, Yeovil, Somerset TA14 6TE
T: (01935) 881337 **E:** p.allard190@btinternet.com
W: www.littlenortonmill.co.uk **£ BOOK ONLINE**

VisitEngland ★★★★ SELF CATERING

Units   8
Sleeps   2-4
PER UNIT PER WEEK
£269.00 - £698.00

📘 🐦

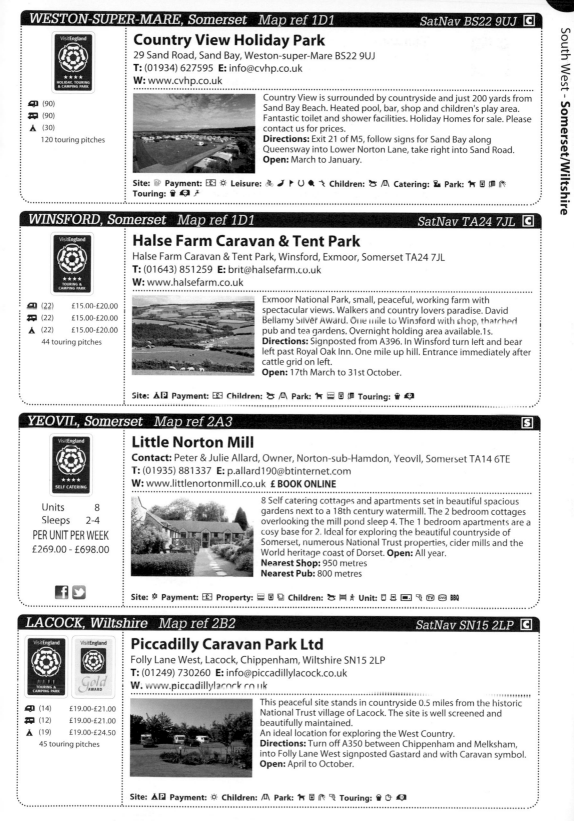

8 Self catering cottages and apartments set in beautiful spacious gardens next to a 18th century watermill. The 2 bedroom cottages overlooking the mill pond sleep 4. The 1 bedroom apartments are a cosy base for 2. Ideal for exploring the beautiful countryside of Somerset, numerous National Trust properties, cider mills and the World heritage coast of Dorset. **Open:** All year.
Nearest Shop: 950 metres
Nearest Pub: 800 metres

Site: ✻ **Payment:** 🖼 **Property:** 🖥 🗑 📺 **Children:** ⍺ ⊞ ⚥ **Unit:** 🗑 🗑 📺 🍴 TV 📀 BBQ

LACOCK, Wiltshire Map ref 2B2
SatNav SN15 2LP **C**

Piccadilly Caravan Park Ltd
Folly Lane West, Lacock, Chippenham, Wiltshire SN15 2LP
T: (01249) 730260 **E:** info@piccadillylacock.co.uk
W: www.piccadillylacock.co.uk

VisitEngland ★★★★ TOURING & CAMPING PARK   VisitEngland Gold AWARD

🚐 (14) £19.00-£21.00
🚏 (12) £19.00-£21.00
⛺ (19) £19.00-£24.50
45 touring pitches

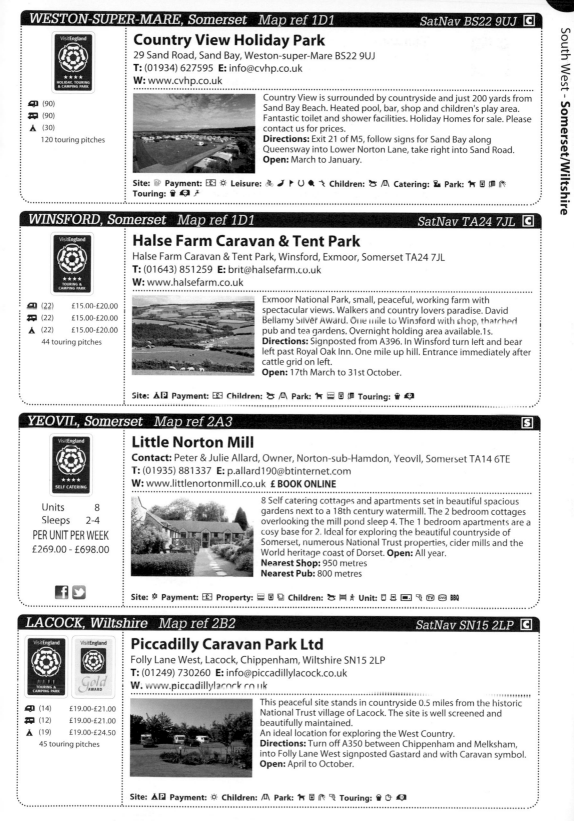

This peaceful site stands in countryside 0.5 miles from the historic National Trust village of Lacock. The site is well screened and beautifully maintained.
An ideal location for exploring the West Country.
Directions: Turn off A350 between Chippenham and Melksham, into Folly Lane West signposted Gastard and with Caravan symbol.
Open: April to October.

Site: ⛺🅿 **Payment:** ☼ **Children:** ⚠ **Park:** 🐕 🗑 📻 🍴 **Touring:** ☎ 🚽 🚐

MELKSHAM, Wiltshire   Map ref 2B2 — SatNav SN12 8EF [H]

SMALL HOTEL

Shaw Country Hotel

Bath Road, Shaw, Nr Melksham, Wiltshire SN12 8EF **T:** (01225) 702836 **F:** (01225) 790275
E: shawcountryhotel@hotmail.co.uk
W: www.shawcountryhotel.com **£ BOOK ONLINE**

B&B PER ROOM PER NIGHT
S: £65.00 - £73.00
D: £90.00 - £95.00
HB PER PERSON PER NIGHT
£86.50 - £94.50

Four hundred year old farmhouse in own grounds, nine miles from Bath. Licensed bar and restaurant, with table d'hote and a la carte menus. All rooms en suite.
Bedrooms: 3 single, 7 double, 3 twin.
Open: All year.

Site: ✿ **Payment:** 💳 **Property:** 🍴 🐕 🖥 🅱 **Children:** 👶 🛏 🛝 **Catering:** 🍽 🍴 **Room:** 📶 ☕ 🕐 📺

PEWSEY, Wiltshire   Map ref 2B2 — SatNav SN9 6HZ [B]

BED & BREAKFAST

Huntly's Farmhouse

Manningford Abbots, Pewsey SN9 6HZ **T:** (01672) 563663 / 07900 211789
E: gimspike@esend.co.uk
W: www.huntlys.co.uk

B&B PER ROOM PER NIGHT
S: £40.00 - £50.00
D: £60.00 - £90.00
EVENING MEAL PER PERSON
£15.00 - £17.00

Peacefully located thatched 18th century farmhouse including horse-stabling/grazing. Within close range of good walking country. Heated outdoor swimming pool. Free range and organic food - a speciality.
Directions: Turn off A345 SW of Pewsey signed Manningford Abbotts. Huntlys is 0.5 mile on right hand side just past turn to Sharcott. Opposite post box in wall.
Bedrooms: 1 double, 1 family. **Open:** All year.

Site: ✿ P **Leisure:** 🏊 🎣 🏌 ♻ 🚴 **Property:** 🐕 🖥 🅱 **Children:** 👶5 **Catering:** (✗ 🍴 **Room:** 📶 ☕ 🕐 📺

SALISBURY, Wiltshire   Map ref 2B3 — SatNav SP5 4LH [B]

Evening Hill

Blandford Road, Coombe Bissett, Salisbury, Wiltshire SP5 4LH **T:** (01722) 718561
E: info@eveninghill.com
W: www.eveninghill.com

B&B PER ROOM PER NIGHT
S: £38.00 - £42.00
D: £50.00 - £55.00

A quiet village location 10 mins from the city of Salisbury. Ideal for visiting Salisbury city and Cathedral, Stonehenge, New Forest, Bath, Southampton, Portsmouth, Winchester.
Directions: 2 miles South of Salisbury on the A354. Drive through the village of Coombe Bissett 500 meters past the church on right hand side.
Bedrooms: 1 double, 1 family.
Open: All year.

Site: ✿ P **Payment:** 💳 **Property:** 🐕 🖥 🍴 **Children:** 👶 🛏 🛝 **Catering:** 🍴 **Room:** 📶 ☕ 🕐 📺 ♿

SALISBURY, Wiltshire   Map ref 2B3 — [S]

HOLIDAY, TOURING & CAMPING PARK

Stonehenge Campsite & Glamping Pods

Contact: Berwick St James, Salisbury SP3 4TQ **T:** (07786) 734732
E: stay@stonehengecampsite.co.uk
W: www.stonehengecampsite.co.uk **£ BOOK ONLINE**

Sleeps   35

Stonehenge Campsite is a beautiful small Gold & multi award-winning Glamping Campsite in a semi-woodland setting. It is perfectly situated close to Stonehenge, Longleat, Bath, Devizes, Wilton, Salisbury, Stourhead & The New Forest.
Open: 12th February to October.

Payment: 💳 **Leisure:** 🎣 🏌 **Property:** 🐕 🖥 🅱 **Children:** 👶

Don't Miss...

Beaulieu National Motor Museum, House and Garden 🏵

Beaulieu, Hampshire SO42 7ZN
(01590) 612345
www.beaulieu.co.uk

In the New Forest, Beaulieu is one of England's top family days out. There's lots to enjoy including the world famous National Motor Museum, home to a stunning and historic collection of automobiles; Palace House, home of the Montagu family; historic Beaulieu Abbey founded in 1204 by Cistercian Monks, and World of Top Gear features vehicles from some of the most ambitious challenges.

Portsmouth Historic Dockyard 🏵

Portsmouth, Hampshire PO1 3LJ
(023) 9283 9766
www.historicdockyard.co.uk

Portsmouth Historic Dockyard offers a great day out for all the family and spans over 800 years of British Naval history. The state-of-the-art Mary Rose Museum is home to the remains of Henry VIII's flagship and an astounding collection of 400 year old artefacts recovered from the sea.

The Royal Pavilion Brighton 🏵

Brighton, East Sussex BN1 1EE
03000 290900
www.brightonmuseums.org.uk/royalpavilion

This spectacularly extravagant seaside palace was built for the Prince Regent, later King George IV, between 1787 and 1823. Housing furniture, works of art and a splendid balconied tearoom overlooking the gardens, it is one the most extraordinary and exotic oriental buildings in the country.

Turner Contemporary Art Gallery

Margate, Kent, CT19 1HG
(01843) 233000
www.turnercontemporary.org

Situated on Margate's seafront, Turner Contemporary is a welcoming space that offers world-class exhibitions of contemporary and historical art, events and activities. Taking inspiration from Britain's best-known painter JMW Turner and designed by internationally acclaimed David Chipperfield Architects, this gleaming structure hovering over the town is the largest exhibtiion space in the South East outside of London and admission to the gallery is free.

Windsor Castle

Windsor, Berkshire SL4 1NJ
(020) 7766 7304
www.royalcollection.org.uk

Built by Edward III in the 14th century and restored by later monarchs, Windsor Castle is the largest and oldest occupied castle in the world and has been the family home of British kings and queens for almost 1,000 years. It is an official residence of Her Majesty the Queen and encapsulates more than 900 years of English history. St George's Chapel within the Castle Precincts is the spiritual home of the Order of the Garter, the oldest order of chivalry in the world.

South East

Berkshire, Buckinghamshire, Hampshire, Isle of Wight, Kent, Oxfordshire, Surrey, Sussex

The River Thames sketches broad curves through the beech woodlands of the Chiltern Hills. The region's varied countryside brings ramblers to the open chalk downlands and to the ancient woodlands of the Weald. The beach resorts of the South, dotted along 257 miles of coastline, are perfect for sailing, kite surfing and sandcastles. Or enjoy the many historic towns from timbered Rye in Sussex to the university town of Oxford. There are gardens here in profusion and unmissable historic sites like Blenheim Palace, Canterbury Cathedral and the gardens of Great Dixter. Queen Victoria's favourite holidays were spent on the Isle of Wight and the island retains the style of a more leisurely time, only a short ferry ride away.

Oxfordshire
Buckinghamshire
Berkshire
Surrey   Kent
Hampshire
Sussex
Isle of Wight

Explore – South East

Berkshire

Renowned for its royal connections, the romantic county of Berkshire counts Windsor Castle as its most famous building. Cliveden House, former seat of the Astor family and now a famous hotel, is nearby. Highclere Castle, the setting for Downton Abbey, as well as Eton College and Ascot Racecourse can be found here too.

For fun-filled days out, explore the models and exciting events at fabulous Legoland in Windsor, or take budding scientists in the family to The Lookout Discovery Centre at Bracknell and The Living Rainforest at Thatcham for plenty of interactive hands-on activities.

Buckinghamshire

Buckinghamshire, to the North East of the region, is home to the most National Trust properties in the country including the magnificent French chateau-style Waddesdon Manor near Aylesbury, idyllic Claydon House near Buckingham and Hughenden in High Wycombe, the former home of Victorian Prime Minister, Benjamin Disraeli. And don't forget to get some fresh air in the magnificent 'Capability' Brown landscape at Stowe, now a famous public school.

The city of Milton Keynes has its infamous concrete cows and the delights of its vast shopping centre but there's plenty more to see and do in the county. Experience a hands-on history lesson at the fascinating Chiltern Open Air Museum or get your adrenalin pumping and test your head for heights with a zip wire adventure at Go Ape Wendover Woods. For a gentler pace, enjoy a tranquil bike ride through beautiful countryside along the meandering Thames.

Hampshire & Isle Of Wight

Historic Winchester is a must-visit for its charming medieval streets, imposing Cathedral, vibrant galleries and stylish, independent shops. The ancient heaths and woodlands of the New Forest National Park were once a royal hunting ground for William the Conqueror and deer, ponies and cattle continue to roam free. Cycle, walk or go horseriding in this tranquil, car-free environment or visit attractions such as the National Motor Museum at Beaulieu and Exbury Gardens & Steam Railway for a great day out.

Coastal Hampshire, with the Solent, Southampton Water and the Isle of Wight, is one of the sailing playgrounds of England. Discover the history of England's naval past and explore its historic ships at Portsmouth Historic Docklands or climb the Spinaker Tower for far-reaching views of the coast. Stroll gently around the picturesque village of Lymington or explore the cliffs along the coast. The Isle of Wight can be reached by ferry and has amazing beaches, exciting events such as Bestival, or a step back in time; Osborne House and Carisbrooke Castle are among its historic gems.

Kent

Kent, 'The Garden of England' is a diverse county full of romantic villages, distinctive coast houses and unmissable heritage attractions. Leeds Castle, surrounded by its shimmering lake and set in 500 acres of spectacular parkland and gardens, has attractions and events aplenty. Take a tour of Kent's rural past with a scenic cruise along the River Medway to Kent Life, a museum and working farm with animals galore and a real sense of nostalgia for bygone days.

At the northeast tip of the county, where stunning sea and skyscapes famously inspired JMW Turner, Margate is home to the acclaimed Turner Contemporary art gallery and the Shell Grotto, a subterranean wonder lined with 4.6 million shells. Broadstairs hosts an acclaimed annual folk festival taking place all over the town, there's hardly a venue that isn't bursting with song, music and dance. Ramsgate is also a firm favourite, with its sophisticated café culture, marina and award-winning sandy beach.

Oxfordshire

Oxford's dreaming spires, echoing quads and cloistered college lawns have a timeless beauty. The Ashmolean Museum, Britain's oldest public museum, opened in 1683 and contains gold and jewellery believed to have belonged to King Alfred, the lantern carried by Guy Fawkes and riches from ancient Egypt and Greece. The Bodleian Library, founded in 1596, contains over one million volumes, including a copy of every book published in the UK since 1900. Just north of Oxford at Woodstock sits magnificent Blenheim Palace, the birthplace of Sir Winston Churchill. Oxfordshire's quiet paths and roads are perfect for cycling, and charming picture postcard villages like Great Tew make excellent rest points.

Surrey

Ashdown Forest covers 6400 acres of upland, with a large deer, badger and rare bird population. The heights of Box Hill and Leith Hill rise above the North Downs to overlook large tracts of richly wooded countryside, containing a string of well protected villages. The Devil's Punchbowl, near Hindhead, is a two mile long sandstone valley, overlooked by the 900-ft Gibbet Hill. Farnham, in the west of the country, has Tudor and Georgian houses flanking the 12th century castle. Nearby Aldershot is the home of the British Army and county town Guildford is a contemporary business and shopping centre with a modern cathedral, theatre and university. The North of the county borders Greater London and includes the 2400 acre Richmond Park, Hampton Court Palace and Kew Gardens.

Sussex

Sussex is a popular county for those wanting a short break from the hustle and bustle of London. Cosmopolitan Brighton, surely the capital of East Sussex, oozes culture, boutique hotels, marina, shops and 'buzz'. The eccentric Royal Pavilion testifies to its history as the Regency summer capital of Britain.

To the West is the impressive Arundel Castle, with its famous drama festival, nearby popular marinas and Wittering sands. Bognor Regis is a traditional seaside resort with a blue flag beach and the usual attractions. Littlehampton, with its award-winning beaches and architecture including the East Beach Café and the Stage by the Sea, is a popular destination and a great base for exploring the beautiful Sussex Coast.

To the East the impressive Beachy Head and Seven Sisters cliffs provide a dramatic backdrop for Eastbourne. The Sussex section of the South Downs National Park stretches from Beachy Head to Harting Down with miles of open chalk grassland, lush river valleys and ancient forests to explore.

If heritage is your thing then Sussex has a plethora of historic houses and gardens and three of the historic Cinque Ports. Rye in particular, with its cobbled streets, transports the visitor back three centuries. The 1066 Story is told at Battle, near Hastings and Groombridge Place, Great Dixter and Borde Hill and these are just a few that feature stunningly beautiful heritage gardens.

Visit – South East

Berkshire

Ascot CAMRA Beer Festival
Ascot Racecourse, October
An action packed day of flat racing and an array of
over 280 real ales, ciders and perries to sample at
the Ascot CAMRA Beer Festival as well as traditional
pub games, a quiz and live music.

French Brothers Ltd
Windsor, Berkshire SL4 5JH
(01753) 851900
www.boat-trips.co.uk
Large range of public trips on weather-proof
vessels departing from Windsor, Runnymede
and Maidenhead.

Go Ape! Bracknell, Swinley Forest
Berkshire RG12 7QW
(0333) 920 6904
www.goape.co.uk/days-out/bracknell
Go Ape! and tackle a high-wire forest adventure course
of rope bridges, Tarzan swings and zip slides up to 35
feet above the forest floor.

Highclere Castle and Gardens
Newbury, Berkshire RG20 9RN
(01635) 253210
www.highclerecastle.co.uk
Visit the spectacular Victorian Castle which was the
setting for Downton Abbey. Splendid State Rooms,
Library and Egyptian Exhibition in the Castle Cellars,
plus gardens inspired by Capability Brown.

LEGOLAND® Windsor
Berkshire SL4 4AY
(0871) 222 2001
www.legoland.co.uk
A theme park and Lego-themed hotel, with over
55 interactive rides and attractions, there's just too
much to experience in one day!

The Look Out Discovery Centre
Bracknell, Berkshire RG12 7QW
(01344) 354400
www.bracknell-forest.gov.uk/thelookoutdiscoverycentre
A hands-on, interactive science exhibition with over
80 exhibits, set in 1,000 hectares of Crown woodland.

Reading Festival
August, Reading, Berkshire
www.readingfestival.com
The Reading and Leeds Festivals are a pair of annual
music festivals that take place simultaneously.

REME Museum of Technology
Lyneham, Chippenham SN15 4XX
(01249) 894869
www.rememuseum.org.uk
Due to reopen in 2017 after relocating to Lyneham.
The museum shows the developing technology
used by the Royal Electrical and Mechanical
Engineers in maintaining and repairing the army's
equipment since 1942.

Royal Ascot Races
June, Ascot, Berkshire SL5 7JX
(0844) 346 3000
www.ascot.co.uk/Royal-Ascot
Britain's most valuable race meeting, attracting
many of the world's finest racehorses to compete
for more than £5.5milllion in prize money.

Buckinghamshire

Aerial Extreme Milton Keynes
Milton Keynes, Buckinghamshire MK15 0DS
0845 652 1736
www.aerialextreme.co.uk/locations/milton-keynes
Amaze yourself as you take each of the challenges head on.

Bekonscot Model Village and Railway
Beaconsfield, Buckinghamshire HP9 2PL
(01494) 672919
www.bekonscot.co.uk
Use your imagination in this unique world of make-believe that has delighted generations of visitors.

Gulliver's Land
Milton Keynes, Buckinghamshire MK15 0DT
(01925) 444888
www.gulliversfun.co.uk/gullivers-land-milton-keynes
Family theme park with 30 rides aimed at children between 2 and 12 years.

Kop Hill Climb
Princes Risborough, Buckinghamshire
www.kophillclimb.org.uk
In the 1900s Kop Hill Climb was one of the most popular hill climbs in the country for cars and motorcycles. Now the spirit of the climb is revived.

Marlow Regatta
June, Eton Dorney, Buckinghamshire
www.themarlowregatta.com
Marlow Regatta is one of the multi-lane regattas in the British Rowing calendar.

Milton Keynes Theatre
Milton Keynes, Buckinghamshire MK9 3NZ
(0844) 871 7627
www.atgtickets.com/venues/milton-keynes-theatre
Managed by the Ambassador Theatre Group, this modern 1400 seater theatre and entertainment centre offers West End and world class production and events, making every visit memorable.

National Trust Stowe
Buckinghamshire MK18 5EQ
(01280) 817156
www.nationaltrust.org.uk/stowe
Over 40 temples and monuments, laid out against an inspiring backdrop of lakes and valleys.

Roald Dahl Festival
Aylesbury Town Centre, Buckinghamshire
www.aylesburyvaledc.gov.uk/dahl
An annual celebration of the famous author, including a 500-strong parade of pupils, teachers and musicians with puppets and artwork based on the Roald Dahl stories.

Roald Dahl Museum and Story Centre
Great Missenden, Buckinghamshire HP16 0AL
(01494) 892192
www.roalddahl.com/museum
Where Roald Dahl (1916-1990) lived and wrote many of his well-loved books.

Waddesdon Manor
Aylesbury, Buckinghamshire HP18 0JH
(01296) 820414
www.waddesdon.org.uk
This National Trust property houses the Rothschild Collection of art treasures and wine cellars. It also features spectacular grounds with an aviary, parterre and woodland playground, licensed restaurants, gift and wine shops.

Xscape
Milton Keynes, Buckinghamshire MK9 3XS
(01908) 357025
www.xscape.co.uk/milton-keynes
Xscape, Milton Keynes offers a unique combination of extreme sports and leisure activities for all ages.

Hampshire & Isle Of Wight

Alton Summer Beer Festival
June, Alton, Hampshire GU34 2LX
www.altonbeerfestival.co.uk
Celebrating the cultural heritage of Alton as a traditional area for brewing, based on the clear waters rising from the source of the River Wey, and locally grown hops.

Blackgang Chine
Chale, Isle of Wight PO38 2HN
(01983) 730330
www.blackgangchine.com
The UK's oldest amusement park overlooking the stunning South coast of the Isle of Wight. Great family fun in over 40 acres of spectacular cliff top gardens.

Cowes Week
July - August, Cowes, Isle of Wight
www.aamcowesweek.co.uk
Cowes Week is one of the longest-running regular regattas in the world with up to 40 daily races for around 1,000 boats.

Dinosaur Isle
Sandown, Isle of Wight PO36 8QA
(01983) 404344
www.dinosaurisle.com
Britain's first purpose built dinosaur museum and visitor attraction, in a spectacular pterosaur shaped building, on Sandown's blue flag beach. Walk back through fossilised time and meet life sized replica dinosaurs.

Exbury Gardens and Steam Railway
Beaulieu, Hampshire SO45 1AZ
(023) 8089 1203
www.exbury.co.uk
World famous woodland garden, home to the Rothschild Collection of rhododendrons, azaleas, camellias, rare trees and shrubs, with its own steam railway.

Isle of Wight Festival
June, Newport, Isle of Wight
www.isleofwightfestival.com
Annual music festival featuring some of the UK's top acts and bands.

Isle of Wight Walking Festival
May, Isle of Wight
www.isleofwightwalkingfestival.co.uk
The festival boasts 16 days of unbeatable, informative and healthy walks.

Marwell Zoo
Winchester, Hampshire SO21 1JH
(01962) 777407
www.marwell.org.uk
A chance to get close to the wonders of the natural world – and play a big part in helping to save them.

New Forest and Hampshire Show
July, New Park, Brockenhurst, Hampshire SO42 7QH
(01590) 622400
www.newforestshow.co.uk
A celebration of traditional country pursuits, crafts, produce and entertainment.

Osborne House
East Cowes, Isle of Wight PO32 6JX
(01983) 200022
www.english-heritage.org.uk/daysout/properties/osborne-house
Step into Queen Victoria's favourite country home and experience a world unchanged since the country's longest reigning monarch died here just over 100 years ago.

Paultons Family Theme Park
Romsey, Hampshire SO51 6AL
(023) 8081 4442
www.paultonspark.co.uk
A great family day out with over 60 different attractions and rides included in the price!

Shanklin Chine
Shanklin, Isle of Wight PO37 6BW
(01983) 866432
www.shanklinchine.co.uk
Historic gorge with dramatic waterfalls and nature trail. The Isle of Wight's oldest tourist attraction, which first opened in 1817.

Southampton Boat Show
September, Southampton, Hampshire TW20 8BF
(01784) 473377
www.southamptonboatshow.com
See the best boats and marine brands gathered together in one fantastic water-based show.

Ventnor Botanic Gardens
St. Lawrence, Isle of Wight PO38 1UL
(01983) 855397
www.botanic.co.uk
Basking in the microclimate of The Undercliff, Ventnor Botanic Garden on the Isle of Wight is one of the great gardens of Britain. A place where the pleasure of plants can be enjoyed to the fullest.

Winchester Hat Fair
June - July, Winchester, Hampshire
www.hatfair.co.uk
Named after the tradition of throwing donations into performer's hats, it's Britain's longest running festival of street theatre and outdoor arts.

Kent

Bedgebury National Pinetum & Forest
Cranbrook, Kent TN17 2SJ
(01580) 879820
www.forestry.gov.uk/bedgebury
Ideal for cycling, walking, running and riding and adventure play. Visit the National Pinetum, one of the world's finest conifer collections, perfect for picnics.

Canterbury Cathedral
Canterbury, Kent CT1 2EH
(01227) 762862
www.canterbury-cathedral.org/
One of the oldest and most famous Christian structures in England, stunning Canetrbury Cathedral is a holy place and part of a World Heritage Site.

Deal Castle
Deal, Kent CT14 7BA
(01304) 372762
www.english-heritage.org.uk/visit/places/deal-castle
One of the finest Tudor artillery castles built by the order of King Henry VIII. Explore the castle's interior and outside, admire the squat, rounded bastions and canons of its defences.

Deal Festival of Music and the Arts
June/July, Deal, Kent
(01304) 370220
www.dealfestival.co.uk
Experience great classical and contemporary music from some of the world's finest music-makers, as well as theatre, opera, cinema and dance .

Dickens Festival
June, Rochester, Kent
www.visitkent.co.uk/events/9576
A weekend of colourful celebration honouring one of England's greatest writers with costumed parades, street acts, competitions, readings and fair.

Hever Castle & Gardens
Hever, Edenbridge Kent TN8 7NG
(01732) 865224
www.hevercastle.co.uk
A romantic 13th century moated castle with magnificently furnished interiors, award-winning gardens, miniature Model House Exhibition, Yew Maze and a unique Splashing Water Maze.

The Historic Dockyard Chatham
Chatham, Kent ME4 4TE
(01634) 823800
www.thedockyard.co.uk
A unique, award-winning maritime heritage destination with a fantastic range of attractions, iconic buildings and historic ships to explore, plus a fabulous programme of touring exhibitions, events and activities.

Kent & East Sussex Railway
Tenterden, Kent TN30 6HE
(01580) 765155
www.kesr.org.uk
Rural light railway enables visitors to experience travel and service from a bygone age aboard restored Victorian coaches and locomotives.

Leeds Castle
Maidstone, Kent ME17 1PL
(01622) 765400
www.leeds-castle.com
With 500 acres of beautiful parkland and gardens, daily activities, flying falconry displays, special events and attractions including a hot air balloon festival and a triathlon, Leeds Castle is one of the best days out in Kent.

Quex Park & Powell-Cotton Museum
Birchington, Kent CT7 0BH
(01843) 842168
www.quexpark.co.uk
Quex Park is home to the Powell-Cotton Museum and the Powell-Cotton family's extraordinary collection of natural history, ethnography and fine and decorative arts.

Rochester Castle
Kent ME1 1SW
(01634) 335882
www.english-heritage.org.uk/visit/places/rochester-castle
One of the finest keeps in England. Also the tallest, measures 113 feet high, 70 feet square and has walls 12 feet thick in places, partly built on the Roman city wall. Good views from the battlements over the River Medway.

Oxfordshire

Blenheim Palace
Woodstock, Oxfordshire OX20 1PP
(0800) 849 6500
www.blenheimpalace.com
Birthplace of Sir Winston Churchill and home to the Duke of Marlborough, Blenheim Palace, one of the finest baroque houses in England, is set in over 2,000 acres of landscaped gardens.

Didcot Railway Centre
Oxfordshire OX11 7NJ
(01235) 817200
www.didcotrailwaycentre.org.uk
Living museum recreating the golden age of the Great Western Railway. Steam locomotives and trains, Brunel's broad gauge railway, engine shed and small relics museum.

Henley Royal Regatta
June - July, Henley, Oxfordshire
01491 572153
www.hrr.co.uk
Attracting thousands of visitors over a five-day period and spectators will be thrilled by over 200 races of international standard.

Oxford Official Guided Walking Tour
www.experienceoxfordshire.org/official-tours
A fascinating and entertaining way to explore and learn about this unique city, its history, University, famous people and odd traditions. Covering a wide range of topics from an introduction to the city and its University to Inspector Morse, Harry Potter, J.R.R. Tolkien and more.

Surrey

British Wildlife Centre
Lingfield, Surrey RH7 6LF
(01342) 834658
www.britishwildlifecentre.co.uk
The best place to see and learn about Britain's own wonderful wildlife, with over 40 different species including deer, foxes, otters, badgers, pine martens and red squirrels.

Guildford Cathedral
Surrey GU2 7UP
(01483) 547860
www.guildford-cathedral.org
New Anglican Cathedral, the foundation stone of which was laid in 1936. Notable sandstone interior and marble floors. Restaurant and shops.

Investec Derby
June, Epsom Racecourse, Surrey
www.epsomderby.co.uk
The biggest horse race in the flat-racing calendar.

Loseley Park
Guildford, Surrey GU3 1HS
(01483) 304440
www.loseleypark.co.uk
A beautiful Elizabethan mansion standing in ancient Surrey Parkland. Still the home of the More-Molyneux family, it is remarkably unchanged since 1562 when Sir William More laid the first stones.

RHS Garden Wisley

Woking, Surrey GU23 6QB
0845 260 9000
www.rhs.org.uk/wisley
Enjoy a day out at the world-class Wisley garden, stretching over 240 glorious acres. Join in the fun with all year round events.

RHS Hampton Court Palace Flower Show
www.rhs.org.uk/shows-events
One of the biggest events in the horticulture calendar.

Thorpe Park
Chertsey, Surrey KT16 8PN
(0871) 663 1673
www.thorpepark.com
Thorpe Park Resort is an island like no other, with over 30 thrilling rides, attractions and live events.

Wings & Wheels
August, Dunsfold Aerodrome, Surrey GU6 8TB
(01483) 542226
www.wingsandwheels.net
A popular family day out featuring an outstanding variety of dynamic aviation, motoring displays and iconic cars.

Sussex

1066 Battle Abbey and Battlefield
East Sussex TN33 0AD
(01424) 775705
www.english-heritage.org.uk/visit/places/1066-battle-of-hastings-abbey-and-battlefield
An abbey founded by William the Conqueror on the site of the Battle of Hastings.

Arundel Festival
August, Arundel, Sussex
www.arundelfestival.co.uk
Ten days of the best music, theatre, art and comedy.

Arundel Wetland Centre
West Sussex BN18 9PB
(01903) 883355
www.wwt.org.uk/visit/arundel
WWT Arundel Wetland Centre is a 65-acre reserve in an idyllic setting, nestled at the base of the South Downs National Park.

Brighton Festival
May, 29 New Road, Brighton BN1 1UG
(01273) 709709
www.brightonfestival.org
A sensational programme of art, theatre, dance, music, literature and family shows starting with a Children's Parade winding its way through the city.

Brighton Lanes
Brighton, East Sussex
www.visitbrighton.com/shopping/the-lanes
From quirky stores, vintage antiques and boutiques to live music, funky restaurants and cutting edge art, Brighton Lanes is crammed with interesting independent shops and watering holes.

Brighton Fringe
Brighton, Sussex
www.brightonfringe.org
One of the largest fringe festivals in the world, offering cabaret, comedy, classical concerts, club nights, theatre and exhibitions, as well as street performances.

British Airways i360
Brighton BN1 2LN
(03337) 720360
www.britishairwaysi360.com
Take a flight into the skies and see Sussex as you've never seen it before. The 450 feet high British Airways i360 will offer breath-taking 360 degree views of up to 26 miles from the world's first vertical cable car.

Chichester Cathedral
West Sussex PO19 1PX
(01243) 782595
www.chichestercathedral.org.uk
A magnificent Cathedral with treasures ranging from medieval stone carvings to world famous 20th century artworks.

Denmans Garden
Fontwell, West Sussex BN18 0SU
(01243) 542808
www.denmans-garden.co.uk
Beautiful 4 acre garden designed for year round interest through use of form, colour and texture. Beautiful plant centre, award-winning and fully licensed Garden Café.

Eastbourne Beer Festival
October, Winter Gardens, Eastbourne, Sussex
(01323) 415415
www.eastbournebeerfestival.co.uk
Eastbourne's annual beer festival features over 120 cask ales, plus wines, international bottled beers, ciders and perries. Each session features live music.

Eastbourne Music & Arts Festival
Febuary, Eastbourne, Sussex
(01323) 729013
www.eastbournefestival.co.uk
The Eastbourne Music & Arts Festival is a held annually in Eastbourne since1961.

England's Medieval Festival
August, Herstmonceux Castle, Sussex
www.englandsmedievalfestival.com
A celebration of the Middle Ages.

Fishers Adventure Farm Park
Billingshurst, West Sussex RH14 0EG
(01403) 700063
www.fishersfarmpark.co.uk
Award-winning Adventure Farm Park and open all year. Ideally suited for ages 2-11 years. Huge variety of animals, rides and attractions from the skating rink, to pony rides, toboggan run, bumper boats, theatre shows and more!

Glorious Goodwood
August, Chichester, Sussex
www.goodwood.com
Also known as the 'Qatar Goodwood Festival'. Bursting with fabulous fashions, succulent strawberries, chilled Champagne and top horse racing stars, as well as music and dancing.

Glyndebourne Festival
May - August, Lewes, Sussex BN8 5UU
www.glyndebourne.com
An English opera festival held at Glyndebourne, an English country house near Lewes.

Great Dixter House and Gardens
Rye, East Sussex TN31 6PH
(01797) 252878
www.greatdixter.co.uk
An example of a 15th century manor house with antique furniture and needlework. The house is restored and the gardens were designed by Lutyens.

London to Brighton Bike Ride
June, Ends on Madeira Drive, Brighton, Sussex
www.bhf.org.uk/get-involved/events/bike-rides
The annual bike ride from the capital to the coast in aid of the British Heart Foundation. The UK's largest charity bike ride with 27,000 riders.

Pashley Manor Gardens
Wadhurst, East Sussex TN5 7HE
(01580) 200888
www.pashleymanorgardens.com
Pashley Manor Gardens offer a blend of romantic landscaping, imaginative plantings, fine old trees, fountains, springs and large ponds plus exciting special events.

Petworth House and Park
West Sussex GU28 9LR
(01798) 342207
www.nationaltrust.org.uk/petworth
Discover the National Trust's finest art collection displayed in a magnificent 17th century mansion within a beautiful 700-acre park. Petworth House contains works by artists such as Van Dyck, Reynolds and Turner.

RSPB Pulborough Brooks
West Sussex RH20 2EL
(01798) 875851
www.rspb.org.uk
Set in the scenic Arun Valley with views to the South Downs, the two mile circular nature trail leads around this beautiful reserve.

Tourist Information Centres

When you arrive at your destination, visit the Tourist Information Centre for quality assured help with accommodation and information about local attractions and events, or email your request before you go.

Aldershot	Prince's Hall	01252 320968	aldershotvic@rushmoor.gov.uk
Ashford	Ashford Gateway Plus	01233 330316	tourism@ashford.gov.uk
Banbury	Castle Quay Shopping Centre	01295 753752	banbury.tic@cherwell-dc.gov.uk
Battle	Yesterdays World	01797 229049	battletic@rother.gov.uk
Bexley (Hall Place)	Central Library	0208 3037777	touristinfo@bexleyheritagetrust.org.uk
Bicester	Unit 86a Bicester Village	01869 366266	bicestervisitorcentre@bicestervillage.com
Bracknell	The Look Out Discovery Centre	01344 354409	thelookout@bracknell-forest.gov.uk
Brighton	Brighton Centre Box Office	01273 290337	visitor.info@visitbrighton.com
Buckingham	The Old Gaol Museum	01280 823020	buckinghamtic@touismse.com
Burford	33a High Street	01993 823558	burford.vic@westoxon.gov.uk
Burgess Hill	Burgess Hill Town Council	01444 238202	touristinformation@burgesshill.gov.uk
Canterbury	Beaney House	01227 862162	canterburyinformation@canterbury.gov.uk
Chichester	The Novium	01243 775888	chitic@chichester.gov.uk
Deal	The Landmark Centre	01304 369576	info@deal.gov.uk
Dover	Dover Museum	01304 201066	tic@doveruk.com
Eastbourne	Cornfield Road	0871 663 0031	tic@eastbourne.gov.uk

Faringdon	The Corn Exchange	01367 242191	tic@faringdontowncouncil.gov.uk
Faversham	Fleur de Lis Heritage Centre	01795 534542	ticfaversham@btconnect.com
Folkestone	1-2 Guildhall Street	01303 258594	tourism@folkestone-tc.gov.uk
Fordingbridge	Kings Yard	01425 654560	fordingbridgetic@tourismse.com
Gosport	Gosport TIC, Bus Station Complex	023 9252 2944	tourism@gosport.gov.uk
Gravesend	Towncentric	01474 337600	info@towncentric.co.uk
Guildford	155 High Street	01483 444333	tic@guildford.gov.uk
Hastings	Queens Square	01424 451111	hic@hastings.gov.uk
Hayling Island	Central Beachlands	023 9246 7111	tourism@havant.gov.uk
Henley-on-Thames	Town Hall,	01491 578034	vic@henleytowncouncil.gov.uk
High Wycombe	High Wycombe Library	01494 421892	tourism_enquiries@wycombe.gov.uk
Horsham	9 Causeway	01403 211661	visitor.information@horsham.gov.uk
Lewes	187 High Street	01273 483448	lewes.tic@lewes.gov.uk
Littlehampton	The Look & Sea Centre	01903 718984	visitorcentre@lookandsea.co.uk
Lymington	St Barbe Museum	01590 676969	info@thenewforest.co.uk
Lyndhurst & New Forest	New Forest Museum	023 8028 2269	Info@thenewforest.co.uk
Maidenhead	Maidenhead Library	01628 796502	maidenhead.tic@rbwm.gov.uk
Maidstone	Maidstone Museum	01622 602169	tourism@maidstone.gov.uk
Marlow	Marlow Library	01628 483597	marlowoffice@wycombe.gov.uk
Midhurst	North Street	01730 817322	jbudd@chichester.gov.uk
Oxford	15-16 Broad Street	01865 686430	info@experienceoxfordshire.org
Petersfield	County Library	01730 268829	petersfieldinfo@btconnect.com
Portsmouth	D-Day Museum	023 9282 6722	vis@portsmouthcc.gov.uk
Princes Risborough	Princes Risborough Library	01844 274795	risborough_office@wycombe.gov.uk
Ringwood	The Furlong	01425 470896	information@nfdc.gov.uk
Rochester	95 High Street	01634 338141	visitor.centre@medway.gov.uk
Romsey	13 Church Street	01794 512987	romseytic@testvalley.gov.uk
Royal Tunbridge Wells	Unit 2 The Corn Exchange	01892 515675	touristinformationcentre @tunbridgewells.gov.uk
Sandwich	The Guildhall	01304 613565	tourism@sandwichtowncouncil.gov.uk
Seaford	37 Church Street	01323 897426	seaford.tic@lewes.gov.uk
Sevenoaks	Stag Community Arts Centre	01732 450305	tic@sevenoakstown.gov.uk
Swanley	Library & Information Centre	01322 614660	touristinfo@swanley.org.uk
Tenterden	Tenterden Gateway	01233 330316	tourism@ashford.gov.uk
Thame	Town Hall	01844 212833	oss@thametowncouncil.gov.uk
Thanet	The Droit House	01843 577577	visitorinformation@thanet.gov.uk
Tonbridge	Tonbridge Castle	01732 770929	tonbridge.castle@tmbc.gov.uk
Winchester	Guildhall	01962 840500	tourism@winchester.gov.uk
Windsor	Old Booking Hall	01753 743900	windsor.tic@rbwm.gov.uk
Witney	3 Welsh Way	01993 775802	witney.vic@westoxon.gov.uk

Regional Contacts and Information

For more information on accommodation, attractions, activities, events and holidays in South East England, contact one of the following regional or local tourism organisations. Their websites have a wealth of information and many produce free publications to help you get the most out of your visit.

www.visitsoutheastengland.com
email enquiries@tourismse.com or
call (023) 8062 5400.

www.visitnewbury.org.uk
www.visitbuckinghamshire.org
www.visit-hampshire.co.uk
www.visitisleofwight.co.uk
www.visitkent.co.uk
www.experienceoxfordshire.org
www.visitsurrey.com
www.visitbrighton.com

Stay – South East

Entries appear alphabetically by town name in each county. A key to symbols appears on page 6

HURLEY, Berkshire   Map ref 2C2   SatNav SL6 5NN

VisitEngland
★★★★
HOLIDAY PARK

Hurley Riverside Park

Hurley, Near Henley-on-Thames SL6 5NE
T: (01628) 824493 **E:** info@hurleyriversidepark.co.uk
W: www.hurleyriversidepark.co.uk **£ BOOK ONLINE**

🚐	(138)	£15.00-£30.00
🚙	(138)	£15.00-£30.00
⛺	(130)	£13.00-£28.00
🏠	(10)	£360.00-£600.00

200 touring pitches

SPECIAL PROMOTIONS
Touring Park Loyalty Card. Membership Card. Giveaways and offers on Facebook and Twitter. Short breaks available in Hire Caravan Holiday Homes and ReadyTents one week prior to arrival.

Family-run park alongside the River Thames, ideal for LEGOLAND® Windsor, Henley-on-Thames, Oxford & London. Tents, tourers, motorhomes & RVs welcome. Heated shower blocks, laundry, shop, nature trail, playground and outdoor table tennis tables, riverside picnic grounds, slipway, fishing in season and free Wi-Fi. 2 day LEGOLAND® tickets available. Caravan Holiday Homes and Tent hire also available.

Directions: M4 J8/9 or M40 J4, onto A404(M), third exit to Henley (A4130). Past Hurley Village, turn right into Shepherds Lane.

Open: March to October.

Payment: 💷 ☀ **Leisure:** 🎣 ⚲ ∪ **Children:** 🐴 ⛰ **Catering:** 🍴 **Park:** 🐕 🚮 🚻 📶 **Touring:** 💧 ♿ 🚐 ⚡

READING, Berkshire   Map ref 2C2   SatNav RG7 1SP

VisitEngland
★★★
TOURING & CAMPING PARK

Wellington Country Park - Touring Caravan & Campsite

Odiham Road, Riseley, Nr Reading RG7 1SP
T: (0118) 932 6444 **F:** (0118) 932 6445 **E:** info@wellington-country-park.co.uk
W: www.wellington-country-park.co.uk **£ BOOK ONLINE**

🚐	(56)	£17.00-£38.50
🚙	(56)	£17.00-£38.50
⛺	(30)	£15.50-£31.50

86 touring pitches

Set within beautiful woodlands, fees include 2 people and unlimited access to Country Park with nature trails, animal farm, play areas, miniature railway, sand pits and mini golf. Easy access from both M3 & M4. Please note: the Sat Nav postcode will not take you to the entrance of the Country Park or Campsite. Please see website for details. **Directions:** Hampshire/Berkshire border between Reading/Basingstoke. Do not use Sat Nav. M4 junction 11 A33 to Basingstoke. M3 junction 5 B3349 to Reading. **Open:** March to November.

Payment: 💷 ☀ **Leisure:** ♿ ∪ **Children:** 🐴 ⛰ **Catering:** ✗ 🍴 **Park:** 🐕 🚮 🚻 📶 **Touring:** 💧 ♿ 🚐

WINDSOR, Berkshire   Map ref 2D2   SatNav RG42 6LD

VisitEngland
★★★
HOTEL

Stirrups Country House Hotel

Maidens Green, Bracknell RG42 6LD **T:** (01344) 882284 **F:** (01344) 882300
E: reception@stirrupshotel.co.uk
W: www.stirrupshotel.co.uk **£ BOOK ONLINE**

Stirrups, with its Tudor origins, is located between Bracknell, Ascot and Windsor and is the perfect venue for visits to Legoland Windsor (three miles). Round off your day by relaxing in the oak-beamed bar, by the inglenook fire, prior to dinner. Please contact for prices. **Directions:** Stirrups lies on the B3022, 200 metres south of the crossroads in Maidens Green Village. **Bedrooms:** 19 double, 4 twin, 7 family, 6 suite - all en suite. **Open:** All year.

Site: ✿ P **Payment:** 💷 **Property:** 🍴 🚮 🚻 🅿 ◐ **Children:** 🐴 🛏 🚼 **Catering:** (✗ 🍴 🍽 **Room:** 📺 🔌 ☎ 🎧 📻 ♨ ✉

GREAT MISSENDEN, Buckinghamshire   Map ref 2C1   SatNav HP16 0AX [B]

Forge House

Forge House, 10 Church Street, Great Missenden, Buckinghamshire HP16 0AX
T: (01494) 867347 / 07717 949710

B&B PER ROOM PER NIGHT
D: £70.00 - £80.00

Set in the wooded Chiltern Hills, quiet central village location with 7 restaurants available. A charming 18th century beamed house traditionally refurbished with three en suite double bedrooms; set in the home village of Roald Dahl. Forge House welcomes walkers and cyclists alike and we are only a 10 minute walk to the railway station in Great Missenden and is only a 35 minute trip on the Chiltern line to Marylebone central London station. Please contact for prices for single occupancy. Self-Catering facilities available please enquiry when booking. **Bedrooms:** 2 double rooms, 1 twin room, 1 single room, all en suite. **Open:** All year.

Site: P Payment: € Leisure: Property: Children: 5 Catering: Room:

FAREHAM, Hampshire   Map ref 2C3   [S]

Cowes View Coastguard Cottage

Contact: Mel Vennis, Hill Head, Fareham, Portsmouth, Hampshire PO14 3JJ
T: (01329) 664236 / 07712 650805 E: enquiries@cowesview.co.uk
W: www.cowesview.co.uk

Units   1
Sleeps   1-5

PER UNIT PER WEEK
£445.00 - £845.00

SPECIAL PROMOTIONS
Weekend breaks start at £325, minimum 2 nights during winter months, weekly lets between March and November.

Welcome to Cowes View, your seaside home from home, a place where smugglers were stopped bringing whisky and tobacco ashore and later where coastguards aided seafaring folk. Now you can soak up the history, the whisky, the sea and a fantastic panoramic ever changing view across 'The Solent'. Lie in bed, listen to the sea lapping against the shore, watch beautiful sunsets, smell the sea, enjoy the air and relax. Visit HMS Victory, the New Forest, South Downs, Isle of Wight or just enjoy a beach walk directly from the cottage. Suitable for couples, families, valentines and wedding nights all year.

Open: All year 365 nights.
Nearest Shop: 1 mile, Stubbington village
Nearest Pub: 100m, Osborne View Pub

Site: Leisure: Property: Children: Unit: BBQ

The Three Lions

Stuckton, Fordingbridge SP6 2HF **T:** (01425) 652489 **F:** (01425) 656144
E: the3lions@btinternet.com
W: www.thethreelionsrestaurant.co.uk

B&B PER ROOM PER NIGHT
S: £79.00
D: £125.00
HB PER PERSON PER NIGHT
£70.00 - £85.00

SPECIAL PROMOTIONS
Weekend Two Day
Break £235 incl
continental breakfast
£360 with 3 course
dinners Mid Week
£215 to £340
respectively.

A Restaurant with Rooms in the New Forest. Come and stay, relax and enjoy English/French cuisine cooked by Mike a constantly hands on (former) Michelin starred chef. Cosy informal bar, log fire, conservatory and gardens with sauna and hot tub. Three times Hampshire Restaurant of the Year, Good Food Guide. National Newcomer of the Year, Good Hotel Guide. We are family, cyclist and walker friendly and accept pets.

Directions: 15 minutes M27 Junction 1. 15 minutes Salisbury. Locate Total garage east of Fordingbridge, follow brown tourist signs to the Three Lions.

Bedrooms: 2 double, 2 twin, 3 family.
Open: All year.

Site: ✿ Payment: 🏧 € Leisure: 🏊 ♪ ▶ ♻ Property: 🐾 🐴 🖥 📺 Children: 🐕 🛏 🚶 Catering: 🍽 🍴
Room: 🍷 🕯 📺 ☕ 🍳

Beach House

Milford on Sea, Lymington, Hampshire SO41 0PT **T:** (01590) 643044
E: beachhouse.reception@hall-woodhouse.co.uk
W: www.beachhousemilfordonsea.co.uk **£ BOOK ONLINE**

B&B PER ROOM PER NIGHT
D: £95.00 - £170.00
EVENING MEAL PER PERSON
£15.00 - £25.00

Situated on the edge of the New Forest, 200 yards from the beach with breathtaking views of the Isle of Wight and the Needles, the Beach House is a Grade II listed Victorian mansion built in 1897. Originally built for the Siemens Family as their 'Beach House', it's a beautiful example of Arts and Crafts architecture with restored oak-panelled interior, stained glass windows and vintage furniture.

Directions: From M27: take Junction 1 or 2, take A337 signposted to Lyndhurst. Drive through Lyndhurst and Brokenhust, through Lymington, take B3058, stay on, Beach House on left.

Bedrooms: 15 unique en suite rooms all finished to a luxurious, comfortable standard with flatscreen TV, bluetooth radio and tea & coffee making facilities.
Open: All year.

Site: ✿ P Payment: 🏧 Property: 🐴 🖥 ⌀ Children: 🐕 🚶 Catering: ◖ 🍴 Room: 🍷 🕯 📺 ☕ 🍴

LYMINGTON, Hampshire   Map ref 2C3   [S]

Downton Holiday Park

Contact: Pauline Ley-Greaves, Assistant Manager, Downton Holiday Park, Shorefield Road, Milford-on-Sea, Lymington, Hampshire SO41 0LH **T:** (01590) 642515 / (01425) 476131
F: (01590) 642515 **E:** downtonoffice@btconnect.com **W:** www.downtonholidaypark.co.uk

Units   23
Sleeps   1-8
PER UNIT PER WEEK
£200.00 - £720.00

Downton Holiday Park is a small, peaceful park, close to the New Forest and less than 5 minutes drive from the beach Milford-on-Sea. We have a four star rating from Visit England and we are also members of New Forest Tourism, Bournemouth Tourism Services and the British Holiday and Home Parks Association. We have 74 Caravans, of which 23 are available for hire. We are perfectly placed for the ideal holiday, whatever your interests. **Open:** March to October. **Nearest Shop:** 200 yards **Nearest Pub:** 500 yards

Payment: 💷 **Leisure:** 🚲 ⚡ **Property:** 🐕 🖥 🗐 📠 **Children:** 🐎

NEW MILTON, Hampshire   Map ref 2B3   [S]

Glen Orchard Holiday Park

Contact: Loraine Whittle, Proprietor, Walkford Lane, New Milton BH25 5NH
T: (01425) 616463 **E:** info@glenorchard.co.uk
W: glenorchard.co.uk **£ BOOK ONLINE**

Units   18
Sleeps   2-6
PER UNIT PER WEEK
£160.00 - £725.00

Small family park in secluded, landscaped setting close to beaches, forest, riding, golf and fishing. Convenient for Bournemouth, Christchurch, Lymington, Southampton and Isle of Wight. **Open:** March to October.

Payment: 💷 **Leisure:** 🚲 🎣 🏇 ⛵ ⚡ **Property:** 🖥 🗐 **Children:** 🐎

NEW MILTON, NEW FOREST, Hampshire   Map ref 2B3   SatNav BH23 5QL   [H]

Chewton Glen

New Milton, New Forest, Hampshire BH25 6QS **T:** (01425) 282212
E: reservations@chewtonglen.com
W: www.chewtonglen.com

VisitEngland
Awards for
Excellence 2016
SILVER WINNER

B&B PER ROOM PER NIGHT
D: £370.00 -
£1500.00
HB PER PERSON PER NIGHT
£470.00 - £1620.00

SPECIAL PROMOTIONS
Two night minimum
stay at weekends.

An English Original. Chewton Glen is a luxury country house hotel and spa set in 130 acres of Hampshire countryside on the edge of the New Forest National Park, and just a few minutes walk from the sea. A very special place, Chewton Glen is a proud member of Relais & Châteaux, is one of the finest luxury hotels in the UK and has been voted 'Best Holiday Hotel' in the Condé Nast Traveller Readers' Travel Awards more than once. The unsurpassed heritage of effortlessly gracious English hospitality and the balance between heritage and evolution is what makes Chewton Glen a 5 star, luxury country house hotel and spa that constantly surprises.

Directions: Please contact us for directions.

Bedrooms: 35 double, 23 suites, 12 treehouse suites.
Open: All year.

Site: ☘ **Payment:** 💷 € **Leisure:** 🚲 🎣 🏇 ⛵ ⛳ 🏓 ⚓ ⚡ **Property:** 🅿 🏊 🖥 🗐 🌙 **Children:** 🐎 🎠 🧸
Catering: 🍽 🍴 **Room:** 🗝 📞 📺 📻 ♨

PITT, Hampshire   Map ref 2C3   S

South Winchester Lodges

Contact: Lesley Ross, South Winchester Golf Club, Romsey Road, Winchester, Hampshire SO22 5SW **T:** (01962) 820490 **E:** info@southwinchesterlodges.co.uk
W: www.southwinchesterlodges.co.uk **£ BOOK ONLINE**

Units   14
Sleeps   1-6
PER UNIT PER WEEK
£649.00 - £1280.00

Award-winning, two and three bedroom, five star lodges, some with hot tubs, beautifully set on South Winchester Golf Course just 3 miles from the city centre of Winchester.
Short breaks available from £420.00.
Open: All year.
Nearest Shop: 1 miles
Nearest Pub: 1 miles

Site: ✿ **P** **Payment:** ▣ **Leisure:** ♿ ♪ ▶ ♼ **Property:** ★ ▤ ▣ ▣ **Children:** ⚘ ▦ ☂ **Unit:** ▯ ▤ ▣ ▣ ▦ ▯ ▣ ▣ ▣ BBQ

PORTSMOUTH, Hampshire   Map ref 2C3   SatNav PO1 3HS   H

Royal Maritime Club

75-80 Queen Street, Portsmouth PO1 3HS **T:** (023) 9282 4231 **F:** (023) 9229 3496
E: info@royalmaritimeclub.co.uk
W: www.royalmaritimeclub.co.uk **£ BOOK ONLINE**

B&B PER ROOM PER NIGHT
S: £53.00 - £73.00
D: £92.00 - £145.00
EVENING MEAL PER PERSON
£15.75 - £18.50

SPECIAL PROMOTIONS
Minimum 3 night breaks Sunday to Thursday from £56.00 pp per night. Friday and Saturday from £65 pp per night.

Situated at the heart of Portsmouth's unique naval heritage area. Within walking distance of HMS Victory, HMS Warrior, the Mary Rose, Gunwharf Quays shopping complex. Rail, coach, ferry links nearby.

Directions: Take the M275 Portsmouth(W) and then follow signs to Historic Waterfront/Historic Dockyard.

Bedrooms: 20 single, 33 double, 19 twin, 8 family, 20 superior.
Open: All year except Christmas and New Year.

Payment: ▣ **Leisure:** ⚲ **Property:** ▾ ▤ ▣ ◗ **Children:** ⚘ ▦ ☂ **Catering:** ▾ ▦ **Room:** ⚲ ✦ ▣ TV ▱

WINCHESTER, Hampshire   Map ref 2C3   SatNav SO23 9SR   B

12 Christchurch Road

12 Christchurch Road, Winchester SO23 9SR **T:** (01962) 854272 / 07879 850076
E: pjspatton@yahoo.co.uk

B&B PER ROOM PER NIGHT
S: £55.00 - £60.00
D: £65.00 - £70.00

Elegant Victorian house furnished with style. Easy, pleasant walk to city centre, cathedral, museums, shops and water meadows. Breakfast in conservatory, overlooking beautiful gardens (NGS), with homemade bread, preserves and local produce.
Directions: Please contact us for directions.
Bedrooms: 1 double, 1 twin. Comfortable and well furnished.
Open: All year except Christmas and New Year.

Property: ★ ▤ **Children:** ⚘ ▦ ☂ **Catering:** ▦ **Room:** ⚲ ✦

NEWPORT, Isle of Wight   Map ref 2C3   [S]

VisitEngland
★★★★
SELF CATERING

Newbarn Country Cottages

Contact: Steve Harvey, Newbarn Farm, Newbarn Lane, Gatcombe, Newport, Isle of Wight PO30 3EQ **T:** (01983) 721202 / 07739 868201 **E:** newbarncountrycottages@gmail.com
W: www.newbarncountrycottages.co.uk **£ BOOK ONLINE**

Units   3
Sleeps   2-6
PER UNIT PER WEEK
£250.00 - £800.00

Three beautiful barn conversions in a secluded downland valley in the centre of the Isle of Wight, Parlour Cottage sleeping up to 6 (4 adults and 2 children) and Stable and Dairy Cottages sleeping 4 people. Being centrally located all of the islands attractions are within easy reach and the rural location is ideal for walkers or mountain bikers. **Open:** All year.
Nearest Shop: 2 miles
Nearest Pub: 3 miles

Site: **P** Leisure: ♿ ► ∪ Property: 🔥 🖥 🔆 🖲 Children: 🚼¹ ♨ ⚲ Unit: 🖥 🖵 🔆 🔆 📺 ⊕ 📀

RYDE, Isle of Wight   Map ref 2C3   SatNav PO33 1QJ   [C]

VisitEngland
★★★★★
TOURING &
CAMPING PARK

Whitefield Forest Touring Park

Brading Road, Ryde PO33 1QJ
T: (01983) 617069 **E:** pat&louise@whitefieldforest.co.uk
W: www.whitefieldforest.co.uk

🚐 (50)   £17.50-£26.00
🚍 (50)   £17.50-£26.00
🛖 (50)   £17.50 £26.00
100 touring pitches

Award-winning campsite in the picturesque woodland of Whitefield Forest. Near to the sandy beaches of Ryde & Sandown on a good bus route, ideal for caravans, motor homes and tents. Special offers available on ferry travel & for over 50's.
Directions: Just off A3055 follow to Brading, at Tesco's roundabout straight across, site approx half mile on left hand side.
Open: 31st March to 8th October 2017.

Payment: 💳 ☀ Leisure: 🚭 ► ∪ Children: 🚼 ⚠ Catering: 🛒 Park: 🐾 🚌 🖥 🎦 Touring: 🚿 🔥 🚽 🔥

SANDOWN, Isle of Wight   Map ref 2C3   SatNav PO36 8JR   [B]

VisitEngland
★★★
GUEST
ACCOMMODATION

The Montpelier

5 Pier Street, Sandown PO36 8JR **T:** (01983) 403964 / 07771 936651
E: steve@themontpelier.co.uk
W: www.themontpelier.co.uk

B&B PER ROOM PER NIGHT
S: £29.00 - £35.00
D: £58.00 - £70.00

SPECIAL PROMOTIONS
Check our website for
ferry inclusive specials.

The Montpelier is situated opposite the pier and beaches with the High street just around the corner. We offer B&B, room-only and ferry-inclusive from Southampton. Rooms are en suite, most with sea views and all have a fridge. Room only £4pn less.

Directions: Make your way to Sandown Pier and Esplanade and as you come into Pier Street we are the blue building 15 metres down on your left.

Bedrooms: 1 single, 3 double, 2 twin, 2 family.
Open: All year.

Payment: 💳 € Leisure: 🚭 ► Property: 🖥 Children: 🚼 ♨ Catering: 🍴 Room: 🍵 ⚙ 📺

VENTNOR, *Isle of Wight*   *Map ref 2C3*   S

West Rew Farm Cottages

Contact: Felicity Corry, Proprietor, Rew Lane, Wroxall, Ventnor, Isle of Wight PO38 3AU
T: (01983) 855165 **E:** info@littlespanfarm.co.uk
W: www.westrewfarmcottages.co.uk **£ BOOK ONLINE**

Units   3
Sleeps   2-6
PER UNIT PER WEEK
£220.00 - £650.00

Newly converted cottages with spiral staircase, situated on a working farm in area of outstanding natural beauty on the South West side of the Island. 2 miles from Ventnor and a golf course. Close to bridle and footpaths, ideal for walking and family holidays, a short drive to the sandy beaches of Ventnor, Shanklin & Sandown.
Open: All year.
Nearest Shop: 0.25 miles
Nearest Pub: 0.5 miles

Site: ❀ P Property: 🐎 🚐 🖥 Children: 🐾¹ 🚶 Unit: 📺 🗑 🍴 🎧 📀

WROXALL, *Isle of Wight*   *Map ref 2C3*   *SatNav PO38 3EP*   C

Appuldurcombe Gardens Holiday Park

Appuldurcombe Road, Wroxall, Nr. Ventnor, Isle of Wight PO38 3EP
T: (01983) 852597 **F:** (01983) 856225 **E:** info@appuldurcombegardens.co.uk
W: www.appuldurcombegardens.co.uk

🚐 (50)   £18.40-£30.70
🚎 (40)   £18.40-£30.70
⛺ (40)   £18.40-£30.70
🏕 (40)   £254.80-£914.90
130 touring pitches

Picturesque holiday park within an Area of Outstanding Natural Beauty. Situated within 14 acres of lush secluded grounds & only minutes by car to glorious beaches & attractions. 40 static caravans within a walled orchard & 130 pitches with a selection of pitch options. Prices based on 2 people sharing (excl. static caravans).
Directions: Head to Newport & take A3020 towards Shanklin & Ventnor. Through Blackwater to Rookley, Godshill & Sandford. Reach Whiteley Bank roundabout, right to Wroxall. **Open:** Feb-Nov.

f 𝕏

Site: ♨ ▲🅿 Payment: 💷 ☀ Leisure: ♨ 🎣 🏌 ♻ ⚓ 🎯 Children: 🐾 🎢 Catering: ✕ 🍴 Park: 🐾 🎵 🚐 🗑 🔥 Touring: 🚽 🛁 🚿 🎏

The Solent, Hampshire ©VisitBritain Images Andrew Pickett

ASHFORD, Kent Map ref 3B4　　　SatNav TN25 5NB B

Bulltown Farmhouse Bed & Breakfast

Bulltown Lane, West Brabourne, Ashford, Kent TN25 5NB **T:** (01233) 813505
E: lily.wilton@bulltown.co.uk
W: www.bulltown.co.uk

B&B PER ROOM PER NIGHT
S: £50.00 - £60.00
D: £90.00

Stunning 15th century timber framed farmhouse with wealth of beams surrounded by cottage garden in Area of Outstanding Natural Beauty. Rooms have unspoilt views. All en suite. Guest lounge with large inglenook fireplace. Local produce used. **Directions:** See website for directions but under 4 miles from Junction 10 M20. **Bedrooms:** 1 double, 1 twin, 1 family. **Open:** All year.

Site: ✿ P **Payment:** € **Leisure:** ♿ ♪ ▶ ∪ **Property:** ▦ ▤ **Children:** ⛄ ▦ ✿ **Catering:** ▦ **Room:** ♨ ✋

CANTERBURY, Kent Map ref 3B3　　　S

Broome Park Golf and Country Club

Contact: Canterbury Road, Barham, Canterbury, Kent CT4 6QX **T:** (0800) 358 6991
E: EuHotels@diamondresorts.com
W: www.DiamondResortsandHotels.com **£ BOOK ONLINE**

Units　14
Sleeps　1-6

PER UNIT PER WEEK
£420.00 - £1393.00

SPECIAL PROMOTIONS
Visit our website or call today for seasonal discounts and great savings.

This huge private estate has a historical building at its centre. Broome Park is a relaxing resort with modern log cabins, fine dining, indoor swimming and golf. The 17th century main house has the restaurant and bar. The accommodation is spread throughout the grounds, in well-equipped woodland cabins. The cabins feature a TV in each bedroom, 2 bathrooms, and a fully-fitted kitchen.

The Broome Park grounds feature a full championship golf course, where there are discounts for hotel guests. The Jacobean Restaurant has an antique crystal chandelier and beautiful countryside views.

Open: All year.
Nearest Shop: 2 miles
Nearest Pub: 2 miles

Units: 2 Bedroom Lodges with 1 double room, 1 twin room and full kitchen unit. Each unit also boasts 2 complete bathroom units.

Site: ✿ P **Payment:** ▦ **Leisure:** ▶ ♣ ♒ ♒ **Property:** ▦ ▣ **Children:** ⛄ ▦ ✿
Unit: ▦ ▦ ▦ ▦ ♨ TV ▦ ☏

CANTERBURY, Kent Map ref 3B3　　　SatNav CT1 3JT B

Kipps Independent Hostel

40 Nunnery Fields, Canterbury CT1 3JT **T:** (01227) 786121 **E:** kippshostel@gmail.com
W: www.kipps-hostel.com **£ BOOK ONLINE**

B&B PER ROOM PER NIGHT
S: £25.00 - £35.00
D: £20.00 - £30.00
BED ONLY PER NIGHT
£10.00 - £24.50

Self catering backpackers hostel only a short walk from the Cathedral and City Centre. We offer accommodation for individuals and Groups. Excellent facilities including kitchen, garden, lounge free Wi-Fi, and nightly events. **Directions:** Please go to our website www.kipps-hostel.com for directions. **Bedrooms:** Private/family and dormitory rooms. **Open:** All year.

Site: ✿ **Payment:** ▦ € **Leisure:** ♣ **Property:** ▦ ▣ TV **Catering:** ▦ **Bedroom:** ♨ ☏

CRANBROOK, Kent   Map ref 3B4

VisitEngland
★★★
SELF CATERING

Units   1
Sleeps   2-3

PER UNIT PER WEEK
£300.00 - £350.00

Bakersbarn Annexe

Contact: Mrs Hooper, Owner, Golford Road, Cranbrook, Kent County TN17 3NW
T: (01580) 713344 **E:** hooper.jm@btinternet.com
W: www.bakersbarn.co.uk

Bakersbarn is a non-smoking accommodation in a quiet rural situation, within 7 minutes walk from the town centre of Cranbrook. All rooms overlook the garden and grazing land and are well equipped. The bedroom has optional zipped twin beds and all linen and electricity is included. The bathroom has a bath with overhead shower, toilet and hand basin. Fully furnished kitchen.
Open: All year. **Nearest Shop:** 0.25 miles **Nearest Pub:** 0.25 miles

Site: ✿ P Property: 🔲 🔃 Unit: 🖥 📷 📺 📀

EDENBRIDGE, Kent   Map ref 2D2

SatNav TN8 7NG B

VisitEngland
★★★★★
GUEST ACCOMMODATION

VisitEngland
Gold
AWARD

B&B PER ROOM PER NIGHT
S: £105.00 - £140.00
D: £125.00 - £295.00

SPECIAL PROMOTIONS
Includes complimentary access to the Castle and gardens.

Hever Castle Luxury Bed & Breakfast

Hever Castle, Hever, Edenbridge, Kent TN8 7NG **T:** (01732) 861800 **F:** (01732) 867860
E: stay@hevercastle.co.uk
W: www.hevercastle.co.uk/stay/bed-breakfast **£ BOOK ONLINE**

Surrounded by glorious Kent countryside, Hever Castle in Kent offers luxury Bed and Breakfast in the Astor Wing of Hever Castle, an Edwardian Wing created by William Waldorf Astor, designed in Tudor style. This period property boasts a fine collection of 28, stunning five-star Gold graded bedrooms. On offer you will find an abundance of rich fabrics, crisp linens, panelled walls, perhaps a golden chaise longue or a glimpse of the Castle through leaded windows.
All bedrooms are en suite and individually styled, some offering four poster beds, some roll top baths and some walk in showers. All rooms blend modern day comforts with antique furnishings and original features. The fine collection of bedrooms offers a selection of double rooms, twin rooms, single rooms and some rooms that are suitable for families with young children.

Directions: Please see website.

Bedrooms: Service en Chambre leather bound refreshment boxes, luxurious toiletries, lounge facilities & billiards room.
Open: All year.

f y

Site: ✿ P Payment: 💳 Leisure: ⚑ ⚲ Property: 🛎 🖥 🏥 Children: 🧸 🛏 🚼 Catering: 🍽 🍴
Room: 🍵 💧 📞 📺 🔌 🧺

EDENBRIDGE, Kent Map ref 2D2 [S]

Units 1
Sleeps 2-8

PER UNIT PER WEEK
£1785.00 - £3250.00

SPECIAL PROMOTIONS
Short breaks available throughout the year, contact Hever Castle for further information.

Medley Court - Hever Castle

Contact: Miss Kate Rowbottom, Sales Manager, Medley Court at Hever Castle, Hever Castle, Hever, Edenbridge TN8 7NG **T:** (01732) 861744 **F:** (01732) 867860
E: krowbottom@hevercastle.co.uk
W: www.hevercastle.co.uk/stay/medley-court/ **£ BOOK ONLINE**

Dating back to 1903, Medley Court is a luxurious four bedroom property forming part of the Astor Wing. The charming, double-moated Hever Castle and surrounding formal lawns provide a stunning backdrop to this beautiful holiday cottage in a truly historic location. Although Medley Court is now just over one hundred years old, its appearance is that of a Tudor house, the standard of decoration and comfort is outstanding and it still retains the warm, relaxed feel of a family home.

Open: All year.
Nearest Shop: 5 miles
Nearest Pub: 0.5 miles

Site: ✿ **P Payment:** FE **Leisure:** ♪ ▶ ⚲ **Property:** ▭ 🗄 🖳 **Children:** 🐴 🛏 🛝
Unit: 🗌 🗄 🖭 📶 📺 🎧 📼 🗍

HERNHILL, Kent Map ref 3B3 SatNav ME13 9JW [B]

B&B PER ROOM PER NIGHT
S: £48.00 - £58.00
D: £80.00 - £90.00

Church Oast

Church Oast, Hernhill, Faversham ME13 9JW **T:** (01227) 750974 **E:** Jill@geliot.plus.com
W: www.churchoast.co.uk

A warm welcome and luxury accommodation in converted Oast House in quiet picturesque village. Well equipped bedrooms with en suite or private facilities. Award-winning breakfasts served in stunning conservatory with views over garden and orchards. Guest lounge.

Meals available in nearby pub and plenty of other eating places nearby.

Near to Canterbury, Whitstable and Faversham

Directions: From London M2 then A299 Margate first exit and follow signs to Hernhill. From Dover A2 to M2 roundabout 4th exit A299 then as above.

Bedrooms: 2 double, 1 flexible/family.
Open: All year.

Site: ✿ **P Payment:** € **Leisure:** ♪ ▶ ⋃ **Property:** ▦ **Children:** 🐴 🛏 **Catering:** 🍽 **Room:** 🗄 ♨

MAIDSTONE, Kent   Map ref 3B3

Coldblow Farm

VisitEngland 3★ - 4★ SELF CATERING

Contact: Bookings Office, Coldblow Lane, Thurnham, Maidstone, Kent ME14 3LR
T: (01622) 730439 9am-2pm **E:** bookings@coldblowfarm.co.uk
W: www.coldblowfarm.co.uk

Units   5
Sleeps 2-70

Coldblow Farm is situated on top of the Kent Downs overlooking Maidstone in 'An Area of Outstanding Natural Beauty'. Coldblow has a range of self-catering holiday accommodation with two cottages suitable and graded for disabled guests.
Nearest Shop: 2 miles

Site: ✿ P **Leisure:** ↱ ∪ **Property:** ∥ 🐕 🖼 🗑 🏠 🖼 **Children:** 🎠 🏃
Unit: 🗄 🗒 🖥 🗑 🔧 📺 dvd BBQ

MAIDSTONE, Kent   Map ref 3B3

Lime Tree Cottages

VisitEngland ★★★ SELF CATERING

Contact: Peter & Stella Hasler, Owners, 4 Lime Tree Cottages, Faversham Road, Lenham, Kent ME17 2EY **T:** (01622) 851310 / 07777 661716 **E:** pvhasler@gmail.com
W: www.kentcottage.com

Units   1
Sleeps 1-4
PER UNIT PER WEEK
£300.00 - £410.00

A 100+ year old cottage on the historic Pilgrims Way (AONB) is an ideal base to explore Kent - easy access to London and Europe. Only 5 minute drive from Leeds Castle and 30 minutes to Canterbury or Rochester. A warm welcome awaits you.
Open: All year.
Nearest Shop: 0.5 miles
Nearest Pub: 0.5 miles

Site: ✿ P **Property:** 🐕 🖼 🗑 🗒 **Children:** 🎠 🍴 🏃 **Unit:** 🖥 🗑 🔧 📺 dvd ∅ BBQ 📞

MAIDSTONE, Kent   Map ref 3B3   SatNav ME14 2BD

The Limes

VisitEngland ★★ GUEST ACCOMMODATION **VisitEngland Silver AWARD**

118 Boxley Road, Maidstone ME14 2BD **T:** (01622) 750629 / 07889 594700
E: info@thelimesmaidstone.co.uk
W: www.thelimesmaidstone.co.uk **£ BOOK ONLINE**

B&B PER ROOM PER NIGHT
S: £50.00
D: £90.00

Large Georgian house, 2 star guest accommodation. Close to town centre, motorways, railway stations and shopping centres. Good location for walkers and cyclists. Off-road parking. Silver award for breakfast and a 5 star hygiene rating. **Directions:** From M2 Junction 3 take A229 to Maidstone. From M20 Junction 6 A229 Signposted Penenden Heath. Turn right at roundabout for town centre.
Bedrooms: 3 single, 1 twin.
Open: All year except Christmas and New Year.

Site: ✿ P **Leisure:** ♪ ↱ ∪ **Property:** 🖼 🏥 **Children:** 🎠12 **Catering:** 🍽 **Room:** 🔧 🚿 📞 📺

Need more information?

Visit our websites for detailed information, up-to-date availability and to book your accommodation online. Includes over 20,000 places to stay, all of them star rated.
www.visitor-guides.co.uk

RAMSGATE, Kent Map ref 3C3
SatNav CT11 8DT **H**

VisitEngland
★★★
HOTEL

Comfort Inn Ramsgate

Victoria Parade, Ramsgate, Kent CT11 8DT **T:** (01843) 592345 **F:** (01843) 580157
E: reservations@comfortinnramsgate.co.uk
W: www.comfortinnramsgate.co.uk **£ BOOK ONLINE**

B&B PER ROOM PER NIGHT
S: £39.00 - £70.00
D: £40.00 - £180.00
EVENING MEAL PER PERSON
£5.95 - £13.00

SPECIAL PROMOTIONS
Mention Visit England
when booking and
code LSC10 to receive
a 10% discount on
your stay call (01843)
592345 to book.

Victorian Grade 2 Listed building with modern facilities situated on the cliff top opposite the beach with panoramic sea views. Free Wi-Fi, free parking, well stocked bar selling local ale, restaurant offering wide variety of dishes, Beauty Salon, Gym and Sauna. Sea view rooms, some with enclosed private balcony, Garden. Live Entertainment fortnightly. Afternoon tea available.

Directions: From M2 take the A299 then A253 to Ramsgate. Follow signs for East Cliff. From Victoria Road turn left, hotel is on the left.

Bedrooms: 7 single, 14 double, 9 twin, 7 family, 7 suite.
Open: All year.

Site: ❀ P **Payment:** ▦ € **Leisure:** ♨ ♩ ▶ ♺ ✹ ⋈ ⊞ **Property:** ◉ ⚿ ▱ ▤ ◐ **Children:** ♘ ⊨ ⚶ **Catering:** (✕ ⍾ 🍴 **Room:** ☍ ♨ ☎ ⊡ 🗱

ROYAL TUNBRIDGE WELLS, Kent Map ref 2D2
SatNav TN4 9SS **B**

VisitEngland
★★
BED & BREAKFAST

Badgers End Bed & Breakfast

47 Thirlmere Road, Royal Tunbridge Wells, Kent TN4 9SS **T:** (01892) 533176

B&B PER ROOM PER NIGHT
S: £35.00
D: £60.00

Modern house in quiet cul-de-sac with large garden backing onto woodland. Close to A26. Full English breakfast. Freeview TV plus broadband. Tea and coffee making facilities. Non smoking establishment throughout.
Directions: 1.5 miles from Tunbridge Wells station. 1 mile from shopping centre. Varying directions, given upon request.
Bedrooms: 1 single, 1 double.
Open: All year except Christmas.

Leisure: ▶ **Property:** ▱ **Catering:** 🍴 **Room:** ☍ ♨ ⊡ ▣

Leeds Castle, Kent ©VisitBritain

ROYAL TUNBRIDGE WELLS, Kent   Map ref 2D2   [S]

VisitEngland
★★★★
SELF CATERING

Plaisance

Contact: Mrs Angela Worsell, Office Manager, Itaris Properties, 12 Mount Ephraim, Royal Tunbridge Wells, Kent TN4 8AS **T:** (01892) 511065 **E:** enquiries@itaris.co.uk **W:** www.itaris.co.uk

| Units | 5 |
| Sleeps | 2-4 |

PER UNIT PER WEEK
£330.00 - £515.00

SPECIAL PROMOTIONS
Weekly bookings from Saturday to Saturday.

Royal Tunbridge Wells is surrounded by beautiful and unspoilt countryside and is the ideal location for a short break or relaxing holiday. Our self-contained and fully equipped holiday apartments are situated in the very heart of Tunbridge Wells within walking distance of its many amenities, and transport by bus or train. The famous Pantiles with its shops, cafés and restaurants, occasional markets and music events are a must for visitors.

Open: All year.
Nearest Shop: 0.5 miles
Nearest Pub: 0.10 miles

Units: Gas and electricity are charged as used during the months of October to the end of March.

Site: P **Payment:** 💷 **Leisure:** 🚲 🎵 ♪ **Property:** 🖥 🗄 🔲 🗐 🎱 **Children:** 🛏 🎠 🚶
Unit: 🗄 💻 📺 🔲 📀

ABINGDON, Oxfordshire   Map ref 2C1   SatNav OX14 3BT   [B]

VisitEngland
★★★
INN

The Railway Inn

Station Road, Culham, Culham Station Nr Abingdon, Oxfordshire OX14 3BT
T: (01235) 528046 **E:** info@railwayinnculham.co.uk
W: www.railwayinnculham.co.uk

B&B PER ROOM PER NIGHT
S: £60.00
D: £81.00
EVENING MEAL PER PERSON
£8.00 - £16.00

Bed and breakfast. Evening meals range from homemade pies to steaks. Free house. Cask ales. Free parking. Friendly staff. No Sunday evening meals and no Monday lunch. No dogs policy.
Directions: A415 2 miles East of Abingdon (near Culham). Adjacent to main rail, London Paddington to Oxford. Close to A34, M40 and M4. 1 mile from Thames Path.
Bedrooms: 4 double, 3 twin, 2 family and 1 Double de Luxe.
Open: All year except Christmas.

Site: ✿ P **Payment:** 💷 **Leisure:** 🎵 ♪ **Property:** 🖥 **Children:** 🛏 🚶 **Catering:** 🍷 🍽 **Room:** 👤 🔲 📺

ABINGDON-ON-THAMES, Oxfordshire   Map ref 2C1   SatNav OX14 2BE   [B]

VisitEngland
★★★★
GUEST HOUSE

VisitEngland
Gold
AWARD

Abbey Guest House

136 Oxford Road, Abingdon-on-Thames, Oxford OX14 2AG
T: (01235) 537020 / 07976 627252 **E:** info@abbeyguest.uk
W: www.abbeyguest.uk **£ BOOK ONLINE**

B&B PER ROOM PER NIGHT
S: £60.00 - £85.00
D: £100.00 - £110.00

We are a quiet, 'Home from Home', non smoking, multi-award winning, highly accessible B&B, in the historic town of Abingdon-on-Thames. Guests enjoy private parking, excellent bus services and local amenities, Fair Trade items and free Wi-Fi. **Directions:** Oxford Road is the A4183. Detailed walking & driving directions, and information if travelling by bus, train or plane is available on the website. **Bedrooms:** Lift installed, ensures 7 en suite rooms accessible. **Open:** All year. Added charge for Christmas & New Year.

🇫 🐦

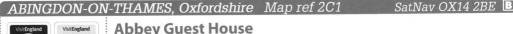

Site: ✿ P **Payment:** 💷 **Property:** 🖥 🛏 **Children:** 🛏 🚶
🚶 **Catering:** 🍽 **Room:** 🔲 👤 📺 📀 🛗

SatNav OX17 1AZ **C**

Anita's Touring Caravan Park

The Yews, Church Farm, Banbury OX17 1AZ
T: (01295) 750731 / 07966 171959 **F:** (01295) 750731 **E:** anitagail@btopenworld.com
W: www.oxfordshirecamping.co.uk

VisitEngland
★★★★
TOURING &
CAMPING PARK

🚐 (36)	£18.00-£24.00
🚍 (36)	£18.00-£24.00
⛺ (20)	£14.00-£18.00
🏠 (6)	£30.00-£130.00

Anita's is a friendly family run site in North Oxforshire on the edge of Mollington village. Clean facilities, shop, reception, hard and grass pitches, camping, camping pods and cottages.
Directions: M40 Junction 11 Banbury take 3rd roundabout to Southam for 4 miles, 150 yards past Mollington, turn-off on left. Brown signs.
Open: All year.

Site: A🅿 **Payment:** 🔢 **Leisure:** 🎣 ⚲ ∪ **Children:** 🏕 **Catering:** 🛒 **Park:** 🐾 🚐 🅿 **Touring:** 🔌 🔆 🚐

SatNav OX26 1TE **H**

Bicester Hotel Golf and Spa

Bicester Hotel Golf and Spa, Green Lane, Chesterton, Bicester, Oxfordshire OX26 1TE
T: (01869) 241204 **E:** carol.barford@bicesterhgs.com
W: www.bicesterhotelgolfandspa.com **£ BOOK ONLINE**

VisitEngland
★★★★
HOTEL

B&B PER ROOM PER NIGHT
S: £85.00 - £170.00
D: £95.00 - £180.00

A unique, independently run 52 bedroomed hotel with extensive leisure and spa facilities and an 18 hole golf course, set in 134 acres. Close to Bicester Village and other local attractions.
Directions: Just minutes from Junction 9 of M40 motorway. Direct rail links into London and Birmingham from Bicester North.
Bedrooms: 19 standard double, 13 standard twin, 14 superior double, 4 feature rooms, 2 suite.
Open: All year except Christmas day.

🇫 🐦

Site: ✿ P **Payment:** 🔢 **Leisure:** 🏊 🎣 ⚲ ∪ 🏌 🎿 🗗 ⚲ **Property:** 📶 🍽 🖥 ● **Children:** 🏕 🎠 ☂ **Catering:** (✗ 🍷 🍴 **Room:** ☎ 🛏 🔌 📺

SatNav RG9 3NY **B**

The Baskerville

Station Road, Lower Shiplake, Henley-on-Thames RG9 3NY **T:** (01189) 403332
E: enquiries@thebaskerville.com
W: www.thebaskerville.com **£ BOOK ONLINE**

VisitEngland
★★★★
INN

VisitEngland
Silver
AWARD

B&B PER ROOM PER NIGHT
S: £100.00 - £200.00
D: £110.00 - £200.00
EVENING MEAL PER PERSON
£27.00 - £36.00

SPECIAL PROMOTIONS
Daily changing
specials.

Quality, award-winning, traditional family run village inn situated on the Thames Path, a short walk from Shiplake station and just minutes from Henley-on-Thames. Outstanding food with menus that evolve with the seasons using fresh local produce. Excellent wine list, cosy, comfortable bar with a good choice of cask-conditioned ales. 50 cover restaurant and a garden with seating for 100.

Directions: From Henley-on-Thames, take Reading road for 2 miles, turn left down Station Road for 0.5 mile. Baskerville is on right after cross roads before station.

Bedrooms: 2 double, 1 twin, 1 family.
Open: All year.

🇫 🐦

Site: ✿ P **Payment:** 🔢 **Leisure:** 🎣 **Property:** 🍽 🐾 🚭 🌿 **Children:** 🏕 🎠 ☂ **Catering:** (✗ 🍷 🍴 **Room:** ☎ 🛏 🔌 📺

MILTON-UNDER-WYCHWOOD, Oxfordshire   Map ref 2B1   SatNav OX7 6JH   B

BED & BREAKFAST ★★★★

Silver AWARD

B&B PER ROOM PER NIGHT
S: £60.00 - £80.00
D: £80.00 - £90.00

Hillborough House

The Green, Shipton Road, Milton-under-Wychwood, Near Burford OX7 6JH
T: (01993) 832352 **F:** (01993) 832352 **E:** hillboroughhouse@btinternet.com
W: www.hillboroughhouse.co.uk **£ BOOK ONLINE**

A Victorian village house with spacious en suite rooms overlooking the green with views to distant hills. You will be assured of a warm welcome and a great breakfast.
Directions: Please contact us for directions.
Bedrooms: 1 double, 1 twin, 1 family, all en suite.
Open: All year except Christmas.

Site: **P** Leisure: ♿ 🏊 ▶ ∪ Property: 🐾 🖥 🖨 Children: 🛏 🎠 🚶 Catering: 🍴 Room: 🔌 🍵 🎧 📺 📀 🔌

OXFORD, Oxfordshire   Map ref 2C1   SatNav OX2 8DX   B

★★★
GUEST ACCOMMODATION

B&B PER ROOM PER NIGHT
S: £40.00 - £50.00
D: £60.00 - £70.00

Arden Lodge

34 Sunderland Avenue, Oxford OX2 8DX **T:** (01865) 552076 **F:** (01865) 512265
E: ardenlodge34@googlemail.com
W: www.ardenlodgeoxford.co.uk

Arden Lodge is a modern, detached house set in a tree-lined avenue, in one of Oxford's most select areas. It offers 3 attractively furnished bedrooms, with private facilities, colour TV and beverage tray. An excellent base for touring; within easy reach of the Cotswolds, London, Stratford and Warwick. The position is convenient for Oxford City Centre, parks, river, meadows, golf course and country inns, including the world famous Trout Inn as featured in 'Inspector Morse'. Ample parking is available, and there is an excellent bus service, with Oxford City Centre about 10 minutes away.

Directions: Please contact us for directions.

Bedrooms: 1 single, 1 double, 1 twin.
Open: All year except Christmas.

Site: **P** Leisure: ▶ Property: 🖥 Children: 🎠 🚶 Catering: 🍴 Room: 🔌 🍵 📞 📺

OXFORD, Oxfordshire   Map ref 2C1   SatNav OX2 7PL   B

★★★★
GUEST ACCOMMODATION

B&B PER ROOM PER NIGHT
S: £85.00 - £95.00
D: £125.00 - £160.00

Cotswold House

363 Banbury Road, Oxford OX2 7PL **T:** (01865) 310558 **E:** d.r.walker@talk21.com
W: www.cotswoldhouse.co.uk **£ BOOK ONLINE**

A well-situated and elegant property, offering excellent accommodation and service. Cotswold House is in a most desirable part of Oxford. Free parking and Wi-Fi.
Directions: Exit Oxford ring road on North side, following sign to Summertown. We are half a mile on right as you head towards city centre.
Bedrooms: 2 single, 2 double, 1 twin, 2 family, 1 deluxe suite.
Open: All year.

Site: **P** Payment: 💳 Property: 🖥 Children: 🎠³ Room: 🔌 🍵 📺 🔌

OXFORD, Oxfordshire Map ref 2C1
SatNav OX1 4PL **B**

Newton House Guest House B&B Oxford
82-84 Abingdon Road, Oxford OX1 4PL **T:** (01865) 240561
E: stay@newtonhouseoxford.co.uk
W: www.newtonhouseoxford.co.uk **£ BOOK ONLINE**

B&B PER ROOM PER NIGHT
S: £66.00 - £110.00
D: £74.00 - £116.00

SPECIAL PROMOTIONS
Ask about special
offers.

Close to Oxford's city centre, on foot, bus, coach, train or car. A perfect opportunity to visit Oxford's university central city attractions, research facilities, museums, hospitals. Family-run with a personal touch, free Wi-Fi, car park, English traditional breakfast, vegetarian and continental. Special diets catered for.

Direct booking discount available if booking via our website - www.newtonhouseoxford.co.uk

Directions: Situated on A4144 (OX1 4PL) Postal code 1/2 mile (800 metres) from the city centre 10 to 15 minute walk see us on google maps.

Bedrooms: 8 double, 4 twin, 2 family, all en suite.
Open: All year.

Site: P Payment: ⊞ € Leisure: ⚬ ♪ Property: ▦ ◗ Children: ⛺ 🍴 ⚓ Catering: 🍽
Room: 🍴 ⚬ ☎ ⊡ 📺 ⚓

STANDLAKE, Oxfordshire Map ref 2C1
SatNav OX29 7PZ **C**

Hardwick Parks
Downs Road, Standlake, Witney OX29 7PZ
T: (01865) 300501 **F:** (01865) 300037 **E:** info@hardwickparks.co.uk
W: www.hardwickparks.co.uk **£ BOOK ONLINE**

🚐 (196)	£16.00-£26.50
🚌 (196)	£16.00-£26.50
⛺ (196)	£11.00-£19.00
🏕 (17)	£295.00 £600.00

196 touring pitches

Beautiful 180 acre family holiday park situated in stunning Oxfordshire countryside, close to Oxford and Cotswolds; suitable for caravans, tents and motor homes with holiday caravans to hire/ for sale. Clubhouse, shop, Watersports on park.
Directions: Four and a half miles from Witney, signposted from the A415.
Open: Easter to end of October.

Site: ⛺ ▲🅿 Payment: ⊞ ☼ Leisure: ♪ Children: ⛺ 🅰 Catering: ✕ 🍴 Park: 🐕 ▦ 🗑 🚻 ⚓ **Touring:** 🚽 🚿 🔌 ⚡

THAME, Oxfordshire Map ref 2C1
S

The Hollies
Contact: Miss Julia Tanner, The Hollies, c/o Little Acre, High Street, Tetsworth, Thame OX9 7AT **T:** (01844) 281423 / 07798 625252 **F:** (01844) 281423
E: info@theholliesthame.co.uk **W:** theholliesthame.co.uk **£ BOOK ONLINE**

Units   1
Sleeps   1-6
PER UNIT PER WEEK
£595.00 - £795.00

Luxury four-bedroom dorma bungalow with peaceful gardens, five minutes' walk from centre of Thame, historic market town. Ideal location for Oxford, Cotswolds, NT & London. Good bus service.
Open: All year.
Nearest Shop: 0.25 miles
Nearest Pub: 0.25 miles

Site: ⚘ **P** Leisure: ⚬ ♪ ♦ ♺ Property: 🐕 ▦ 🖼 Children: ⛺ Unit: 🗄 📺 ⚓ 🍴 📺 📻 ☎

For **key to symbols** see page 6

WOODSTOCK, Oxfordshire   Map ref 2C1

SatNav OX20 1HT **B**

The Duke of Marlborough

A44 Woodleys, Woodstock, Oxford OX20 1HT   T: (01993) 811460   F: (01993) 810165
E: sales@dukeofmarlborough.co.uk
W: www.dukeofmarlborough.co.uk

B&B PER ROOM PER NIGHT
S: £75.00 - £110.00
D: £90.00 - £140.00
EVENING MEAL PER PERSON
£9.95 - £30.00

Family-run and friendly and well known locally for its good food. Situated close to Woodstock. Nearby Blenheim Palace and Oxford. Ideally situated for exploring the surrounding countryside.
Directions: We are positioned on the A44 Oxford to Stratford road just 2 miles North of Woodstock at the junction with the B4437.
Bedrooms: 4 double, 2 twin, 5 family, 2 suites.
Open: All year.

Site: ❀ P Leisure: ♪ ▶ ∪ Property: ▤ Children: ▦ Catering: ❤✕ ♟ 🍴 Room: ✆ ♨ ☏ ☎ 📺 ♿

EAST MOLESEY, Surrey   Map ref 2D2

SatNav KT8 9DD **B**

Kings Arms

2 Lion Gate, Hampton Court Road, East Molesey, Surrey KT8 9DD   T: (02089) 771729
E: kingsarms.hamptoncourt@hall-woodhouse.co.uk
W: www.kingsarmshamptoncourt.co.uk   **£ BOOK ONLINE**

B&B PER ROOM PER NIGHT
S: £75.00 - £120.00
D: £85.00 - £170.00
EVENING MEAL PER PERSON
£15.00 - £25.00

The Kings Arms is a 300 year old inn located on the Northern edge of Hampton Court Palace just outside the Lions Gate. The building is steeped in history and in parts dates back to 1658. Originally built as a 'house of disrepute' for the soldiers garrisoned at Hampton Court Palace, today the inn offers guests characterful and unique rooms perfect for a relaxing stay.

Directions: Located on the edge of Hampton Court Palace on the A308, we have 4 parking spaces for guests. On-street parking is limited to 4 hours, long stay parking is available in Bushy Park.

Bedrooms: Our historic inn and rooms are steeped in charm and character. Each of our bedrooms show off genuine period features and home comforts.
Open: All year.

Payment: 💳 Property: ▤ ∅ Children: 🧸 ♟ Catering: ❤✕ ♟ Room: ✆ ♨ 📺

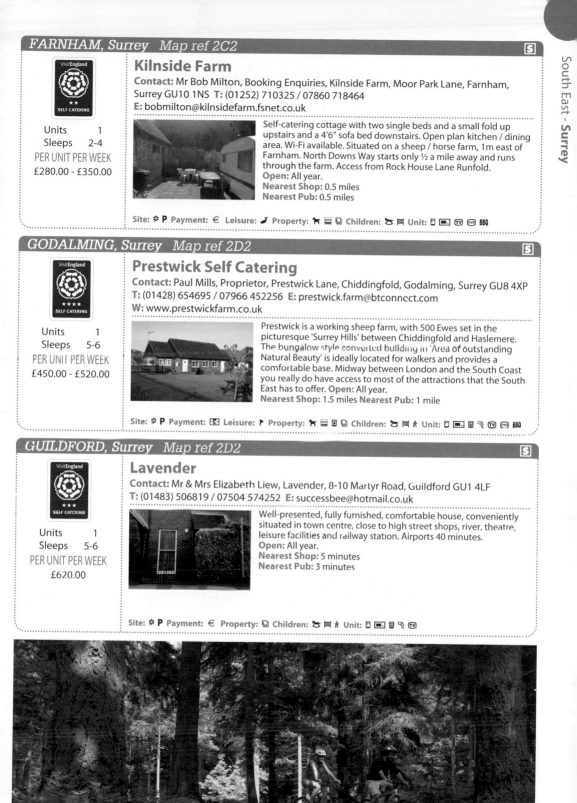

FARNHAM, Surrey   Map ref 2C2

VisitEngland
★★
SELF CATERING

Units 1
Sleeps 2-4
PER UNIT PER WEEK
£280.00 - £350.00

Kilnside Farm

Contact: Mr Bob Milton, Booking Enquiries, Kilnside Farm, Moor Park Lane, Farnham, Surrey GU10 1NS **T:** (01252) 710325 / 07860 718464
E: bobmilton@kilnsidefarm.fsnet.co.uk

Self-catering cottage with two single beds and a small fold up upstairs and a 4'6" sofa bed downstairs. Open plan kitchen / dining area. Wi-Fi available. Situated on a sheep / horse farm, 1m east of Farnham. North Downs Way starts only ½ a mile away and runs through the farm. Access from Rock House Lane Runfold.
Open: All year.
Nearest Shop: 0.5 miles
Nearest Pub: 0.5 miles

Site: ✿ P Payment: € Leisure: ♪ Property: ♖ 🖾 🖳 Children: ⚘ 🏛 Unit: 🗋 🖃 TV 🗔 BBQ

GODALMING, Surrey   Map ref 2D2

VisitEngland
★★★★
SELF CATERING

Units 1
Sleeps 5-6
PER UNIT PER WEEK
£450.00 - £520.00

Prestwick Self Catering

Contact: Paul Mills, Proprietor, Prestwick Lane, Chiddingfold, Godalming, Surrey GU8 4XP
T: (01428) 654695 / 07966 452256 **E:** prestwick.farm@btconnect.com
W: www.prestwickfarm.co.uk

Prestwick is a working sheep farm, with 500 Ewes set in the picturesque 'Surrey Hills' between Chiddingfold and Haslemere. The bungalow style converted building in 'Area of outstanding Natural Beauty' is ideally located for walkers and provides a comfortable base. Midway between London and the South Coast you really do have access to most of the attractions that the South East has to offer. **Open:** All year.
Nearest Shop: 1.5 miles **Nearest Pub:** 1 mile

Site: ✿ P Payment: 🖽 Leisure: ▶ Property: ♖ 🖾 🖳 Children: ⚘ 🏛 ♀ Unit: 🗋 🖃 🗔 ◖ TV 🗔 BBQ

GUILDFORD, Surrey   Map ref 2D2

VisitEngland
★★★
SELF CATERING

Units 1
Sleeps 5-6
PER UNIT PER WEEK
£620.00

Lavender

Contact: Mr & Mrs Elizabeth Liew, Lavender, 8-10 Martyr Road, Guildford GU1 4LF
T: (01483) 506819 / 07504 574252 **E:** successbee@hotmail.co.uk

Well-presented, fully furnished, comfortable house, conveniently situated in town centre, close to high street shops, river, theatre, leisure facilities and railway station. Airports 40 minutes.
Open: All year.
Nearest Shop: 5 minutes
Nearest Pub: 3 minutes

Site: ✿ P Payment: € Property: 🖳 Children: ⚘ 🏛 ♀ Unit: 🗋 🖃 🗔 ◖ TV

Bolderwood, New Forest, Hampshire ©VisitBritain Daniel Bosworth

BARNHAM, *Sussex* Map ref 2D3 [S]

Orchard Cottage Holidays

Contact: Mrs Lorraine Holden, Owner, Orchard Cottage Holidays, High Ground Orchards, High Ground Lane, Barnham, Nr Bognor Regis, West Sussex PO22 0BT **T:** 07484 003978
E: lorraine@orchardcottageholidays.org.uk
W: www.orchardcottageholidays.org.uk **£ BOOK ONLINE**

Units 4
Sleeps 2-4

PER UNIT PER WEEK
£400.00 - £900.00

SPECIAL PROMOTIONS
Short breaks by
negotiation.

Four-two bedroom flint cottages, newly-built to highest specification. Near to well supplied, popular village close to downs and sea. Perfect base to explore Chichester, Arundel and West Sussex area. Rural outlook, ample parking and easy level access. Both bedrooms en suite (one downstairs). Own sunny conservatory. Private, secure individual gardens with patio.

Open: All year.
Nearest Shop: 0.5 miles
Nearest Pub: 0.5 miles

Site: ✿ P **Payment:** 💷 **Leisure:** ⚓ ♪ ► ∪ **Property:** 🖥 🗖 🕾 ⛱ **Children:** 🐴 🏠 ⛺
Unit: 🗖 🗄 📼 🗄 🖇 📺 🕹 📀

BOGNOR REGIS, *Sussex* Map ref 2C3 SatNav PO22 7AH [B]

White Horses Bed & Breakfast

Clyde Road, Felpham, Bognor Regis, West Sussex PO22 7AH **T:** (01243) 824320
E: whitehorsesbandb@btinternet.com
W: www.whitehorsesfelpham.co.uk

B&B PER ROOM PER NIGHT
S: £55.00
D: £85.00

White Horses is located in a quiet cul-de-sac overlooking the sea and Felpham beach. A modernised flint and brick house offering quality accommodation. A 3 mile promenade adjacent affords easy sea-side walking. Pubs and food outlets nearby.
Directions: Please see website.
Bedrooms: En suite, flat screen TV, hairdryer & tea/coffee tray.
Open: All year.

Site: ✿ P **Payment:** 💷 € **Leisure:** ► **Property:** 🖥 **Children:** 🐴 🏠 ⛺ **Room:** 🖇 ♨ 📺

BRIGHTON, *Sussex* Map ref 2D3 SatNav BN2 9JA [B]

Kipps Brighton

76 Grand Parade, Brighton BN2 9JA **T:** (01273) 604182 **E:** kippshostelbrighton@gmail.com
W: www.kipps-brighton.com **£ BOOK ONLINE**

BED ONLY PER NIGHT
£15.00 - £80.00

Award-winning hostel situated in the heart of Brighton. We offer private rooms as well as dormitory rooms. Excellent facilities, including a self catering kitchen, lounge & outside patio. Views overlooking the historic Royal Pavillion.
Directions: We are situated in the centre of Brighton. Visit our website to print off a map.
Bedrooms: 1 single, 6 doubles, 4 twins, & dormitory rooms.
Open: All year.

Site: ✿ **Payment:** 💷 € **Leisure:** ⚓ ♪ ► ∪ **Property:** 🖥 🕹 📺 🖇 **Catering:** 🍴 🍷 **Room:** 🖐
Bedroom: 🖐

BRIGHTON, Sussex   Map ref 2D3
SatNav BN1 2PQ H

The Brighton Hotel
143-145 Kings Road, Brighton, East Sussex BN1 2PQ **T:** (01273) 820555 **F:** (01273) 821555
E: reception@thebrightonhotel.com
W: www.thebrightonhotel.co.uk **£ BOOK ONLINE**

B&B PER ROOM PER NIGHT
S: £45.00 - £185.00
D: £55.00 - £220.00
EVENING MEAL PER PERSON
£19.00 - £23.00

SPECIAL PROMOTIONS
Special price for dinner menu, 2 course £17 and 3 course only £21. Late check out discount of £5 per hour from 11am to 2pm maximum. The normal cost of this would be £10 per hour.

The Grade II listed The Brighton Hotel is one of the most charming hotels in Brighton, where you are guaranteed a warm and personal welcome. It is located on the seafront directly opposite the famous Brighton Bandstand, very close to the West Pier and to the British Airways i360 attraction.

The best rates are only ever found direct with us via our website or calling us on (01273) 820555.

Directions: Brighton Train Station is walking distance from the Hotel, when you leave the Station follow the signs for Taxi & exit Station. Walk straight to the seafront and turn right, towards the West Pier.

Bedrooms: Bright and warmly furnished rooms with private bathrooms. Also includes a flat screen TV, ironing facilities, hair dryer and tea and coffee station.
Open: The hotel is open all year. 24 hour Reception.

Site: P Payment: Leisure: Property: Children: Catering: Room:

CHICHESTER, Sussex   Map ref 2C3
SatNav PO19 1PX B

4 Canon Lane
Chichester, West Sussex PO19 1PX **T:** (01243) 813586
E: bookings@chichestercathedral.org.uk
W: www.chichestercathedral.org.uk / www.cathedralenterprises.co.uk

B&B PER ROOM PER NIGHT
S: £79.00
D: £117.00 - £138.00

SPECIAL PROMOTIONS
Seasonal Discounts - 25% discount on bedroom rates from 1st December 2016 to 31st March 2017 (not including breakfast)

4 Canon Lane is a beautifully restored eight bedroom house situated in the historic precincts of Chichester Cathedral.

All bedrooms are en suite, with tea & coffee facilities and offer stunning views of the Cathedral or gardens. Breakfast is available in the dining room of the house which looks out into the private garden.

Free Wi-Fi & parking available. Advance booking essential.

Directions: Turn though the archway into Canon Lane off South Street and 4 Canon Lane is the last house on the left before the next archway.

Bedrooms: 4 x large double / twins, 3 x standard doubles & 1 x single room with disabled access.
Open: All year excluding Christmas and New Year.

Site: P Payment: Property: Children: Catering: Room:

CHICHESTER, Sussex   Map ref 2C3   S

VisitEngland ★★★★ SELF CATERING

VisitEngland Gold AWARD

Laneside

Contact: Mrs Clare Sherlock, General Manager, Millstream Hotel, Bosham Lane, Bosham, Chichester, West Sussex PO18 8HL   **T:** (01243) 573234   **F:** (01243) 573459
E: info@millstreamhotel.com   **W:** www.millstreamhotel.com   **£ BOOK ONLINE**

| Units | 3 |
| Sleeps | 2-10 |

PER UNIT PER WEEK
£350.00 - £750.00

SPECIAL PROMOTIONS
Please contact us for prices.

Three apartments, which are located just 200 metres from the shores of Chichester Harbour. Laneside is owned and managed by the Millstream Hotel - in whose AA 2 Rosette Restaurant dinner can be taken. Sleeps 10 in three units.

Open: All year.
Nearest Shop: 0.6 miles
Nearest Pub: 0.3 miles

Units: Three individual apartments, 2 x two bedroom apartments and 1 x one bedroom apartment with the bedroom on the ground floor. All with separate bathroom.

Site: ✿ Property: 🛏 Unit: 📺 📶 📀 BBQ

CHICHESTER, Sussex   Map ref 2C3   S

VisitEngland ★★★★ SELF CATERING

Matchbox Stable Cottage

Contact: Margaret Nightingill, Manager, Woodland Cottage, 21 Orchard Way, Fontwell, West Sussex BN18 0SH   **T:** (01243) 814770 / 07990 905849
E: margaretnightingill246@btinternet.com
W: www.matchboxstablecottage.co.uk   **£ BOOK ONLINE**

| Units | 1 |
| Sleeps | 2 |

PER UNIT PER WEEK
£300.00 - £475.00

A comfortable cottage for two people nestled in the downland village of Singleton in West Sussex. Originally built as stabling in 1850's the stable has been converted into a delightful flint cottage whilst keeping the unique charm of the old stables.
Ideally placed for visiting many local places of interest. The Weald and Downland Open Air Museum and West Dean Gardens are within walking distance. **Open:** All year.
Nearest Shop: 2 miles **Nearest Pub:** 900 yards

Site: **P** Property: 🛏 🛋 Unit: 🛏 🛋 📺 📀

Need more information?

Visit our websites for detailed information, up-to-date availability and to book your accommodation online. Includes over 20,000 places to stay, all of them star rated.

www.visitor-guides.co.uk

CHICHESTER, Sussex   Map ref 2C3
SatNav PO18 8HL   **H**

Millstream Hotel
Bosham Lane, Bosham Nr Chichester, West Sussex PO18 8HL **T:** (01243) 573234
F: (01243) 573459 **E:** info@millstreamhotel.com
W: www.millstreamhotel.com **£ BOOK ONLINE**

B&B PER ROOM PER NIGHT
S: £79.00 - £149.00
D: £135.00 - £245.00
HB PER PERSON PER NIGHT
£87.00 - £155.00

SPECIAL PROMOTIONS
Please contact for à la carte menu prices.

This charming English country hotel is situated in picturesque Bosham, just 4 miles west of Chichester. The bright and airy en suite bedrooms are all individually decorated. The Millstream Restaurant serves modern British cuisine and has 2 AA Rosettes. Alternatively, Marwick's Brasserie provides a contemporary and relaxed eating environment. Guests can enjoy afternoon tea in the gardens or lounge.

Directions: Please visit www.millstreamhotel.com/map

Bedrooms: Bedrooms are individually decorated, en suite, with fresh milk and water in the fridge, tea & coffee making facilities and dressing gowns.
Open: All year.

Site: ❋ P Payment: ▦ Property: ⌖ ▦ ⛨ ❂ Catering: ⟨✗ ⚑ Room: ⌇ ♨ ☎ ⎙ ♨ ▤

CHICHESTER, Sussex   Map ref 2C3
SatNav PO19 7HW   **B**

The Cottage
22B Westhampnett Road, Chichester, W. Sussex PO19 7HW **T:** (01243) 774979
E: thecottagechichester@gmail.com
W: www.chichester-bedandbreakfast.co.uk or thecottage-chichester.co.uk **£ BOOK ONLINE**

B&B PER ROOM PER NIGHT
S: £60.00 - £100.00
D: £60.00 - £100.00

Just off the A27. A short walk from the town centre with its Cathedral, cinema, bowling, shops, rail & bus stations, restaurants & pubs. Goodwood Festival of Speed & Revival, Airfield, golfing & horse racing. The Tangmere Aviation Museum.
Directions: Westhampnett Road is located on the eastern side of Chichester and is close to Portfield Retail park and Goodwood just off the A27. **Bedrooms:** 1 double, 1 twin with complimentary tea tray and TV. **Open:** All year except Christmas and New Year.

Site: P Payment: ▦ Property: ▦ Children: ⛱ Catering: ▥ Room: ♨ ⎙ ♨

CROWBOROUGH, Sussex   Map ref 2D3
S

Hodges
Contact: Mrs Hazel Colliver, Hodges, Eridge Road, Steel Cross TN6 2SS **T:** (01892) 652386 / 07887 505718 **E:** hazel.colliver@hodges.uk.com
W: www.hodges.uk.com

Units   1
Sleeps   1-3
PER UNIT PER WEEK
£375.00 - £430.00

Ground floor luxury accommodation. Kitchen. Large double bed. Superking bed/en suite. Sitting/dining room, triple aspect adjoining small sunny conservatory. Owners plantaholic garden for guest use. Perfect for NT and South Gardens
Longer lets by negotiation.
Sleeps 3.
Open: All year.
Nearest Shop: 1 mile
Nearest Pub: 1mile

Leisure: ♪ ⚲ Property: ▦

EASTBOURNE, Sussex   Map ref 2D3

SatNav BN24 5NG **C**

Fairfields Farm Caravan & Camping Park

Eastbourne Road, Westham, Pevensey BN24 5NG
T: (01323) 763165 **F:** (01323) 469175 **E:** enquiries@fairfieldsfarm.com
W: www.fairfieldsfarm.com

🚐 (60)	£18.00-£28.00	
🚍 (60)	£18.00-£28.00	
⛺ (60)	£18.00-£28.00	

60 touring pitches

SPECIAL PROMOTIONS
Special promotions available throughout the season, please contact us for more details.

A quiet country touring site on a working farm. Clean facilities, lakeside walk with farm pets and free fishing for campers. Close to the beautiful seaside resort of Eastbourne, and a good base from which to explore the diverse scenery and attractions of South East England. Overnight holding area available. Free Wi-Fi is also available on site.

Directions: From A27 Pevensey roundabout, travel through Pevensey towards castle, then through Westham. Turn left (B2191) towards Eastbourne. Over level crossing and we are on left.

Open: 1st April to 31st October.

Site: ⛺🅿 **Payment:** 💷 ☀ **Leisure:** ♪ ▶ ∪ **Children:** ⚲ **Catering:** ⚲ **Park:** 🐕 🚽 🔒 ♺ ♺
Touring: 🔘 🔘 🔘 ♨

HEATHFIELD, Sussex   Map ref 3A4

S

Graywood Canvas Cottages

Contact: Stephanie Wakeham-Dawson, Owner, Graywood Farm, Graywood Lane,
East Hoathly, East Sussex BN8 6QT **T:** 07715 630665
E: bookings@graywoodcanvascottages.co.uk
W: www.graywoodcanvascottages.co.uk **£ BOOK ONLINE**

Units	3
Sleeps	2-5

PER UNIT PER WEEK
£650.00 - £850.00

Gold standard Glamping in the heart of Sussex on a small farm. Our yurts have large windows, french doors and a clear dome for star gazing. There is a gallery bedroom and a super-king ground floor bedroom. Each yurt has an inside bathroom with shower and a complete kitchen with dishwasher and washer/dryer. Luxury sofas and hypnosis mattresses provide ultimate comfort. Full heating available. **Open:** Easter to Mid November.
Nearest Shop: 3 km **Nearest Pub:** 3 km

Site: ✿ P **Payment:** 💷 **Property:** 📱 **Children:** ⚲ 🛏 🚼 **Unit:** 🚿 ♨ 🍴 📺 ♺ 📺 📶 BBQ

HENFIELD, Sussex   Map ref 2D3

SatNav BN5 9RQ **B**

No1 The Laurels B&B

1 The Laurels, Martyn Close, Henfield, West Sussex BN5 9RQ **T:** (01273) 493518
E: bookings@no1thelaurels.co.uk
W: www.no1thelaurels.co.uk **£ BOOK ONLINE**

B&B PER ROOM PER NIGHT
S: £45.00 - £55.00
D: £80.00 - £90.00

A detached house faced with traditional knapped Sussex flint stones. Comfortable rooms, a warm welcome, easy access to Brighton. Many places of interest nearby.
Directions: Please refer to website.
Bedrooms: 1 single, 2 double and 1 twin.
Open: All year.

Site: ✿ P **Payment:** 💷 **Property:** 🖥 **Children:** ⚲ **Catering:** 🍴 **Room:** ♺ ♨ 📺

The Official Tourist Boards Guide to **Star-Rated Places to Stay 2017**

HORSHAM, Sussex Map ref 2D2

VisitEngland ★★★★ SELF CATERING

Cottesmore Lodges

Contact: Beryl Grantham-Hill, Accommodation Manager, Cottesmore Golf & Country Club, Buchan Hill, Pease Pottage, West Sussex RH11 9AT **T:** (01293) 528256 **F:** (08448) 717221
E: accommodation@cottesmoregolf.co.uk **W:** www.cottesmoregolf.co.uk

Units	7
Sleeps	1-4

PER UNIT PER WEEK
£560.00 - £800.00

The attractive and cosy self-catering Norwegian log cabins have two en suite bedrooms. The cottages overlook the fairway of Cottesmore's 8th hole on the Griffin course. Residents will be able to use all the facilities the club has to offer.
Open: All year.
Nearest Shop: 1 mile
Nearest Pub: 1/2 Mile

Site: ❀ P Payment: Leisure: Property: Children: Unit: BBQ

LEWES, Sussex Map ref 2D3

VisitEngland ★★★ SELF CATERING

White Lion Farm Cottages

Contact: Mrs Diana Green, Owner, White Lion Farm, Shortgate, East Sussex BN8 6PJ
T: (01825) 840288 **E:** dgreen384@btinternet.com
W: www.whitelionfarmcottages.co.uk

Units	2
Sleeps	2-4

PER UNIT PER WEEK
£180.00 - £310.00

Two converted holiday cottages, tastefully decorated throughout and provide comfortable accommodation for up to four people in each. Each cottage is completely separate with its own entrance, private patio and small garden with wonderful rural views and parking area. Each cottage has a spacious double bedroom, a good sized bathroom with a shower and large living room with a sofa-bed and a well equipped kitchen area with amenities.
Open: All year. **Nearest Shop:** 3 miles **Nearest Pub:** 3 miles

Site: ❀ P Leisure: Property: Children: Unit: BBQ

MAYFIELD, Sussex Map ref 2D3

VisitEngland ★★★★ SELF CATERING

Hoopers Farm Cottage

Contact: Sarah Ratcliffe, Owner, Vale Road, Mayfield, East Sussex TN20 6BD
T: (01435) 873310 / 07721 009549 **E:** info@hoopersfarmcottage.co.uk
W: www.hoopersfarmcottage.co.uk

Units	1
Sleeps	6

PER UNIT PER WEEK
£400.00 - £800.00

Mayfield, East Sussex - cosy converted barn in secluded location, within walking distance of historic village. Spectacular views across the Weald.
Open: All year.
Nearest Shop: 5 minutes
Nearest Pub: 5 minutes

Site: ❀ P Leisure: Property: Children: Unit: BBQ

MIDHURST, Sussex Map ref 2C3

VisitEngland ★★★★ SELF CATERING

Long Meadow

Contact: Bridget Adler, Long Meadow, Hoyle Lane, Heyshott, Midhurst GU29 0DX
T: (01798) 867102 / 07885 699479 **E:** mail@bridgetadler.com
W: www.selfcateringinsussex.co.uk

Units	1
Sleeps	2-6

PER UNIT PER WEEK
£450.00 - £675.00

Outstanding views, quiet, rural location, newly refurbished. Close to Midhurst, Petworth, Cowdray Park, Goodwood, Chichester and the Coast. There is an upstairs double bedroom with en suite shower room and a downstairs twin bedroom with bathroom. Separate well equipped kitchen, sitting room with dining area.
Well presented with off road parking. **Open:** All year.
Nearest Shop: 4 miles
Nearest Pub: 1 mile

WALKERS FAMILIES CYCLISTS Site: ❀ P Property: Unit: BBQ

Rye Lodge Hotel

Hilders Cliff, Rye, East Sussex TN31 7LD **T:** (01797) 223838 **F:** (01797) 223585
E: info@ryelodge.co.uk
W: www.ryelodge.co.uk **£ BOOK ONLINE**

B&B PER ROOM PER NIGHT
D: £130.00 - £250.00

SPECIAL PROMOTIONS
Book direct via our
website and save 10%
with discount code
"DIRECT10"

Staying at Rye Lodge is always an enjoyable experience at any time of the year. The surroundings are elegant, the atmosphere relaxed - and the service second to none! Luxurious rooms and suites furnished to the highest standards with all the little extras that make such a difference. Award-winning restaurant, Leisure Centre with swimming pool and Sauna. Private car park.

Directions: Please visit:
www.ryelodge.co.uk/rye-lodge-maps

Bedrooms: All rooms en suite with shower or bath.
Open: All year.

Site: P Payment: 🖃 **Leisure:** 🏊 ♨ ♨ **Property:** 🐕 🖥 🏛 **Children:** ⛱ 🛏 🧒 **Catering:** (✗ 🍷 🍴
Room: 🍵 🚽 📞 📺 🔌

The Quarter House

Contact: Sally Bayly, Owner, Rye Cottages, The Mint, Rye TN31 7EN **T:** (01797) 222498 / 07956 280257 **E:** info@ryecottages.net
W: www.ryecottages.net / www.cottages4you.co.uk/cottages/the-quarter-house-25320

Units   1
Sleeps   1-4

PER UNIT PER WEEK
£290.00 - £650.00

SPECIAL PROMOTIONS
Short breaks available.

Enchanting Grade II listed 17th century 2-storey apartment in the heart of Medieval Rye. Original beams & floorboards, open log fire, Jacuzzi bath & Wi-Fi. Wander Rye's cobbled streets & Church Square, visit its historic pubs, restaurants, tea shops, art galleries, antique & boutique shops, & independent cinema & café

All within easy reach are Kent & Sussex walks & bike paths; beautiful beaches, wind/kite surfing, dinghy sailing/kayaking; Dungeness & Rye Harbour Nature Reserves & Bird Sanctuaries; the historic towns of Battle, Hastings and Canterbury; & Bodiam, Leeds & Dover Castles.

Open: All year.
Nearest Shop: 0.01 miles
Nearest Pub: 0.01 miles

Units: Both bedrooms are on the top floor & are separated by a large chimney breast & the stairs, so there is visual privacy but sound may carry.

Leisure: 🚲 🎣 ♨ **Property:** 🐕 🖥 🏛 **Children:** ⛱ 🛏 **Unit:** 🖥 🔌 📺 🔌 📀 ⌀

RYE, Sussex Map ref 3B4
SatNav TN31 7EL **H**

VisitEngland
★★★
HOTEL

The River Haven Hotel
Quayside, Winchelsea Road, Rye TN31 7EL **T:** (01797) 227982 **F:** (01797) 227983
E: info@riverhaven.co.uk
W: www.riverhaven.co.uk **£ BOOK ONLINE**

B&B PER ROOM PER NIGHT
S: £60.00 - £85.00
D: £80.00 - £110.00
HB PER PERSON PER NIGHT
£58.50 - £73.50

Family-run hotel with restaurant. English breakfast, flat screen Freeview TVs, en suite bathrooms. Standard, superior & garden rooms with river views. Special breaks. Disability-friendly. Large car park free parking for guests. **Directions:** From Channel Ports & London M20 to exit 10 to Brenzett. Take A259 to Rye and follow ring road. Hotel is adjacent to the Quay.
Bedrooms: 13 double, 3 twin, 6 family.
Open: All year except Christmas.

Site: ✿ Payment: 💳 Leisure: ⚹ ♪ ▸ Property: ⚓ 🖥 ● Children: ⛱ 🏠 ⚘ Catering: 🍷 🍴 Room: ☕ ⚘ 📞 📺 ⚒

SELSEY, Sussex Map ref 2C3
S

VisitEngland
★★★★★
HOLIDAY PARK

Green Lawns Holiday Park (Bunn Leisure)
Contact: Paddock Lane, Selsey, Chichester, West Sussex PO20 9EJ **T:** (01243) 606080
F: (01243) 606068 **E:** holidays@bunnleisure.co.uk
W: www.bunnleisure.co.uk **£ BOOK ONLINE**

Units   10
Sleeps   8

PER UNIT PER WEEK
£220.00 - £1075.00

SPECIAL PROMOTIONS
From £130.

The smallest and most peaceful park, offers leafy lanes, duck ponds and open green spaces, but with access to all Bunn Leisure's facilities and entertainment. Enjoy everything on offer with top class facilities, indoor & outdoor swimming pools, gym, kids clubs, TV character visits, evening entertainment from top acts such as Billy Ocean, The Three Degrees and Leo Sayer. Enjoy the many food outlets and restaurants, free park bus and Bunni Express.

Directions: From A27 Chichester by pass take B2145 to Selsey, West Sussex. Green Lawns is on your right just before you enter the town.

Open: March to January.
Nearest Shop: 100 metres
Nearest Pub: 100 metres

Payment: 💳 Leisure: ⚹ ♪ ▸ ∪ ⚲ ❄ ⚱ ⚲ Property: 🐕 🖥 🗑 🖳 📱 Children: ⛱ 🏠 ⚘
Unit: 🗄 🖥 📺 📀

f ▸

For **key to symbols** see page 6

SatNav PO20 9EL [C]

★★★★★
TOURING PARK

Warner Farm Camping & Touring Park

Warner Lane, Selsey, Chichester, West Sussex PO20 9EL
T: (01243) 604499 **E:** touring@bunnleisure.co.uk
W: www.warnerfarm.co.uk

🚐 (80)   £20.00-£67.50
🚎 (50)   £20.00-£67.50
⛺ (120)   £20.00-£40.00
250 touring pitches

Great value, fun filled family camping & touring holidays. Well maintained standard, electric and full services pitches. Stay here and make the most of all Bunn Leisure's facilities and entertainment. Enjoy everything on offer, indoor & outdoor swimming pools, gym, kids clubs, TV character visits, evening entertainment from top acts such as Billy Ocean, The Three Degrees and Leo Sayer. Enjoy the many food outlets and restaurants, free park bus and Bunni Express.

Directions: From A27 Chichester by-pass take B2145 to Selsey. Warner Farm is clearly signed on the right once you are in town.

Open: March to January.

Site: 📷 **Payment:** 💷 ☼ **Leisure:** ♿ ♪ ▶ ∪ 🔍 ≶ ⚲ ⚲ **Children:** ⛄ ⚲ **Catering:** ✕ 🍴
Park: 🐾 ♪ 🖥 🗄 📠 🚿 **Touring:** 🔌 🚻 🚿 🚿

[S]

★★★★
HOLIDAY PARK

West Sands Holiday Park (Bunn Leisure)

Contact: Mill Lane, Selsey, Chichester, West Sussex PO20 9BH **T:** (01243) 606080
F: (01243) 606068 **E:** holidays@bunnleisure.co.uk
W: www.bunnleisure.co.uk **£ BOOK ONLINE**

Units   140
Sleeps   6-10

PER UNIT PER WEEK
£220.00 - £1075.00

SPECIAL PROMOTIONS
Short breaks from only
£130.

The liveliest of our 4 parks on the South Coast offering family fun in a fantastic seaside location with a mile long stretch of glorious beach.

We offer top class facilities, indoor and outdoor swimming pools, kids clubs, TV character visits, evening entertainment from top acts such as Billy Ocean, The Three Degrees and Leo Sayer. Enjoy a range of eating out experiences at the many food outlets, take advantage of the free park bus and Bunni Express.

Directions: From A27 Chichester by-pass take B2145 to Selsey. West Sands is clearly signed on right once you are in the town.

Open: March to January.
Nearest Shop: 100 metres
Nearest Pub: 100 metres

Ⓕ Ⓣ

Payment: 💷 **Leisure:** ♿ ♪ ▶ ∪ 🔍 ≶ ⚲ ⚲ **Property:** 🐾 🖥 🗄 📠 **Children:** ⛄

SELSEY, Sussex Map ref 2C3

White Horse Holiday Park (Bunn Leisure)

Contact: Paddock Lane, Selsey, Chichester, West Sussex PO20 9EJ **T:** (01243) 606080
F: (01243) 606068 **E:** holidays@bunnleisure.co.uk
W: www.bunnleisure.co.uk **£ BOOK ONLINE**

VisitEngland ★★★★ HOLIDAY PARK

Units 10
Sleeps 6

PER UNIT PER WEEK
£220.00 - £1075.00

SPECIAL PROMOTIONS
From £130.00.

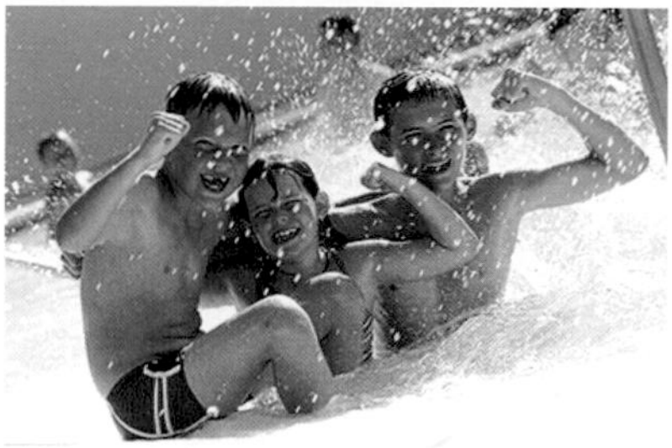

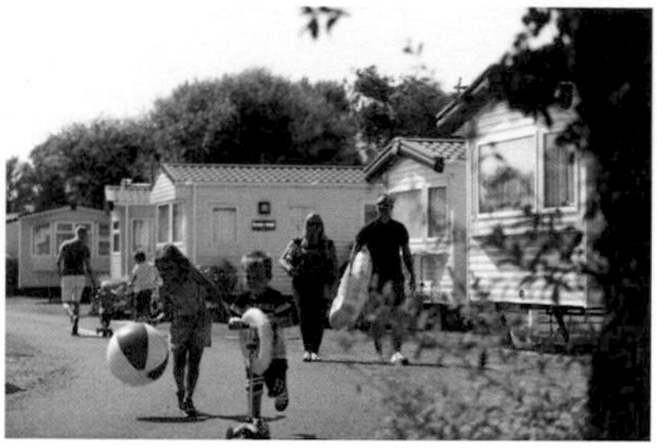

With its coveted award for its traditional atmosphere, White Horse Holiday Park is perfect for families, but with access to all that Bunn Leisure has to offer.

Enjoy the top class facilities, indoor & outdoor swimming pools, gym, kids clubs, TV character visits, evening entertainment from top acts such as Billy Ocean, The Three Degrees and Leo Sayer. Enjoy the many food outlets and restaurants, free park bus and Bunni Express.

Directions: From A27 Chichester by-pass take the B2145 to Selsey and enter via Green Lawns Holiday Park which is on the right just before entering the town.

Open: March to January.
Nearest Shop: 100 metres
Nearest Pub: 100 metres

Payment: **Leisure:** **Property:** **Children:**

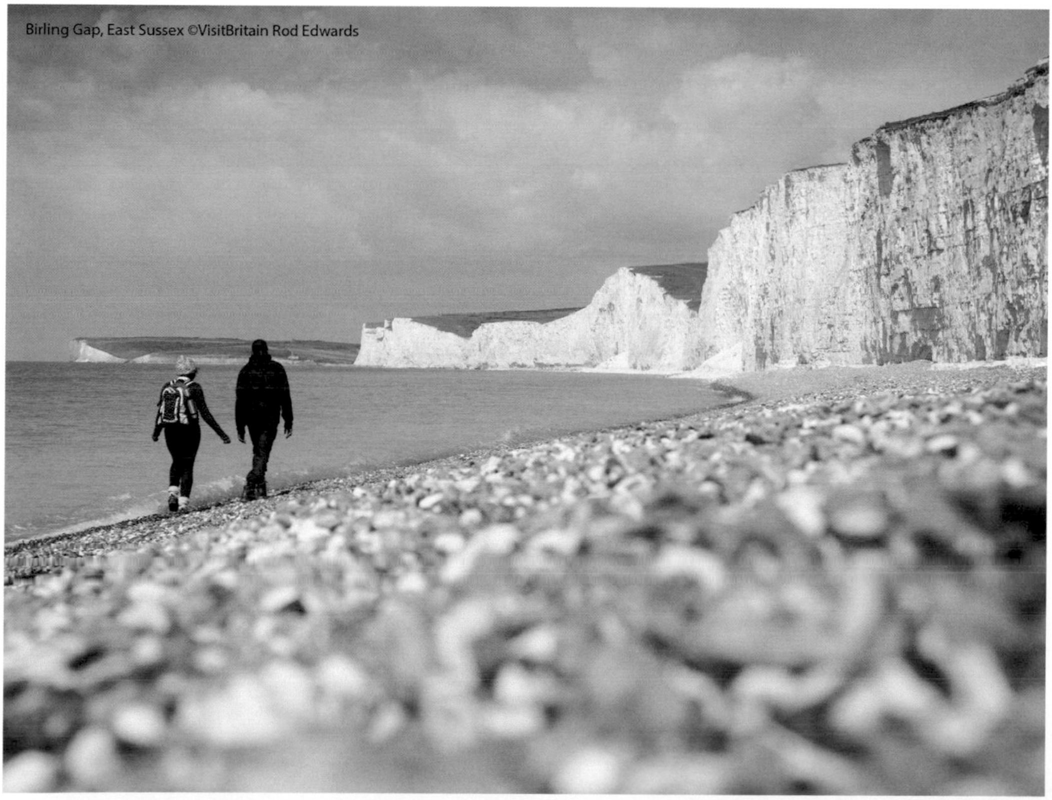

Birling Gap, East Sussex ©VisitBritain Rod Edwards

Don't Miss...

Buckingham Palace

London, SW1A 1AA
(020) 7766 7300
www.royalcollection.org.uk
Buckingham Palace is the office and London residence of Her Majesty
The Queen. It is one of the few working royal palaces remaining in the
world today. The State Rooms are used extensively by The Queen and
Members of the Royal Family and during August and September, when
The Queen makes her annual visit to Scotland, the Palace's nineteen
state rooms are open to visitors.

Houses of Parliament

Westminster, London SW1A 0AA
(020) 7219 4114
www.parliament.uk/visiting
Tours offer a unique combination of one thousand years of history,
modern day politics, and stunning art and architecture. Visit the Queen's
Robing Room, the Royal Gallery and the Commons Chamber, scene
of many lively debates. Stylish afternoon tea in the Terrace Pavillion
overlooking the River Thames can be added to many tours.

Madame Tussauds

Marylebone Road, London, NW1 5LR
(0871) 894 3000
www.madametussauds.com/London/
Experience the legendary history, glitz and glamour of Madame
Tussauds London. Visit the 14 exciting, interactive zones and come face-
to-face with some of the world's most famous stars. From Shakespeare to
David Beckham you'll meet leading figures from sport, showbiz, politics
and even royalty. Strike a pose with Usain Bolt, get up close and personal
with One Direction, receive a royal audience with Her Majesty the
Queen, or even plant a cheeky kiss on Prince Harry's cheek.

National Gallery

Westminster WC2N 5DN
(020) 7747 2885
www.nationalgallery.org.uk
Founded in 1824, housing one of the greatest collections of Western
European painting in the world, with over 2,300 paintings dating from
the mid-13th century to 1900. Discover inspiring art by world-class artists
including Botticelli, Caravaggio, Leonardo da Vinci, Monet, Raphael,
Rembrandt, Titian, Vermeer and Van Gogh. The Gallery aims to encourage
the widest possible access to the pictures as well as studying and caring
for the collection, which is on show 361 days a year, free of charge.

Natural History Museum

Kensington and Chelsea SW7 5BD
(020) 7942 5000
www.nhm.ac.uk
The world's most prestigious and pre-eminent museum of natural
history, exhibiting a vast range of specimens from various segments of
natural history. Revealing how the jigsaw of life fits together - animal,
vegetable or mineral, the best of our planet's most amazing treasures are
here for you to see - for free. Alongside the collection, a packed calendar
of year round activities, temporary exhibitions and special events as
diverse as David Attenborough's virtual reality Great Barrier Reef dive
and Crime Scene Live, an interactive night at the museum combining
real science and crime fiction, offers something for everyone.

London

Grand landmarks, gorgeous gardens, spectacular shopping, exciting attractions, museums, galleries, theatres, sporting venues and all the buzz and history of one of the world's greatest capital cities - London's treasures are beyond measure. A single trip is never enough and you'll find yourself returning time and again to take in the many unforgettable sights and experiences on offer.

London

Explore – London

In the Central/West End area the most visited sights are the now public rooms of Buckingham Palace, the National Gallery in Trafalgar Square, Tate Britain on Millbank, Westminster Abbey, Houses of Parliament and Cabinet War Rooms.

Westminster Abbey, nearly a thousand years old, has tombs of many English kings, queens, statesmen and writers. The British Museum in Bloomsbury houses one of the world's largest elections of antiquities, including the Magna Carta, the Elgin Marbles and the first edition of Alice in Wonderland. This entire area can be viewed from The London Eye on the South Bank.

No visit to London is complete without a spot of shopping. Head for bustling Oxford Street and the stylish shops on Regent Street and Bond Street, check out the trendy boutiques around Carnaby Street, or visit the iconic Liberty store.

For entertainment, enjoy a wide range of theatre, bars, restaurants and culture in Covent Garden and don't forget to take in a musical or an offbeat play and the amazing nightime atmosphere around Leicester Square. Madame Tussauds features all your favourite celebrities and super heroes, or if you fancy an historical fright, visit the London Dungeon near Tower Bridge or explore the streets of old London on a Jack-the-Ripper tour. London's parks are its green lungs. St James, the oldest, was founded by Henry VIII in 1532. Hyde Park, bordering Kensington, Mayfair and Marylebone, is the largest at 630 acres and one of the greatest city parks in the world. You can enjoy any number of outdoor activities, visit the Serpentine Galleries for contemporary art or Speakers' Corner, the most famous location for free speech in the world. Regents Park, with its zoo and outdoor theatre, lies north of Oxford Circus and was given to the nation by the Prince Regent.

In the North of the capital, trendy Camden is an eclectic mix of intriguing and unique experiences. Locals and visitors alike hunt for vintage treasures in the open air markets at Camden Lock and far-out attire in the alternative shops that line the high street, or spend time celebrity spotting or strolling along Regent's Canal. There's a different kind of food at every turn, from street vendors to swanky sushi restaurants, and Camden is also home to an extraordinary array of bars, live music and arts venues including the Roundhouse.

Heading East, St Pauls Cathedral in the city of London was redesigned by Sir Christopher Wren and the nearby the Tower of London, a medieval fortress dominated by the White Tower and dating from 1097, houses The Crown Jewels, guarded by the famous Beefeaters. Even further East, the Queen Elizabeth Olympic Park is the exciting legacy of the 2012 Olympic Games and is situated at the heart of a new, vibrant East London.

To the South East of the capital, Canary Wharf is one of London's main financial centres and contains many of Europe's tallest buildings, including the second-tallest in Great Britain, One Canada Square. Take a trip up the tallest tallest building in Great Britain, the Shard, to pick out all the landmarks and trace the Thames all the way to the sea. On the south bank, opposite Docklands, attractions include the National Maritime Museum incorporating the Royal Greenwich Observatory, the Cutty Sark and The O2, one of London's premier entertainment venues.

In November, the Lord Mayors Show will feature a parade of over 6,000 people, military marching bands, acrobats, a procession of decorated floats, a gilded State Coach that the Lord Mayor travels and starts with an RAF flypast. After the procession London's City Guides will be on hand to lead free guided tours of the City's more strange and wonderful corners, and in the evening fireworks will light up the sky over the river. Visit their website for more information, www.lordmayorsshow.org.

Visit – London

 Attractions with this sign participate in the Visitor Attraction Quality Assurance Scheme.

Apsley House
Westminster W1J 7NT
(020) 7499 5676
www.english-heritage.org.uk
This great 18th century town house pays homage to the Duke's dazzling military career, which culminated in his victory at Waterloo in 1815.

Bank of England Museum
Bartholomew Lane, London EC2R 8AH
(020) 7601 5545
www.bankofengland.co.uk/museum
Housed within the impressive walls of the Bank of England, this fascinating museum takes you through the history of the bank since its foundation in 1694 to its role today as the nation's central bank.

Bateaux London Restaurant Cruisers
Westminster WC2N 6NU
(020) 3504 8278
www.bateauxlondon.com
Bateaux London offers lunch and dinner cruises, combining luxury dining, world-class live entertainment and five-star customer care.

The Boat Race
April, Putney Bridge
www.theboatrace.org
Boat crews from the universities of Oxford and Cambridge battle it out on the Thames.

British Museum
Camden WC1B 3DG
(020) 7323 8299
www.britishmuseum.org
Collections that span over two million years of human history and culture, all under one roof.

Changing the Guard
Buckingham Palace, London SW1A 1AA
www.changing-guard.com
Watch the Changing the Guard ceremony at Buckingham Palace for an impressive display of British pomp and ceremony at 11.30am every day.

Chinese New Year
January, Various venues
www.visitlondon.com/tag/chinese-new-year
London's Chinese New Year celebrations are the largest outside Asia, with parades, performances and fireworks.

Chiswick House
Chiswick, London W4 2RP
(020) 8995 0508
www.chgt.org.uk
Among the most glorious examples of 18th century British architecture, the celebrated villa of Lord Burlington with impressive grounds, features Italianate garden with statues, temples, obelisks and urns. The gardens are the birthplace of the English Landscape Movement and have inspired countless gardens.

Churchill Museum and Cabinet War Rooms
Westminster SW1A 2AQ
(020) 7930 6961
www.iwm.org.uk/visits/churchill-war-rooms
Learn more about the man who inspired Britain's finest hour at the highly interactive and innovative Churchill Museum, the world's first major museum dedicated to life of the 'greatest Briton'. Step back in time and discover the secret.

Cutty Sark King
William Walk, London SE10 9HT
www.rmg.co.uk/cutty-sark
Discover what life was like on board the legendary sailing ship Cutty Sark, the world's sole surviving tea clipper, and fastest ship of her time - now an award-winning visitor attraction.

Eltham Palace
Greenwich SE9 5QE
(020) 8294 2548
www.english-heritage.org.uk
A spectacular fusion of 1930s Art Deco villa and magnificent 15th century Great Hall. Surrounded by period gardens.

The Globe Theatre
Bankside, London SE1 9DT
(020) 7902 1400
www.shakespearesglobe.com
Globe Exhibition & Tour and Globe Education seek to further the experience and international understanding of Shakespeare in performance.

Goldsmiths Hall
Foster Lane, London EC2V 6BN
(020) 7606 7010
www.thegoldsmiths.co.uk
One of the Twelve Great Livery Companies of the City of London. The Goldsmiths' Company, based at the magnificent Goldsmiths' Hall in the City of London, regularly holds exhibitions and events to promote contemporary jewellers and silversmiths.

Greenwich Heritage Centre
Greenwich SE18 4DX
(020) 8854 2452
www.greenwichheritage.org
Local history museum with displays of archaeology, natural history and geology. Also temporary exhibitions, schools service, sales point and Saturday club.

Hampton Court Palace
Richmond upon Thames KT8 9AU
(020) 3166 6000
www.hrp.org.uk/hampton-court-palace
This magnificent palace set in delightful gardens was famously one of Henry VIII's favourite palaces.

HMS Belfast
Southwark SE1 2JH
(020) 7940 6300
www.iwm.org.uk/visits/hms-belfast
HMS Belfast, launched 1938, served throughout WWII, playing a leading part in the destruction of the German battle cruiser Scharnhorst and in the Normandy Landings.

Hyde Park
London W2 2UH
(0300) 061 2114
www.royalparks.org.uk/parks/hyde-park
Explore one of the greatest city parks in the world, with outdoor sports, a spectacular children's playground, a packed calendar of open air events and a number of fascinating buildings and monuments, such as The Serpentine Bridge, the famous Archiles statue and the Diana Memorial Fountain.

Imperial War Museum
Southwark SE1 6HZ
(020) 7416 5000
www.iwm.org.uk/visits/iwm-london
This award-winning museum tells the story of conflict involving Britain and the Commonwealth since 1914. See thousands of imaginatively displayed exhibits, from art to aircraft, utility clothes to U-boats.

Kensington Palace State Apartments
Kensington and Chelsea W8 4PX
(020) 3166 6000
www.hrp.org.uk/kensington-palace
Home to the Royal Ceremonial Dress Collection, which includes some of Queen Elizabeth II's dresses worn throughout her reign, as well as 14 of Diana, Princess of Wales' evening dresses.

Kenwood House
Camden NW3 7JR
(020) 8348 1286
www.english-heritage.org.uk/visit/places/kenwood
Beautiful 18th century villa with fine interiors, and a world class collection of paintings. Also fabulous landscaped gardens and an award-winning restaurant.

London Dungeon
County Hall, Riverside Building SE1 7PB
0871 423 2240
www.thedungeons.com/London
Exciting, scary and fun - the London Dungeon has a new home on the Southbank and lots of new scary stories about London's history for you to discover. Steel your nerves for some terrifying new experiences and hrilling new scary rides!

London Eye River Cruise Experience
Lambeth SE1 7PB
(0871) 781 3000
www.londoneye.com
See London from a different perspective and enjoy a unique 40 minute circular sightseeing cruise on the river Thames.

London Fashion Week Festival
Febuary, 180 Strand WC2R
www.londonfashionweekfestival.com
London's largest and most exclusive designer shopping event. This four-day showcase brings you the ultimate fashion experience.

London Festival of Architecture
June, Various locations
www.londonfestivalofarchitecture.org
A city-wide celebration of architectural experimentation, thinking and practice. See London's buildings in a new light during the Festival of Architecture.

London Film Festival
October, Various venues
www.bfi.org.uk/lff
A two-week showcase of the world's best new films, the BFI London Film Festival is one of the most anticipated events in London's cultural calendar, screening more than 300 features, documentaries and shorts from almost 50 countries.

London Transport Museum
Westminster WC2E 7BB
(020) 7379 6344
www.ltmuseum.co.uk
The history of transport for everyone, from spectacular vehicles, special exhibitions, actors and guided tours to film shows, gallery talks and children's craft workshops.

London Wetland Centre
Richmond upon Thames SW13 9WT
(020) 8409 4400
www.wwt.org.uk/wetland-centres/london
A unique wildlife visitor attraction just 25 minutes from central London. Run by the Wildfowl and Wetlands Trust (WWT), it is acclaimed as the best urban site in Europe to watch wildlife. Stroll among the lakes, ponds and gardens.

London Zoo
Regent's Park, London NW1 4RY
(020) 7722 3333
www.zsl.org/zsl-london-zoo
Come face to face with some of the hairiest, scariest, tallest and smallest animals on the planet - right in the heart of the capital.

Lord's Tour
Westminster NW8 8QN
(020) 7616 8500
www.lords.org/lords/things-to-do/tours-of-lords
Guided tour of Lord's Cricket Ground including the Long Room, MCC Museum, Real Tennis Court, Mound Stand and Indoor School.

Museums At Night
May, Various venues
www.museumsatnight.org.uk
Explore arts and heritage after dark at museums across London. Packed with special events, from treasure trails to pyjama parties, Museums at Night is a great opportunity to explore culture in a new light.

Museum of London
City of London EC2Y 5HN
(020) 7001 9844
www.museumoflondon.org.uk
Step inside Museum of London for an unforgettable journey through the capital's turbulent past.

National Maritime Museum
Greenwich SE10 9NF
(020) 8312 6565
www.rmg.co.uk/national-maritime-museum
Britain's seafaring history housed in an impressive modern museum. Themes include exploration, Nelson, trade and empire, passenger shipping, luxury liners, maritime London, costume, art and the sea, the future and environmental issues.

National Portrait Gallery
Westminster WC2H 0HE
(020) 7306 0055
www.npg.org.uk
The National Portrait Gallery houses the world's largest collection of portraits. Visitors come face to face with the people who have shaped British history from Elizabeth I to David Beckham. Entrance is free.

Notting Hill Carnival

August, Various venues

www.visitlondon.com

Join London's biggest street party as the Notting Hill Carnival fills the streets of West London with Caribbean colours, music and tempting food stalls. A spectacular event!

RHS Chelsea Flower Show

May, Royal Hospital Chelsea

www.rhs.org.uk/shows-events/rhs-chelsea-flower-show

Experience the greatest flower show in the world at London's Royal Hospital Chelsea. The Chelsea Flower Show has been held in the grounds of the Royal Hospital Chelsea, London every year since 1913, apart from gaps during the two World Wars. Once Britain's largest flower show, it is still the most prestigious.

Ride London 2017

July, London

www.prudentialridelondon.co.uk

RideLondon is the world's greatest festival of cycling and takes place the weekend immediately after the Tour de France. With several events to enjoy on closed roads over a summer weekend in July there's really something for everyone.

Royal Academy of Arts

Piccadilly, London W1J 0BD

(020) 7300 8000

www.royalacademy.org.uk

Located in the heart of London, with a varied programme of exciting exhibitions and events, the Royal Academy of Arts has something for everyone in 2017.

Royal Air Force Museum Hendon

Barnet NW9 5LL

(020) 8205 2266

www.rafmuseum.org.uk

Take off to the Royal Air Force Museum, located on the former Hendon Aerodrome, and flypast the history of aviation with an exciting display of suspended aircraft, touch screen technology, simulator rides, hands-on section, film shows, licensed restaurant.

Royal Observatory Greenwich

Greenwich SE10 8XJ

(020) 8312 6565

www.rmg.co.uk/royal-observatury

Stand on the Greenwich Meridian Line, Longitude Zero, which divides East and West. Watch the time-ball fall at 1 o'clock, and explore your place in the universe at London's only planetarium.

Science Museum

Kensington and Chelsea SW7 2DD

0333 241 4000

www.sciencemuseum.org.uk

The Science Museum is world-renowned for its historic collections, awe-inspiring galleries, family activities and exhibitions - and it's free!

Somerset House

Westminster WC2R 1LA

(020) 7845 4600

www.somersethouse.org.uk

This magnificent 18th century building houses the celebrated collections of the Courtauld Institute of Art Gallery, Gilbert Collection and Hermitage Rooms. During summer months 55 fountains dance in the courtyard, and in winter you can skate on one of London's favourite ice rinks.

Southbank Centre

Lambeth SE1 8XX

(020) 7960 4200

www.southbankcentre.co.uk

A unique arts centre with 21 acres of creative space, including the Royal Festival Hall, Queen Elizabeth Hall and The Hayward.

Southwark Cathedral

Southwark SE1 9DA

(020) 7367 6700

www.cathedral.southwark.anglican.org

Oldest Gothic church in London (c.1220) with interesting memorials connected with the Elizabethan theatres of Bankside.

Tate Britain

Westminster SW1P 4RG

(020) 7887 8888

www.tate.org.uk/visit/tate-britain

Presenting the world's greatest collection of British art in a dynamic series of new displays and exhibitions.

Tate Modern
Southwark SE1 9TG
(020) 7887 8888
www.tate.org.uk/visit/tate-modern
The national gallery of international modern art and is one of London's top free attractions. Packed with challenging modern art and housed within a disused power station on the south bank of the River Thames.

Tower Bridge Exhibition

Southwark SE1 2UP
(020) 7403 3761
www.towerbridge.org.uk
Inside Tower Bridge Exhibition you will travel up to the high-level walkways, located 140 feet above the Thames and witness stunning panoramic views of London before visiting the Victorian Engine Rooms.

Tower of London
Tower Hamlets EC3N 4AB
(020) 3166 6000
www.hrp.org.uk/tower-of-london
The Tower of London spans over 900 years of British history. Fortress, palace, prison, arsenal and garrison, it is one of the most famous fortified buildings in the world, and houses the Crown Jewels, armouries, Yeoman Warders and ravens.

Victoria and Albert Museum
Kensington and Chelsea SW7 2RL
(020) 7942 2000
www.vam.ac.uk
The V&A is the world's greatest museum of art and design, with collections unrivalled in their scope and diversity.

The View from The Shard
London SE1 9SG
(08444) 997111
www.theviewfromtheshard.com
The View from The Shard is the premium visitor attraction at the top of Western Europe's tallest building, and London's newest landmark, The Shard, designed by Master Architect Renzo Piano.

Virgin Money London Marathon
April, Various venues
www.virginmoneylondonmarathon.com
Whether you run, walk or cheer from the sidelines, this is a London sporting institution you won't want to miss.

Wembley Stadium Tours

Brent HA9 0WS
0800 169 9933
www.wembleystadium.com/wembley-tours.aspx
Until your dream comes true, there's only one way to experience what it's like winning at Wembley - take the tour.

William Morris Gallery
Lloyd Park, Forest Road, Walthamstow E17 4PP
(020) 8496 4390
www.wmgallery.org.uk
The William Morris Gallery is devoted to the life and legacy of one of Britain's most remarkable designers and is housed in the grade II* listed Georgian house that was his family home in North-East London from 1848 to 1856.

Wimbledon Lawn Tennis Championships
July, Wimbledon
www.wimbledon.com
(020) 8944 1066
The world of tennis descends on Wimbledon in South West London every summer for two weeks of tennis, strawberries and cream, and good-natured queuing.

Wimbledon Lawn Tennis Museum

Merton SW19 5AG
(020) 8944 1066
www.wimbledon.com/en_GB/museum_and_tours/index.html
A collection of memorabilia dating from 1555, including Championship Trophies, Art Gallery, and special exhibitions, reflecting the game and championships of today.

Tourist Information Centres

When you arrive at your destination,
visit a Tourist Information Centre for quality assured
help with accommodation and information about local
attractions and events, or email your request before you go.

City of London
St Paul's Churchyard
(020) 7332 3456
pro@cityoflondon.gov.uk

Greenwich
Pepys House
0870 608 2000
tic@visitgreenwich.org.uk

Harrow
Gayton Library
(020) 8427 6012
gayton.library@harrow.gov.uk

Regional Contacts and Information

Find everything you need to plan your trip on visitlondon. com, the official London website. Here you can download free London maps and guides: transport maps of London, the latest London Planner and the Welcome to London Guide. We do not mail out printed maps and guides as all our London guides, news, editorial and listings are available for free online.

For more information while you're in London, visit one of London's Tourist Information Centres or download our free Official London Cityguide App.

Travel and Transport in London
If you have questions about travelling in London, including Oyster cards, ticket prices, journey planning, booking a taxi and the congestion charge, please visit the Transport for London website or call 0343 222 1234 or Textphone 020 7918 3015.

Stay – London

Entries appear alphabetically by town name in each county. A key to symbols appears on page 6

LONDON, Inner London Map ref 2D2 SatNav WC2R 0JJ H

Strand Palace Hotel
372 Strand, London WC2R 0JJ T: (020) 7379 4737
E: reservations@strandpalacehotel.co.uk
W: strandpalacehotel.co.uk £ BOOK ONLINE

Historic hotel in the heart of the West End, close to the City. Contemporary rooms are complemented by award-winning restaurants serving British and Indian cuisine, a gin cocktail bar and superb afternoon teas. Meeting venues available.
Directions: Minutes from Charing Cross, Waterloo, Embankment, Covent Garden and Temple stations. Well served by many bus routes, plus taxi drop off and pick up.
Bedrooms: Single, twin, double & king rooms. A/C offered.
Open: All year.

Payment: Leisure: Property: Children: Catering: Room:

LONDON E4, Inner London Map ref 2D2 SatNav E4 7RA C

Lee Valley Campsite - Sewardstone
Sewardstone Road, Chingford, London E4 7RA
T: (020) 8529 5689 F: (020) 8559 4070
E: sewardstonecampsite@vibrantpartnerships.co.uk
W: www.visitleevalley.org.uk/wheretostay £ BOOK ONLINE

(65)	£14.50-£22.50	
(65)	£14.50-£22.50	
(35)	£14.50-£22.50	
(17)	£35.00-£45.00	

65 touring pitches

Lee Valley Campsite, Sewardstone is less than 40 minutes from central London and is close to the scenic Hertfordshire and Essex countryside. Come camping, caravanning or stay in one of our cosy cocoons or woodland cabins – it's perfect for families, couples or groups of friends looking for affordable accommodation in London.

Directions: The campsite is situated on the A112 between Chingford and Waltham Abbey to the South of the M25. Leave M25 at junction 26 and follow the signs. **Open:** 1st March to 31st January.

Site: Payment: Leisure: Children: Catering: Park: Touring:

LONDON N4, Inner London Map ref 2D2 SatNav N4 2LX H

Kent Hall Hotel
414 Seven Sisters Road, Finsbury Park, London N4 2LX T: (020) 8802 0800
F: (020) 8802 9070 E: info@kenthallhotel.co.uk
W: www.kenthallhotel.co.uk £ BOOK ONLINE

B&B PER ROOM PER NIGHT
S: £50.00 - £55.00
D: £60.00 - £70.00

Budget hotel located next to Manor House Station (Piccadilly Line Zone 2). 15 minutes from Central London by Tube. Within walking distance of Arsenal Football Stadium. Direct from Heathrow and Eurostar terminals. For Groups and Tourists.
Directions: Exit 5 from Manor House station - Piccadilly Line.
Bedrooms: All room have private bathroom, TV, fridge, Wi-Fi.
Open: All year. 24 hours per day.

Site: P Payment: Property: Children: Room:

Lee Valley Camping and Caravan Park - Edmonton

Meridian Way, Edmonton, London N9 0AR
T: (020) 8803 6900 **F:** (020) 8884 4975 **E:** edmontoncampsite@vibrantpartnerships.co.uk
W: www.visitleevalley.org.uk/wheretostay **£ BOOK ONLINE**

VisitEngland
★★★
TOURING & CAMPING PARK

🚐 (100)   £14.50-£22.50
🚎 (100)   £14.50-£22.50
🅰 (60)   £14.50-£22.50
🏠 (12)   £245.00-£315.00
100 touring pitches

SPECIAL PROMOTIONS
Please visit our website to view our special offers which run throughout the year.

A peaceful site that puts you in easy each of both central London and the many attractions of Lee Valley Regional Park. With excellent facilities including an on-site shop and children's play area, plus an 18 hole golf and FootGolf course, athletics centre and cinema all located within the complex. Overnight holding area available.

Directions: Leave M25 at J25, follow signs for City. Turn left for Freezywater at traffic lights, follow signs for Lee Valley Leisure Complex.

Open: All year.

Site: 🅰🅿 Payment: 💷 ☼ Leisure: 🎣 🏌 ∪ Children: 🛝 🎠 Catering: 🛒 Park: 🐾 🚽 🚿 🛁 🛉 Touring: 🔌 🔥 💧 ✐

The Old Bakery

Contact: The Old Bakery, Hoppers Road, Winchmore Hill, Enfield, London N21 3NF
T: 07979 637480 (please use text message if possible) **E:** enquiry@oldbakerylondon.co.uk
W: www.oldbakerylondon.co.uk

VisitEngland
★★★★
SELF CATERING

VisitEngland
Gold
AWARD

Units   2
Sleeps   2-4

PER UNIT PER WEEK
£500.00 - £950.00

SPECIAL PROMOTIONS
Please call for more information.

THE OLD BAKERY is an historic house in the Conservation area of Winchmore Hill, a leafy North London suburb with excellent shops, cafés, restaurants and pubs. We are 2 minutes from a station and 30 from London's theatres and museums. We offer two high quality apartments.

CHALKLEY'S APARTMENT (sleeps 4) is in the most historic part of the Old Bakery, dating from circa 1000AD. Beautiful brick fireplaces and beamed ceilings make for an atmospheric holiday home, with elegant furniture, designer fabrics and contemporary bathrooms and kitchen. 4* Gold Award.

THE STABLES COTTAGE (sleeps 2) is a romantic hideaway for two in the secluded, walled garden of The Old Bakery with direct access to the street. The cottage is stylishly furnished and well equipped and has its own patio area. The bedroom is in the eaves.

Open: All year.
Nearest Shop: 75 yards
Nearest Pub: 150 yards

Units: The Stables sleeps 2 and Chalkley's sleeps up to 4 and they both have a minimum stay of 4 nights.

Site: ❀ P Property: 🚽 🚿 🛁 Children: 🛝 Unit: 🚽 🚿 📺 📻 🛁

LONDON SW20, Inner London   Map ref 2D2   [S]

Thalia Holiday Home

Contact: Mr Peter & Mrs Ann Briscoe-Smith, Owners, 150 Westway, Raynes Park, Wimbledon, London SW20 9LS **T:** (020) 8542 0505 **E:** info@thaliaholidayhome.co.uk
W: www.thaliaholidayhome.co.uk

VisitEngland
★★★★ SELF CATERING

Units   1
Sleeps   5-6
PER UNIT PER WEEK
£800.00

Thalia is a three-bedroomed house in the residential suburban area of West Wimbledon. Home from home, with easy access to central London. Wi-Fi/LAN broadband. Special offers: £50 discount on complete 2nd & subsequent weeks of same booking. Bookings can start and end on any day of the week.
Open: All year.
Nearest Shop: 0.2 miles
Nearest Pub: 0.5 miles

Site: ✿ P Property: ▦ ▣ Children: ⏰ ▥ ⚡ Unit: ▯ ▯ ▣ ▣ ⚡ TV ⊙

LONDON SW3, Inner London   Map ref 2D2   [S]

The Apartments - Chelsea & Marylebone

Contact: Kasia Tymoczko, General Manager, 36 Draycott Place, Chelsea, London SW3 2SA
T: (020) 7589 3271 **F:** (020) 7589 3274 **E:** sales@theapartments.co.uk
W: www.theapartments.co.uk **£ BOOK ONLINE**

VisitEngland
3★-4★ SELF CATERING

VisitEngland
Gold AWARD

Units   41
Sleeps   1-4
PER UNIT PER WEEK
£1092.00 - £2982.00

The Apartments is a family run, boutique serviced apartment business, with over 15 years experience. We offer a selection of stylish studios & one bedroom apartments, in two of London's premier locations. Housed in predominantly period buildings, each apartment is individually designed with modern fitted kitchens & bathrooms, and a full range of modern amenities. Includes complimentary Wi-Fi. **Open:** All year including Christmas & New Year. **Nearest Shop:** 0.10 miles **Nearest Pub:** 0.10 miles

Payment: ▣ Property: ⁄ ▦ ▯ ▣ Children: ⏰ ▥ ⚡ Unit: ▯ ▣ ▣ ⚡ TV ⊙ ☎

LONDON W6, Inner London   Map ref 2D2   SatNav W6 9QL   [B]

Temple Lodge Club Ltd

Temple Lodge, 51 Queen Caroline Street, Hammersmith, London W6 9QL
T: (020) 8748 8388 **E:** templelodgeclub@btconnect.com
W: www.templelodgeclub.com

VisitEngland
★★★ GUEST ACCOMMODATION

VisitEngland
Silver AWARD

B&B PER ROOM PER NIGHT
S: £58.00 - £90.00
D: £76.00 - £120.00

SPECIAL PROMOTIONS
Please see website for special promotions.

Hidden away from the hustle and bustle of central Hammersmith, yet a surprisingly short walk from its main transport hub, this listed building provides a quiet and relaxing haven after the exertions of a busy day or night out.

Breakfast is hearty, vegetarian and mainly organic. Bedrooms are comfortably furnished, light and airy. Most rooms, including library, look out onto our secluded garden.

Directions: Exit Hammersmith tube towards the Apollo Theatre, turn left towards the river and Hammersmith Bridge, next door but one is Temple Lodge. Enter small courtyard, come to blue front door and ring doorbell!

Bedrooms: 5 single with companion bed if needed, 4 double (1 en suite, 1 private bathroom, 1 shower only in room, 1 facilities on corridor) 2 twin-bedded.
Open: All year.

Site: ✿ Payment: ▣ Property: ⚑ ▦ ⚕ Catering: ▥ Room: ⚡ ♨

LONDON WC1N, Inner London   Map ref 2D2   SatNav WC1N 2AD [B]

VisitEngland ★★★★ GUEST ACCOMMODATION
VisitEngland Silver AWARD

Goodenough Club
23 Mecklenburgh Square, London WC1N 2AD **T:** (020) 7769 4727
E: reservations@goodenough.ac.uk
W: www.club.goodenough.ac.uk **£ BOOK ONLINE**

B&B PER ROOM PER NIGHT
S: £99.00 - £224.00
D: £134.00 - £409.00

Occupies 5 Georgian town houses in the heart of Bloomsbury, walking distance to West End, Covent Garden and the Eurostar. Luxurious Garden Suites are available and a Health club day is available charged nearby. **Directions:** Goodenough Club is well located for all the major London airports and train stations and within walking distance of London Euston & King's Cross. **Bedrooms:** TV, Wi-Fi, hairdryer and hospitality tray. **Open:** 365 days a year.

Site: Payment: Leisure: Property: Children: Catering: Room:

TEDDINGTON, Outer London   Map ref 2D2   SatNav TW11 9NU [H]

VisitEngland ★★★★ COUNTRY HOUSE HOTEL
VisitEngland Silver AWARD

Lensbury
Broom Road, Teddington TW11 9NU **T:** (020) 8614 6400 **F:** (020) 8614 6445
E: accommodation@lensbury.com
W: www.lensbury.com **£ BOOK ONLINE**

B&B PER ROOM PER NIGHT
S: £90.00 - £190.00
D: £105.00 - £210.00
HB PER PERSON PER NIGHT
£110.00 - £230.00

SPECIAL PROMOTIONS
Weekend offer if you stay two or three nights. Best rate available. Prices include Breakfast, Car Parking, Wi-Fi internet and use of extensive leisure facilities including a 25m pool.

The Lensbury is a 4 star hotel, conference centre and premium leisure centre located in 25 acres of grounds on the banks of the river Thames at Teddington in West London. With 171 en suite bedrooms, an excellent purpose-built conference centre and superb leisure facilities, The Lensbury is a "one stop shop" for the business or leisure visitor. Free car parking and Wi-Fi, 25 metre Swimming pool.

Directions: Near Heathrow & Gatwick Airports. Motorways: 15 minutes from the M25. 10 minutes from the M3. Rail: 35 minutes to London Waterloo. Complimentary shuttle bus to local station Monday to Friday peak times.

Bedrooms: Standard Rooms, Superior, Executive, Deluxe, Disabled room and a Family room. Rooms can take up to a maximum of 4 people. **Open:** All year.

Site: P Payment: Leisure: Property: Children: Catering: Room:

For **key to symbols** see page 6

Don't Miss...

Audley End House & Gardens
Saffron Walden, Essex CB11 4JF
(03703) 331181
www.english-heritage.org.uk
At Audley End near Saffron Walden, you can discover one of England's grandest stately homes. Explore the impressive mansion house, uncover the story behind the Braybrooke's unique natural history collection, visit an exhibition where you can find out about the workers who lived on the estate in the 1800s and even try dressing the part with dressing up clothes provided.

The Broads
Norwich, Norfolk NR13 3QD
(01603) 610734
www.broads-authority.gov.uk
The Norfolk Broads with its scenic waterways, rare wildlife and rich history has National Park status. This ancient mosaic of lakes, land and rivers covering 303 square kilometres in the east of England, is the UK's largest protected wetland and boasts a variety of habitats including fen, carr woodland and grazing marshes, as well as pretty villages and no less than 11,000 species of wildlife. Walking, cycling, fishing, boating, wildlife spotting, the list of things to do here is endless and there is something for all ages to enjoy.

Kings College Cambridge 🏵
King's Parade, Cambridge CB2 1ST
(01223) 331100
www.kings.cam.ac.uk
Founded in 1441 by Henry VI (1421-71), King's is one of the 31 colleges in the University of Cambridge. Regarded as one of the greatest examples of late Gothic English architecture, it has the world's largest fan-vault and the chapel's stained-glass windows and wooden chancel screen are considered some of the finest from their era. The chapel's choir, composed of male students at King's and choristers from the nearby King's College School, is one of the most accomplished and renowned in the world and every year on Christmas Eve the Festival of Nine Lessons and Carols is broadcast from the chapel to millions of listeners worldwide.

Holkham Hall 🏵
Wells-next- the-Sea, Norfolk, NR23 1AB
(01328) 710227
www.holkham.co.uk
Steeped in history, magnificent Holkham Hall on the North Norfolk Coast, is a stunning Palladian mansion with its own nature reserve. It is home to many rare species of flora and fauna, a deer park and one of the most beautiful, unspoilt beaches in the country. Step back in time in the Bygones Museum or explore the 18th century walled gardens which are being restored, while the children have fun in the woodland adventure play area.

ZSL Whipsnade Zoo 🏵
Dunstable, Bedfordshire LU6 2LF
(03442) 251826
www.zsl.org/zsl-whipsnade-zoo
Set on 600 acres in the rolling Chiltern Hills, Whipsnade is home to more than 2500 species and you can get close to some of the world's hairiest, scariest, tallest and smallest animals here. Meet the animals, take a steam train ride, visit the Hullabazoo Farm or even be a keeper for the day.

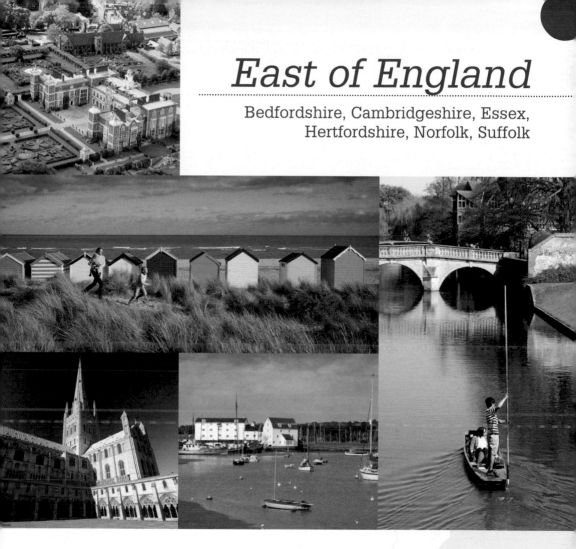

East of England

Bedfordshire, Cambridgeshire, Essex, Hertfordshire, Norfolk, Suffolk

Loved for its unspoiled character, rural landscape, architecture and traditions, the East of England is full of beautiful countryside, idyllic seaside, historic cities and vibrant towns. The Norfolk Broads and Suffolk Coast have always been popular with yachtsmen and the North Norfolk Coast has become a fashionable getaway in recent years. Cambridge is steeped in history and oozes sophistication, while Bedfordshire, Hertfordshire and Essex each have their own charms, with pockets of beauty and fascinating heritage. This is a diverse region where you'll find plenty to keep you busy.

Explore – East of England

Bedfordshire & Hertfordshire

History, the arts, family entertainment and relaxing, unspoilt countryside - this area has it all. Bedfordshire has plenty of attractions, from exotic animals at Whipsnade Zoo to vintage aeroplanes at The Shuttleworth Collection and notable historic houses. Woburn Abbey, the still inhabited home of the Dukes of Bedford, stands in a 3000-acre park and is part of one of Europe's largest drive-through game reserves. The 18th century mansion's 14 state apartments are open to the public and contain an impressive art collection.

Hertfordshire also has its fair share of stately homes, with Hatfield House, built from 1707 by Robert Cecil, first Earl of Salisbury, leading the way. Nearby Knebworth House is the venue for popular summer concerts and events. Both will be familiar as the backdrop to many recent blockbuster movies.

Roman walls, mosaic floors and part of an amphitheatre are still visible at Verulanium, St Albans and Much Hadham, where the Bishops of London used to have their country seat, is a showpiece village. Welwyn Garden City, one of Britain's first 20th century new towns retains its leafy character and art deco charm.

Cambridgeshire & Essex

Cambridge is a city of winding streets lined with old houses, world-famous colleges and churches, while the gently flowing Cam provides a serene backdrop to the architectural wonders. Kings College Chapel, started by Henry VI in 1446 should not be missed and the Fitzwilliam Museum founded by Henry VI in 1446, is one of Europe's treasure houses, with antiquities from Greece and Rome. First class shopping can be found in the quirky stores and exquisite boutiques tucked away along cobbled streets and there's a vast choice of places to eat and drink.

Further afield, Cambridgeshire is a land of lazy waterways, rolling countryside, bustling market towns and quaint villages. Climb grand sweeping staircases in the stately homes of the aristocracy or relax as you chug along in a leisure boat, watching the wildlife in one of the wonderful nature reserves. The English perpendicular gothic cathedrals of Peterborough and Ely began life as abbey churches as long ago as AD 670.

Western Essex is dotted with pretty historic market towns and villages like Thaxted and Saffron Walden and plenty of historic sites. County town Colchester was founded by the Romans and its massive castle keep, built in 1067 on the site of the Roman Temple of Claudius, houses a collection of Roman antiquities. Explore the beautiful gardens and 110ft Norman Keep at Hedingham Castle, which also holds jousting and theatre performances.

Some of the region's loveliest countryside lies to the North, on the Suffolk Border around Dedham Vale where Constable and Turner painted, while further east you can find family seaside resorts such as Walton on the Naze and Clacton-on-Sea. Following the coast south, the Blackwater and Crouch estuaries provide havens for yachts and pleasure craft. Inland, Layer Marney Tower is a Tudor palace with buildings, gardens and parkland dating from 1520 in a beautiful, rural Essex setting. The county city of Chelmsford has a historic 15th century cathedral and Hylands House is a beautiful Grade II* listed neo-classical villa, set in over 500 acres of Hylands Park.

Norfolk

Norfolk is not as flat as Noel Coward would have you believe, as any cyclist will tell you, but cycling or walking is still a great way to see the county. In the west Thetford Forest is said to be the oldest in England while in the east, the county is crisscrossed by waterways and lakes known as The Broads - apparently the remains of medieval man's peat diggings!

The county town of Norfolk and unofficial capital of East Anglia is Norwich, a fine city whose cathedral walls are decorated with biblical scenes dating from 1046. There are 30 medieval churches in central Norwich and many other interesting historic sites, but modern Norwich is a stylish contemporary city with first rate shopping and cultural facilities. Sandringham, near Kings Lynn in the North West of the county, is the royal palace bought by Queen Victoria for the then Prince of Wales and where the present Queen spends many a family holiday.

The North Norfolk coast has become known as 'Chelsea-on-Sea' in recent years and many parts of the region have developed a reputation for fine dining. From Hunstanton in the west to Cromer in the east, this stretch of coastline is home to nature reserves, windswept beaches and quaint coastal villages. Wells-next-the-Sea, with its long sweeping beach bordered by pine woodland has a pretty harbour with small fishing boats where children fish for crabs.

Suffolk

Suffolk is famous for its winding lanes and pastel painted, thatched cottages. The county town of Ipswich has undergone considerable regeneration in recent years, and now boasts a vibrant waterfront and growing arts scene. For history lovers, Framlingham Castle has stood intact since the 13th century and magnificent churches at Lavenham, Sudbury and Long Melford are well worth a visit.

The Suffolk Coast & Heaths 'Area of Outstanding Natural Beauty' has 155 square miles of unspoilt wildlife-rich wetlands, ancient heaths, windswept shingle beaches and historic towns and villages for you to explore. Its inlets and estuaries are extremely popular with yachtsmen. Gems such as Southwold, with its brightly coloured beach huts, and Aldeburgh are home to some excellent restaurants. Snape Maltings near Aldeburgh offers an eclectic programme of events including the world famous Aldeburgh Festival of music. The historic market town of Woodbridge on the River Deben, has a working tide mill, a fabulous riverside walk with an impressive view across the river to Sutton Hoo and an abundance of delightful pubs and restaurants.

In the South of the county, the hills and valleys on the Suffolk-Essex border open up to stunning skies, captured in paintings by Constable, Turner and Gainsborough. At the heart of beautiful Constable Country, Nayland and Dedham Vale 'Area of Outstanding Natural Beauty' are idyllic places for a stroll or leisurely picnic.

Visit – East of England

 Attractions with this sign participate in the **Visitor Attraction Quality Assurance Scheme.**

Bedfordshire

Dunstable Downs Kite Festival
July, Dunstable, Bedfordshire LU6 2GY
www.dunstablekitefestival.co.uk
Enjoy a fantastic atmosphere as professional kite teams put on show-stopping diplays. With family activities, local artists and entertainment, there's something for everyone.

Luton International Carnival
May, Luton, Bedfordshire
www.luton.gov.uk
The highlight is the spectacular carnival parade – an eye-catching, breathtaking procession through the town centre, superbly reflecting the diverse mix of cultures in Luton. Enjoy the decorated floats, music and dance as you watch the parade go by.

Thurleigh Farm Centre
Thurleigh, Bedfordshire MK44 2EE
(01234) 771597
www.thurleighfarmcentre.co.uk
A wonderful working farm; have excellent fun with indoor activities including trampolines and mini quad biking, and the tea room with delightful homemade cakes.

Woburn Abbey
Woburn, Bedfordshire MK17 9WA
(01525) 290333
www.woburnabbey.co.uk
Home of the Duke of Bedford, a treasure house with outstanding collections of art, furniture, silver, gold and extensive gardens.

Woburn Safari Park
Bedfordshire MK17 9QN
(01525) 290407
www.woburnsafari.co.uk
Drive through the safari park with species such as white rhino, elephants, tigers and black bears in natural groups just a windscreen's width away, or even closer!

Wrest Park
Silsoe, Luton, Bedfordshire, MK45 4HR
(0370) 333 1181
www.english-heritage.org.uk
Enjoy a great day out exploring one of Britain's most spectacular French style mansions and 'secret' gardens. With hidden gems including a thatched-roof Bath house, ornate marble fountain, Chinese Temple and bridge and over 40 statues, as well as a kids audio trail and play area, it's popular with families and garden lovers alike.

Cambridgeshire

Cambridge Folk Festival
July, Cherry Hinton, Cambridgeshire
www.cambridgelivetrust.co.uk/folk-festival
Top acts make this a must-visit event for folk fans.

Cambridge University Botanic Garden
1 Brookside, Cambridge CB2 1 JE
(01223) 336265
www.botanic.cam.ac.uk/Botanic
Opened to the public in 1846, the Cambridge University Botanic Garden develops & displays over 8,000 plant species in 40 acres of landscapes.

Duxford Air Show
September, Duxford, nr Cambridge, Cambridgeshire
www.iwm.org.uk/duxford
Set within the spacious grounds of the famous former First and Second World War airfield, the Duxford Air Show features an amazing array of aerial displays.

Elton Hall
Elton, Cambridgeshire PE8 6SH
(01832) 280468
www.eltonhall.com
Historic house with a fine collection of paintings, furniture, antiquarian books, bibles and Henry VIII's prayer book, together with beautiful ornate gardens and arboretum.

Imperial War Museum Duxford
Cambridge CB22 4QR
(01223) 835000
www.iwm.org.uk/duxford
Visit this historic airfield and museum of aviation history and discover the stories of people who lived and worked at RAF Duxford. With its air shows, unique history and atmosphere, nowhere else combines the sights, sounds and power of aircraft quite like it.

Kings College Chapel
Cambridge CB2 1ST
(01223) 331100
www.kings.cam.ac.uk
It's part of one of the oldest Cambridge colleges sharing a wonderful sense of history and tradition with the rest of the University. The Chapel is a splendid example of late Gothic architecture.

The National Stud
Newmarket, Cambridgeshire CB8 0XE
(01638) 663464
www.nationalstud.co.uk
The beautiful grounds and facilities are a renowned tourist attraction in the eastern region.

Oliver Cromwell's House
Ely, Cambridgeshire CB7 4HF
(01353) 662062
www.olivercromwellshouse.co.uk
Visit the former Lord Protector's family's home and experience an exhibition on 17th century life, on the doorstep of Ely Cathedral.

Peterborough Dragon Boat Festival
June, Peterborough Rowing Lake,
Thorpe Meadows, Cambridgeshire
www.peterboroughdragonboatfestival.com
Teams of up to 11 people, dragon boats and all equipment provided, no previous experience required. Family entertainment and catering stalls.

The Raptor Foundation
Huntingdon, Cambridgeshire PE28 3BT
(01487) 741140
www.raptorfoundation.org.uk
Bird of prey centre, offering 3 daily flying displays with audience participation, gift shop, Silent Wings Tearoom, Raptor crafts shop.

Essex

Adventure Island
Southend-on-Sea, Essex SS1 1EE
(01702) 443400
www.adventureisland.co.uk
One of the best value 'theme parks' in the South East with over 60 great rides and attractions for all ages. No admission charge, you only 'pay if you play'.

Central Museum and Planetarium
Southend-on-Sea, Essex SS2 6EW
(01702) 212345
www.southendmuseums.co.uk
An Edwardian building housing displays of archaeology, natural history, social and local history.

Clacton Airshow
August, Clacton Seafront, Essex
www.clactonairshow.com
An impressive two days of aerobatic displays taking to the skies whilst a whole host of exhibition, trade stands, food court and on-site entertainment are available at ground level.

Colchester Medieval Festival
June, Lower Castle Park, Colchester, Essex
www.oysterfayre.co.uk
With many of the peripheral activities that this major annual event of the period would have offered. It remembers a time when folk from the countryside and neighbouring villages would travel to the 'Big Fair' in the town.

Colchester Zoo
Essex CO3 0SL
(01206) 331292
www.colchester-zoo.com
Be transported into a world full of magnificent animals waiting to be discovered. Learn about the animals as you see them up close and why not watch one of many daily displays.

Hedingham Castle
Essex CO9 3DJ
(01787) 460261
www.hedinghamcastle.co.uk
Standing in 160 acres of spectacular landscape, Hedingham Castle is a 900 year old Normal castle filled with romance, heritage and history.

Maldon Mud Race
May, Maldon, Essex
www.maldonmudrace.com
The annual Maldon Mud Race is a wacky fun competition in which participants race to become the first to finish a 400m dash over the bed of the River Blackwater.

RHS Garden Hyde Hall
Chelmsford, Essex CM3 8AT
0845 265 8071
www.rhs.org.uk/hydehall
A garden of inspirational beauty with an eclectic range of horticultural styles from traditional to modern providing year round interest.

Royal Gunpowder Mills
Waltham Abbey, Essex EN9 1JY
(01992) 707370
www.royalgunpowdermills.com
A spectacular 170-acre location for a day of family fun. Special events including Spitfire flypast, award-winning Secret History exhibition, tranquil wildlife walks, guided land train tours and rocket science gallery.

Sea-Life Adventure
Southend-on-Sea, Essex SS1 2ER
(01702) 442200
www.sealifeadventure.co.uk
With more than 30 display tanks and tunnels to explore, there are loads of fishy residents to discover at Sea-Life Adventure.

Southend Carnival
August, Southend-on-Sea, Essex
www.southendcarnival.weebly.com
A wide range of exciting and enjoyable events for everyone held over eight days. Now one of the largest community events in South East Essex, and includes a thrilling fun fair and the colourful carnival procession along Southend Seafront!

Hertfordshire

Ashridge Gardens
Berkhamsted, Hertfordshire HP4 1NS
(01442) 841009
www.ashridgehouse.org.uk
Originally designed by Humphry Repton in the early 19th century, Ashridge Gardens are 190 acres of pure beauty and tranquillity. Please contact for advice on tours.

Cathedral and Abbey Church of St Alban
St. Albans, Hertfordshire AL1 1BY
(01727) 860780
www.stalbanscathedral.org
St Alban is Britain's first Christian Martyr and the Cathedral, with its shrine, is its oldest place of continuous worship. The building's amazing mix of architectural styles bears witness to the many centuries of its life, first as a monastic Abbey and now as a Cathedral.

Chilli Festival
August, Benington Lordship Gardens, Stevenage, Hertfordshire
www.beningtonlordship.co.uk
A popular family event attracting thousands of visitors over three days, offering a chance to buy Chilli plants, products and sample foods from around the world.

Hertfordshire County Show
May, Redbourn, Hertfordshire
www.hertsshow.com
County show with Trade Stands, award-winning Food Hall, exclusive 'Made in Hertfordshire' marquee, Countryside Arena, and much much more.

Knebworth House
Hertfordshire SG3 6PY
(01438) 812661
www.knebworthhouse.com
Historic house, home to the Lytton family since 1490. Knebworth Park offers a great day out for all the family, with fun activities for children and lots to do for all ages, including Adventure Playground, Dinosaur Trail, a walk through history in Knebworth House and Gardens and special events throughout the summer.

Potters Bar Museum
Hertfordshire EN6 4HN
(01707) 654179
www.facebook.com/pottersbarmuseum
Go back in time at Potters Bar Museum with pottery and artefacts revealing history from Potters Bar and the surrounding area. See fossils, stones, and even parts of a Zeppelin that crashed into Potters Bar in 1916.

Norfolk

Banham Zoo
Norwich, Norfolk NR16 2HE
(01953) 887771
www.banhamzoo.co.uk
A 50-acre wildlife spectacular which will take you on a journey to experience tigers, leopards and zebra plus some of the world's most exotic, rare and endangered animals.

Blickling Hall, Gardens and Park
Norwich, Norfolk NR11 6NF
(01263) 738030
www.nationaltrust.org.uk/blickling-estate
A Jacobean redbrick mansion with a garden, orangery, parkland and lake. Spectacular long gallery, plasterwork ceilings and fine collections of furniture, pictures and books. You can walk across much of the 950 acres of woodland, parkland and historic countryside using waymarked routes and the estate also connects with other national paths.

Bressingham Steam and Gardens
Low Rd, Bressingham, Norfolk IP22 2AA
(01379) 686900
www.bressingham.co.uk
Where world renowned gardener and horticulturist Alan Bloom combined his passion for plants and gardens with his love of steam to create a truly unique experience for all the family.

Cromer Pier
Cromer, Norfolk NR27 9HE
www.cromerpier.com
Cromer Pier is a Grade II listed, 12 year old, award-winning, seaside pier on the north coast of Norfolk. The pier is the home of the Cromer Lifeboat Station and the Pavilion Theatre and absolutely the best crab fishing spot on the coast.

Fritton Lake Country World
Great Yarmouth, Norfolk NR31 9HA
(01493) 484008
www.frittonlakeoc.co.uk
A woodland and lakeside haven with a children's assault course, putting, an adventure playground, golf, fishing, boating, wildfowl, heavy horses, cart rides, falconry and flying displays.

Great Yarmouth Maritime Festival
September, Great Yarmouth, Norfolk
www.great-yarmouth.co.uk/maritime-festival
A mix of traditional and modern maritime vessels will be moored on South Quay for visitors to admire and go aboard.

Norwich Castle Museum and Art Gallery
Norfolk NR1 3JU
(01603) 493625
www.museums.norfolk.gov.uk
One of Norwich's most famous landmarks, the ancient Norman keep dominates the city and is one of the most important buildings of its kind in Europe. Explore the Castle's history as a palace and later as a prison, and enjoy the fabulous collections of fine art.

Royal Norfolk Show
June, Norwich, Norfolk
www.royalnorfolkshow.co.uk
Offering 10 hours of entertainment each day from spectacular grand ring displays, traditional livestock and equine classes, to a live music stage, celebrity guests and over 650 stands.

Sainsbury Centre for Visual Arts
UEA, Norwich, Norfolk NR4 7TJ
(01603) 593199
www.scva.ac.uk
Containing a collection of world art, it was one of the first major public buildings to be designed by the architect Norman Foster.

Sandringham
King's Lynn, Norfolk PE35 6EN
(01485) 545400
www.sandringhamestate.co.uk
The Norfolk country retreat of H.M. The Queen and HRH The Duke of Edinburgh. A fascinating house, an intriguing museum and the best of the Royal gardens.

Suffolk

Aldeburgh Music Festival
June, Snape Maltings, Suffolk IP17 1SP
www.aldeburgh.co.uk
The Aldeburgh Festival of Music and the Arts offers an eclectic mix of concerts, operas, masterclasses, films and open air performances at different venues in the Aldeburgh/Snape area in Suffolk.

Gainsborough's House
Sudbury, Suffolk CO10 2EU
(01787) 372958
www.gainsborough.org
Gainsborough's House is the only museum situated in the birthplace of a great British artist. The permanent collection is built around the works of leading English painter Thomas Gainsborough, alongside other temporary exhibitions.

Go Ape! High Wire Forest Adventure - Thetford
Suffolk IP27 0AF (0845) 094 9732
www.goape.co.uk
Experience an exhilarating course of rope bridges, tarzan swings and zip slides... all set high in the trees above the forest floor.

Ickworth House, Park and Gardens
Bury St. Edmunds, Suffolk IP29 5QE
(01284) 735270
www.nationaltrust.org.uk/ickworth
Fine paintings, a beautiful collection of Georgian silver, an Italianate garden and stunning parkland.

Latitude Festival
July, Southwold, Suffolk
www.latitudefestival.com
Primarily a music festival but also has a full spectrum of art including film, comedy, theatre, cabaret, dance and poetry.

National Horseracing Museum and Tours
Newmarket, Suffolk CB8 8JH
(01638) 667333
www.nhrm.co.uk
Family-friendly venue embracing fine and decorative art, social history, archive material and photos. Discover the stories of racing from its early origins at Newmarket to its modern-day heroes.

RSPB Minsmere Nature Reserve
Saxmundham, Suffolk IP17 3BY
(01728) 648281
www.rspb.org.uk/minsmere
One of the UK's premier nature reserves, offering excellent facilities for people of all ages and abilities.

Smiths Row
Bury St Edmunds, Suffolk IP33 1BT
(01284) 762081
www.smithsrow.org
A contemporary art gallery and craft workshop; relax in The Art Lounge with an exhibition book, or take part in a workshop to develop your crafting skills.

Somerleyton Hall and Gardens
Lowestoft, Suffolk NR32 5QQ
(0871) 222 4244
www.somerleyton.co.uk
12 acres of landscaped gardens to explore including our famous 1864 Yew Hedge Maze. Guided tours of the Hall.

Suffolk Show
May - June, Ipswich, Suffolk
www.suffolkshow.co.uk
Animals, food and drink, shopping...there's lots to see and do at this popular county show.

Sutton Hoo
Woodbridge, Suffolk IP12 3DJ
(01394) 389700
www.nationaltrust.org.uk
Anglo-Saxon burial site set on a stunning 255 acre estate with breathtaking views over the River Debe.

Tourist Information Centres

When you arrive at your destination, visit the Tourist Information Centre for quality assured help with accommodation and information about local attractions and events, or email your request before you go.

Aldeburgh	48 High Street	01728 453637	atic@suffolkcoastal.gov.uk
Aylsham	Bure Valley Railway Station	01263 733903	aylsham.tic@broadland.gov.uk
Beccles	The Quay	01502 713196	admin@beccles.info
Bedford	Thurlow Street	01234 718112	travelandtourism@bedford.gov.uk
Bishop's Stortford	2 Market Square	01279 655831	tic@bishopsstortford.org
Brentwood	Town Hall	01277 312500	
Burnham Deepdale	Deepdale Information	01485 210256	stay@deepdalebackpackers.co.uk
Bury St Edmunds	6 Angel Hill	01284 764667	tic@stedsbc.gov.uk
Cambridge	Peas Hill	01223 791500	info@visitcambridge.org
Clacton-on-Sea	Town Hall	01255 686633	clactontic@tendringdc.gov.uk
Colchester	Castle Park	01206 282920	vic@colchester.gov.uk
Cromer	Louden Road	01263 512497	cromerinfo@north-norfolk.gov.uk
Diss	Meres Mouth	01379 650523	dtic@s-norfolk.gov.uk
Dunstable	Priory House	01582 891420	tic@dunstable.gov.uk
Ely	Oliver Cromwell's House	01353 662062	tic@eastcambs.gov.uk
Felixstowe	Crescent Road	01394 383789	ftic@suffolkcoastal.gov.uk
Great Yarmouth	25 Marine Parade	01493 846346	tourism@great-yarmouth.gov.uk
Hertford	10 The Wash	01992 584322	tic@hertford.gov.uk
Holt	3 Pound House	01263 713100	holtinfo@north-norfolk.gov.uk
Hoveton	Station Road	01603 782281	hovetontic@broads-authority.gov.uk
Hunstanton	Town Hall	01485 532610	info@visithunstanton.info
Ipswich	St Stephens Church	01473 258070	tourist@ipswich.gov.uk
King's Lynn	The Custom House	01553 763044	kings-lynn.tic@west-norfolk.gov.uk
Lavenham	Lady Street	01787 248207	lavenhamtic@babergh.gov.uk
Letchworth Garden City	33-35 Station Road	01462 487868	tic@letchworth.com
Maldon	Wenlock Way	01621 856503	tic@maldon.gov.uk
Newmarket	63 The Guineas	01638 719749	tic.newmarket@forest-heath.gov.uk
Norwich	The Forum	01603 213999	tourism@norwich.gov.uk
Peterborough	41 Bridge Street	01733 452336	vic@peterborough.gov.uk
Saffron Walden	1 Market Place	01799 524002	tourism@saffronwalden.gov.uk
Sandy	Rear of 10 Cambridge Road	01767 682 728	tourism@sandytowncouncil.gov.uk
Sheringham	Station Approach	01263 824329	sheringhaminfo@north-norfolk.gov.uk
Skegness	Embassy Theatre	0845 6740505	skegnessinfo@e-lindsey.gov.uk
Southend-on-Sea	Pier Entrance	01702 215620	vic@southend.gov.uk
St Albans	Old Town Hall	01727 864511	tic@stalbans.gov.uk
Stowmarket	The Museum of East Anglian Life	01449 676800	tic@midsuffolk.gov.uk
Sudbury	Sudbury Library	01787 881320 / 372331	sudburytic@sudburytowncouncil.co.uk
Swaffham	1 London Street	01760 722255	tic@swaffhammuseum.co.uk
Waltham Abbey	2-4 Highbridge Street	01992 660336	tic@walthamabbey-tc.gov.uk
Wells-Next-The-Sea	Staithe Street	01328 710885	wellsinfo@north-norfolk.gov.uk
Whitlingham	Whitlingham Country Park	01603 756094	whitlinghamtic@broads-authority.gov.uk
Wisbech	2-3 Bridge Street	01945 464058	info@wisbechinfo.org.uk
Witham	61 Newland Street	01376 502674	tic@witham.gov.uk
Woodbridge	Woodbridge Library	01394 383789	customer.services.scdc@eastsuffolk.gov.uk
Wymondham	Market Cross	01953 604721	wymondhamtic@btconnect.com

Regional Contacts and Information

For more information on accommodation, attractions, activities, events and holidays in the East of England, contact the following regional tourism organisation. Their website has a wealth of information.

Visit East Anglia
(0333) 302 4202
www.visiteastofengland.com

Stay –
East of England

Entries appear alphabetically by town name in each county. A key to symbols appears on page 6

BEDFORD, Bedfordshire Map ref 2D1 S

Dovecote Self-Catering

Contact: Ros and Ian Northern, Owners, Priory Farm, Lavendon Road, Harrold, Bedford MK43 7EE **T:** (01234) 720293 **E:** info@dovecoteselfcatering.co.uk
W: www.dovecoteselfcatering.co.uk

Units   3
Sleeps   1-11
PER UNIT PER WEEK
£400.00 - £680.00

Three comfortable self-catering cottages in the picturesque village of Harrold. The Dovecote is a range of traditional stone and brick built buildings set around a sunny courtyard. Each cottage has an individual character but they all have modern facilities. The countryside is on your doorstep, but we are near good pubs and shopping. We welcome families young and old as well as business people. **Open:** All year.
Nearest Shop: 350 metres **Nearest Pub:** 250 metres

Site: ✿ P **Payment:** 💳 **Property:** 📺 🔒 🏠 **Children:** 🧸 🛏 ♿ **Unit:** 🛏 🍴 💻 🔊 📶 📺 📀

CAMBRIDGE, Cambridgeshire Map ref 2D1 S

Glebe Cottage

Contact: Mrs Fiona Key, Owner, 44 Main Street, Hardwick, Cambridge, Cambridgeshire CB3 7QS **T:** (01954) 212895 **E:** info@camcottage.co.uk
W: www.camcottage.co.uk **£ BOOK ONLINE**

Units   1
Sleeps   2
PER UNIT PER WEEK
£400.00 - £450.00

Recently refurbished, the soft furnishings of velvet drapes and blinds bring a warm cosy feel. New kitchen with dishwasher. Upstairs brand new en suite bathroom to double bedroom. Views of over two acres of established garden with furniture and BBQ. A little bit of paradise and a quiet spot but close enough to the city and transport links.

Open: All year except Christmas - New Year.
Nearest Shop: 0.5 miles
Nearest Pub: 300 yards

Site: ✿ P **Leisure:** 🚲 ♪ ↑ ∪ **Property:** 📺 🔒 🏠 **Children:** 🧸 **Unit:** 🛏 🍴 💻 🔊 📶 📺 📀 BBQ

Highfield Farm Touring Park

Long Road, Comberton, Cambridge CB23 7DG
T: (01223) 262308 **F:** (01223) 262308 **E:** enquiries@highfieldfarmtouringpark.co.uk
W: www.highfieldfarmtouringpark.co.uk

🚐 (60)   £15.50-£26.00
🚙 (60)   £15.50-£26.00
⛺ (60)   £14.00-£26.00
120 touring pitches

A popular, family-run park with excellent facilities close to the University City of Cambridge and Imperial War Museum, Duxford. Ideally situated for touring East Anglia and within easy access of the Cambridge park and rides. Prices for Caravans and motorvans are based on two people with electric included. Please view our website for further information.

Directions: From Cambridge take the A1303 to Bedford. After 3 miles, left at roundabout, follow sign to Comberton. From M11 junction 12, A603 to Sandy. Then B1046 to Comberton.

Open: April to October.

Site: ▲🅿 **Payment:** € ☼ **Leisure:** ♪ ▶ ∪ **Children:** ⛄ ⚠ **Catering:** ⛴ **Park:** ✝ 🗑 🗄 🐾 **Touring:** 🚰 🕁 🚐 ♫

Southampton Guest House

7 Elizabeth Way, Cambridge CB4 1DE **T:** (01223) 357780 **F:** (01223) 314297
E: southamptonhouse@btinternet.com
W: www.southamptonguesthouse.com

B&B PER ROOM PER NIGHT
S: £40.00 - £55.00
D: £60.00 - £65.00

Victorian property with friendly atmosphere, only 15 minutes walk along riverside to city centre, colleges and shopping mall.
Directions: Please contact us for directions.
Bedrooms: 1 single, 1 double, 3 family.
Open: All year.

Site: P **Payment:** € **Property:** ▦ **Children:** ⛄ 🏃 **Room:** 🍵 ♨ 📞 📺 👔

River Cam, Cambridge ©VisitBritain Britain on View

CAMBRIDGE, Cambridgeshire Map ref 2D1 S

The Bull Pen

Contact: Sally & Nick Charter, Owner, Chapman's Farm, 167 Alms Hill, Bourn, Cambridge CB23 2SZ **T:** (01954) 719292 / 07712 121777
E: thebullpen.chapmansfarm@btinternet.com **W:** www.explorecambridgeshire.co.uk

Units 1
Sleeps 1-6

PER UNIT PER WEEK
£700.00 - £1200.00

SPECIAL PROMOTIONS
3 days minimum booking

Enjoy countryside & city with this high quality modern barn conversion. The Bull Pen, located 8 miles west of Cambridge in the Cambridgeshire village of Bourn, has been designed to keep a feel for its history. A comfortable and peaceful place with; open plan living area, exceptionally well equipped, patio & BBQ for warm summer days and underfloor heating & triple glazed for cosy winter days. All the rooms look across traditional pasture. With lovely walks to local cafés & restaurants; it is ideal for a holiday combining 'time in' the city and 'time-out' of the city. Easy off road parking.

Open: All year.
Nearest Shop: 1 mile
Nearest Pub: 1 mile

Units: 3 bedrooms: Kingsize double with en suite (1st floor), Superking/ or twins with wetroom (ground floor), Kingsize/ or twins with shower room (ground).

HUNTINGDON, Cambridgeshire Map ref 3A2 SatNav PE28 9AJ C

Quiet Waters Caravan Park

Hemingford Abbots, Huntingdon, Cambridgeshire PE28 9AJ
T: (01480) 463405 **F:** (01480) 463405 **E:** quietwaters.park@btopenworld.com
W: www.quietwaterscaravanpark.co.uk

(18) £19.00-£23.00
(18) £19.00-£23.00
(2) £19.00-£23.00
(9) £320.00-£450.00
18 touring pitches

A quiet, family owned riverside park in the centre of a picturesque village. Fishing, boating & excellent walking area. Luxury holiday static caravans and touring pitches, seasonal pitches also available. Disabled facilities available.
Directions: Junction 25 off the A14, 13 miles from Cambridge, 5 miles from Huntingdon.
Open: 1st April to 30th October.

HUNTINGDON, Cambridgeshire Map ref 3A2 SatNav PE28 3DE C

Stroud Hill Park

Fen Road, Pidley, Huntingdon, Cambridgeshire PE28 3DE
T: (01487) 741333 **E:** stroudhillpark@gmail.com
W: www.stroudhillpark.co.uk

(60) £25.00-£27.00
(60) £25.00-£27.00
(20) £17.00-£19.00
60 touring pitches

Stroud Hill Park is a privately owned, exclusively adult, touring caravan site in Pidley, Cambridgeshire. The quiet, attractive, rural site provides a central Cambridgeshire location for touring caravans and campers. This premier site has been awarded many industry accolades in recognition of the high standard of the on-site facilities. **Directions:** B1040 From St Ives - A1/A14 Huntingdon - A141 between Huntingdon & Warboys.
Open: All year.

HUNTINGDON, Cambridgeshire   Map ref 3A2 — S

Wyton Lakes Holiday Park

Contact: Banks End, Wyton, Huntingdon, Cambridgeshire PE28 2AA
T: (01480) 412715 / 07785 294419 **E:** loupeter@supanet.com
W: www.wytonlakes.com

Units   60
Sleeps 60-20
PER UNIT PER WEEK
£20.00

Adult-only park. Some pitches beside the on site carp and coarse-fishing lakes. River frontage. Close to local amenities. Toilet and shower block, dishwashing, laundry. 2 Bedroomed chalet for weekly hire. Excellent local bus service.
Open: April to October.

Payment: 💳 **Leisure:** 🎣 **Property:** 🐕 ▣ ⬚

COLCHESTER, Essex   Map ref 3B2   SatNav CO6 4PZ — H

VisitEngland ★★★★ HOTEL   VisitEngland Silver AWARD

Stoke by Nayland Hotel, Golf & Spa

Keepers Lane, Leavenheath, Colchester, Essex CO6 4PZ **T:** (01206) 265835
F: (01206) 265840 **E:** sales@stokebynayland.com
W: www.stokebynayland.com **£ BOOK ONLINE**

VisitEngland Awards for Excellence 2016 SILVER WINNER

B&B PER ROOM PER NIGHT
S: £86.00
D: £108.00

SPECIAL PROMOTIONS
For current special offers please see our website or call (01206) 265835.

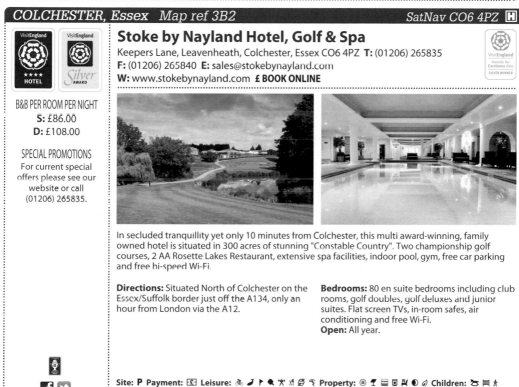

In secluded tranquillity yet only 10 minutes from Colchester, this multi award-winning, family owned hotel is situated in 300 acres of stunning "Constable Country". Two championship golf courses, 2 AA Rosette Lakes Restaurant, extensive spa facilities, indoor pool, gym, free car parking and free hi-speed Wi-Fi.

Directions: Situated North of Colchester on the Essex/Suffolk border just off the A134, only an hour from London via the A12.

Bedrooms: 80 en suite bedrooms including club rooms, golf doubles, golf deluxes and junior suites. Flat screen TVs, in-room safes, air conditioning and free Wi-Fi.
Open: All year.

f 🐦

Site: P Payment: 💳 **Leisure:** 🚴 🎣 🏐 🎯 🎱 ⛳ **Property:** ⓡ 🍴 🖥 ▣ ♨ ◐ ⊘ **Children:** 🍼 🛏 🚸
Catering: (✕ 🍷 🍽 **Room:** 🍵 🛋 📞 ⒶTV 🛁

MERSEA ISLAND, Essex Map ref 3B3

VisitEngland ★★★★★ HOLIDAY PARK

Units 14
Sleeps 2-8

PER UNIT PER WEEK
£260.00 - £850.00

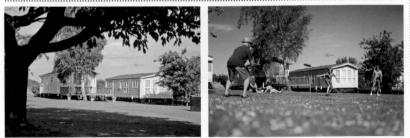

Away Resorts Mersea Island

Contact: Reception, East Mersea CO5 8UA **T:** (01442) 508850 **E:** mersea.island@away-resorts.com
W: www.awayresorts.co.uk

Away Resorts Mersea Island is a beautiful, family-friendly park on the Essex coast offering luxury caravan accommodation among the trees, with spacious surroundings, a private beach and access to the nearby country park for walks and cycling. Set in 22 acres of coastal countryside, the park overlooks the stunning Blackwater Estuary. Our peaceful location provides a safe environment for all age groups to enjoy the countryside, beach and recreational areas. Facilities include a heated swimming pool, clubhouse, tennis court and a convenient on-site shop. New accommodation options available for 2017.

Open: 1st February to 31st December.

Site: **Payment:** **Leisure:** **Property:** **Children:** **Unit:**

ORSETT, Essex Map ref 3B3 SatNav RM16 3LJ

VisitEngland ★★★★ ROOM ONLY

B&B PER ROOM PER NIGHT
S: £35.00 - £47.50
D: £50.00 - £65.00

Jays Lodge

Chapel Farm, Baker Street, Orsett, Grays, Essex RM16 3LJ **T:** (01375) 891663
E: info@jayslodge.co.uk
W: www.jayslodge.co.uk

Barn conversion to provide twelve rooms all with en suite, mini kitchen facility, colour television with Freeview and free Wi-Fi access. Ample, free and secure car parking available.
Directions: Please contact us for directions.
Bedrooms: 2 single, 2 double and 8 twin.
Open: All year except Christmas and New Year.

Site: P **Payment:** **Leisure:** **Property:** **Catering:** **Room:**

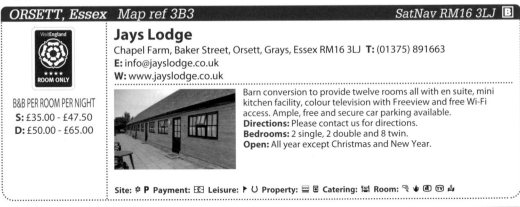

Leigh-on-Sea, Essex ©VisitBritain Jack Barnes

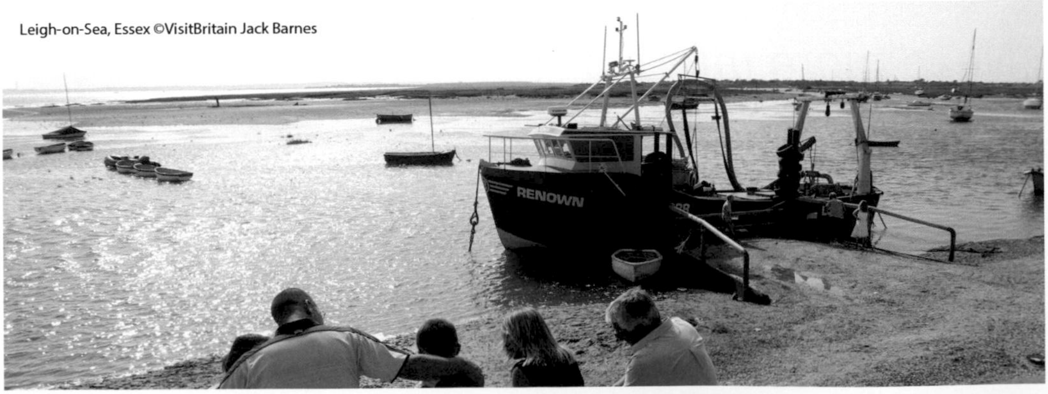

STANSTED MOUNTFITCHET, Essex   Map ref 2D1   S

VisitEngland
3★ - 4★
SELF CATERING

Walpole Farmhouse

Contact: Mrs Jill Walton, Proprietor, Walpole Farmhouse, Cambridge Road, Stansted Mountfitchet CM24 8TA **T:** (01279) 812265 **E:** info@walpolefarmhouse.com **W:** www.walpolefarmhouse.com **£ BOOK ONLINE**

Units   2
Sleeps   1-5

PER UNIT PER WEEK
£300.00 - £450.00

SPECIAL PROMOTIONS
Minimum stay is one week in either property.

Charmingly converted single storey building with its own spacious private garden. Both the Cottage and Studio are tastefully decorated with all modern facilities, including Wi-Fi & ample parking. Ideal for both foreign and UK visitors. Close to Stansted Airport, the UK motorway network, and with easy access to London & Cambridge by train or car. The local train station is a 15 minute walk away. Frequent buses pass-by to Saffron Walden, a picturesque medieval town and to Bishop's Stortford for great shopping, the cinema, and accessing the main commuter railway station.

Open: All year (please call or email for booking).
Nearest Shop: 0.25 miles (& more in village)
Nearest Pub: 0.5 miles (Pubs in Village)
Units: Please see our detailed floor maps & descriptions on www.walpolefarmhouse.com

f

Site: ✿ P Payment: 🖃 Leisure: ⚐ Property: 🐾 🖳 📚 Children: 🧸 🛏 Unit: 📱 🛢 🖥 🗄 🗫 TV DVD

WEST MERSEA, Essex   Map ref 3B3   SatNav CO5 8LS   B

VisitEngland
★★★★
INN

Victory at Mersea

Coast Road, Mersea Island, Colchester CO5 8LS **T:** (01206) 382907
E: info@victoryatmersea.com
W: www.victoryatmersea.com **£ BOOK ONLINE**

B&B PER ROOM PER NIGHT
S: £70.00 - £95.00
D: £80.00 - £120.00
EVENING MEAL PER PERSON
£12.00 - £22.00

f

The Victory is situated on the Mersea waterfront. We have 7 really comfortable, superior quality rooms, individually decorated with a personal touch, some with fantastic estuary views.
Directions: Mersea is clearly signposted from the A12 and you'll find us on the outskirts of the village centre, right on the waterfront.
Bedrooms: 5 double, 1 twin, 1 family.
Open: All year.

Site: ✿ P Payment: 🖃 Leisure: ♿ ♪ ⚐ ↻ Property: 🐾 🖳 Children: 🧸 ⚲ Catering: ⟨✗ ⚱ 🍴 Room: 🗫 ✆ ⏰ TV ♨

For **key to symbols** see page 6

The Old Swan Tea Shop

Contact: Lynda Sullivan, Owner, Hare Street, Buntingford, Hertfordshire SG9 0DZ
T: (01763) 289265 **E:** sullivan@oldswanteashop.co.uk
W: www.oldswanteashop.co.uk

Units   2
Sleeps   4

PER UNIT PER WEEK
£410.00 - £550.00

SPECIAL PROMOTIONS
Please call for more
information.

A picturesque 15th century Hall House set in two acres of garden and orchard, situated on the B1368, the old London to Cambridge coach road; where you will always find a warm and friendly welcome from your hosts Lynda and Bill.

The House is ideally located in the East Hertfordshire countryside to offer easy access to Cambridge, Saffron Walden and other local attractions.

We have a double unit for Bed & Breakfast at £75 per night or £55 for a single person also available. When booking, there is a 20% non-returnable deposit.

Open: All year.
Nearest Shop: 2 miles
Nearest Pub: 2 miles

Units: Bedrooms upstairs and accessed by the spiral staircase. Toilet & shower downstairs.

Site: ✿ P Leisure: ↑ Property: ∥ ☎ 🖳 🖥 🖴 Children: 🐾 🛏 🕴 Unit: 🖬 🖥 📺 🗄 🗄 📺

Lee Valley Caravan Park - Dobbs Weir

Charlton Meadows, Essex Road, Hoddesdon, Hertfordshire EN11 0AS
T: (03000) 030 619 **E:** dobbsweircampsite@vibrantpartnerships.co.uk
W: www.visitleevalley.org.uk/wheretostay **£ BOOK ONLINE**

🚐 (46)   £14.50-£22.50
🚐 (46)   £14.50-£22.50
⚊ (138)   £14.50-£22.50
🏠 (12)   £70.00-£80.00

Lee Valley Caravan Park, Dobbs Weir is nestled in the picturesque countryside of Hertfordshire and Essex and is perfect for a relaxing stay whether in a tent, caravan, motorhome or one of our pre-pitched tents or Wigwams! Your site fee includes free car parking near the local train station, which means you can be exploring the sights of London or Cambridge within an hour. Holiday homes are also available to purchase.

Directions: From the A10 take the Hoddesdon turn off, then at the second roundabout, turn left signposted Dobbs Weir. Lee Valley Caravan Park is on the right within 1 mile.

Open: From 1st March to 31st January.

Site: ⚊📶 Payment: 💷 ☼ Leisure: 🚴 ♪ Children: 🐾 ⚠ Catering: 🍴 Park: ☎ 🖳 🗄 📿
Touring: 🚰 ↻ ♿ ⚒

SOUTH MIMMS, Hertfordshire   Map ref 2D1   S

SELF CATERING

Units   3
Sleeps   2-6

PER UNIT PER WEEK
£250.00 - £330.00

Black Swan

Contact: Mr William Marsterson, Black Swan, 64 Blanche Lane, South Mimms, Potters Bar EN6 3PD **T:** (01707) 644180 / 07932 181441 **F:** (01707) 642344
E: wmarsterson@yahoo.co.uk

Cottage and self-contained flats, 16th century listed building. Rail connections at Potters Bar and London Underground at Barnet allow travel to London within 45 minutes.
Open: All year.
Nearest Shop: 0.25 miles
Nearest Pub: 0.25 miles

Site: ✿ P Property: ⫽ ⛏ 🖥 🗄 🔲 Children: ⛹ 🛏 Unit: 🗄 🔲 🗄 🔌 📺 📀 ☎

BODHAM, Norfolk   Map ref 3B1   S

2★-4★ **SELF CATERING**   **Gold AWARD**

Units   7
Sleeps   2-32

PER UNIT PER WEEK
£395.00 - £3910.00

SPECIAL PROMOTIONS
Please refer to website for details.

Rookery Farm Norfolk

Contact: Mrs Emma McNeil Wilson, Booking Enquiries, Rookery Farm Norfolk, Rookery Farm, West Beckham, Holt, Norfolk NR25 6NX **T:** (01263) 821232
F: (01263) 822242 **E:** holiday@rookeryfarmnorfolk.com
W: www.rookeryfarmnorfolk.com **£ BOOK ONLINE**

The perfect holiday retreat, Rookery Farm offers comfortable, contemporary self-catering accommodation in a tranquil coastal location. We aim to combine luxury, character and everything you could possibly need for a stress free break.

Rookery Farm is tucked away but perfectly placed for all that's good about beautiful north Norfolk with its unspoilt beaches, rolling countryside and charming towns and villages. The barns are set round a garden courtyard; in addition each property has its own private garden with patio, lawn and herb garden. There is a small play area for younger children.

Open: All year.
Nearest Shop: 2.5 miles
Nearest Pub: 0.5 miles

WALKERS FAMILIES CYCLISTS PETS!

Site: ✿ P Payment: 💳 Leisure: ⚑ Property: ⫽ ⛏ 🖥 🗄 🔲 Children: ⛹ 🛏 ⚲
Unit: 🗄 🔲 🗄 🔌 📺 📀 🍳 BBQ

CROMER, Norfolk   Map ref 3C1   S

SELF CATERING

Units   1
Sleeps   1-6

PER UNIT PER WEEK
£300.00

Cliff Hollow

Contact: Ms L Willins, Booking Enquiries, Cliff Haven, 35 Overstrand Road, Cromer NR27 0AL **T:** (01263) 512447 **E:** l.willins@btinternet.com

Cottage in a quiet loop road, 3-5 minutes from the beach, cliffs and town. Secluded garden with garden furniture. Bird watching, walking, golf and cycling all available.
Open: April to October. Christmas, New Year and February half term.
Nearest Shop: 1 mile
Nearest Pub: 1 mile

Site: ✿ P Leisure: 🚲 ♪ ⚑ ↻ ⚲ Property: ⛏ 🔲 Children: ⛹ 🛏 ⚲ Unit: 🗄 🔲 🔌 📺 📀

CROMER, Norfolk Map ref 3C1 S

VisitEngland
★★★★
SELF CATERING

Cromer Country Club

Contact: 127 Overstrand Road, Cromer, Norfolk NR27 0DJ **T:** (0800) 358 6991
E: EuHotels@diamondresorts.com
W: www.DiamondResortsandHotels.com **£ BOOK ONLINE**

Units	85
Sleeps	1-6

PER UNIT PER WEEK
£300.00 - £1414.00

SPECIAL PROMOTIONS
Visit our website or call today for seasonal discounts and great savings.

With views of the picturesque Norfolk coastline, Cromer Country Club is ideally placed for a delightful break in a pleasant Victorian seaside town. Apartments are equipped with practical and modern conveniences and are furnished to a very comfortable standard.

The extensive leisure facilities make the resort a lively family destination. There is a swimming pool, steam room, a pool-side whirlpool and spa area. The Amber Bar and Restaurant offers an extensive menu in pleasant surroundings. Daily specials are created using the best locally sourced ingredients.

Open: All year.
Nearest Shop: 1 mile
Nearest Pub: On site

Units: A choice of Studio, one and two bedroom apartments available. All apartments boast a full kitchen, modern bathroom and TV with DVD player.

Site: ☼ P **Payment:** 💷 **Leisure:** ▶ ◀ ☂ **Property:** 🖥 🔔 🖼 **Children:** 🚲 🛏 ☂ **Unit:** 🖥 💻 🔌 📺 📀 ☎

FAKENHAM, Norfolk Map ref 3B1 S

VisitEngland
★★★★
SELF CATERING

VisitEngland
Gold
AWARD

2 Westgate Barns

Contact: Bettina Gresham, Wareham Road, Binham, Norfolk NR21 0DQ **T:** (01483) 473653
E: enquiries@westgatebarn.co.uk
W: www.westgatebarn.co.uk

Units	1
Sleeps	2-8

PER UNIT PER WEEK
£761.00 - £1380.00

SPECIAL PROMOTIONS
Short breaks available - contact us for details

Luxury self-catering accommodation sleeping up to eight people, situated close to the North Norfolk coast in the beautiful village of Binham. The barn is equipped to a high standard with under floor heated solid oak flooring throughout the ground floor and a wood burning stove in the living room. With many modern amenities the barn still retains its charm and character.

Open: All year.
Nearest Shop: 0.5 miles
Nearest Pub: 0.5 miles

Site: ☼ P **Property:** 🖥 🔔 🖼 **Children:** 🚲 🛏 ☂ **Unit:** 🖥 🖥 💻 🔔 📺 🎮 📀 🍳 BBQ

FAKENHAM, Norfolk   Map ref 3B1

3★ - 4★ SELF CATERING

Moor Farm Stable Cottages

Contact: Paul Davis, Owner, Moor Farm, The Street, Foxley, Dereham NR20 4QP
T: (01362) 688523   **F:** (01362) 688523   **E:** mail@moorfarmstablecottages.co.uk
W: www.moorfarmstablecottages.co.uk

Units   16
Sleeps   3-10
PER UNIT PER WEEK
£300.00 - £1100.00

Situated on a working farm a courtyard of 2/3/4 bedroomed converted stables and barns. Central for North Norfolk coast, Sandringham, Broads and Norwich. Fishing in owner's lakes. Indoor heated swimming pool and spa.
Open: All year including Christmas and New Year.
Nearest Shop: 1 mile
Nearest Pub: 1 mile

Site: ✿ P Leisure: ♪ ↖ Property: 🐾 ▦ ▣ ▦ Children: ➴ ▦ ⋇ Unit: ▫ ▪ ▣ ▦ TV DVD BBQ ☎

FIELD DALLING, Norfolk   Map ref 3B1

VisitEngland SELF CATERING ★★★★   **VisitEngland Gold AWARD**

Hard Farm Barns

Contact: Mrs Angela Harcourt, Hard Farm Barns, Hard Farm House, Little Marsh Lane, Field Dalling, Holt, Norfolk NR25 7LL   **T:** (01328) 830655 / 07790 631760
E: angela@hardfarm.co.uk   **W:** www.hardfarm.co.uk   **£ BOOK ONLINE**

Units   3
Sleeps   1-2

PER UNIT PER WEEK
£265.00 - £425.00

SPECIAL PROMOTIONS
Weekend breaks from £195, low season or last minute.

Spacious 4* Gold Award barn conversions sleeping 2, beautifully furnished and equipped with pretty gardens. The ancient flint barns retain their character with original beams and offer warmth and comfort all year round with full central heating. Oak Barn is ground floor, Beech and Ash are over 2 floors. They offer twin or super king beds, all have spacious bathrooms. Hard Farm is the ideal peaceful location for Holt, Blakeney and North Norfolk Coast with its abundance of bird-watching and walking opportunities. A pet is welcome in Ash Barn only. Wi-Fi. Personally supervised and a warm welcome.

Open: All year.
Nearest Shop: 1.5 miles
Nearest Pub: 1.5 miles

Units: 3 Barns each sleeping 2 people, one ground floor.

Site: ✿ P Property: 🐾 ▦ ▣ Unit: ▫ ▪ ▣ ▦ ↖ TV ◉ DVD

Burlington Palm Hotel

North Drive, Great Yarmouth NR30 1EG **T:** (01493) 844568 **F:** (01493) 331848
E: enquiries@burlington-hotel.co.uk
W: www.burlington-hotel.co.uk **£ BOOK ONLINE**

B&B PER ROOM PER NIGHT
S: £55.00 - £120.00
D: £80.00 - £160.00
EVENING MEAL PER PERSON
£18.50 - £34.00

SPECIAL PROMOTIONS
Nightly discounts for extended stays. Check website for special offers.

Seafront Hotel overlooking Great Yarmouth's Golden Sands. We are a short walk from all the main attractions and 1.5 miles from the train station. We are also the only Hotel in Great Yarmouth with a heated indoor swimming pool. Catering for Old and Young, Private, Business and Groups customers. Free Off Road Car Parking for all.

Directions: From the A12 or A47 follow signs for Seafront turn left, we are on North Drive about 600 Yards north of the Britannia Pier.

Bedrooms: 7 single, 22 double, 21 twin, 18 family.
Open: All year except 28th December to 2nd January.

Site: P Payment: Leisure: **Property:** **Children:** **Catering:**
Room:

Clippesby Hall

Hall Lane, Clippesby, Norfolk NR29 3BL
T: (01493) 367800 **F:** (01493) 367809 **E:** holidays@clippesby.com
W: www.clippesbyhall.com **£ BOOK ONLINE**

(104)   £12.50-£39.00
(104)   £12.50-£39.00
(126)   £12.50-£39.00
(4)   £465.00-£1165.00
(11)   £325.00-£1595.00
125 touring pitches

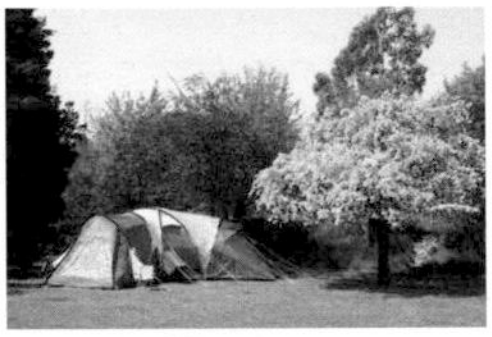

Clippesby Hall is a 5 star touring & camping holiday park in the heart of the Norfolk Broads, with Gold awards from David Bellamy Conservation and the Green Tourism Business Scheme. Family-friendly, with loads to do on and off site.
Directions: From the A47, between Norwich & Great Yarmouth, take the A1064 at Acle (Caister-on-sea road), turn left at Clippesby on the B1152, turn first left.
Open: All year (Easter to October for catering).

Site: **Payment:** **Leisure:** **Children:** **Catering:**
Park: **Touring:**

GREAT YARMOUTH, Norfolk   Map ref 3C1   S

VisitEngland
★★★★★
HOLIDAY PARK

Units	13
Sleeps	1-8

PER UNIT PER WEEK
£325.00 - £1595.00

SPECIAL PROMOTIONS
Short breaks of 3 nights available during Spring, Autumn and Winter, charged from 65% of weekly price.

Clippesby Hall Holiday Park

Contact: John Lindsay, Park owner, Clippesby Hall, Clippesby, Norfolk NR29 3BL
T: (01493) 367800 **F:** (01493) 367809 **E:** holidays@clippesby.com
W: www.clippesbyhall.com **£ BOOK ONLINE**

The self-catering accommodation at Clippesby Hall is located in the heart of the Norfolk Broads, at an award-winning, independent, family holiday park, suitable for all ages. There is a wide range of accommodation available, from one-bedroom apartments, two-bedroom cottages, and three-bedroom Pine Lodges, to four-bedroom houses. Fully fitted kitchens, bathrooms and all heating are included, together with bed linen. The holiday park has its own bar, restaurant, cafe, outdoor pool, tennis, mini-golf, cycle hire, bike trails, and childrens play areas. Great scenery and beaches.

Open: All year (café, bar, resturant and pool April to October).
Nearest Shop: 3 miles
Nearest Pub: 2 miles

Units: 1-4 bedroom apartments, cottages and lodges set in 34 acre holiday park.

Site: ✿ P **Payment:** 💷 **Leisure:** 🏊 🎣 ⚲ ⚲ **Property:** 🐾 🖼 📶 🛋 **Children:** 🐟 🎡 🎠
Unit: 📷 📺 📶 🍴 TV DVD BBQ 📞

GREAT YARMOUTH, Norfolk   Map ref 3C1   SatNav NR29 3QG   C

VisitEngland
★★★★
CAMPING PARK

🚐	£13.00-£26.00
🚗	£13.00-£26.00
⛺	£13.00-£26.00

70 touring pitches

The Grange Touring Park

Yarmouth Road, Ormesby St Margaret, Great Yarmouth, Norfolk NR29 3QG
T: (01493) 730306 **E:** info@grangetouring.co.uk
W: www.grangetouring.co.uk

In a sylvan setting three miles north of Great Yarmouth. 70 touring/tent/motorvan level grassy pitches with lighting, made-up roadways and high standard toilet/shower/disabled facilities. Graded four star/ticks with Quality in Tourism and the AA.
Directions: We are just five minutes drive from Great Yarmouth at the junction of the A149 and B1159.
Open: Mid March to End September.

Site: ⛺P **Payment:** 💷 € **Leisure:** 🎣 **Children:** 🐟 🎡 **Park:** 🖼 📶 🚿 📵 **Touring:** 🔌 🔧 🚰

GREAT YARMOUTH, Norfolk   Map ref 3C1   SatNav NR30 1TB   C

VisitEngland
★★★★★
HOLIDAY PARK

🚐	(180)	£21.00-£66.00
🚗	(180)	£21.00-£66.00
⛺	(180)	£21.00-£66.00
🛖	(48)	£217.00-£1071.00
🏠	(386)	£167.00-£1142.00

180 touring pitches

Vauxhall Holiday Park

Acle New Road, Great Yarmouth, Norfolk NR30 1TB
T: (01493) 857231 **F:** (01493) 331122 **E:** info@vauxhallholidays.co.uk
W: www.vauxhall-holiday-park.co.uk **£ BOOK ONLINE**

Five star Vauxhall Holiday Park in Great Yarmouth, Norfolk is a long established holiday park offering superb accommodation, camping mega pods and touring facilities. Offers family holidays, short breaks and music weekender events.
Directions: Please contact us for directions.
Open: All year.

Site: ⛺P **Payment:** 💷 **Leisure:** 🏊 🎣 ⚲ ⚲ **Children:** 🐟 🎡 **Catering:** ✕ 🍴 **Park:** 🎵 🖼 📶 📵 ⓘ
Touring: 🔌 🔧 🚰 🚰

HOLT, Norfolk Map ref 3B1 S

Garden Cottage

Units 1
Sleeps 2-4
PER UNIT PER WEEK
£330.00 - £575.00

Contact: Rosemary Kimmins, Owner, Chequers, Bale Road, Sharrington, Norfolk NR24 2PG
T: (01263) 860308 / 07779 267330 **E:** rosemary@kimmins1.wanadoo.co.uk

This high quality conversion of an 18th century building overlooks a large garden in a quiet village convenient to Holt, Blakeney and the whole North Norfolk coast. Fitted and furnished to the highest standard with one double and one twin bedroom, bathroom with over bath shower, downstairs cloakroom, fully fitted kitchen. Comfortable sitting room with digital TV, DVD and free Wi-Fi. No pets allowed. Please note that we do not cater for children under 15. **Open:** All year except Christmas and New Year. **Nearest Shop:** 1 mile **Nearest Pub:** 1.5 miles

Site: ❋ P Leisure: ⌇ Property: ∥ ▦ 🗑 🏊 Unit: 🗄 🖥 🗄 ⚡ 📺 📀

HOLT, Norfolk Map ref 3B1 S

Manor Farm Holiday Barns

Units 6
Sleeps 4-10
PER UNIT PER WEEK
£420.00 - £2660.00

Contact: Manor Farm House, Lower Bodham, Holt, Norfolk NR25 6PU **T:** (01263) 710240
E: bookings@manorfarmholidaybarns.co.uk
W: www.manorfarmholidaybarns.co.uk **£ BOOK ONLINE**

Manor Farm Holiday Barns is a beautiful complex of 6 superb grade two listed barns which have been lovingly and sympathetically converted to an extremely high standard. Each barn provides spacious, luxurious and comfortable holiday accommodation whilst retaining the original features and character of traditional brick and flint Norfolk farm buildings, from which you can enjoy and explore the beautiful North Norfolk countryside. **Open:** All year.

Site: ❋ P Payment: 💳 Property: ▦ 🗑 🏊 Children: 🧸 ▥ 🎿 Unit: 🗄 🖥 🗄 ⚡ 📺 ④ 📀 🍖 BBQ

HUNSTANTON, Norfolk Map ref 3B1 S

Chilvers

Units 1
Sleeps 1-6

PER UNIT PER WEEK
£525.00 - £1100.00

SPECIAL PROMOTIONS
Short breaks (minimum 3 nights) available during school term time. Change over day is Saturday. Other days may be available out of season. Towels available. Contact owner to discuss your requirements.

Contact: Harriet Huntsman, Owner, Stockpot, 27 Hall Orchard Lane, Welbourn, Lincoln LN5 0NG **T:** (01400) 273474 / 07778 002858 **E:** hhuntsman@btinternet.com
W: www.chilverscosycottage.co.uk **£ BOOK ONLINE**

- A charming Victorian cottage, modernised and well equipped.
- Spectacular views and direct access onto the salt marsh.
- Downstairs comprises a sitting room with open fire, flatscreen TV and DVD player, a dining room and kitchen with hob, oven, microwave, fridge-freezer, dishwasher and washing machine.
- The twin, double and superking/twin bedrooms and bathroom are on two floors.
- Heated by electric oil wall mounted radiators.
- Outside is a BBQ and garden furniture.
- Ideally situated for sailing, walking, tennis, golf, bird watching, the Coast Hopper bus, excellent hostelries and dining.

Open: All year.
Nearest Shop: 168 metres
Nearest Pub: 100 metres

Units: The double and superking/twin bedrooms plus the bathroom are on the first floor and the twin room is on the second floor.

Site: ❋ P Property: ▦ 🗑 🏊 Children: 🧸 ▥ 🎿 Unit: 🗄 🖥 🗄 ⚡ 📺 📀 🍖 BBQ

Searles Leisure Resort

Contact: South Beach Road, Hunstanton, Norfolk PE36 5BB   **T:** (01485) 534211
E: bookings@searles.co.uk
W: www.searles.co.uk   **£ BOOK ONLINE**

PER UNIT PER WEEK
£14.00 - £1449.00

Creating happiness for all ages. Searles Leisure Resort has so much to offer, young and old alike. A warm welcome will be had by all guests and our facilities are second to none, only 200 metres from Norfolk's beautiful beaches.

Site: ✿ P Payment: 💷 Leisure: ♿ ⚓ ► ⚲ ⚲ ⚲ Property: 🐾 🛏 🖥 🖥 🎦 Children: 🎠 🎮 🎯
Unit: 🖥 🖥 📺 📀

Overcliff Lodge

46 Cromer Road, Mundesley, Norfolk NR11 8DB   **T:** (01263) 720016
E: enquiries@overclifflodge.co.uk
W: www.overclifflodge.co.uk   **£ BOOK ONLINE**

B&B PER ROOM PER NIGHT
S: £55.00 - £70.00
D: £80.00 - £110.00

Overcliff Lodge is a lovely light, bright seaside house, situated just a few minutes' walk from the Blue Flag sandy beach and village centre. The house offers spacious, comfortable, contemporary accommodation and has a small rear garden.
Directions: Overcliff Lodge is situated at the junction of Gimingham Road and Cromer Road just west of Mundesley.
Bedrooms: All en suite with TV/DVD, tea/coffee facilities.
Open: All year except 1 week in January.

Site: ✿ P Payment: 💷 Leisure: ► ↺ Property: 🖥 🏠 ⌀ Catering: 🍴 Room: 🍵 ♨ 📺 📀

MUNDESLEY, Norfolk   Map ref 3C1   S

VisitEngland
★★★★
SELF CATERING

Units   1
Sleeps   1-4

PER UNIT PER WEEK
£389.00 - £555.00

SPECIAL PROMOTIONS
3 nights from £284.00 -
£404.00.

Seaescape Cottage

Contact: Valerie Daniels, Mill Farmhouse, Weybread, Diss IP21 5RS **T:** (01379) 586395
E: valerie@seaescapecottage.com
W: www.norfolkcottages.co.uk/cottage-details/1366

A newly refurbished, Victorian two storey end terrace cottage overlooking Gold Park in the centre of Mundesley, with two bedrooms sleeping up to four people. Kitchen, lounge, dining area, first floor bathroom with shower over bath. Patio doors from the kitchen leading to a small garden. With parking next to cottage.

Bookings for cottage with Norfolk Country Cottages.

Open: All year.
Nearest Shop: 0.25 miles
Nearest Pub: 0.25 miles

Site: ✿ P Leisure: ♪ Property: 🖼 Children: ⅀ Unit: 🗄 🖥 🗄 ⚲ TV DVD BBQ

NORTH RUNCTON, Norfolk   Map ref 3B1   SatNav PE33 0RA   C

VisitEngland
★★★★★
HOLIDAY, TOURING
& CAMPING PARK

🚐 (150)   £15.00
🚏 (150)   £15.00
⛺ (150)   £8.00
🏠 (8)   £350.00
     150 touring pitches

Kings Lynn Caravan & Camping Park

New Road, North Runcton, King's Lynn, Norfolk PE33 0RA
T: (01553) 840004 **E:** klcc@btconnect.com
W: www.kl-cc.co.uk **£ BOOK ONLINE**

Set in approximately ten acres of beautiful mature parkland, the site is situated on the edge of the village of North Runcton, one mile from the Hardwick roundabout where the A47, A10, A149 and A17 meet. Situated in a prime position for touring Norfolk and the Fens, which are both 'Areas of Outstanding Natural Beauty', it is also the nearest campsite to the historic port and market town of Kings Lynn. Fishing, golf, riding, bowling and clay pigeon shooting are a few of the sports available locally. Can also book by telephone.

Directions: On arrival at Kings Lynn take the A47   **Open:** All year.
Swaffham/Norwich road approx 2 miles from
large roundabout where A10, A47 meet. Turning
to North Runcton on right hand side, campsite
entrance about 150 yards on.

Site: ▲🅿 Payment: 💷 € Leisure: ♪ ▶ ♺ Children: ⅀ 🄰 Catering: 🍴 Park: 🐕 🚮 🗄 🚽 🕍 🚿
Touring: 🚰 ♺ 🗑 🔧

NORWICH, Norfolk   Map ref 3C1   [S]

Cable Gap Holiday Park

Contact: Coast Road, Bacton, Norfolk NR12 0EW **T:** (01692) 650667
E: holiday@cablegap.co.uk
W: www.cablegap.co.uk **£ BOOK ONLINE**

Units 14	
Sleeps 2-6	
PER UNIT PER WEEK	
£245.00 - £770.00	

Paul and Claire Medd welcome you to their holiday park in Bacton, with caravans enjoying sea views. Direct beach access and dogs welcome. A great place for all.
In addition to caravans we have a 2 bedroom bungalow for less mobile guests with parking, ramped access and a spacious wet-room bathroom.
Open: Mid-March to Mid-November.

Payment: ⊞ **Leisure:** ♪ **Property:** ⊢ ☲ ⓑ ⊒ **Children:** ⊃ ⊞ ⅋ **Unit:** ▣ ⓣⓥ ⓓⓥⓓ

SAHAM TONEY, Norfolk   Map ref 3B1   SatNav IP25 7EX   [H]

Broom Hall Country Hotel

Richmond Road, Saham Toney, Thetford IP25 7EX **T:** (01953) 882125 **F:** (01953) 885325
E: enquiries@broomhallhotel.co.uk
W: www.broomhallhotel.co.uk **£ BOOK ONLINE**

B&B PER ROOM PER NIGHT
S: £75.00 - £110.00
D: £85.00 - £185.00
EVENING MEAL PER PERSON
£10.00 - £30.00

SPECIAL PROMOTIONS
Two night breaks, dinner B&B, priced per couple for two nights. Winter from £240.00, Summer from £275.00.

Family-run, Victorian country house offering peace and tranquillity in 15 acres of garden and parkland. Open fire warms winter evenings. After a swim in heated indoor pool, enjoy a cream tea on the terrace or in the conservatory or relax in the Rose Room Bar. Purpose-built, ground floor, disabled rooms. Restaurant or bar meals are available lunchtimes and evenings.

Directions: From A11, take A1075 to Watton. Left at lights, 0.5m right at roundabout. From A47, take A1065 Newmarket, left onto B1108, left at roundabout.

Bedrooms: 9 double, 4 twin, 2 family all en suite, ground floor disabled access rooms.
Open: All year except Christmas and New Year.

Site: ✿ P **Payment:** ⊞ **Leisure:** ⅋ ♪ ⊦ ∪ ⋈ ☇ **Property:** ⊤ ⊢ ☲ ⓑ ⋈ ⌀ **Children:** ⊃ ⊞ ⅋
Catering: ⅋ ⅋ **Room:** ⅋ ⅋ ☎ ⓣⓥ ⅋ ⅋

SHERINGHAM, Norfolk   Map ref 3B1   SatNav NR26 8TU   [C]

Woodlands Caravan Park

Holt Road, Upper Sheringham, Norfolk NR26 8TU
T: (01263) 823802 **E:** info@woodlandscaravanpark.co.uk
W: www.woodlandscaravanpark.co.uk

⊞ (120)	£20.00-£34.00
⊞	£20.00-£34.00
180 touring pitches	

This 4 star North Norfolk touring caravan park is situated in a coastal area of outstanding natural beauty close to Sheringham. Surrounded by beautiful woodland walks with excellent on site facilities.
Directions: Located on the A148 between Holt and Sheringham.
Open: Mid March to End of October.

Site: ⅋ A P **Payment:** ⊞ **Leisure:** ♪ ∪ ⅋ **Children:** ⊃ **Catering:** ⅋ **Park:** ⊢ ♫ ⓑ ⅋ ⅋ **Touring:** ⅋ ⅋ ⅋

Woodlands Holiday Cottages

Contact: Church Road, Long Lane, West Beckham, Norfolk NR25 6NX **T:** (01263) 823802 / (01263) 823850 **E:** info@woodlandsholidaycottages.co.uk
W: www.woodlandsholidaycottages.co.uk

| Units | 2 |
| Sleeps | 1-6 |

PER UNIT PER WEEK
£700.00 - £1550.00

SPECIAL PROMOTIONS
Please enquire for shorter breaks minimum nights 3.

Hay Shed Cottage and Malting House Cottage near Sheringham, North Norfolk are two family owned, luxury holiday cottages. The holiday cottages are converted barns over 120 years old and are situated close to the beautiful North Norfolk Coast including Blakeney, Cley Marshes and Sheringham beach.

The barns have been restored and renovated into luxury 5 star holiday cottages by North Norfolk craftsmen with a very high standard of finish and decoration. The cottages offer luxurious and comfortable holiday accommodation complete with the opportunity for swimming, fishing, walking and cycling.

Nearest Shop: Tesco at Sheringham
Nearest Pub: The Roman Camp Inn

Units: Malting House & Hay Shed Cottage.

Leisure: ♪ **Property:** 🖥 🏠 **Unit:** 📱 📺 🔥 BBQ

Chequers Inn

Griston Road, Thompson IP24 1PX **T:** (01953) 483360
E: richard@thompsonchequers.co.uk
W: www.thompsonchequers.co.uk

SPECIAL PROMOTIONS
3 nights stay for £175.

The Chequers is a 16th century village inn with a thatched roof, still retaining all of its original character. A true country retreat in the heart of Breckland. Local produce and fresh fish a speciality. Local real ales include Wolf, Wherry, Adnams and Greene King IPA to name a few. Please contact for 2017 Rates.

Directions: Twelve miles north east of Thetford, just off the A1075. Snetterton Race Track just a short drive away.

Bedrooms: 2 double, 1 twin.
Open: All year.

Site: ✿ P **Payment:** 💷 **Leisure:** ♪ ▶ **Property:** 🐾 🖥 **Children:** 🧸 🎡 **Catering:** 🍽 🍴
Room: 🍵 💧 📞 💿 📺 🎧

THORNHAM, Norfolk   Map ref 3B1

VisitEngland
★★★
SELF CATERING

Units 1
Sleeps 1-4
PER UNIT PER WEEK
£200.00 - £500.00

Malthouse Cottages 1

Contact: Mrs Leslie Rigby, Owner, Brindle Cottage, 6 Church Hill, Castor PE5 7AU
T: (01733) 380399 **F:** (01733) 380399 **E:** rigbysnushall@hotmail.com
W: malthousecottages.co.uk **£ BOOK ONLINE**

Charming and traditional cottage with open fire and enclosed south-facing garden; in a coastal village. Three pubs, Dheli, Yourt and a Fish and Chip shop. The area is renowned for beautiful beaches, sailing, walking, birdwatching, golfing, horse riding and historic houses including Sandringham. Two double rooms and put-u-up. W/E October/April (minimum 2 night stay).
Open: All year.
Nearest Shop: 0.6 miles **Nearest Pub:** 0.2 miles

Site: ❀ Leisure: ▶ Property: ♉ 🖵 Children: ♋ Unit: 🖵 🖵 🖵 🖵 🖳 📺 ⓔ ⓓⓥⓓ ∅ BBQ ☎

WELLS-NEXT-THE-SEA, Norfolk   Map ref 3B1

VisitEngland
★★★★
SELF CATERING

Units 1
Sleeps 1 4

PER UNIT PER WEEK
£380.00 - £530.00

SPECIAL PROMOTIONS
Short breaks available during low season.
£280
Monday to Friday
(4 nights)
or Friday to Monday
(3 nights)

Hayloft Cottage

Contact: Paula Baldry, 11 Mill Road, Wells-Next-The-Sea, Norfolk NR231HD
T: (01328) 711818 / 07784 872977 **E:** paula.baldry@gmail.com
W: www.hayloftcottage.com **£ BOOK ONLINE**

Sea-side character cottage in Wells-next-the-Sea. 4 star cottage just 200 yards from historic quay which you can see from the garden gate. Sleeps 4 in one double and one twin room. Luxury bathroom with bath and separate shower. The lounge has two comfortable sofas for relaxing after long walks on the beach, TV, radio, ipod dock, and free Wi-Fi.

Fully enclosed patio garden with garden furniture and room to store bikes or kayaks. Parking usually available outside but there is also a dedicated parking space on our drive three minutes walk away.

No charge for up to two well behaved family dogs.

Open: All year. Short breaks September to May.
Nearest Shop: 150 yards
Nearest Pub: 150 yards

Site: ❀ P Property: ♉ 🖵 🖵 Unit: 🖵 🖵 🖳 📺 ⓓⓥⓓ

WICKMERE, Norfolk Map ref 3B1 [S]

Church Farm Barns

Contact: Louise Wood, Church Farm Barns, Regent Street, Wickmere, Norfolk NR11 7NB
T: (01263) 577300 **E:** louise@churchfarmbarnsnorfolk.co.uk
W: www.churchfarmbarnsnorfolk.co.uk

VisitEngland 3★-4★ SELF CATERING

VisitEngland Gold AWARD

Units   3
Sleeps   2-17

PER UNIT PER WEEK
£275.00 - £1240.00

SPECIAL PROMOTIONS
Please contact for
short breaks or last
minute bookings.

Weekend break for two
from £196.00.

Discounts may be
available for booking
all 3 barns sleeping up
to 17.

Lost in rustic and tranquil North Norfolk where time stands still, this luxurious accommodation offers a peaceful retreat for bird watchers, wildlife enthusiasts, dog owners, walkers and cyclists. Blickling (NT), Felbrigg (NT), Sheringham Park (NT), Wolterton and Mannington all within walking distance. Close to attractions: Broads National Park and North Norfolk coast. The smallest barn provides a cosy escape for two, while taken together the barns are a great venue for family parties and reunions. Friendly owners on site.

Open: All year.
Nearest Shop: 1.25 miles
Nearest Pub: 0.75 miles

Units: Corner Barn: 2 double and 1 triple en suite beds (1 ground floor) plus sofa bed.
Owl Barn: 1 double and 2 twin beds.
Bailey's Barn: 1 double.

Site: ❀ P Leisure: ⏵ ♺ ♠ Property: 🐾 📺 🅱 🖵 Children: 🛝 🎠 ⚥ Unit: 🗄 🗜 🖳 🍵 📺 📀 🖭 ∅ BBQ

BURY ST. EDMUNDS, Suffolk Map ref 3B2 [S]

Culford Farm Cottages

Contact: Mr Steve Flack, Culford Farm Cottages, Home Farm, Culford, Bury St Edmunds, Suffolk IP28 6DS **T:** (01284) 728334 / 07725 201086 **E:** enquiries@homefarmculford.co.uk
W: www.culfordfarmcottages.co.uk

VisitEngland 4★-5★ SELF CATERING

Units   3
Sleeps   2-6
PER UNIT PER WEEK
£336.00 - £856.00

Unique, well-equipped farm cottages offering an indoor pool available all year, private hot tubs, and riverside walks on our peacefully located working farm with easy access to Bury St Edmunds and beyond.
Open: All year.
Nearest Shop: 2 miles
Nearest Pub: 2 miles

Site: ❀ P Leisure: ⏵ ♞ Property: 🐾 📺 🅱 🖵 Children: 🛝 🎠 ⚥ Unit: 🗄 🗜 🖳 🅱 🍵 📺 📀 BBQ

BURY ST. EDMUNDS, Suffolk   Map ref 3B2   [S]

Lackford Lakes Barns

Contact: Owner, Lackford Hall, Lackford, Nr Bury St Edmunds, Suffolk IP28 6HX
E: Bookings@LackfordLakesBarns.co.uk
W: www.lackfordlakesbarns.co.uk **£ BOOK ONLINE**

Units   4
Sleeps   4-23

PER UNIT PER WEEK
£450.00 - £1200.00

SPECIAL PROMOTIONS
Weekly and short breaks of 3 or 4 nights with a flexible start date.

Situated within the picturesque and tranquil Lackford Lakes Nature Reserve, our charming accommodation is set in the heart of the beautiful Suffolk countryside, only 5 miles from historic and vibrant Bury St Edmunds, offering 4 self catering holiday cottages sleeping up to 23 guests.

Our grade 2 listed renovated barns are The Cart Lodge (sleeps 7), Holm Oak (sleeps 6), Lark Lodge (sleeps 6) and curlew Cottage (sleeps 4).

Open: All year.
Nearest Shop: 4 miles
Nearest Pub: 2 miles

Units: Grade 2 listed, converted barns of brick, flint and timber, insulated, double glazed, underfloor heating, comfortably furnished with modern bathrooms.

Site: ✿ **P Payment:** 🖭 **Leisure:** ♪ ♪ ♻ ✿ **Property:** ⫽ 🖼 🗄 ⊠ **Children:** ⛷ 🛏 ⚲
Unit: 🗄 🗄 🖥 🗄 ⚲ 📺 📀 ⌕ BBQ

BURY ST. EDMUNDS, Suffolk   Map ref 3B2   [S]

Rede Hall Farm Park

Contact: Mrs Christine Oakley, Partner, Rede Hall Farm Park, Rede Hall Farm, Chedburgh, Bury St Edmunds IP29 4UG **T:** (01284) 850695 **F:** (01284) 850345
E: chris@redehallfarmpark.co.uk **W:** www.redehallfarmpark.co.uk **£ BOOK ONLINE**

Units   2
Sleeps   2-6
PER UNIT PER WEEK
£375.00 - £665.00

Country retreat in old-fashioned farmyard. Jenny Wren has two ground floor double bedrooms and galleried twin room. Nuthatch has two ground floor double en suite bedrooms, sofa bed, single bed in galleried area. Also supplied is a shared Hot Spa Tub. Shepherds Hut sleeps two in a private field with its own Hot Spa Tub. This is only available March to end of September. Patio, BBQ, wood burner etc. **Open:** All year - Shepherds Hut April to October. **Nearest Shop:** 3 miles **Nearest Pub:** 1 miles

Site: ✿ **P Leisure:** ♪ **Property:** 🐾 🖼 ⊠ **Children:** ⛷ 🛏 ⚲ **Unit:** 🗄 🗄 🖥 🗄 ⚲ 📺 📀 BBQ

BURY ST. EDMUNDS, Suffolk   Map ref 3B2   SatNav IP28 6EY   [B]

West Stow Hall

Icklingham Road, West Stow, Bury St. Edmunds IP28 6EY **T:** (01284) 728127
E: eileengilbert54@aol.com
W: www.weststowhall.com

B&B PER ROOM PER NIGHT
S: £75.00 - £80.00
D: £120.00 - £130.00
EVENING MEAL PER PERSON
£15.00 - £30.00

Enjoy the tranquillity and beauty of this historic hall set in six acres of lovely grounds. Large comfortable bedrooms, great breakfasts and a warm welcome are guaranteed. The Studio, with ground floor access, is ideally suited for less mobile guests.
Directions: M11 to A11 direction Mildenhall. Before Mildenhall take A1101 to Bury St Edmunds, left turn West Stow. The hall is clearly signposted on the left. **Bedrooms:** 2 doubles, 1 twin, 1 family.
Open: All year except Christmas and the New Year.

Site: ✿ **P Payment:** 🖭 € **Leisure:** ♿ ♪ ♪ ♻ **Property:** 🐾 🖼 ⊠ **Children:** ⛷ ⚲ **Catering:** 🍴
Room: ⚲ 📶 ☕

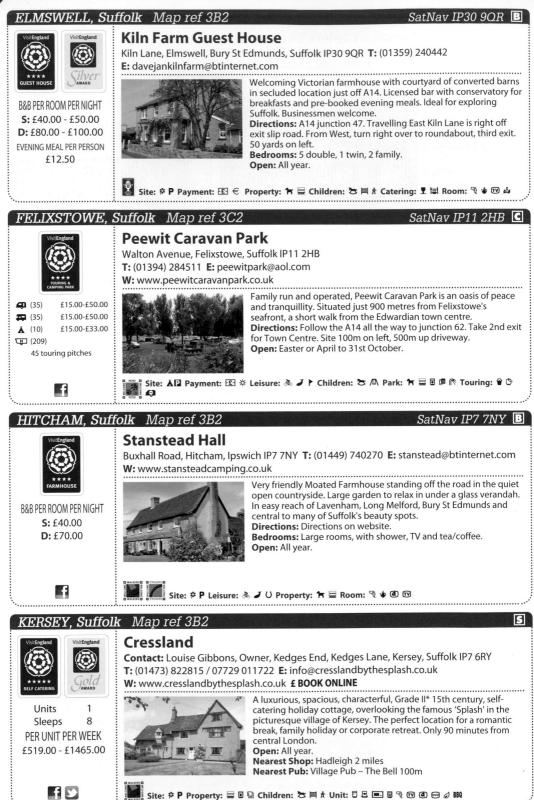

ELMSWELL, Suffolk   Map ref 3B2   SatNav IP30 9QR B

VisitEngland ★★★★ GUEST HOUSE
VisitEngland Silver AWARD

B&B PER ROOM PER NIGHT
S: £40.00 - £50.00
D: £80.00 - £100.00
EVENING MEAL PER PERSON
£12.50

Kiln Farm Guest House

Kiln Lane, Elmswell, Bury St Edmunds, Suffolk IP30 9QR   **T:** (01359) 240442
E: davejankilnfarm@btinternet.com

Welcoming Victorian farmhouse with courtyard of converted barns in secluded location just off A14. Licensed bar with conservatory for breakfasts and pre-booked evening meals. Ideal for exploring Suffolk. Businessmen welcome.
Directions: A14 junction 47. Travelling East Kiln Lane is right off exit slip road. From West, turn right over to roundabout, third exit. 50 yards on left.
Bedrooms: 5 double, 1 twin, 2 family.
Open: All year.

Site: ✿ P Payment: £ € Property: ☎ ⌨ Children: ⛱ ♨ ☂ Catering: ♟ ⚱ Room: ☏ ♨ TV ♒

FELIXSTOWE, Suffolk   Map ref 3C2   SatNav IP11 2HB C

VisitEngland ★★★★ TOURING & CAMPING PARK

🚐 (35)   £15.00-£50.00
🚙 (35)   £15.00-£50.00
⛺ (10)   £15.00-£33.00
🚐 (209)
45 touring pitches

[f]

Peewit Caravan Park

Walton Avenue, Felixstowe, Suffolk IP11 2HB
T: (01394) 284511   **E:** peewitpark@aol.com
W: www.peewitcaravanpark.co.uk

Family run and operated, Peewit Caravan Park is an oasis of peace and tranquillity. Situated just 900 metres from Felixstowe's seafront, a short walk from the Edwardian town centre.
Directions: Follow the A14 all the way to junction 62. Take 2nd exit for Town Centre. Site 100m on left, 500m up driveway.
Open: Easter or April to 31st October.

Site: ⛺🅿 Payment: £ ☀ Leisure: ♿ ♪ ▶ Children: ⛱ ⚠ Park: ☎ ⌨ ▯ ⚑ ♺ Touring: ⛽ ♺

HITCHAM, Suffolk   Map ref 3B2   SatNav IP7 7NY B

VisitEngland ★★★★ FARMHOUSE

B&B PER ROOM PER NIGHT
S: £40.00
D: £70.00

[f]

Stanstead Hall

Buxhall Road, Hitcham, Ipswich IP7 7NY   **T:** (01449) 740270   **E:** stanstead@btinternet.com
W: www.stansteadcamping.co.uk

Very friendly Moated Farmhouse standing off the road in the quiet open countryside. Large garden to relax in under a glass verandah. In easy reach of Lavenham, Long Melford, Bury St Edmunds and central to many of Suffolk's beauty spots.
Directions: Directions on website.
Bedrooms: Large rooms, with shower, TV and tea/coffee.
Open: All year.

Site: ✿ P Leisure: ♿ ♪ ∪ Property: ☎ ⌨ Room: ☏ ♨ ▣ TV

KERSEY, Suffolk   Map ref 3B2   S

VisitEngland ★★★★★ SELF CATERING
VisitEngland Gold AWARD

Units   1
Sleeps   8
PER UNIT PER WEEK
£519.00 - £1465.00

[f] [t]

Cressland

Contact: Louise Gibbons, Owner, Kedges End, Kedges Lane, Kersey, Suffolk IP7 6RY
T: (01473) 822815 / 07729 011722   **E:** info@cresslandbythesplash.co.uk
W: www.cresslandbythesplash.co.uk   £ **BOOK ONLINE**

A luxurious, spacious, characterful, Grade II* 15th century, self-catering holiday cottage, overlooking the famous 'Splash' in the picturesque village of Kersey. The perfect location for a romantic break, family holiday or corporate retreat. Only 90 minutes from central London.
Open: All year.
Nearest Shop: Hadleigh 2 miles
Nearest Pub: Village Pub – The Bell 100m

Site: ✿ P Property: ⌨ ▯ ▤ Children: ⛱ ♨ ☂ Unit: ▯ ▣ ▭ ▯ ☏ TV ◉ ⊙ BBQ

VisitEngland
★★★★★
SELF CATERING

Wheelwrights Cottage

Contact: Doreen Gowan, The Forge, Kersey Upland, Kersey, Ipswich, Suffolk IP7 6EN
T: (01473) 829311 / 07785 572878 **E:** peter@pjgowan.net
W: www.wheelwrightscottage.co.uk **£ BOOK ONLINE**

Units	1
Sleeps	2

PER UNIT PER WEEK
£360.00

SPECIAL PROMOTIONS
£60 per night -
minimum of three
nights.

Two nights are
available at £180.

Wheelwrights is a cottage recently converted from an 18th century wheelwrights barn situated in the wilds of Suffolk, close to the picturesque village of Kersey. Wonderful countryside for walking or cycling. It consists of one bedroom with a 6ft bed, en suite bathroom with bath and shower, fully equipped kitchen and a large lounge with wood-burning stove.

Wheelwrights is situated in the grounds of a 16th century thatched cottage - 'The Forge' in Kersey Upland where the owners live. The villages of Hadleigh, Lavenham, Long Melford and Dedham are a short drive away and Felixstowe beach is only 40 mins.

Open: All year.
Nearest Shop: 2.5 miles
Nearest Pub: 1 mile

Units: Large lounge with wood-burning stove. Fully fitted kitchen. Bedroom with king size bed and en suite bathroom.

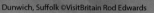
WALKERS ☑ CYCLISTS ☑
WELCOME WELCOME
WALKERS ☑ CYCLISTS ☑

Site: P Leisure: ▶ Property: 🖥 🔲 🔲 **Unit:** 🔲 🔲 🔲 🔲 🔍 📺 🔲 ⌔

Dunwich, Suffolk ©VisitBritain Rod Edwards

LAVENHAM, Suffolk   Map ref 3B2   S

Staddles

Contact: Helen Burgess, Owner, The White Horse, 57-58 Water Street, Lavenham, Suffolk CO10 9RW **T:** (07827) 911539 **E:** helen424@btinternet.com
W: www.staddlescottage-lavenham.co.uk **£ BOOK ONLINE**

Units	1
Sleeps	2

PER UNIT PER WEEK
£425.00 - £575.00

Lavenham is a historic medieval village boasting over 340 listed buildings. Lavenham has a long and colourful history, featuring at different times: Edward de Vere, 17th Earl of Oxford, one of those proposed as the real Shakespeare and Louis Napoleon in the 19th century. Please note short breaks are available. Midweek 4 night stays beginning Monday and 3 night weekend breaks starting Friday. **Open:** All year.
Nearest Shop: 0.10 miles **Nearest Pub:** 0.10 miles

Site: ❁ P Leisure: 🦽 ⚐ ⚲ Property: 🐾 ▦ ⎙ ⛳ Unit: ⎙ ⊟ ▣ 🖥 ⚲ 📺 ◉ 📀 BBQ

LOWESTOFT, Suffolk   Map ref 3C1   S

23 Alandale Drive

Contact: Karen Foster, Owner, Kessingland, Lowestoft, Suffolk NR33 7SD
T: (01223) 576874 / 07952 779046 **E:** karenfoster251@yahoo.co.uk

Units	1
Sleeps	4

PER UNIT PER WEEK
£198.00 - £360.00

Holiday Bungalow in quiet village location, a very quick walk away from the beach. In Kessingland near Lowestoft, Southwold and Broads. Short breaks available. Guide dogs accepted, no pets. Great for walkers, cyclists and bird watchers as the property is located alongside the Suffolk Coastal Path. Buses run regularly to Southworld, Lowesoft and Great Yarmouth. 2 bedrooms, one double bed and an adult bunk bed.
Open: 1st March to 4th January.
Nearest Shop: 1.5 miles
Nearest Pub: 0.5 miles

Site: ❁ P Payment: € Leisure: 🦽 ⚐ ⚲ ⛵ Property: ▦ Children: 🛝 Unit: ⎙ ▣ 📺 📀

PIN MILL, Suffolk   Map ref 3C2   S

Alma Cottage

Contact: Mr John Pugh, Alma Cottage, Culver End, Amberley, Stroud GL5 5AG
T: (01453) 872551 **E:** john.pugh@talk21.com

Units	1
Sleeps	1-4

PER UNIT PER WEEK
£275.00 - £460.00

In centre of Pin Mill, 25m from high water, views over Orwell Estuary. A traditional sailing village, free public access to water, ideal for families, walkers, birdwatchers and painters.
Open: All year.
Nearest Shop: 0.75 miles
Nearest Pub: 0.10 miles

FAMILIES Site: ❁ P Payment: € Leisure: ⚐ Property: 🐾 ▦ ⎙ ⛳ Children: 🛝 ⚘ Unit: ⎙ ▣ 🖥 ⚲ 📺 ◉ 📀 ⚘ ☎

SAXMUNDHAM, Suffolk   Map ref 3C2   S

Buff's Old Barn

Contact: Jeannie Wright, Owner / Managing Director, Woodside Barn Cottages, Buffs Old Barn, Woodside Farm, Church Road, Friston, Saxmundham, Suffolk IP17 1PU
T: (03452) 680788 / 07899 891498 **E:** jeannie@woodsidebarncottages.co.uk
W: www.woodsidebarncottages.co.uk **£ BOOK ONLINE**

Units	1
Sleeps	6

PER UNIT PER WEEK
£553.00 - £1351.00

This converted barn's design makes it great for families to enjoy a relaxing holiday close to the Suffolk Coast. A delightful location on the owner's 32-acre working farm. Own enclosed private garden area, direct access to public footpaths. Located in the pretty village of Friston, a short drive from the coastal delights of Aldeburgh & Southwold. **Open:** All year including Christmas & New Year.
Nearest Shop: 3 Miles **Nearest Pub:** 3 Miles

Site: ❁ P Payment: 💳 Leisure: ⚐ Property: 🐾 ▦ ⎙ ⛳ Children: 🛝¹ 🏓 ⚘ Unit: ⎙ ▣ ⚲ ◉ 📀

SOUTHWOLD, Suffolk   Map ref 3C2

Highsteppers at Blythview

Contact: Patricia Dowding, Owner, Highsteppers Holidays, Summer House, Rectory Road, Middleton, Suffolk IP17 3NR **T:** (01728) 648819 / 07977 196156
E: pat_roy16@hotmail.com **W:** www.highsteppers-suffolk.co.uk

Units	1
Sleeps	2-4

PER UNIT PER WEEK
£370.00 - £590.00

SPECIAL PROMOTIONS
3 night weekend breaks and 4 night weekday breaks available outside peak seasons. Discount of 5% offered for party of 2 people only, using one bedroom only, if booking a full week.

Highsteppers is a 2 storey apartment on the 1st and 2nd floors situated within a converted Georgian Grade II listed building, originally built as a Workhouse for the Blything Union. It also has the benefit of a shared indoor swimming pool, games room and mini-gym. Fully equipped kitchen, good sized lounge and diner on first floor. Two double bedrooms, one en suite and one separate bathroom.

Less than 10 miles from RSPB Minsmere as featured on Springwatch. Stunning views over the Blyth Valley and only 5 miles from Southwold.

Open: All year.
Nearest Shop: 1 mile
Nearest Pub: 1 mile

Units: A beautifully appointed apartment with stunning views over the Blyth Valley. There are 2 double bedrooms, one with shower room and en suite.

Site: P **Leisure:** ♿ ♪ ⏱ ∪ ⚲ ⚲ **Property:** 🔌 **Children:** 🛏5 🏠 🅰 **Unit:** 🔌 🔋 💻 📷 🍳 📺 📀

SOUTHWOLD, Suffolk   Map ref 3C2

Solely Southwold

Contact: Kathy Oliver, Owner, 1 Sawyers Cottage, Norfolk Road, Wangford, Suffolk NR34 8RE **T:** (01502) 578383 **E:** kathy@solely-southwold.co.uk
W: www.solely-southwold.co.uk

Units	4
Sleeps	2-5

PER UNIT PER WEEK
£330.00 - £750.00

Well-appointed central Southwold holiday homes, established in 1995. 2 cottages and 2 flats (1 on the ground floor). Convenient for beach, shops, pubs, restaurants and wonderful walks. Personally managed by the owners to high standards in home-from-home competitively priced accommodation. Free secure Wi-Fi. Book via phone or e-mail. **Open:** All year.
Nearest Shop: 10 metres
Nearest Pub: 50 metres

Site: ♿ P **Payment:** € **Property:** 🔌 🖥 📺 **Children:** 🛏 🏠 **Unit:** 🔌 🔋 💻 📷 🍳 📺 📀 ✏

THORPENESS, Suffolk   Map ref 3C2

House In The Clouds

Contact: Mrs Sylvia Le Comber, House In The Clouds, 4 Hinde House, 14 Hinde Street, London W1U 3BG **T:** (020) 7224 3615 / 07718 455988
E: houseintheclouds@btopenworld.com **W:** www.houseintheclouds.co.uk

Units	1
Sleeps	12

PER UNIT PER WEEK
£2200.00 - £3275.00

Wonderfully-eccentric 'fantasy unmatched in England'. Five bedrooms, three bathrooms, unrivalled views from 'Room at the Top'. Billiards, snooker, table tennis, tennis, boules, bird watching. Sea, golf, Sailing on the Meare, music and walks.
Open: All year.
Nearest Shop: 0.30 miles
Nearest Pub: 0.30 miles

Site: ♿ P **Leisure:** ♿ ♪ ⏱ ∪ ⚲ ⚲ **Property:** 🔌 🖥 📺 **Children:** 🛏 🏠 🅰 **Unit:** 🔌 🔋 💻 📷 🍳 📺 📀 BBQ ☎

WOODBRIDGE, Suffolk   Map ref 3C2

Units   5
Sleeps   2-5
PER UNIT PER WEEK
£285.00 - £665.00

Ore Valley Holiday Cottages

Contact: Justine Howe, Booking Administrator, Sink Farm, Little Glemham, Woodbridge, Suffolk IP13 0BJ **T:** (01728) 602783 / 07796 148220 **E:** cottages@fridaystfarm.co.uk
W: www.orevalleyholidaycottages.co.uk **£ BOOK ONLINE**

The Ore Valley Holiday Cottages are set amidst the rural Suffolk countryside. Just a short drive away from Suffolk's Heritage Coast, these five converted farm stables offer a 4 star self-catering stay for the keen explorer. All of the cottages give you the chance to take in a piece of the breathtaking views that make Suffolk the perfect getaway. **Open:** All year.
Nearest Shop: 3 miles
Nearest Pub: 1 mile

Site: ✿ **P Payment:** ⊞ **Leisure:** ♦ **Property:** ∥ ⌕ ▭ ⊟ ⬚ **Children:** ⛾ ▥ ⅄ **Unit:** ⬚ ⊟ ▭ ⊠ ℛ TV DVD
BBQ

WORTHAM, Suffolk   Map ref 3B2

Units   1
Sleeps   2-11

PER UNIT PER WEEK
£160.00 - £2000.00

SPECIAL PROMOTIONS
Short breaks available:
please contact for
details.

Ivy House Farm

Contact: Mrs Jacky Bradley, Owner, Ivy House Farm, Long Green, Wortham, Diss, Norfolk IP22 1RD **T:** (01379) 898395 / 07946 620217 **E:** prjsbrad@aol.com
W: www.ivyhousefarmcottages.co.uk **£ BOOK ONLINE**

Ivy House Farm is located on a wide medieval common in the sparsely populated village of Wortham on the Norfolk/Suffolk border near Diss. It is a 16th century Suffolk long house set in spacious grounds with its own enclosed garden. This is an excellent centre for making excursions in all directions. Head North to Norwich, Sandringham, the broads & north Norfolk coast or south to Lavenham and Constable country or east to the coast at Gt Yarmouth, Lowestoft, Southwold, Dunwich and Minsmere: head west to Newmarket, Cambridge and Thetford forest or stay at the farm and relax.

Open: All year.   **Units:** Farm house: Sleeps 11.
Nearest Shop: 0.5 miles
Nearest Pub: 0.5 miles

Site: ✿ **P Payment:** € **Leisure:** ⛾ ♪ ⏵ ∪ ♦ ⸮ **Property:** ⌕ ▭ ⊟ ⬚ **Children:** ⛾ ▥ ⅄
Unit: ⬚ ⊟ ▭ ⊠ ℛ TV DVD ∅ BBQ

If you have
access needs...

Guests with hearing, visual or mobility needs can feel confident about booking accommodation that participates in the National Accessible Scheme (NAS).

Look out for the NAS symbols which are included throughout the accommodation directory. Using the NAS could help make the difference between a good holiday and a perfect one!

For more information on the NAS and tips & ideas on holiday travel in England, go to: www.visitengland.com/accessforall

Don't Miss...

Burghley House
Stamford, Lincolnshire PE9 3JY
(01780) 752451
www.burghley.co.uk
Used in films Pride and Prejudice and The Da Vinci Code, the house boasts eighteen magnificent State Rooms and a huge collection of works and art, including one of the most important private collections of 17th century Italian paintings, the earliest inventoried collection of Japanese ceramics in the West and wood carvings by Grinling Gibbons and his followers.

Chatsworth
Bakewell, Derbyshire DE45 1PP
(01246) 565300
www.chatsworth.org
Chatsworth is a spectacular historic house set in the heart of the Peak District in Derbyshire, on the banks of the river Derwent. There are over 30 rooms to explore, including the magnificent Painted Hall and Sculpture Gallery. In the garden, discover water features, giant sculptures and beautiful flowers set in one of Britain's most well-known historic landscapes.

Sherwood Forest
Sherwood Forest Visitor Centre,
Edwinstowe, Nottinghamshire NG21 9HN
(01623) 823202
www.nottinghamshire.gov.uk
Once part of a royal hunting forest and legendary home of Robin Hood, Sherwood Forest National Nature Reserve covers 450 acres of ancient woodlands where veteran oaks over 500 years old grow, as well as being home to a wide variety of flora and fauna. Follow the waymarked trails amongst the leafy glades and spot birds including nightjars, woodlarks, hawfinches, marsh and willow tits. Marvel in the shadow of the historic Major Oak, browse the Visitor Centre shops or relax with a coffee in the Forest Table Restaurant.

Sudbury Hall
Main Road, Sudbury, Ashbourne DE6 5HT
(01283) 585337
www.nationaltrust.org.uk
Discover two contrasting experiences. Sudbury Hall is the lavish country home of the Lords Vernon, offering 17th century craftsmanship. Be amazed by the grandeur of the Great Staircase, Long Gallery and the captivating story which the house tells. The Museum of Childhood is a delight for all ages with something for everyone. Explore the childhoods of times gone by, make stories, play with toys and share your childhood with others.

Twycross Zoo
Hinckley, Leicestershire CV9 3PX
(08444) 741777
www.twycrosszoo.org
Set in more than 80 acres and renowned as a World Primate Centre, Twycross Zoo has around 500 animals of almost 150 species, including many endangered animals and native species in the Zoo's Nature Reserve. Pay a visit to meet the famous orangutans, gorillas and chimpanzees plus many other mammals, birds and reptiles.

East Midlands

Derbyshire, Leicestershire,
Lincolnshire, Northamptonshire,
Nottinghamshire, Rutland

The East Midlands is a region of historic castles and cathedrals, lavish houses, underground caves, a rich industrial heritage and spectacular countryside including the Peak District and the Lincolnshire Wolds. Climb to enchanting hilltop castles for breathtaking views. Explore medieval ruins and battlefields. Discover hidden walks in ancient forests, cycle across hills and wolds, or visit one of the regions many events and attractions.

Lincolnshire
Derbyshire
Nottinghamshire
Rutland
Leicestershire
Northamptonshire

Explore –
East Midlands

Derbyshire

'There is no finer county in England than Derbyshire. To sit in the shade on a fine day and look upon verdure is the most perfect refreshment' according to Jane Austen. Derbyshire is the home of the UK's first National Park, the Peak District, which has been popular with holidaymakers for centuries. It forms the beginning of the Pennine Chain and its reservoirs and hills are second to none in beauty. This is excellent walking, riding and cycling country and contains plenty of visitor attractions and historic sites such as Gullivers Theme Park at Matlock Bath and the 17th century Palladian Chatsworth, seat of the Duke of Devonshire.

Leicestershire & Rutland

Leicester is a cathedral city with a 2000-year history, now host to a modern university, and the county's pastures fuel one of its main exports: cheese. Foxton Locks is the largest flight of staircase locks on the English canal system with two 'staircases' of five locks bustling with narrowboats. Belvoir Castle dominates the rolling agricultural land of the Vale of Belvoir. Rockingham Castle at Market Harborough was built by William the Conqueror and stands on the edge of an escarpment giving dramatic views over five counties and the Welland Valley below. Quietly nestling in the English countryside, England's smallest county of Rutland is an idyllic rural destination with an array of unspoilt villages and two charming market towns, packed with rich history and character, centred on Rutland Water, one of England's largest man-made lakes.

Lincolnshire

Lincolnshire is said to produce one eighth of Britain's food and its wide open meadows are testament to this. Gothic triple-towered Lincoln Cathedral is visible from the Fens for miles around, while Burghley House hosts the famous annual International Horse Trials and is a top tourist attraction. The Lincolnshire Wolds, a range of hills designated an 'Area of Outstanding Natural Beauty' and the highest area of land in eastern England between Yorkshire and Kent, is idyllic walking and cycling country. Also perfect for bird watchers and nature lovers, Lincolnshire's Natural Coast is one of this region's best kept secrets!

Northamptonshire

County town Northampton is famous for its shoe making, celebrated in the Central Museum and Art Gallery, and the county also has its share of stately homes and historic battlefields. Silverstone in the south is home to the British Grand Prix. Althorp was the birthplace and is now the resting place of the late Diana Princess of Wales.

Nottinghamshire

Nottingham's castle dates from 1674 and its Lace Centre illustrates the source of much of the city's wealth, alongside other fine examples of Nottinghamshire's architectural heritage such as Papplewick Hall & Gardens. Legendary tales of Robin Hood, Sherwood Forest and historic battles may be what the county is best known for, but it also hosts world class sporting events, live performances and cutting edge art, and there's plenty of shopping and fine dining on offer too. To the North, the remains of Sherwood Forest provide a welcome breathing space and there are plenty of country parks and nature reserves, including the beautiful lakes and landscape of the National Trust's Clumber Park.

Visit – East Midlands

 Attractions with this sign participate in the Visitor Attraction Quality Assurance Scheme.

Derbyshire

Buxton Festival
July, Buxton, Derbyshire
www.buxtonfestival.co.uk
A summer celebration of the best opera, music and literature, at the heart of the beautiful Peak District.

Creswell Crags
Chesterfield, Derbyshire S80 3LH
(01909) 720378
www.creswell-crags.org.uk
A world famous archaeological site, honeycombed with caves and smaller fissures. Stone tools and remains of animals found in the caves by archaeologists provide evidence for a fascinating story of life during the last Ice Age between 50,000 and 10,000 years ago. It is also home to Britain's only known Ice Age cave art.

Derby Museum and Art Gallery
Derby DE1 1BS
(01332) 641901
www.derbymuseums.org
Derby Museum and Art Gallery holds collections and displays relating to the history, culture and natural environment of Derby and its region.

Derbyshire Food & Drink Fair
May, Derby, Derbyshire DE22 5JH
www.derbyshirefoodanddrinkfair.co.uk
Over 150 stalls will showcase the best local produce from Derbyshire and the Peak District region, as well as unique and exotic foods from further afield.

Gulliver's Kingdom Theme Park
Matlock Bath, Derbyshire DE4 3PG
(01925) 44488
www.gulliversfun.co.uk
With more than 40 rides & attractions, Gulliver's provides the complete family entertainment experience.

Haddon Hall
Bakewell, Derbyshire DE45 1LA
(01629) 812855
www.haddonhall.co.uk
Haddon Hall is a stunning English Tudor and country house on the River Wye at Bakewell in Derbyshire, Haddon Hall is one of England's finest examples of a medieval manor.

Hardwick Hall
Chesterfield, Derbyshire S44 5QJ
(01246) 850430
www.nationaltrust.org.uk/hardwick
Owned by the National Trust, Hardwick Hall is one of Britain's greatest Elizabethan houses. The water-powered Stainsby Mill is fully functioning and the Park has a fishing lake and circular walks.

Heights of Abraham
Matlock, Derbyshire DE4 3NT
(01629) 582365
www.heightsofabraham.com
Country park and famous show caverns set in 60 acres of woodland and reached by cable car over deep limestone gorge in the Peak District.

Kedleston Hall
Derby DE22 5JH
(01332) 842191
www.nationaltrust.org.uk/kedleston-hall
A fine example of a neo-classical mansion built between 1759-65 by the architect Robert Adam and set in over 800 acres of parkland and landscaped pleasure grounds. Administered by The National Trust.

Renishaw Hall and Gardens
Dronfield, Derbyshire S21 3WB
(01246) 432310
www.renishaw-hall.co.uk
The Gardens are Italian in design and were laid out over 100 years ago by Sir George Sitwell. The garden is divided into 'rooms' with yew hedges, flanked with classical statues.

The Silk Mill - Museum of Industry
and History
Derby DE1 3AF
(01332) 641901
www.derbymuseums.org/locations/silk-mill
*The Silk Mill was completed around 1723 and the
re-built Mill now contains displays on local history
and industry.*

Speedwell Cavern and Peak District Cavern
Castleton, Hope Valley, Derbyshire S33 8WA
(01433) 623018
www.speedwellcavern.co.uk
*Speedwell Cavern and Peak District Cavern offer
the chance for amazing adventures in the heart of
the Peak District, with unusual rock formations, the
largest natural cave entrance in the British Isles and
an incredible underground boat trip.*

Sudbury Hall
Ashbourne, Derbyshire DE6 5HT
(01283) 585337
www.nationaltrust.org.uk/sudburyhall/
*Explore the grand 17th century hall with its richly
decorated interior and see life below stairs.* Learn
about George Vernon, the young man who built the
hall you see today at Sudbury in 1660.

Leicestershire & Rutland

Artisan Cheese Fair
April, Melton Mowbray, Leicestershire LE13 1JY
www.artisancheesefair.co.uk
*A chance to taste the huge range of cheeses that
are made locally and further afield. Visitors to the
Artisan Cheese Fair can sample and purchase many
of the 200 popular and rare cheeses on show from
over 60 exhibitors including the leading names in
UK artisan cheese production.*

Ashby-de-la-Zouch Castle
Leicestershire LE65 1BR
(01530) 413343
www.english-heritage.org.uk/visit/places/ashby-de-
la-zouch-castle
*Visit Ashby-de-la-Zouch Castle where you will see
the ruins of this historical castle, the original setting
for many of the scenes of Sir Walter Scott's classic
tale 'Ivanhoe'.*

Bosworth Battlefield Heritage Centre
Market Bosworth, Leicestershire CV13 0AD
(01455) 290429
www.bosworthbattlefield.com
*Delve into Leicestershire's fascinating history at
Bosworth Battlefield Country Park - the site of the
1485 Battle of Bosworth.*

Conkers Discovery Centre
Ashby-de-la-Zouch, Leicestershire DE12 6GA
(01283) 216633
www.visitconkers.com/thingstodo/discoverycentre
*Enjoy the great outdoors and explore over 120 acres
of the award-winning parkland.*

Diwali Festival Leicester
October, various locations
www.visitleicester.info/diwali
*In Leicester Diwali celebrations are one of the
biggest outside of India, with over 35,000 people
attending the 2016 switch on and more attending
Diwali Day itself.*

Easter Vintage Festival
April, Great Central Railway, Leicestershire
www.gcrailway.co.uk
*A real treat for all this Easter with traction engines,
classic cars and buses, fairground rides, trade
stands, a beer tent as well as lots of action on the
double track.*

Great Central Railway
Leicester LE11 1RW
(01509) 632323
www.gcrailway.co.uk
*The Great Central Railway is Britain's only double
track main line steam railway. Enjoy an exciting
calendar of events, a footplate ride or dine in style
on board one of the steam trains.*

Lincoln Castle
Castle Hill, Lincoln LN1 3AA
(01522) 554559
www.lincolncastle.com
*Discover a site steeped in history spanning the
centuries and experience nearly 1000 years of jaw-
dropping history, from battles to the hanging of
criminals and ghostly tales.*

National Space Centre

Leicester LE4 5NS
(0116) 261 0261
www.spacecentre.co.uk
The award-winning National Space Centre is the UK's largest attraction dedicated to space. From the moment you catch sight of the Space Centre's futuristic Rocket Tower, you'll be treated to hours of breathtaking discovery & interactive fun.

Rutland Water

Egleton, Oakham, Rutland LE15 8BT
(01572) 770651
www.rutlandwater.org.uk
There's plenty to keep everyone entertained at Rutland Water, with a huge range of watersports, fantastic fishing, an outdoor adventure centre and nature reserves teeming with wildlife.

Twinlakes Theme Park

Melton Mowbray, Leicestershire LE14 4SB
(01664) 567777
www.twinlakespark.co.uk
Twinlakes Theme Park - packed with variety, fun and endless adventures for every member of your family.

Lincolnshire

Ayscoughfee Hall Museum and Gardens

Spalding, Lincolnshire PE11 2RA
(01775) 764555
www.ayscoughfee.org
Housed in a beautiful wool merchant's house built in 1451 on the banks of the River Welland.

Belton House

Belton, Lincolnshire NG32 2LW
(01476) 566116
www.nationaltrust.org.uk/belton-house
Belton, is a perfect example of an English Country House. The mansion is surrounded by formal gardens and a series of avenues leading to follies within a larger wooded park.

Burghley Horse Trials

August - September, Burghley House, Lincolnshire
www.burghley-horse.co.uk
One of the most popular events in the British equestrian calendar.

Doddington Hall

Lincoln LN6 4RU
(01522) 694308
www.doddingtonhall.com
A Elizabethan mansion by the architect Robert Smythson. The hall stands today as it was completed in 1600 with walled courtyards, turrets and gatehouse.

Hardys Animal Farm

Ingoldmells, Lincolnshire PE25 1LZ
(01754) 872267
www.hardysanimalfarm.co.uk
Learn about the countryside and how a farm works. There are animals for the children to enjoy as well as the history and traditions of the countryside.

Lincolnshire Show

June, Lincolnshire Showground LN2 2NA
(01522) 522900
www.lincolnshireshow.co.uk
Agriculture remains at the heart of the Lincolnshire Show with livestock and equine competitions, machinery displays and the opportunity to find out where your food comes from and to taste it too!

Lincolnshire Wolds Walking Festival

May - June, Louth, Lincolnshire
www.woldswalkingfestival.co.uk
Over 90 walks and bike rides, taking place in an 'Area of Outstanding Natural Beauty' and surrounding countryside.

Normanby Hall Museum and Country Park

Scunthorpe, Lincolnshire DN15 9HU
(01724) 720588
www.normanbyhall.co.uk
Normanby Hall is a classic English mansion set in 300 acres of gardens, parkland, deer park, woods, ornamental and wild birds.

Tattershall Castle

Lincolnshire LN4 4LR
(01526) 342543
www.nationaltrust.org.uk/tattershall-castle
Tattershall Castle was built in the 15th century to impress and dominate by Ralph Cromwell, one of the most powerful men in England. The castle is a dramatic red brick tower.

Northamptonshire

78 Derngate
Northampton NN1 1UH
(01604) 603407
ww.78derngate.org.uk
The only house in England designed by Charles Rennie Mackintosh offering an unforgettable day out.

Althorp
Northampton NN7 4HQ
(01604) 770107
www.spencerofalthorp.com
One of England's finest country houses, and ancestral home of Diana, Princess of Wales.

British Grand Prix
July, Silverstone, Northamptonshire
www.silverstone.co.uk
The only place in the UK to see the world's best Formula One drivers in action.

Coton Manor Garden
Nr Guilsborough, Northampton NN6 8RQ
(01604) 740219
www.cotonmanor.co.uk
A beautiful Old English gardens enclosed by old yew and holly hedges.

Lamport Hall and Gardens
Northamptonshire NN6 9HD
(01604) 686272
www.lamporthall.co.uk
Grade 1 listed building that was home to the Isham family and their collections for over four centuries.

National Waterways Museum - Stoke Bruerne

Towcester, Northamptonshire NN12 7SE
(01604) 862229
www.canalrivertrust.org.uk
Stoke Bruerne is an ideal place to explore the story of our waterways.

Prebendal Manor Medieval Centre
Nassington, Northamptonshire PE8 6QG
(01780) 782575
www.prebendal-manor.co.uk
Visit a unique medieval manor and enjoy the largest recreated medieval gardens in Europe.

Rockingham Castle
Market Harborough, Northamptonshire LE16 8TH
(01536) 770240
www.rockinghamcastle.com
Rockingham Castle stands on the edge of an escarpment giving dramatic views over five counties and the Welland Valley below.

Salcey Forest
Hartwell, Northamptonshire NN7 2HX
(01604) 696239
www.forestry.gov.uk/salceyforest
Wildlife and history are in abundance at Salcey, so come and discover this ancient semi-natural woodland and get a birds eye view on the tremendous Tree Top Way.

Sulgrave Manor
Northamptonshire OX17 2SD
(01295) 760205
www.sulgravemanor.org.uk
Sulgrave Manor is the ancestral home of George Washington's family with authentic furniture shown by friendly guides.

Wicksteed Park
Kettering, Northamptonshire NN15 6NJ
(01536) 512475
www.wicksteedpark.co.uk
Wicksteed Park remains Northamptonshire's most popular attraction and entertainment venue.

Nottinghamshire

Armed Forces Weekend
June, Wollaton Park, Nottingham, Nottinghamshire
www.experiencenottinghamshire.com
Nottingham welcomes the annual national event celebrating our Armed Forces past and present.

Attenborough Nature Centre
Attenborough, Nottingham, NG9 6DY
(01159) 721777
www.attenboroughnaturecentre.co.uk
With a visionary eco-design, set against the backdrop of the beautiful Attenborough Nature Reserve, the Attenboroudgh Nature Centre provides a place for visitors to look, learn and refresh.

Galleries of Justice Museum

Nottingham NG1 1HN
(0115) 952 0555
www.galleriesofjustice.org.uk
There are many ways to explore the museum of Crime and Punishment, with free exhibitions, audio and performance-led tours plus an on-site café and gift shop. You will be delving in to the dark and disturbing past of crime and punishment.

Holme Pierrepont Country Park

Holme Pierrepoint, Nottinghamshire NG12 2LU
(0115) 982 1212
www.nwscnotts.com
Set in 270 acres of beautiful parkland and home to the National Watersports Centre. With excellent water sports facilities, Family Fun Park, Life Fitness Gym and marvellous nature trails for cycling and walking.

Newark Air Museum

Nottinghamshire NG24 2NY
(01636) 707170
www.newarkairmuseum.org
The air museum is located on part of the former World War Two airfield of RAF Winthorpe. Displaying aircraft, helicopters, aeroplanes, aero engines and aviation exhibits. The museum is open to the public every day except December 24th, 25th, 26th and January 1st.

Newark Castle

Newark, Nottinghamshire NG24 1BG
(01636) 655765
www.newark-sherwooddc.gov.uk
At the heart of the town for many centuries the castle has played an important role in historical events. The gardens are pretty, formal gardens bordered by the remaining walls of Newark Castle.

The Newark International Antiques and Collectors Fair

February, Newark, Nottinghamshire NG24 2NY
www.iacf.co.uk/newark
(01636) 702 326
The largest event of its kind in Europe. It is the ultimate treasure hunting ground with 2,500 stands attracting thousands of dealers and buyers from around the globe.

Nottingham Castle

Nottingham NG1 6EL
(0115) 876 1400
www.nottinghamcastle.org.uk
Situated on a high rock, commanding spectacular views over the city and once rivalled the great castles of Windsor and the Tower of London.

Nottinghamshire County Show

May, Newark Showground, Nottinghamshire
www.nottinghamshirecountyshow.com
Promoting farming, food, rural life and heritage in Nottinghamshire and beyond.

Papplewick Hall & Gardens

Nottinghamshire NG15 8FE
www.papplewickhall.co.uk
A fine Adam house, built in 1787 and Grade I listed building with a landscape park, surrounded by tree belts and a woodland garden.

Robin Hood Beer Festival

October, Nottingham Castle, Nottinghamshire
www.beerfestival.nottinghamcamra.org
Set in the stunning grounds of Nottingham Castle, the Robin Hood Beer Festival offers the world's largest selection of real ales and ciders.

Robin Hood Festival

August, Sherwood Forest, Nottinghamshire
www.experiencenottinghamshire.com
Celebrate our most legendary outlaw in Sherwood Forest's medieval village with jousting tournaments, story tellers, comedy acts amd more.

Sherwood Forest Country Park

Nottinghamshire NG21 9HN
(01623) 823202
www.nottinghamshire.gov.uk/sherwoodforestcp
Sherwood Forest Country Park covers 450 acres and incorporates some truly ancient areas of native woodland.

Sherwood Pines Forest Park

Edwinstowe, Nottinghamshire NG21 9JL
(01623) 822447
www.forestry.gov.uk/sherwoodpines
The largest forest open to the public in the East Midlands and centre for outdoor activities.

Tourist Information Centres

When you arrive at your destination, visit the Tourist Information Centre for quality assured help with accommodation and information about local attractions and events, or email your request before you go.

Ashbourne	Town Hall	01335 343666	vic@ashbournetc.co.uk
Ashby-de-la-Zouch	North Street	01530 411767	ashby.tic@nwleicestershire.gov.uk
Bakewell	Old Market Hall	01629 813227	bakewell@peakdistrict.gov.uk
Boston	2 South Street	01205 356656	ticboston@boston.gov.uk
Buxton	The Pavilion Gardens	01298 25106	tourism@highpeak.gov.uk
Castleton	Buxton Road	01629 816572	castleton@peakdistrict.gov.uk
Chesterfield	Rykneld Square	01246 345777	tourism@chesterfield.gov.uk
Derby	Assembly Rooms	01332 643411	tourism@derby.gov.uk
Glossop	Glossop One Stop Shop	0845 1297777	
Grantham	The Guildhall Centre, Council Offices	01476 406166	granthamtic@southkesteven.gov.uk
Horncastle	Wharf Road	01507 601111	horncastleinfo@e-lindsey.gov.uk
Kettering	Municipal Offices	01536 410333	customerservices@kettering.gov.uk
Leicester	51 Gallowtree Gate	0116 299 4444	info@visitleicester.info
Lincoln Castle Hill	9 Castle Hill	01522 545458	visitorinformation@lincolnbig.co.uk
Loughborough	Loughborough Town Hall	01509 231914	loughborough@goleicestershire.com
Louth	Cannon Street	01507 601111	louthinfo@e-lindsey.gov.uk
Mablethorpe	Stanley Avenue	01507 474939	customerservices@e-lindsey.gov.uk
Melton Mowbray	The Library, Wilton Road	0116 305 3646	
Newark	Keepers Cottage, Riverside Park	01636 655765	
Northampton	Sessions House, County Hall	01604 367997	tic@northamptonshire.gov.uk
Nottingham City	1-4 Smithy Row	08444 775 678	tourist.information@nottinghamcity.gov.uk
Retford	40 Grove Street	01777 860780	rctford.tourist@bassetlaw.gov.uk
Rutland Water	Sykes Lane	01780 686800	rutlandwaterinfo@anglianwater.co.uk
Sherwood	Sherwood Heat	01623 824545	sherwoodtic@nsdc.info
Silverstone	Silverstone Circuit	0844 3728 200	Elicia.Bonamy@silverstone.co.uk
Spalding	South Holland Centre	01775 725468 / 764777	touristinformationcentre@sholland.gov.uk
Stamford	Stamford TI Arts Centre	01780 755611	stamtic@southkesteven.gov.uk
Swadlincote	Sharpe's Pottery Museum	01283 222848	tic@sharpespotterymusuem.org.uk
Woodhall Spa	The Cottage Museum	01526 353775	woodhall.spainfo@e-lindsey.gov.uk

Regional Contacts and Information

For more information on accommodation, attractions, activities, events and holidays in the East Midlands, contact one of the following regional or local tourism organisations. Their websites have a wealth of information and many produce free publications to help you get the most out of your visit.

East Midlands Tourism
www.eastmidlandstourism.com

Experience Nottinghamshire
www.experiencenottinghamshire.com

Peak District and Derbyshire
www.visitpeakdistrict.com

Discover Rutland
www.discover-rutland.co.uk

Lincolnshire
(01522) 545458
www.visitlincolnshire.com

VisitNorthamptonshire
www.visitnorthamptonshire.co.uk

Leicestershire
0116 225 4000
www.goleicestershire.com

Stay – East Midlands

Entries appear alphabetically by town name in each county. A key to symbols appears on page 6

Rivendale Caravan & Leisure Park

Buxton Road, Nr Alsop En Le Dale, Ashbourne DE6 1QU
T: (01335) 310311 **F:** (01335) 310100 **E:** enquiries@rivendalecaravanpark.co.uk
W: www.rivendalecaravanpark.co.uk **£ BOOK ONLINE**

🚐 (81)	£18.00-£28.00	
🚚 (81)	£18.00-£28.00	
⛺ (30)	£17.00-£28.00	
🛏 (12)	£40.00-£90.00	
🏠 (2)	£420.00-£895.00	

111 touring pitches

SPECIAL PROMOTIONS
Stay Sunday to
Thursday & get 5 nights
for the price of 4.

Surrounded by spectacular Peak District scenery, convenient for Alton Towers, Chatsworth, Dovedale and Carsington Water. Ideal for cyclists and ramblers with the Tissington Trail 100 metres away and footpaths running directly from site into Dovedale. Choice of pitch surfaces. Yurts, Camping Pods, accessible Pine Lodges & bedroom suites. Fly fishing lake. Overnight holding area.

Directions: Rivendale is situated 6.5 miles north of Ashbourne, directly off the A515 Buxton road on the right-hand side, travelling north.

Open: All year except 3rd to 28th January.

Site: 🏕 ⛺🅿 **Payment:** 💷 ☼ **Leisure:** ᴥ 🎣 ∪ **Children:** 🐴 ⛰ **Catering:** ✕ 🛒 **Park:** 🐾 🚃 🗑 🏕 🎣
Touring: 🚰 ♿ 💧 ⚡

Peak District Spa

Buxton Road, Nr Alsop en le Dale, Ashbourne, Derbyshire DE6 1QU **T:** (01335) 310100
F: (01335) 310100 **E:** PeakDistrictSpa@rivendalecaravanpark.co.uk
W: www.peakdistrictspa.co.uk **£ BOOK ONLINE**

B&B PER ROOM PER NIGHT
S: £61.00 - £83.00
D: £66.00 - £88.00

Occupying a secluded location on part of Rivendale's 37 acre site with its own parking, terrace and garden with superb views over Eaton Dale. Ideal for cycling, walking & outdoor pursuits (fly fishing lake on site). Convenient Chatsworth, Alton Towers, Carsington Water. All rooms with en suites, oak or travertine floors, under floor heating. Ground floor rooms accessible for wheelchairs M1/M2.

Directions: Travelling north from Ashbourne towards Buxton on the A515, find Rivendale on the RHS.

Bedrooms: 2 double, 2 twin. Ground floor rooms with wheelchair access & shower room wet rooms en suite. 1st floor rooms with over bath showers en suite.
Open: All year except closed 2nd to 31st January.

Site: ❈ P **Payment:** 💷 **Leisure:** ᴥ 🎣 ▶ ∪ 🏊 **Property:** 🚃 🗑 🖋 **Children:** 🐴 🛏 ⚲ **Catering:** 🍷 🍴
Room: 🍵 🖐 📻 📺 🔊

ASHBOURNE, Derbyshire   Map ref 4B2 S

VisitEngland ★★★★ SELF CATERING   **VisitEngland Silver AWARD**

Rivendale Caravan & Leisure Park

Contact: Greg Potter, Director, Alsop Rivendale Ltd, Buxton Road, Alsop-en-le-Dale, Derbyshire DE6 1QU **T:** (01335) 310311 / 07850 666648 **F:** (01335) 310100
E: enquiries@rivendalecaravanpark.co.uk
W: www.rivendalecaravanpark.co.uk **£ BOOK ONLINE**

Units 1
Sleeps 1-6

PER UNIT PER WEEK
£455.00 - £896.00

SPECIAL PROMOTIONS
From £420 for a 4 night mid-week break.

Luxurious 3 bedroom accessible lodge built to residential specification with gas central heating and double glazing designed for snug, year-round use. Ramp access to sun-deck & lodge, with profiling bed, shower-room wet-room, electric recliner chair provided, plus hoist etc available upon request. The lodge has a well-equipped kitchen with linen, towels provided and a parking space immediately in front. The ideal base to explore the Peak District & visit the local attractions. 2 bedroom lodge with hot-tub also available for weekly and short breaks.

Open: All year except closes 2nd to 31st January.   **Units:** 1 double bedroom, 1 bunk bedroom
Nearest Shop: On site   (with 2 beds), twin room or single with hoist.
Nearest Pub: On site plus 3 about 2.5 miles

Site: P Payment: ⌸ **Leisure:** ♪ ▶ ♿ **Property:** ∥ 🐾 🖥 🖨 🖵 **Children:** 🛝 ⚡ **Unit:** 🛏 📟 🍴 📺 📀 BBQ

ASHBOURNE, Derbyshire   Map ref 4B2 S

VisitEngland ★★★★★ HOLIDAY PARK

Sandybrook Country Park

Contact: Buxton Road, Ashbourne, Derbyshire DE6 2AQ **T:** (01335) 300000
F: (01335) 342679 **E:** enquiries@sandybrook.co.uk
W: www.sandybrook.co.uk

Units 51
Sleeps 2-8
PER UNIT PER WEEK
£369.00 - £1589.00

Award-winning Sandybrook Country Park has fantastic facilities including a swimming pool, restaurant and children's play area. Many of our luxury lodges include a private hot tub and the park is close to the picturesque market town of Ashbourne and Alton Towers. With its breathtaking views, Sandybrook is an ideal location for exploring the Peak District with an abundance of walks and cycle routes in the local area.
Open: All year.

Site: P Payment: ⌸ **Leisure:** ♪ ▶ ♿ 🎣 **Property:** 🐾 🖥 🖨 🖵 **Children:** 🛝 🎪 ⚡ **Unit:** 🛏 🛁 📟 🖨 🍴 📺 ⚡ 📀 BBQ

BAMFORD, Derbyshire   Map ref 4B2

SatNav S33 0AZ **B**

Yorkshire Bridge Inn

Ashopton Road, Bamford in the High Peak, Hope Valley S33 0AZ **T:** (01433) 651361
F: (01433) 651361 **E:** info@yorkshire-bridge.co.uk
W: www.yorkshire-bridge.co.uk **£ BOOK ONLINE**

B&B PER ROOM PER NIGHT
S: £55.00 - £70.00
D: £70.00 - £120.00

EVENING MEAL PER PERSON
£10.00 - £17.95

SPECIAL PROMOTIONS
Go to our website to
see the latest offers.
Discounts for mid
week breaks available.
For those that would
like to stay longer see
our 5* self-catering
apartments
www.
ladybowerapartments.
co.uk

This famous award-winning Inn enjoys a beautiful setting just a short stroll from the Ladybower Reservoir in the Peak District National Park. Offering a great selection of locally sourced food, cask ales and an imaginative wine list, its a great place to relax and unwind or even stay the night, with delightful modern bedrooms and three 5 Star apartments too. A great find in an idyllic location.

Directions: M1 junction 29, Chesterfield - Baslow - Calver - Hathersage - Bamford. A6013 through Bamford. After 0.5 miles on left-hand side.

Bedrooms: 10 double, 2 twin, 2 family.
Open: All year except Christmas Day.

Site: ✿ P Payment: 💳 Leisure: ♪ ⏵ ☡ Property: 🐴 🖼 Children: 🧒 🛏 ⚲ Catering: 🍴✗ ♟ 🍽
Room: 🔌 🍴 📞 📻 📺 🔌 🖨

BUXTON, Derbyshire   Map ref 4B2

SatNav SK17 9BA **H**

Alison Park Hotel

3 Temple Road, Buxton, Derbyshire SK17 9BA **T:** (01298) 22473 **F:** (01298) 72709
E: reservations@alison-park-hotel.co.uk
W: www.alison-park-hotel.co.uk **£ BOOK ONLINE**

B&B PER ROOM PER NIGHT
S: £54.00 - £60.00
D: £108.00 - £120.00

EVENING MEAL PER PERSON
£16.00 - £18.50

An Edwardian arts and crafts house, set within its own grounds in quiet location, just out of the town centre. The family management of the hotel ensures a warm welcome.
Bedrooms: 3 single, 7 double, 3 twin, 2 family.
Open: All year.

Site: ✿ Payment: 💳 Leisure: 🚴 ⏵ Property: ♟ 🐴 🖼 Children: 🧒 ⚲ Catering: ♟ 🍽 Room: 🔌 🍴 📞 📻 📺 🖨

BUXTON, Derbyshire   Map ref 4B2   SatNav SK17 9TQ C

Beech Croft Farm Caravan & Camping Park

Blackwell-in-the-Peak, Nr Buxton, Derbyshire SK17 9TQ
T: (01298) 85330 **E:** mail@beechcroftfarm.co.uk
W: www.beechcroftfarm.co.uk **£ BOOK ONLINE**

(30)   £22.00-£25.00
(30)   £22.00-£25.00
(40)   £15.00-£18.00
30 touring pitches

SPECIAL PROMOTIONS
5% discount on stays of 7 nights or more.

In the heart of the Peak District, Beech Croft is a small family run site, alongside their small sheep farm. On the Pennine Bridleway with Monsal Trail & Limestone Way close by. All hard standings have 16 amp EHU, water tap and TV aerial socket and there is also a separate camping field which all have access to 10amp EHU. Environmentally friendly underfloor heated toilet & shower block. Free Wi-Fi.

Directions: Midway between Buxton & Bakewell being 6 miles to each town. Signposted & easily accessible from the A6.

Open: Hard standings open all year.

Site: A ⚑ **Payment:** £ ☼ **Children:** ⛱ **Catering:** 🛒 **Park:** 🐕 🚽 🚻 ⛺ **Touring:** 🚰 🔌 🚿

BUXTON, Derbyshire   Map ref 4B2   SatNav SK17 6BD H

Old Hall Hotel

The Square, Buxton SK17 6BD **T:** (01298) 22841 **F:** (01298) 72437
E: reception@oldhallhotelbuxton.co.uk
W: www.oldhallhotelbuxton.co.uk **£ BOOK ONLINE**

B&B PER ROOM PER NIGHT
S: £69.00 - £89.00
D: £79.00 - £205.00
EVENING MEAL PER PERSON
£20.00 - £28.00

SPECIAL PROMOTIONS
Chatsworth House Breaks, Theatre Breaks and Special Seasonal Promotions available throughout the year.

This historic hotel, reputedly the oldest in England, offers a warm and friendly service. Ideally located opposite Pavillion Gardens and Edwardian opera house, we serve pre and post theatre dinner in our restaurant and wine bar. Rooms available on B&B and half-board basis. The perfect Peak District base.

Directions: Map available, please see our website for full directions.

Bedrooms: 14 classic double and twin bedrooms, 11 standard doubles, 6 executive doubles and twins, 4 four poster beds, 2 singles and a flat.
Open: All year.

Site: ✿ **Payment:** £ **Leisure:** ♨ ♪ ♟ ↻ **Property:** ♟ 🐕 🚻 🏠 ♨ ◗ **Children:** ⛱ 🛏 ♿
Catering: ❌ 🍽 🍴 **Room:** 🚿 🛏 ☎ 📺 📺 📻

BUXTON, Derbyshire Map ref 4B2

Pyegreave Cottage

Contact: Mr & Mrs N C Pollard, Pyegreave Cottage, Pyegreave Farm, Combs, High Peak SK23 9UX **T:** (01298) 813444 **F:** (01298) 815381 **E:** r.pollard@allenpollard.co.uk
W: www.pyegreavecottage.com **£ BOOK ONLINE**

Units	1
Sleeps	1-2

PER UNIT PER WEEK
£295.00 - £410.00

Character stone cottage maintained to a high standard, situated within the Peak District National Park. Spectacular views. Ideal for walking, golf, theatre, fishing, cycling and climbing. Idyllic and tranquil hideaway.
Open: All year.
Nearest Shop: 3 miles
Nearest Pub: 1 mile

Site: ✿ P Payment: 🗲 € Leisure: 🚲 ♪ ↑ ☾ Property: 🖥 🔲 Children: ⛟ Unit: 🗋 🗒 ▣
🔲 🔲 📺 🔲 DVD BBQ 📞

CASTLETON, Derbyshire Map ref 4B2

Riding House Farm Cottages

Contact: Mrs Denise Matthews, Owner, Riding House Farm, Castleton, Hope Valley, Derbyshire S33 8WB **T:** (01433) 620257 **E:** denise@riding-house-cottages.co.uk
W: www.riding-house-cottages.co.uk **£ BOOK ONLINE**

Units	2
Sleeps	2-4

PER UNIT PER WEEK
£340.00 - £595.00

Newly converted farm cottages in the heart of the Peak District National Park. Both cottages are equipped to a very high standard, with charm, character and in a stunning location. Castleton caves and castle, Chatsworth House and Haddon Hall all nearby. From your doorstep you can take the footpath directly to Lose Hill Ridge enjoy another spectacular view over the Edale Valley to Kinder scout **Open:** All year. **Nearest Shop:** 1 mile **Nearest Pub:** 1 mile

Site: ✿ P Leisure: 🚲 ♪ ↑ ☾ Property: 🐾 🔲 🔲 Children: ⛟ 🛏 † Unit: 🗋 🗒 ▣ 🔲 🔲 📺 ▣
DVD BBQ

CHESTERFIELD, Derbyshire Map ref 4B2 SatNav S40 4EE

Abigails Guest House

62 Brockwell Lane, Chesterfield S40 4EE **T:** (01246) 279391 **F:** (01246) 854468
E: gail@abigails.fsnet.co.uk
W: www.abigailsguesthouse.co.uk

B&B PER ROOM PER NIGHT
S: £38.00
D: £58.00

Relax taking breakfast in the conservatory overlooking Chesterfield and surrounding moorlands. Garden with pond, private car park. Best B&B winners 2000. Free Wi-Fi.
Directions: Please contact us for directions.
Bedrooms: 2 single, 3 double, 2 twin.
Open: All year.

Site: ✿ P Payment: 🗲 Leisure: ♪ ↑ 🔍 Property: 🐾 🔲 🔲 Children: ⛟ 🛏 † Catering: 🍴
Room: 🔲 🔲 📞 📺 🔲 🔲 🔲

CHESTERFIELD, Derbyshire Map ref 4B2

The Little Trout

Contact: Chris Mapp, Chef Patron, Tickled Trout, 35 Valley Road, Barlow, Derbyshire S18 7SL **T:** (01142) 891111 **E:** stay@littletroutbarlow.com
W: www.tickledtroutbarlow.com/escape-little-trout

Units	2
Sleeps	4-5

PER UNIT PER WEEK
£369.00 - £573.00

The Little Trout is a superbly finished holiday cottage nestled in the heart of Barlow - a picturesque village with fantastic views over the breathtaking North Derbyshire countryside and great access to the Peak District. The cottage is conveniently positioned next door to the award-winning and popular Tickled Trout pub, which offers delicious locally produced food and drink and privately owned. **Open:** All year. **Nearest Shop:** 3 miles **Nearest Pub:** Next door

Site: P Payment: 🗲 Leisure: ♪ ↑ 🔍 Property: 🐾 🔲 🔲 🔲 Children: ⛟ † Unit: 🗋 🗒 ▣ 🔲 🔲 📺 DVD

HARTINGTON, Derbyshire   Map ref 4B2

Units   1
Sleeps   4
PER UNIT PER WEEK
£300.00 - £500.00

Ash Tree Cottage

Contact: Mrs Clare Morson, Ash Tree Cottage, Nettletor Farm, Mill Lane, Hartington, Nr Buxton SK17 0AN **T:** (01298) 84247 / 07517 220972 **E:** nettletorfarm@btconnect.com
W: www.nettletorfarm.co.uk

Single storey cottage, sleeps four and private parking for two cars. Own contained patio and garden area. Ideally located for Hartington village and picturesque walks into the dales.
Open: All year.
Nearest Shop: 5 minute walk
Nearest Pub: 5 minute walk

Site: ❀ P Leisure: ॐ ✍ ⋃ Property: 🖥 🖳 Children: 🐎 🏠 🅰 Unit: 🖥 🖵 TV 🄳 DVD BBQ

HARTINGTON, Derbyshire   Map ref 4B2

Units   2
Sleeps   6-8
PER UNIT PER WEEK
£370.00 - £590.00

Staley Cottage / Victoria House

Contact: Mrs Judith Flower, Heathcote Grange, Heathcote, Hartington, Derbyshire SK17 0AY **T:** (01298) 84918 / 07523 497602 **E:** judith198@btinternet.com
W: www.hartingtoncottages.com

These two spacious properties have been maintained for 30 years to a high standard.
1 Staley Cottage: 3 bedrooms, double facilities, dining room, lounge, laundry room, large garden and parking. Log fire and summer house.
Victoria House: 3-4 bedrooms, double facilities, kitchen, dining room, lounge, laundry room, garden, garden room and parking.
Open: All year. **Nearest Shop:** 200 yards **Nearest Pub:** 200 yards

Site: ❀ P Leisure: ॐ Property: 🖥 🖳 🖳 Children: 🐎 🏠 🅰 Unit: 🖥 🖵 🖳 🄳 🔌 TV DVD 🔊 BBQ ☎

HATHERSAGE, Derbyshire   Map ref 4B2

Units   1
Sleeps   4-6
PER UNIT PER WEEK
£320.00 - £480.00

Pat's Cottage

Contact: John & Bobbie Drakeford, 110 Townhead Road, Dore S17 3GB
T: (01142) 366014 / 07850 200711 **E:** johnmdrakeford@hotmail.com
W: www.patscottage.co.uk **£ BOOK ONLINE**

An attractive 18th century stone cottage, sympathetically refurbished, retaining original features including black beams. Use of owners swimming pool included in season. On the edge of the Peak District and the city of Sheffield.
Open: All year.
Nearest Shop: 0.30 miles
Nearest Pub: 0.30 miles

Site: ❀ P Leisure: ▶ ⋃ ⚘ Property: 🐕 🖥 🖳 Children: 🐎 🏠 🅰 Unit: 🖵 🖳 🔌 TV DVD BBQ

MATLOCK, Derbyshire   Map ref 4B2

Units   112
Sleeps   2-8
PER UNIT PER WEEK
£415.00 - £1965.00

f t

Darwin Forest Country Park

Contact: Darley Moor, Two Dales, Matlock DE4 5PL **T:** (01629) 732428
F: (01629) 735015 **E:** enquiries@darwinforest.co.uk
W: www.darwinforest.co.uk

Award-winning Darwin Forest provides the perfect base for exploring the stunning Derbyshire Peak District. Many of our luxury lodges include a private hot tub and our fabulous on-site facilities include a swimming pool, spa, gym, indoor and outdoor play areas and an award-winning restaurant. Our 5 star park is close to Chatsworth House and an abundance of spectacular walking and cycling routes.
Open: All year.

Site: P Payment: 💷 Leisure: ॐ ▶ ⋃ ⚘ ⚘ ⚘ Property: 🐕 🖥 🖳 🖳 Children: 🐎 🏠 🅰 Unit: 🖵 🖥 🖵 🖳 🔌 TV 🄳 DVD BBQ

MATLOCK, Derbyshire   Map ref 4B2   S

VisitEngland
★★★★
SELF CATERING

Units   18
Sleeps   4-9

PER UNIT PER WEEK
£395.00 - £1600.00

SPECIAL PROMOTIONS
Late deals and group booking discounts available please call (01629) 735859.

Darwin Lake Holiday Village

Contact: Yvonne, Customer Services, Darwin Lake Holiday Village, Jaggers Lane, Darley Moor, Nr. Matlock DE4 5LH **T:** (01629) 735859 **E:** enquiries@darwinlake.co.uk **W:** www.darwinlake.co.uk

Lovely rural location on the edge of Darwin Forest with views over the lake and access to 10 acres of grounds. "Spacious stone cottages with fine facilities, in a beautiful, tranquil woodland setting."

Darwin Lake is a small, private, well-maintained holiday village built of carefully crafted stone built houses, situated around a stunning 3 acre lake and village green with its own red telephone box. There is a large hall available should you wish to hold a celebration or event, and a delightful woodland walk by the lake. These superbly located holiday properties are 4* rated by VisitEngland

Open: All year.
Nearest Shop: 0.5miles
Nearest Pub: 0.5 miles

Units: Many en suite bedrooms and zip and link beds available, Hall available for Weddings and events, corporate clients catered for, stags and hens parties.

Site: P Payment: 🗠 **Leisure:** 🏊 ♪ ↾ ∪ **Property:** ∥ 🐎 🖾 🖥 🍳 **Children:** 🐾 🛏 🏃
Unit: 🗄 🗄 🖳 🖌 🖎 📺 📀 BBQ

ASHBY-DE-LA-ZOUCH, Leicestershire   Map ref 4B3   S

VisitEngland
★★★★
SELF CATERING

Units   1
Sleeps   4

PER UNIT PER WEEK
£500.00 - £650.00

SPECIAL PROMOTIONS
1 night stay £150, short breaks available.

Forest Lodge

Contact: Andrew Sumnall, Owner, The Rowans, Spring Lane, Packington, Ashby de la Zouch, Leicestershire LE65 1WU **T:** (01530) 411984 / 07709 032390 **E:** hillfarmpackington@hotmail.co.uk **W:** www.hillfarmpackington.co.uk **£ BOOK ONLINE**

Luxury rural retreat located on the outskirts of a village in The National Forest. Near historic Ashby de la Zouch, major tourist attractions, off road cycle centre and country walks. Relaxing hot tub overlooks beautiful countryside. Rare breed animals and farm shop on site selling home produce. Clay Pigeon Shooting, Champneys Health Spa resort nearby (2 miles). Golf Courses within 5 miles, 2 leisure centres within 5 miles. Pony trekking / horse riding - we can accommodate your own horse on our livery yard. Children welcome from any age. The log cabin is furnished to a high standard and includes TV and DVD player, a music centre, washing machine and dishwasher, and a fully equipped kitchen. The cabin has 2 kingsize bedrooms, 1 of which can be spilt into single beds. There are 2 bathrooms, 1 of which is en suite. Linen and towels are provided.

Open: All year.
Nearest Shop: 1 mile
Nearest Pub: 1 mile

Units: 1 unit, sleeps 4. Hot Tub and horse riding on site, kitchen has all mod cons. Parking available.

WALKERS ▨ FAMILIES ▨ CYCLISTS ▨ PETS▨
WALKERS ▨ FAMILIES ▨ CYCLISTS ▨ PETS▨

f

Site: ✿ **P Leisure:** 🏊 ↾ ∪ **Property:** ∥ 🐎 🖥 🍳 **Children:** 🐾 **Unit:** 🗄 🗄 🖳 🖌 🖎 📺 📀

ASHBY-DE-LA-ZOUCH, Leicestershire   Map ref 4B3   S

VisitEngland ★★★★ SELF CATERING

Normans Barn

Contact: Mrs Isabel Stanley, Proprietor, F Stanley & Son, Ingles Hill Farm, Burton Road, Ashby-de-la-Zouch LE65 2TE **T:** (01530) 412224 **E:** isabel_stanley@hotmail.com
W: www.normansbarn.co.uk

Units   1
Sleeps   2-5
PER UNIT PER WEEK
£380.00 - £570.00

Luxuriously appointed barn conversion incorporating minstrels' gallery. Both double bedrooms (one twin) en suite. On working farm including 130 acres of woodland walks. Easy access to M42, NEC, Calke Abbey and Castle Donington Park/Airport, Nottingham, Leicester and Derby. 1 mile from Ashby-de-la-Zouch.
Open: All year plus Christmas and New Year.
Nearest Shop: 0.5 miles
Nearest Pub: 0.5 miles

Site: ❀ P Leisure: 🏊 ♪ ⏵ ∪ Property: 🐴 🚍 🖭 ▯ Children: 🐾 Unit: ▯ ▤ 🖵 ▯ ⛄ 📺 ◉ 📀

BARROW UPON SOAR, Leicestershire   Map ref 4C3   S

VisitEngland ★★★ SELF CATERING

Kingfisher Cottage

Contact: Mr David Petty, 8072 Little Britton Road, Yonges Island, South Carolina, U.S.A 29449 **T:** +1-843-889-1299 / +1-215-869-2182 **F:** +1-843-889-1299
E: dvdpetty1@gmail.com **W:** www.AnEnglishCottage.com **£ BOOK ONLINE**

Units   1
Sleeps   1-6
PER UNIT PER WEEK
£400.00 - £600.00

Semi-detached roadside cottage comprising two reception rooms, two bedrooms, two bathrooms and rear garden to canal. Quiet part of village, convenient for shops and transport. Friendly pub nearby.
Open: All year.
Nearest Shop: 0.3 miles
Nearest Pub: 0.10 miles

Site: ❀ P Leisure: ♪ ∪ Property: 🖭 Children: 🐾 Unit: ▯ ▤ 🖵 ▯ ⛄ 📺 ◉ 📀 ⌀ BBQ ☎

MELTON MOWBRAY, Leicestershire   Map ref 4C3   S

VisitEngland ★★★ SELF CATERING   **VisitEngland Gold AWARD**

1 The Green

Contact: Lynn Lawton, Owner, 1 The Green, Muston, Nottinghamshire NG13 0FQ
E: lynnlawton@mac.com
W: www.onethegreen.co.uk

Units   1
Sleeps   2-6
PER UNIT PER WEEK
£360.00 - £635.00

4 bedroom detached cottage with front garden and patio. Off street parking. In quiet village in the Vale of Belvoir. Log fire, 2 single and 2 double bedrooms, bathroom, shower, downstairs toilet, Gas Central Heating and a lockable outside store for bikes.
Open: All year.
Nearest Shop: 2 miles
Nearest Pub: 0.6 miles

Site: ❀ P Leisure: ♪ ⏵ ∪ Property: 🐴 🚍 🖭 ▯ Children: 🐾 🎠 ⚴ Unit: ▯ 🖵 ▯ 📺 📀 ⌀ BBQ ☎

ALFORD, Lincolnshire   Map ref 4D2   S

VisitEngland ★★★★ SELF CATERING   **VisitEngland Gold AWARD**

Woodthorpe Hall Country Cottages

Contact: Woodthorpe Leisure Park, Woodthorpe, Alford, Lincolnshire LN13 0DD
T: (01507) 450294 **E:** enquires@woodthorpeleisurepark.co.uk
W: www.woodthorpeleisurepark.co.uk **£ BOOK ONLINE**

Units   4
Sleeps   2-6
PER UNIT PER WEEK
£240.00 - £590.00

Cottages overlooking golf course, quiet location with all the modern amenities. One cottage has its own sauna, wet room and hot tub. There is fishing, golf, holistic salon and a restaurant and bar with garden and aquatic centres close by.
Short breaks available.
Open: All year.
Nearest Shop: 0.20 miles
Nearest Pub: 0.20 miles

f

Site: ❀ P Payment: 💳 Leisure: ♪ ⏵ Property: 🐴 🚍 🖭 ▯ Children: 🐾 🎠 ⚴ Unit: ▯ ▤ 🖵 ▯ ◉ 📀

ALFORD, Lincolnshire   Map ref 4D2 SatNav LN13 0DD C

Woodthorpe Leisure Park

Woodthorpe, Alford, Lincolnshire LN13 0DD
T: (01507) 450294 E: enquiries@woodthorpeleisurepark.co.uk
W: www.woodthorpeleisurepark.co.uk **£ BOOK ONLINE**

🚐 (6)
🛖 (3)
🛻 (7)
🚲 (18)
66 touring pitches

Woodthorpe is a 5 Star park on the edge of the Lincolnshire Wolds a short drive from the seaside. Ideal for all we offer Lodges with hot tubs, Glamping pods, Cottages, Caravans & Touring. On site Pub (serving food), golf, fishing & shop.
Directions: On the B1373 Alford to Withern Road. 7 miles inland from Mablethorpe. Only 20 minutes drive from market town of Louth.
Open: All year. See website for more information.

Site: 🏠 ✿ A🅿 Payment: 💷 ☼ Leisure: ♪ ⏵ Children: ⛄ ⚠ Catering: ✕ 🍱
Park: 🐾 🔥 🛖 🐾 ⛺ Touring: 🚐 ♿

BICKER, Lincolnshire   Map ref 3A1 SatNav PE20 3AN H

Supreme Inns

Bicker Bar, Bicker, Boston PE20 3AN T: (01205) 822804 E: enquiries@supremeinns.co.uk
W: www.supremeinns.co.uk **£ BOOK ONLINE**

B&B PER ROOM PER NIGHT
S: £60.50 - £68.00
D: £60.50 - £68.00

EVENING MEAL PER PERSON
£12.00 - £25.00

SPECIAL PROMOTIONS
Dinner, Bed & Breakfast £99 based on 2 people sharing.

Situated in Bicker Bar near Boston in Lincolnshire, the Boston Supreme Inn hotel has 55 large and well equipped bedrooms all with en suite facilities. All rooms have internet access, telephone points, flat screen televisions. We have a modern, relaxing bar area, serving homemade bar meals all day, every day. The award-winning Haven restaurant is also open in the evenings.

Directions: Located on the junction between the A17/A52.

Bedrooms: 32 double, 21 twin, 2 suite.
Open: All year.

Site: ✿ Payment: 💷 Leisure: ♪ ⏵ Property: 🍷 🛏 🗄 ◐ Children: ⛄ 🛏 🚶 Catering: 🍽 🍴
Room: 🔌 🛁 ☎ 📺 🎧

BOSTON, Lincolnshire   Map ref 3A1   S

The Forge and The Smithy

Contact: Johanne Roberts, Chapel Road, Tumby Woodside, Boston, Lincolnshire PE22 7SP
T: (01526) 342943 **E:** enquiries@the4ge.co.uk
W: www.the4ge.co.uk

VisitEngland ★★★★ SELF CATERING

Units 2
Sleeps 2-5

PER UNIT PER WEEK
£250.00 - £650.00

SPECIAL PROMOTIONS
Minimum of 3 nights.

The Forge (sleeps 5) and the Smithy (sleeps 2) are detached self catering cottages located in rural Lincolnshire and situated within their own enclosed and quiet garden with secure private car parking. Both are (4*) Four Star Visit England plus awarded Highly Commended by Tastes of Lincolnshire. For recent visitor comments please refer to our website - www.the4ge.co.uk. Both cottages are fully equipped and include bedding and towels. Sorry no pets. Please contact or see www.the4ge.co.uk for price list.

Open: All year.
Nearest Shop: 2.5 miles
Nearest Pub: 2 miles

Units: The Forge: sleeps 5.
The Smithy: sleeps 2.

Site: ✿ P Leisure: ♪ Property: 📺 🗄 📶 Children: 🌳 🏠 ✚ Unit: 🗄 🍴 📺 📶 ♨ TV DVD

BRATTLEBY, Lincolnshire   Map ref 4C2   S

The Stable

Contact: Jerry Scott, Owner, The Stable Cottage, Sunnyside, East Lane, Brattleby, Lincoln LN1 2SQ **T:** (01522) 730561 / 07990 786931 **E:** jerry@lincolncottages.co.uk
W: www.lincolncottages.co.uk

VisitEngland ★★★★ SELF CATERING

Units 1
Sleeps 2-4
PER UNIT PER WEEK
£275.00 - £475.00

200 year old stone and pantile cottage of character. In a quiet conservation village six miles (scenic drive) from the historic cathedral city of Lincoln. Tastefully furnished and decorated. Self-contained cottage garden with views over open fields. Great location for exploring Lincolnshire.
Open: All year.
Nearest Shop: 1.5 miles
Nearest Pub: 1 mile

Site: ✿ P Property: 📺 🗄 📶 Children: 🌳 ✚ Unit: 🗄 📺 📶 ♨ TV DVD

HOGSTHORPE, Lincolnshire   Map ref 4D2   S

Helsey House Holiday Cottages

Contact: Elizabeth Elvidge, Joint Owner, Helsey House Holiday Cottages, Helsey House, Helsey, Hogsthorpe, Skegness PE24 5PE **T:** (01754) 872927 / 07740 909765
E: info@helseycottages.co.uk **W:** www.helseycottages.co.uk £ BOOK ONLINE

VisitEngland ★★★★ SELF CATERING

Units 2
Sleeps 1-5
PER UNIT PER WEEK
£375.00 - £520.00

Situated in the private grounds of Helsey House. Each award-winning cottage converted from original cattle stalls. Furnished to the highest standard. Single storey cottages with no steps. Rural location but close to quiet sandy beaches. Ample parking within the grounds. Large play area and heated outdoor pool (summer only). Special needs families, less mobile guests and pets are all welcome! **Open:** All year.
Nearest Shop: 3 miles **Nearest Pub:** 3 miles

Site: ✿ P Leisure: ♪ ⛵ ♺ 🎣 Property: 🐴 📺 🗄 📶 Children: 🌳 🏠 ✚ Unit: 🗄 📺 ♨ TV 🍴 DVD BBQ

INGOLDMELLS, Lincolnshire Map ref 4D2 S

VisitEngland
★★★★
SELF CATERING

Skegness Water Leisure Park - Bungalows

Contact: Reception, Skegness Water Leisure Park, Walls Lane, Skegness PE25 1JF
T: (01754) 899400 **F:** (01754) 897867 **E:** enquiries@skegnesswaterleisurepark.co.uk
W: www.skegnesswaterleisurepark.co.uk

| Units | 3 |
| Sleeps | 5 |

PER UNIT PER WEEK
£340.00 - £575.00

Recently refurbished luxury holiday bungalows just ¼ mile from award-winning beaches. Sited on award-winning family friendly holiday park, just 10 minutes walk from golden beaches.
Open: 1st March to 30th November each year.
Nearest Shop: 0.10 miles
Nearest Pub: 0.10 miles

Site: ⚘ P **Payment:** 💷 **Leisure:** ♪ ▶ ☺ **Property:** 🐾 🗄 🖥 🖵 **Children:** ⛷ 🍴 🚿 **Unit:** 🗄 🖥 📶 📺 BBQ

LINCOLN, Lincolnshire Map ref 4C2 SatNav LN41PD H

AA
★★★
Country House Hotel

Branston Hall Hotel

Branston Park, Lincoln Road, Branston LN4 1PD **T:** (01522) 793305 **F:** (01522) 790734
E: info@branstonhall.com
W: www.branstonhall.com **£ BOOK ONLINE**

B&B PER ROOM PER NIGHT
S: £89.00 - £139.00
D: £139.00 - £199.00
EVENING MEAL PER PERSON
£32.50

SPECIAL PROMOTIONS
For best offers and promotions check our website which is updated constantly with new promotions and offers.

Country house elegance. Branston Hall is situated just 3 miles away from the centre of Lincoln. It sits within 88 acres of idyllic grounds, has ample free parking and offers luxurious accommodation coupled with award-winning food.

It boasts individually styled rooms including 4 posters, family rooms and honeymoon suites as well as an indoor swimming pool, sauna and Jacuzzi and gym.

Directions: GPS: 53.194389, -0.482629. Visit our website for more details.

Bedrooms: A selection of doubles, twins, family rooms, honeymoon suites and 4 poster beds all en suite, Sky TV and Wi-Fi available at great prices.
Open: Every day 24 hours per day.

Site: P **Leisure:** 🏊 🧖 💆 🎣 **Property:** 🖥 **Catering:** 🍴 **Room:** 🧳 🗄 📺 💆 📺

LINCOLN, Lincolnshire Map ref 4C2 SatNav LN6 0EY C

VisitEngland
★★★
TOURING PARK

Hartsholme Country Park Camp Site

Skellingthorpe Road, Lincoln LN6 0EY
T: (01522) 873578 **E:** hartsholmecp@lincoln.gov.uk
W: www.lincoln.gov.uk/hartsholmecampsite

🚐	£16.60-£22.00
🚏	£16.60-£22.00
⛺ (8)	£10.00-£22.00

25 touring pitches

Our 3 star English Tourism rated site offers flat, level grassy pitches set in mature wooded parkland. Easy access to city centre and local attractions. We have one camping pod available. Please call or view our web pages for more details.
Directions: Main entrance is on the B1378 (Skellingthorpe Road). It is signposted from the A46 (Lincoln Bypass) and from the B1003 (Tritton Road).
Open: 1st March to 31st October.

Payment: 💷 ☼ **Leisure:** ♪ **Children:** ⛷ 🎢 **Catering:** ✗ 🛒 **Park:** 🐾 🌲 **Touring:** 🚾 🚮

LOUTH, Lincolnshire   Map ref 4D2   **S**

Louth Barn

Contact: Ronnie & Louise Millar, Louth Barn, Grosvenor House, 74 Keddington Road, Louth, Lincolnshire LN11 0BA **T:** (01507) 609381 / 07986 524395
E: enquiries@louthbarn.com **W:** www.louthbarn.com **£ BOOK ONLINE**

Units	1
Sleeps	2-4

PER UNIT PER WEEK
£340.00 - £471.00

Situated on the edge of Louth our converted Victorian barn is adjacent to the main house. Relaxing, comfortable, well-equipped, super-king size bed, internet, shared mature garden, summerhouse, playhouse, swings, own patio, covered parking. Extensive DVD Library, Lego and Brio available, also outdoor table football, pool table and table tennis available. **Open:** All year.
Nearest Shop: 0.20 miles
Nearest Pub: 0.20 miles

MARKET RASEN, Lincolnshire   Map ref 4C2   **S**

Masondale Holiday Cottage

Contact: Mr Neil Cooper, Otby House Farm, Walesby, Lincolnshire LN8 3UU
T: (01673) 838530 / 07768 714281 **E:** n.cooper@otby-lake.co.uk
W: www.otby-lake.co.uk **£ BOOK ONLINE**

Units	1
Sleeps	6

PER UNIT PER WEEK
£400.00 - £575.00

Spacious peaceful farm cottage converted to high quality 4 star self catering accommodation. Perfect base for outdoor activities or a totally relaxing break. Panoramic views. Livery. Quite exceptional trout fishing. Masondale Cottage sits at the edge of the Lincolnshire Wolds with unrivalled panoramic views of the Vale of Ancholme looking across to Lincoln Cathedral prominent on the horizon.
Open: All year. **Nearest Shop:** 4 miles **Nearest Pub:** 4 miles

---

SKEGNESS, Lincolnshire   Map ref 4D2   SatNav PE25 1JF   **C**

Skegness Water Leisure Park

Walls Lane, Skegness PE25 1JF
T: (01754) 899400 **F:** (01754) 897867 **E:** enquiries@skegnesswaterleisurepark.co.uk
W: www.skegnesswaterleisurepark.co.uk **£ BOOK ONLINE**

🚐	£18.00-£25.50
🚍	£20.00-£28.50
⛺	£20.00-£27.50
🏠 (11)	£36.00-£46.00
🏕 (3)	£340.00-£575.00
250 touring pitches	

Family-orientated caravan and camping site 'Where the coast meets the countryside'. Ten minute walk to award-winning beaches with scenic, rural views. Close to Butlins and Fantasy Island.
Directions: A52 north from Skegness 2.5 miles. Turn left at Cheers pub into Walls Lane. Site entrance is 400 yards on the left hand side.
Open: March to November.

Sign up for our newsletter

Visit our website to sign up for our e-newsletter and receive regular information on events, articles, exclusive competitions and new publications.
www.visitor-guides.co.uk

SKEGNESS, Lincolnshire   Map ref 4D2   SatNav PE25 2TY [B]

GUEST HOUSE

B&B PER ROOM PER NIGHT
D: £51.00 - £58.00

Stepping Stones

4 Castleton Boulevard, Skegness PE25 2TY **T:** (01754) 765092
E: info@stepping-stones-hotel.co.uk
W: www.stepping-stones-hotel.co.uk **£ BOOK ONLINE**

Small and friendly we are 50 yards from the prom and all its attractions, including Natureland, bowling greens and the theatre. Within walking distance of town centre. Breakfast menu.
Directions: A158 head straight through all lights towards sea. A52 south turn right at Ship Inn. A52 north, 2nd right (Scarborough Ave.) until pier, left, left.
Bedrooms: 3 double, 1 twin, 2 family all en suite.
Open: All year except Christmas.

Site: P Payment: Children: Catering: Room:

WEST BARKWITH, Lincolnshire   Map ref 4D2   [S]

SELF CATERING

Units   4
Sleeps   2-4
PER UNIT PER WEEK
£240.00 - £310.00

Glebe Farm Apartments

Contact: Stephen Campion, Glebe Farm Apartments, The Barn, Glebe Farm, West Barkwith, Market Rasen LN8 5LF **T:** (01673) 858919 / 07885 676482
E: enquiries@glebeapart.co.uk **W:** www.glebeapart.co.uk **£ BOOK ONLINE**

Converted farm buildings into cosy apartments in rural countryside. Large grounds to enjoy, including free fishing in well-stocked lake. Online booking.
Open: All year.
Nearest Shop: 1 mile
Nearest Pub: 1 mile

Site: P Leisure: Property: Children: Unit: BBQ

WOODHALL SPA, Lincolnshire   Map ref 4D2   SatNav LN10 6QH [C]

TOURING & CAMPING PARK

 (70)   £17.00-£29.00
 (70)   £17.00-£29.00
 (12)   £10.00-£29.00
98 touring pitches

Petwood Caravan Park

Stixwould Road, Woodhall Spa, Lincolnshire LN10 6QH
T: (01526) 354799 **E:** info@petwoodcaravanpark.co.uk
W: www.petwoodcaravanpark.co.uk

We are a 4 star family caravan park, offering superb facilities, set in the heart of the beautiful inland resort of Woodhall Spa. The village is just a 5 minute walk from the site and has a variety of excellent restaurants and shops. Please contact for 2017 Rates.

Open: 17th March to 15th October.

Site: Payment: Children: Park: Touring:

WOODHALL SPA, Lincolnshire   Map ref 4D2

SatNav LN10 6UJ **B**

Village Limits Country Pub, Restaurant & Motel

Stixwould Road, Woodhall Spa, Lincolnshire LN10 6UJ **T:** (01526) 353312
E: info@villagelimits.co.uk
W: www.villagelimits.co.uk **£ BOOK ONLINE**

B&B PER ROOM PER NIGHT
S: £45.00 - £55.00
D: £80.00 - £90.00
EVENING MEAL PER PERSON
£8.50 - £25.00

SPECIAL PROMOTIONS
15% discount for 4 nights or more. Other low season special offers available.

Select Lincolnshire Food & Accommodation Winners 2006-2016. Free Wi-Fi throughout. All rooms en suite with a peaceful rural location. There is ample parking available.

Great home cooked food using seasonal and local ingredients, local beers and excellent wine available with a warm welcome.

Start your day with a hearty award-winning full breakfast.

Directions: On Stixwould Road, next to Woodhall Country Park. 500m past Petwood Hotel. 1 mile to Woodhall Spa centre. 1.5 miles to Woodhall Spa Golf Club.

Bedrooms: 8 twin.
Open: Open all year except Christmas Day til New Year.

Site: ⚲ P Payment: 💷 Property: 🚆 Children: 👶 ♿ Catering: (✗ 🍽 ⛄ Room: 📞 🚿 📺 ⚖

WOODHALL SPA, Lincolnshire   Map ref 4D2

SatNav LN10 6UJ **C**

Woodhall Country Park

Stixwould Road, Woodhall Spa LN10 6UJ
T: (01526) 353710 **E:** info@woodhallcountrypark.co.uk
W: www.woodhallcountrypark.co.uk **£ BOOK ONLINE**

🚐 (100) £20.00-£29.00
🚎 (100) £20.00 £29.00
⛺ (35) £16.00-£26.00
🛖 (6)
100 touring pitches

Woodhall Country Park is a unique 5 star camping and touring experience, set in tranquil woodlands in the heart of a conservation area in Lincolnshire. You will enjoy the natural surroundings of the park and feel close to nature, surrounded by woodland and wildlife. The new facilities offered here are ideal for touring caravans and tents – with camping pods & luxury lodges also available for hire.

Directions: Woodhall Country Park is located on the outskirts of Woodhall Spa, Lincolnshire.

Open: 1st March to 30th November.

Site: ⚲ A P Payment: 💷 ☼ Leisure: 🚲 ♪ ▶ Children: 👶 Park: 🐕 🚽 🚿 Touring: 🚽 🚽 ♪

PETERBOROUGH, Northamptonshire   Map ref 3A1   S

Hall Farm Kings Cliffe

Contact: Ms Sarah Winfrey, Hall Farm Kings Cliffe - SC & GA, Hall Farm, Hall Yard, Kings Cliffe PE8 6XQ **T:** (01780) 470796 / 07906 502494 **E:** info@hallfarmkingscliffe.co.uk
W: www.hallfarmkingscliffe.co.uk **£ BOOK ONLINE**

| Units | 2 |
| Sleeps | 1-2 |

PER UNIT PER WEEK
£315.00 - £450.00

SPECIAL PROMOTIONS
Please contact us for prices.

Hall Farm Kings Cliffe is in a quiet village location within easy reach of Stamford, Oundle, Rutland Water and Peterborough and offers two types of self-catering accommodation each with its own private entrance and furnished to a high standard.

The Stables Cottage is on two floors in a 17th century stable block and faces into a courtyard. It provides stylish comfortable living with old oak beams and ancient stone.

The Archway Apartment is recently refurbished with windows overlooking the church and an old stone courtyard. With old oak beams and high ceilings it has a fresh modern style.

Open: All year except Christmas and New Year.
Nearest Shop: 0.10 miles
Nearest Pub: 0.10 miles

Units: Both the Cottage and Apartment have a super-king size bed that can be separated to make two single beds if required.

Site: P Leisure: ♪ Property: 🖥 🖳 Children: 🍼12 🛏 Unit: 🖩 📺 🍳 🕯 📺 🎧 📀

Stamford, Lincolnshire ©VisitBritain Tony Pleavin

WELLINGBOROUGH, Northamptonshire   Map ref 3A2   S

The Old Watermill

Contact: Mrs. Anne Newman, Hardwater Mill, Hardwater Road, Great Doddington, Wellingborough NN29 7TD **T:** (01933) 276870 / 07702 512022 **F:** (01933) 276870
E: sales@watermillholidays.co.uk **W:** www.watermillholidays.co.uk

Units   1
Sleeps   2-4
PER UNIT PER WEEK
£360.00 - £630.00

A charming and historic former watermill, Grade II listed. The well equipped accommodation is on three floors. One four-poster double and one twin bedroom. Central heating Double glazed. Plenty of old elm beams and oak floors. Pets welcome, garden plus riverside walks. Special Christmas and New Year breaks available.
Open: All year.
Nearest Shop: 1 mile
Nearest Pub: 1.5 miles

Site: ❀ P Leisure: ♪ Property: 🐾 🖥 🖵 Children: 🧒10 Unit: 🛏 🖥 ▣ 🖥 ♨ 📺 📀 ✐

NEWARK, Nottinghamshire   Map ref 4C2   S

Rose and Sweet Briar Cottages

Contact: Mrs Janet Hind, Owner, Rose and Sweet Briar Cottages, Hill Farm, Kersall, Newark, Nottinghamshire NG22 0BJ **T:** (01636) 636274 **E:** hind-hillfarm@hotmail.co.uk
W: www.roseandsweetbriar.co.uk

Units   2
Sleeps   2-4
PER UNIT PER WEEK
£130.00 - £285.00

Single storey cottages set in 1½ acre of private grounds of Hill farm in the hamlet of Kersall, Nr Newark (no longer working farm). Quiet location, beautiful views, large garden, off road parking. Close to Newark, Southwell, Ollerton, Edwinstowe and within easy travelling distance of Lincoln and Nottingham. Ideal location for exploring Sherwood Forest / Robin Hood country. Sorry no pets/no smoking.
Open: All year. **Nearest Shop:** 5 miles **Nearest Pub:** 1 mile

Site: ❀ P Leisure: ♿ ♪ ▶ ♾ Property: 🖵 Children: 🧒 Unit: 🛏 ▣ 🖥 ♨ 📺 📀

NOTTINGHAM, Nottinghamshire   Map ref 4C2   S

Woodview Cottages

Contact: Jane Morley, Woodview Cottages, Newfields Farm, Owthorpe NG12 3GE
T: (01949) 81985 / 07949 973470 **F:** (01949) 81580 **E:** enquiries@woodviewcottages.co.uk
W: www.woodviewcottages.co.uk

Units   2
Sleeps   1-4
PER UNIT PER WEEK
£400.00 - £575.00

A haven of tranquillity, two idyllic stone cottages in a beautiful setting 8 miles from Nottingham/Leicester. Picturesque gardens and beautiful woodland views. Each cottage is maintained by the owner ensuring high standards and comprises a well-equipped kitchen, comfortable living/dining-room with wood-burning stove and exposed beams; 2 bedrooms with exposed stone work, 1 double and 1 twin accommodating up to 4 people; bathroom/W.C. with shower cubicle. Ideal for nature lovers and wildlife enthusiasts.
Open: All year. **Nearest Shop:** 3 miles **Nearest Pub:** 3 miles

Site: ❀ P Payment: 💳 Leisure: ♪ Property: 🖥 🖵 Children: 🛏 Unit: 🛏 🖥 ▣ 🖥 ♨ 📺 🎧 📀

For **key to symbols** see page 6

BROOKE, Rutland   Map ref 4C3   S

★★★
SELF CATERING

| Units | 1 |
| Sleeps | 2-9 |

PER UNIT PER WEEK
£550.00 - £750.00

SPECIAL PROMOTIONS
Weekend breaks off-season or as late availability: 2 nights £375; 3 nights £405; 2 nights late departure Sunday (6pm) £399.

America Lodge

Contact: Mrs Lesley MacCartney, Proprietor, The Office, America Lodge, Brooke LE15 8DF
T: (01572) 723944 / 07850 937653 **F:** (01572) 759399 **E:** americalodge@btconnect.com
W: www.americalodge.co.uk

A lovely secluded farmhouse close to Rutland Water, just south of Oakham, the County Town of Rutland. Views over classic rolling English Countryside. Graded high 3 star. Private garden and grounds, large well appointed kitchen. Very central in UK. Will sleep 9 plus a cot. Refurbished December 2013 www.americalodge.co.uk.

Open: All year.
Nearest Shop: 3 miles
Nearest Pub: 2 miles

Units: Farmhouse accommodation.

Site: ❀ **P Leisure:** ♿ ♪ ▸ ∪ **Property:** 🐾 🖼 🔲 **Children:** 🍼 🛏 ⚲ **Unit:** 🔲 🗄 📺 🎬 📺 💿 🎮 📀 BBQ

OAKHAM, Rutland   Map ref 4C3   SatNav LE15 8AH   H

★★★
HOTEL

SPECIAL PROMOTIONS
Special promotions always available, please see our website for full details.

Barnsdale Lodge Hotel

The Avenue, Rutland Water, Oakham LE15 8AH **T:** (01572) 724678 **F:** (01572) 724961
E: reception@barnsdalelodge.co.uk
W: www.barnsdalelodge.co.uk

Enjoy a relaxing break on the beautiful north shore of Rutland Water. We offer you anything from a wedding to an intimate dinner for two. Our informal dining areas are reflected in our seasonal bistro menu. Our bedrooms are all comfortably and individually decorated and have garden or countryside views.

Directions: Please see our website for map and full directions.

Bedrooms: 7 single, 27 double, 9 twin, 1 family
Open: All year.

Site: ❀ **Payment:** 💷 **Leisure:** ♿ ♪ ▸ ∪ ⚹ **Property:** 🍴 🐾 🖼 🔲 ◐ **Children:** 🍼 🛏 ⚲ **Catering:** 🍷 🍴
Room: 📞 📺 🎬 📺 💻 📠

There are hundreds of "Green" places to stay and visit in England from small bed and breakfasts to large visitor attractions and activity holiday providers. Businesses displaying this logo have undergone a rigorous verification process to ensure that they are sustainable (green) and that a qualified assessor has visited the premises.

We have indicated the accommodation which has achieved a Green award... look out for the 🌱 symbol in the entry.

Don't Miss...

Dudley Zoological Gardens ❀

Dudley, West Midlands DY1 4QB
(01384) 215313
www.dudleyzoo.org.uk
DZG is unique - a zoo with hundreds of animals set around an
11th century castle incorporating the world's largest single collection
of Tecton buildings and the country's only vintage chairlift – all sited
on a 40-acre wooded hillside with a rich geological history. From lions
and tigers to snakes and spiders, animal feeding, face painting, land
train and fair rides, there's something for everyone.

The Iron Bridge Gorge Museum ❀

Telford, Shropshire TF8 7DG
(01952) 433424
www.ironbridge.org.uk
The Ironbridge Gorge is a remarkable and beautiful insight into the
region's industrial heritage. Ten award-winning Museums spread along
the valley beside the wild River Severn - still spanned by the world's first
Iron Bridge, where you can peer through the railings and conjure a
vision of sailing vessels heading towards Bristol and the trading markets
of the world.

The Potteries Museum & Art Gallery

Stoke-on-Trent ST1 3DW
(01789) 204016
www.stokemuseums.org.uk/visit/pmag
Travel back in time and discover the history of The Potteries including
the world's greatest collection of Staffordshire ceramics, a World War II
Spitfire, decorative arts and natural history. A warm and friendly
welcome awaits at one of Britain's leading museums where the
unique combination of 'product and place' is celebrated in its
outstanding displays.

Shakespeare's Birthplace Trust ❀

Stratford-upon-Avon, Warwickshire CV37 6QW
www.shakespeare.org.uk
A unique Shakespeare experience with outstanding archive and library
collections, inspiring educational and literary event programmes.
Discover the Tudor town house that was Shakespeare's Birthplace.
Visit Mary Arden's Farm, the childhood home of Shakespeare's mother.
Explore the lavish rooms and tranquil gardens of Hall's Croft. Fall in
love with romantic Anne Hathaway's Cottage, the quintessentially
English thatched family home of Shakespeare's wife. Take in the period
splendour of Nash's House and learn about Shakespeare's final
home at New Place where he died in 1616.

Warwick Castle

Warwickshire CV34 4QU
(08712) 652000
www.warwick-castle.co.uk
Battlements, towers, turrets, History, magic, myth and adventure -
Warwick Castle is a Scheduled Ancient Monument and Grade 1 listed
building packed with things to do, inside and out.

Heart of England

Herefordshire, Shropshire,
Staffordshire, Warwickshire,
West Midlands, Worcestershire

The Heart of England: a name that defines this lovely part of the country so much better than its geographical name: The Midlands. Like a heart it has many arteries and compartments, from the March counties of Shropshire and Herefordshire, through Birmingham and the West Midlands, birthplace of the Industrial Revolution. It is a region rich in history and character and you'll find pretty villages, grand castles and plenty of canals and waterways to explore.

Staffordshire

Shropshire

West
Midlands

Warwick-   Worcester-
shire   shire

Herefordshire

Explore –
Heart of England

Coventry & Warwickshire

From castles and cathedrals to art galleries, museums and exciting events, this region captivates visitors from all over the world.

Stratford-upon-Avon draws visitors from all over the world who want to follow in the footsteps of William Shakespeare, Stratford's most famous son. The famous theatre is an essential night out for drama from Shakespeare and his contemporaries. The city of Warwick is dominated by its 14th century castle and its museums, and plenty of family activities are staged throughout the year. Historic Coventry has over 400 listed buildings and is most famous for its cathedrals, with the modern Church of St Michael sitting majestically next to the 'blitzed' ruins of its 14th century predecessor.

Herefordshire

Herefordshire's ruined castles and Iron Age and Roman hill-forts recall a turbulent battle-scarred past. Offa's Dyke, constructed by King Offa of Mercia in the 8th century marks the border with Wales but today the landscape is peaceful, with delightful small towns and villages and Hereford cattle grazing in pastures beside apple orchards and hop gardens.

Hereford has an 11th century cathedral and is home to one of the largest medieval map of the world, the Mappa Mundi. In the West, the Wye meanders through meadows and valleys. Hay-on-Wye is now best known for its annual Literary Festival and plethora of second hand bookshops.

Shropshire

Tucked away on the England/Wales border, Shropshire is another March county that saw much conflict between English and Welsh, hostilities between warring tribes and invading Romans.

The Wrekin and Stretton Hills were created by volcanoes and in the South, the Long Mynd rises to 1700 ft with panoramic views of the Severn plain. Ironbridge, near Telford, is where the Industrial Revolution began with the building of the world's first cast iron bridge. County town Shrewsbury was an historic fortress town built in a loop of the river Severn and these days joins Ludlow, with its 11th century castle, as one of the gastronomic high spots of Britain.

There are many splendid historic and architectural gems in Shropshire, from Jacobean coaching inns in the heart of picturesque market towns to historic mansions of brick, like stately Weston Park, the architectural masterpiece of Lady Elizabeth Wilbraham.

Staffordshire

Staffordshire, squeezed between the Black Country to the south and Manchester to the north, conceals many heritage treasures and an exciting industrial history. It is home to the Potteries, a union of six towns made famous by Wedgwood, Spode and other ceramic designers, celebrated at the many museums and visitor centres.

Lichfield, just north of Birmingham is the birthplace of Samuel Johnson and has a magnificent three-spired 13th century cathedral, while some of England's finest houses and most beautiful gardens are also to be found in the county. Fabulous examples include the award-winning landscaped gardens on the Trentham Estate and the 'Capability' Brown parkland at Chillington Hall. Meanwhile, the unspoilt ancient heathland of Cannock Chase, leafy woodlands of the National Forest and secluded byways of South Staffordshire all offer the chance to further enjoy the great outdoors.

West Midlands

The Industrial revolution of the 19th century led to the growth of Birmingham into Britain's second city - the city of a thousand trades. Its prosperity was based on factories, hundreds of small workshops and a network of canals, all of which helped in the production of everything from needles and chocolate to steam engines and bridges. Nowadays the city has one of the best concert halls in Europe, excellent shopping and a regenerated waterside café culture.

The West Midlands is an urban area which still represents the powerhouse of Central Britain. Wolverhampton has been called Capital of the Black Country, made famous through its ironwork and Walsall, birthplace of Jerome K Jerome, has three museums. Affluent Sutton Coldfield and Solihull have proud civic traditions and a number of pretty parks. Many of Solihull's rural villages sit along the Stratford-upon-Avon canal and offer plenty of picturesque pubs along the tow path from which to watch the gentle meander of passing narrow boats.

Worcestershire

The beautiful county of Worcestershire has a fantastic selection of historic houses and gardens to discover and Worcester itself has a famous cathedral, cricket ground, and 15th century Commandery, now a Civil war museum.

Great Malvern, still a Spa town, is famous as the birthplace of Sir Edward Elgar, who drew much of his inspiration from this countryside and who is celebrated at the annual Malvern Festival. The old riverside market town of Evesham is the centre of the Vale of Evesham fruit and vegetable growing area which, with the tranquil banks of the river Avon and the undulating hills and peaceful wooded slopes of the Cotswolds, offers some of the prettiest landscapes in the country.

Droitwich, known in Roman times as Salinae, still has briny water in its spa baths and can trace the origins of salt extraction in the area back to prehistoric times, it even holds an annual 'Salt Festival' to celebrate this unique heritage.

Visit – Heart of England

Coventry & Warwickshire

Coventry Cathedral - St Michael's ⊕
West Midlands CV1 5AB
(024) 7652 1200
www.coventrycathedral.org.uk
*Glorious 20th century Cathedral, with stunning
1950's art & architecture, rising above the stark
ruins of the medieval Cathedral destroyed by air
raids in 1940.*

Compton Verney ⊕
Stratford-upon-Avon CV35 9HZ
(01926) 645500
www.comptonverney.org.uk
*Award-winning art gallery housed in a grade I listed
Robert Adam mansion.*

Godiva Festival
July, Coventry, Warwickshire
www.godivafestival.com
*The Godiva Festival is the UK's biggest free family
festival held over a weekend in the War Memorial
Park, Coventry. The event showcases some of the
finest local, national and International artists, live
comedy, family entertainment, Godiva Carnival,
and lots more.*

Heritage Open Days
September, Coventry, Warwickshire
www.heritageopendays.org.uk
*Celebrating England's architecture and culture
by allowing visitors free access to interesting
properties that are either not usually open or would
normally charge an entrance fee. Also including
tours, events and activities that focus on local
architecture and culture.*

Kenilworth Castle and Elizabethan Garden
Warwickshire CV8 1NE
(01926) 852078
www.english-heritage.org.uk/kenilworth
One of the most spectacular castle ruins in England.

Packwood House
Solihull, Warwickshire B94 6AT
(01564) 782024
www.nationaltrust.org.uk/packwood-house
Tudor house, park and garden with notable topiary.

Ragley Hall ⊕
Stratford-upon-Avon, Warwickshire B49 5NJ
(01789) 762090
www.ragley.co.uk
*Set in 27 acres of beautiful formal gardens. For a fun
family day out Ragley Hall, Park & Gardens really
does have something for everyone!*

Ryton Pools Country Parks
Coventry, Warwickshire CV8 3BG
(024) 7630 5592
www.warwickshire.gov.uk/parks
*The 100 acres of Ryton Pools Country Park are just
waiting to be explored. The many different habitats
are home to a wide range of birds and other wildlife.*

Stratford River Festival
July, Stratford, Warwickshire
www.stratforward.co.uk/events/stratford-river-festival
*Bringing the waterways of Stratford alive, with
boatloads of family fun, on the first weekend of July.*

Three Counties Show
June, Malvern, Warwickshire
www.threecounties.co.uk/threecounties
*Three jam-packed days of family entertainment and
fun, all in celebration of the great British farming
world and countryside.*

Herefordshire

Eastnor Castle
Ledbury, Herefordshire HR8 1RL
(01531) 633160
www.eastnorcastle.com
Fairytale Georgian Castle dramatically situated in the Malvern Hills. Surrounded by a beautiful deer park, arboretum and lake, this award-winning tourist attraction is a fun filled family day out.

Goodrich Castle
Ross-on-Wye, Herefordshire HR9 6HY
(01600) 890538
www.english-heritage.org.uk/goodrich
Come and relive the turbulent history of Goodrich Castle with our free audio and then climb to the battlements for breathtaking views over the Wye Valley.

The Hay Festival
May / June, Hay-on-Wye, Herefordshire
www.hayfestival.com
Some five hundred events see writers, politicians, poets, scientists, comedians, philosophers and musicians come together on a greenfield site for a ten day fesitval of ideas and stories at the Hay Festival.

Hereford Cathedral
Herefordshire HR1 2NG
(01432) 374200
www.herefordcathedral.org
Some of the finest examples of architecture from Norman times to the present day. Its most famous treasure is Mappa Mundi, a medieval map of the world dating from the 13th century.

Hereford Museum and Art Gallery
Herefordshire HR4 9AU
(01432) 260692
www.herefordshire.gov.uk/museums
Hereford Museum and Art Gallery, housed in a spectacular Victorian gothic building, has been exhibiting artefacts and works of fine and decorative art connected with the local area since 1874. The Art Gallery hosts regularly changing exhibitions of contemporary and historic art and themed object displays.

Hergest Croft Gardens
Kington, Herefordshire HR5 3EG
(01544) 230160
www.hergest.co.uk
The gardens extend over 50 acres, with more than 4000 rare shrubs and trees. With over 60 champion trees and shrubs it is one of the finest collections in the British Isles. With a Gift Shop and Tearooms the Gardens are the perfect place to explore and relax.

Ledbury Heritage Centre
Herefordshire, HR8 1DN
(01531) 635680
www.herefordshire.gov.uk/museums
The story of Ledbury's past displayed in a timber-framed building in the picturesque lane leading to the church. Learn about the poets John Masefeild and Elizabeth Barrett Browning and try your hand at timber framing.

Shropshire

Bridgnorth Cliff Railway
Bridgnorth, Shropshire, WV16 4AH
(01746) 762124
www.bridgnorthcliffrailway.co.uk
Take a journey on the oldest and steepest funicular inland electric cliff railway in the country between High Town and Low Town. Visit spectacular shops, gardens, and enjoy the views that Charlies I named the finest in his kingdom.

The British Ironwork Centre
Oswestry, Shropshire SY11 4JH
(0800) 6888386
www.britishironworkcentre.co.uk
A treasure trove of magnificent animal sculptures and decorations, including of a 13ft-high gorilla made from an incredible 40,000+ spoons donated by people from all over the world. Now home to the largest collection of birds of prey in Shropshire.

Darby Houses (Ironbridge)
Telford, Shropshire TF8 7EW
(01952) 433424
www.ironbridge.org.uk/our-attractions/darby-houses
The Darby Houses are one of the ten Ironbridge Gorge Museums. Experience the everyday life of Coalbrookdale's ironmasters in the former homes of the Darby family.

Enginuity
Telford, Shropshire TF8 7DG
(01952) 433424
www.ironbridge.org.uk/our-attractions/enginuity
Enginuity is one of the ten Ironbridge Gorge Museums. Enjoy a fun-filled family day out at this science and technology centre. At Enginuity you can turn the wheels of your imagination, test your horse power and discover how good ideas are turned in to real things.

English Haydn Festival
June, Bridgnorth, Shropshire
www.englishhaydn.com
Focusing on Joseph Haydn's music and his life in Vienna, in particular during the years leading up to his death in 1809 and his friendship and influence on Beethoven and Schubert, performed in St. Leonards Church, Bridgnorth.

Ludlow Food & Drink Festival
September, Ludlow, Shropshire
www.foodfestival.co.uk
More than 180 top quality independent food and drink producers inside Ludlow Castle.

Much Wenlock Priory
Shropshire TF13 6HS
(01952) 727466
www.english-heritage.org.uk/wenlockpriory
Wenlock Priory, a ruined 12th century monastery, with its stunning clipped topiary, has a pastoral setting on the edge of lovely Much Wenlock.

RAF Cosford Air Show
June, Shifnal, Shropshire
www.cosfordairshow.co.uk
This RAF-organised show usually features all the airshow favourites, classic and current British and foreign aircraft, exhibits and trade stalls all on this classic RAF airbase

Royal Air Force Museum Cosford
Shifnal, Shropshire TF11 8UP
(01902) 376200
www.rafmuseum.org
The award-winning museum houses one of the largest aviation collections in the United Kingdom along with being home to the National Cold War Exhibition. FREE Admission.

Severn Valley Railway – The Engine House
Highley, Shropshire
(01746) 862387
www.svr.co.uk/EngineHouse.aspx
The stunning Engine House Centre at Highley takes you on a fascinating journey behind the scenes. Marvel at the massive locomotives, delve into the intriguing history of Britain's railways, enjoy themed exhibitions and meet the engine that collided with a camel!

Shrewsbury Folk Festival
August, Shrewsbury, Shropshire
www.shrewsburyfolkfestival.co.uk
Shrewsbury Folk Festival has a reputation for delivering established artists from the UK alongside acts celebrating folk traditions from across the world who will take you on a voyage of discovery, bringing you ever-changing musical colours with their breathtaking performances.

Stokesay Castle
Craven Arms, Shropshire SY7 9AH
(01588) 672544
www.english-heritage.org.uk/stokesaycastle
Stokesay Castle, nestles in peaceful South Shropshire countryside near the Welsh Border. It is one of more than a dozen English Heritage properties in the county.

V Festival
August, Weston Park, Shropshire
www.vfestival.com
Legendary rock and pop festival held annually during the penultimate weekend in August.

Wenlock Olympian Games
July, Much Wenlock, Shropshire
www.wenlock-olympian-society.org.uk
The games that inspired the modern Olympic Movement.

Wroxeter Roman City
Shrewsbury, Shropshire SY5 6PH
(01743) 761330
www.english-heritage.org.uk/wroxeter
Wroxeter Roman City, or Viroconium, to give it its Roman title, is thought to have been one of the largest Roman cities in the UK with over 200 acres of land, 2 miles of walls and a population of approximately 5,000.

Staffordshire

Abbots Bromley Horn Dance
September, Abbots Bromley, Staffordshire
www.abbotsbromley.com/horn_dance
Ancient ritual dating back to 1226. Six deer-men, a fool, hobby horse, bowman and Maid Marian perform to music provided by a melodian player.

Aerial Extreme Trentham
Staffordshire ST12 9HR
0845 652 1736
www.aerialextreme.co.uk/locations/staffordshire
Our tree based adventure ropes course, set within the tranquil grounds of Trentham Estate is a truly spectacular journey. All ages are guaranteed a bucket load of fun.

Etruria Industrial Museum
Staffordshire ST1 4RB
(07900) 267711
www.etruriamuseum.org.uk
Discover how they put the 'bone' in bone china at the last working steam-powered potters mill in Britain. Includes a Bone and Flint Mill and family-friendly interactive exhibition.

Leek Food Festival
March, Staffordshire, ST13 6AD
www.leekfoodanddrink.co.uk
The Leek Food Festival is host over 70 stalls and hot vendors, a beer festival tent, and experience Leek's fabulous shops and pubs at the same time.

Lichfield Cathedral
Staffordshire WS13 7LD
(01543) 306100
www.lichfield-cathedral.org
A medieval Cathedral, one of the oldest places of Christian worship in Britain, with 3 spires in the heart of an historic City set in its own serene Close.

Midlands Grand National
March, Uttoxeter Racecourse, Staffordshire
www.uttoxeter-racecourse.co.uk
The biggest fixture in Uttoxeter's calendar and the second longest Steeplechase in the country at 4 miles and 1 1/2 furlongs.

National Memorial Arboretum
Lichfield, Staffordshire DE13 7AR
(01283) 245100
www.thenma.org.uk
150 acres of trees and memorials, planted as a living tribute to those who have served, died or suffered in the service of their Country.

The Roaches
Upper Hulme, Leek, Staffordshire ST13
www.visitpeakdistrict.com
The Roaches (or Roches) is a wind-carved outcrop of gritstone rocks that rises above the waters or Tittesworth reservoir, between Leek in Staffordshire and Buxton in Derbyshire. It's impressive gritstone edges and craggy rocks are loved by walkers and climbers alike.

Stone Food & Drink Festival
October, Stone, Staffordshire
07564 378916
www.stonefooddrink.org.uk
Growing from humble beginnings in the town's Georgian High Street into one of the Midlands' biggest and busiest food festivals.

Tamworth Castle
Staffordshire B79 7NA
(01827) 709629
www.tamworthcastle.co.uk
The number one Heritage attraction located in the town. Explore over 900 years of history in the magnificent Motte and Bailey Castle.

Trentham Gardens
Stoke-on-Trent, Staffordshire, ST4 8JG
(01782) 646646
www.trentham.co.uk/trentham-gardens
Enjoy beautiful show gardens; take a woodland stroll along the mile-long lake, or get active in the adventure playground.

World of Wedgwood
Stoke-on-Trent, Staffordshire ST12 9ER
(01782) 282986
www.worldofwedgwood.com
Enjoy the past, buy the present and treasure the experience. The World of Wedgwood offers a unique chance to immerse yourself in the heritage of Britain's greatest ceramics company.

West Midlands

Barber Institute of Fine Arts
Edgbaston, West Midlands B15 2TS
(0121) 414 7333
www.barber.org.uk
British and European paintings, drawings and sculpture from the 13th century to mid 20th century, including Old Master and Impressionist collections. The Barber Institute also hosts an impressive range of concert programmes throughout the year.

Bewdley Museum
Bewdley, DY12 2AE
0845 603 5699
www.bewdleymuseum.co.uk
Set in a historic Butchers Shambles, Bewdley Museum offers a fascinating insight to the history of Bewdley with gardens, interesting displays and demonstrations using craft.

Birmingham Botanical Gardens
Edgbaston, Birmingham B15 3TR
(0121) 454 1860
www.birminghambotanicalgardens.org.uk
Visit the ornamental gardens and glasshouses spaning from tropical rainforest to arid desert climates. A lively birdhouse, wildlife trails and a seasonal butterfly house also sit attractively amongst the fifteen acres of flourishing gardens and foliage.

Birmingham Literature Festival
October, Birmingham, West Midlands
www.birminghamliteraturefestival.org
Celebrating the city's literature scene, the Birmingham Literature Festival takes places every year with its trademark mix of literature events, talks and workshops.

Birmingham International Jazz and Blues Festival
July, Birmingham, West Midlands
www.visitbirmingham.com
The festival presents around 175 performances each year in around 40 venues. Musicians and fans come to the city from every corner of the UK as well as from further afield and significantly, almost all of the events are free to the public.

Black Country Living Museum
Dudley, West Midlands DY1 4SQ
(0121) 557 9643
www.bclm.co.uk
Britain's friendliest open-air museum - visit original shops and houses, ride on fair attractions, take a look down the underground coalmine.

Frankfurt Christmas Market & Craft Fair
November-December, Birmingham, West Midlands
www.germanchristmasmarketbirmingham.com
The largest authentic German market outside Germany and Austria and the centrepiece of the city's festive event calendar.

Great Malvern Priory
Malvern, WR14 2AY
(01684) 561020
www.greatmalvernpriory.org.uk
Great Malvern Priory was founded as Benedictine Priory in 1085 and has been changing and developing for centuries. See different stages of life and appreciate the beautiful architecture in this parish church dedicated to St Mary and St Michael.

Ikon Gallery
Brindley Place, Birmingham B1 2HS
(0121) 248 0708
www.ikon-gallery.org
Ikon is an internationally acclaimed contemporary art venue housed in the Grade II listed, neo-gothic former Oozells Street Board School, designed by John Henry Chamberlain in 1877.

Moseley Folk Festival
September, Birmingham, West Midlands
www.moseleyfolk.co.uk
Offering an inner city Shangri-la bringing together people from all ages and backgrounds to witness folk legends playing alongside their contemporaries.

Thinktank-Birmingham Science Museum
West Midlands B4 7XG
(0121) 348 8000
www.thinktank.ac
Thinktank is Birmingham's science museum where the emphasis is firmly on hands on exhibits and interactive fun.

Worcestershire

The Almonry Museum & Heritage Centre
Evesham, Worcestershire WR11 4BG
(01386) 446944
www.almonryevesham.org
The 14th century house has 12 rooms of exhibits from 2000 years of Evesham history and pleasant gardens to the rear.

Greyfriars House
Worcester WR1 2LZ
(01905) 23571
www.nationaltrust.org.uk/greyfriars
The National Trust's Greyfriars House and Garden, Worcestershire, built in 1480 by a wealthy merchant, is a fine timbered Medieval merchants house and walled garden.

Hanbury Hall
Droitwich Spa, Worcestershire WR9 7EA
(01527) 821214
www.nationaltrust.org.uk/hanburyhall
Early 18th century house, garden & park owned by the Vernon family for nearly 300 years. Choose from one of the scenic walks and make the most of your day by exploring the estate and surrounding countryside.

West Midland Safari and Leisure Park
Bewdley, Worcestershire DY12 1LF
(01299) 402114
www.wmsp.co.uk
Are you ready to SAFARI and come face to face with some of the fastest, tallest, largest and cutest animals around? The park is home to some of the world's most beautiful and endangered exotic animal species. The leisure park features 28 rides and attractions, there is something here to suit the whole family.

Worcester Cathedral
Worcestershire WR1 2LA
(01905) 732900
www.worcestercathedral.co.uk
Worcester Cathedral is one of England's most magnificent and inspiring buildings, as it rises majestically above the River Severn. It has been place of prayer and worship for 14 centuries.

Worcester City Art Gallery & Museum
Worcestershire WR1 1DT
(01905) 25371
www.museumsworcestershire.org.uk
The art gallery & museum runs a programme of exhibitions/events for all the family. Explore the fascinating displays, exhibitions, café, shop and Worcestershire Soldier Galleries. The collections and exhibitions are many and varied, covering centuries of the county's history right up to the present day.

Tourist Information Centres

When you arrive at your destination, visit the Tourist Information Centre for quality assured help with accommodation and information about local attractions and events, or email your request before you go.

Bewdley	Load Street	0845 6077819	bewdleytic@visitwyreforest.co.uk
Bridgnorth	The Library	01746 763257	bridgnorth.tourism@shropshire.gov.uk
Bromyard	The Bromyard Centre	01885 488133	enquiries@visitbromyard.co.uk
Church Stretton	High Street	01694 722113	secretary@churchstretton-tc.gov.uk
Droitwich Spa	St Richard's House	01905 774312	heritage@droitwichspa.gov.uk
Ellesmere, Shropshire	The Boathouse Visitor Centre	01691 622981	ellesmere.tourism@shropshire.gov.uk
Evesham	The Almonry	01386 446944	tic@almonry.ndo.co.uk
Hereford	1 King Street	01432 268430	reception@visitherefordshire.co.uk
Ironbridge	Museum of The Gorge	01952 433424	tic@ironbridge.org.uk
Kenilworth	Kenilworth Library	01926 852595	wdirect-ken@warwickshire.gov.uk
Ledbury	38 The Homend	0844 5678650	info@vistledbury.info
Leek	Stockwell Street	01538 483741	tourism@staffsmoorlands.gov.uk
Leominster	1 Corn Square	01568 616460	reception@leminstertourism.co.uk
Lichfield	St. Marys Church	01543 412112	info@visitlichfield.com
Ludlow	Mill Street	01584 875053	visitors@ludlowassemblyrooms.co.uk
Malvern	21 Church Street	01684 892289	info@visitthemalverns.org
Market Drayton	49 Cheshire Street	01630 653114	marketdrayton.scf@shropshire-cc.gov.uk
Much Wenlock	The Museum - Visitor Information Centre	01952 727679 / 01743 258891	muchwenlock.tourism@shropshire.gov.uk
Newcastle-Under-Lyme	Newcastle Library	01782 297313	tic.newcastle@staffordshire.gov.uk
Nuneaton	Nuneaton Library	0300 5558171	
Oswestry Town	The Heritage Centre	01691 662753	ot@oswestry-welshborders.org.uk
Redditch	Palace Theatre	01527 60806	info.centre@bromsgroveandredditch.gov.uk
Ross-on-Wye	Market House	01989 562768	tic-ross@herefordshire.gov.uk
Royal Leamington Spa	Royal Pump Rooms	01926 742762	vic@warwickdc.gov.uk
Rugby	Rugby Art Gallery Museum	01788 533217	visitor.centre@rugby.gov.uk
Shrewsbury	Barker Street	01743 258888	visitorinfo@shropshire.gov.uk
Solihull	The Core Library	0121 704 6977	libraries@solihull.gov.uk
Stafford	Stafford Gatehouse Theatre	01785 619619	visitorinfo@staffordbc.gov.uk
Stoke-On-Trent	Bethesda Street	01782 236000	stoke.tic@stoke.gov.uk
Stratford-Upon-Avon	Bridge Foot	01789 264293	tic@discover-stratford.com
Tamworth	Lichfield Street	01827 709581	tic@tamworth.gov.uk
Telford	The Telford Shopping Centre	01952 238008	tourist-info@telfordshopping.co.uk
Upton Upon Severn	The Heritage Centre	01684 594200	upton-info@visitthemalverns.org
Warwick	Visit Warwick	01926 492212	info@visitwarwick.co.uk
Whitchurch (Shropshire)	High Street	01948 664577	info@whitchurchcouncil.co.uk
Worcester	The Guildhall	01905 726311	touristinfo@visitworcester.com
Coventry	Barley Lane	024 7622 5616	tic@coventry.gov.uk

Regional Contacts and Information

For more information on accommodation, attractions, activities, events and holidays in the Heart of England, contact one of the following regional or local tourism organisations. Their websites have a wealth of information and many produce free publications to help you get the most out of your visit.

Marketing Birmingham
www.visitbirmingham.com

Visit Coventy & Warwickshire
(024) 7622 5616
www.visitcoventryandwarwickshire.co.uk

Visit Herefordshire
(01432) 268430
www.visitherefordshire.co.uk

Shakespeare Country
www.shakespeare-country.co.uk

Shropshire Tourism
(01743) 261919
www.shropshiretourism.co.uk

Destination Staffordshire
www.enjoystaffordshire.com

Stoke-on-Trent
(01782) 236000
www.visitstoke.co.uk

Destination Worcestershire
(01905) 673617
www.visitworcestershire.org

Stay –
Heart of England

Entries appear alphabetically by town name in each county. A key to symbols appears on page 6

HEREFORD, Herefordshire   Map ref 2A1   [S]

Monnington House Monnington on Wye

Contact: Anna Pearson Gregory, Owner/Manager, Monnington on Wye, Nr Hereford, Herefordshire HR4 7NL **T:** (01672) 563571 / 07879 886068 **E:** anna@pearsongregory.co.uk
W: www.monningtonhouse.co.uk **£ BOOK ONLINE**

Units   1
Sleeps   18
PER UNIT PER WEEK
£3000.00 - £6000.00

Awarded Winner of Best Self Catering House Herefordshire 2016 by Visit Herefordshire. Luxurious farmhouse sleeping 18 in 9 spacious bedrooms and 9 bathrooms on Wye Valley Walk.
Large 2 acre garden plus playing field with 2 football goals. Games room with pool table and table football and table tennis room. Close to 2 cycling routes (bike shed on site) and there is a pub within 16 minutes' walk. Dogs by arrangement, please enquire.
Open: All year. **Nearest Shop:** 1.8 **Nearest Pub:** 1.4

Site: ❀ P Payment: 💷 Leisure: 🚲 ⚘ 🎣 Property: ⚡ 🐾 🖼 📺 🏠 🎦 Children: 🛏 🍴 🏃
Unit: 📶 🍴 🖥 📻 🎮 📺 📀 🌀 BBQ 🔔

HEREFORD, Herefordshire   Map ref 2A1   SatNav HR2 7BP

AA ★★★ Hotel

Three Counties Hotel

Belmont Road, Hereford HR2 7BP **T:** (01432) 299955 **F:** (01432) 275114
E: enquiries@threecountieshotel.co.uk
W: www.threecountieshotel.co.uk **£ BOOK ONLINE**

B&B PER ROOM PER NIGHT
S: £69.00 - £85.00
D: £84.00 - £100.00
EVENING MEAL PER PERSON
£14.95 - £35.00

Excellently appointed hotel set in 3.5 acres. Emphasis on traditional, friendly service. Tasteful bedrooms, restaurant and bar offer today's guests all modern comforts. Free Wi-Fi in all public areas and selected bedrooms. Town centre 1.5 miles.
Directions: Please see website.
Bedrooms: 18 double, 42 twin.
Open: All year.

Site: ❀ Payment: 💷 Property: ⚡ 🐾 🖼 🌐 ◑ Children: 🛏 🍴 🏃 Catering: 🍷 🍽 Room: 🖥 🔌 🔔 📻 📺 🛁

KINGTON, Herefordshire   Map ref 2A1   [S]

VisitEngland 4★-5★ SELF CATERING   VisitEngland Gold AWARD

White Heron Properties

Contact: Jo Hilditch, Managing Director, Whittern Farms Ltd, Lyonshall, Kington HR5 3JA
T: (01544) 340241 **F:** (01544) 340253 **E:** info@whiteheronproperties.com
W: www.whiteheronproperties.com **£ BOOK ONLINE**

Units   5
Sleeps   2-32
PER UNIT PER WEEK
£500.00 - £4800.00

SPECIAL PROMOTIONS
We offer Friday to Sunday, Friday to Monday and Monday to Friday as standard stays.

We have five lovely properties in rolling Herefordshire countryside. They vary from pet friendly small cottages to large contemporary accommodation for house parties, all with en suite bedrooms. The largest has a swimming pool, sauna, hot tub, table tennis, cinema, Wii, Xbox and even a squash court.

We can host small conferences, weddings, hen parties or just provide luxurious accommodation for a romantic weekend away in the country. With great service from a friendly team we can offer full catering, or leave it all to you - the choice is yours, whichever you choose you will not be disappointed! Prices shown are based on a small unit. Please contact for larger unit rates.

Open: All year.
Nearest Shop: 3 miles
Nearest Pub: 2 miles

Units: At White Heron properties we have a total of 23 bedrooms in 5 properties, some en suite.

Site: ❀ P Payment: 💷 Leisure: 🎣 ⚘ ⛱ 🎣 ⚘ Property: ⚡ 🖼 🌐 🏠 Children: 🛏 🍴 🏃
Unit: 📶 🖥 📻 🎮 📺 📀 🌀 BBQ 🔔

f 🐦

ROSS-ON-WYE, Herefordshire   Map ref 2A1   S

VisitEngland ★★★★ SELF CATERING

Units 1
Sleeps 1-4
PER UNIT PER WEEK
£310.00 - £525.00

Bramley Cottage

Contact: Lucy Snell, c/o Bramley House, Pencoyd, Harewood End, Hereford HR2 8JY
T: (01989) 730416 / 07747 041026   **E:** lucy@bramleyholidaycottage.co.uk
W: www.bramleyholidaycottage.co.uk

Bramley Cottage lies in the heart of the Wye Valley. 5 miles from Ross on Wye and near the cathedral town of Hereford. It provides the perfect location from which to explore the stunning countryside, whether on foot along the banks of the Wye to Symonds Yat or on bikes in the Forest of Dean, or just canoeing gently down the river. **Open:** All year.
Nearest Shop: 2 miles
Nearest Pub: 1.25 miles

Site: ✿ P **Property:** ☙ ▦ 🖥 🖵 **Children:** ▥ ☂ **Unit:** 🖵 🍴 ▣ 🖥 🍳 TV 📀 BBQ

ROSS-ON-WYE, Herefordshire   Map ref 2A1   S

VisitEngland ★★★ SELF CATERING

Units 2
Sleeps 2-4
PER UNIT PER WEEK
£285.00 - £520.00

Game Larders & Old Bakehouse

Contact: Miss Anthea McIntyre, Game Larders & Old Bakehouse, Wythall Estate, Walford, Ross-on-Wye HR9 5SD   **T:** (01989) 562688   **F:** (01989) 566531
E: bookings@wythallestate.co.uk   **W:** www.wythallestate.co.uk

Wythall is a 16th century half-timbered manor house in a secluded setting, with garden, duck pond and wooded grounds. You will enjoy peace and quiet here and see an abundance of wildlife. The cottages are self-contained and set in the west wing of the house. They are well equipped, warm and comfortable and have digital television with freeview channels and DVD player and free Wi-Fi access. **Open:** All year.
Nearest Shop: 2 miles **Nearest Pub:** 1 mile

Site: ✿ P **Property:** ☙ ▦ 🖵 **Children:** ☂ ▥ ☂ **Unit:** 🖥 ▣ 🍳 TV 📀

BROSELEY, Shropshire   Map ref 4A3   SatNav TF12 5EW   B

VisitEngland ★★★★ GUEST ACCOMMODATION   **VisitEngland** Silver AWARD

B&B PER ROOM PER NIGHT
S: £45.00 - £55.00
D: £75.00 - £90.00

Broseley House

1 The Square, Broseley, Ironbridge TF12 5EW   **T:** (01952) 882043
E: info@broseleyhouse.co.uk
W: www.broseleyhouse.co.uk

Period townhouse, one mile from Ironbridge. Unique, comfortable bedrooms with Wi-Fi, freeview, plus many thoughtful extras and close good local amenities. Walkers, cyclists welcome. Self catering also available.
Directions: Refer to the website or call for directions.
Bedrooms: 3 double, 1 twin, 2 family.
Open: All year.

🏆 **Site:** ✿ **Payment:** 💷 **Property:** ☙ ▦ 🖥 **Children:** ☂⁵ **Catering:** 🍴 **Room:** 🍳 ♨ TV 📀 🔌 🛁

CLUN, Shropshire   Map ref 4A3   SatNav SY7 8JA   B

VisitEngland ★★★ INN

B&B PER ROOM PER NIGHT
S: £40.00 - £45.00
D: £65.00 - £70.00
EVENING MEAL PER PERSON
£8.95 - £15.95

The White Horse Inn

The Square, Clun, Shropshire SY7 8JA   **T:** (01588) 418161   **E:** room@whi-clun.co.uk
W: www.whi-clun.co.uk   **£ BOOK ONLINE**

Small, friendly 'Good Pub Guide' listed pub with well-appointed en suite family bedrooms in traditional style.
Wide-ranging menu available in dining room.
Specialising in Real Ales with own micro-brewery.
Directions: In the centre of Clun.
Bedrooms: 2 twin, 2 double.
Open: All year except Christmas.

WALKERS CYCLISTS PETS! **Site:** ✿ **Payment:** 💷 **Leisure:** 🎵 **Property:** ☙ ▦ 🖥 ⌀ **Children:** ☂ ▥ ☂ **Catering:** ◖✗ 🍷 🍴 **Room:** 🍳 ♨ TV

Castle House Lodgings

Contact: Sonja Belchere, The Custodian, Castle House Lodgings, Ludlow Castle, Castle Square, Ludlow, Shropshire SY8 1AY **T:** (01584) 874465 **F:** (01584) 874465
E: info@ludlowcastle.com **W:** www.castle-accommodation.com **£ BOOK ONLINE**

| Units | 3 |
| Sleeps | 1-4 |

PER UNIT PER WEEK
£895.00 - £1230.00

SPECIAL PROMOTIONS
Three night weekend break
(Friday to Sunday)

Four night break
(Monday to Thursday)

Seven night break
(Friday to Thursday).

Castle House Lodgings comprise of three 4-5* self catering apartments, full of character features and finished to the highest of standards, set within the walls of Ludlow Castle. Each apartment provides a sitting room/dining room, fully equipped kitchen, two twin bedrooms and two bathrooms and a car parking space.

Open: All year.
Nearest Shop: 0.10 miles
Nearest Pub: 0.10 miles

Site: P Payment: 📧 **Leisure:** 🚴 🏌 ∪ **Property:** 🐾 🖥 📷 🏊 **Children:** 🛝 🎱 🎿
Unit: 🍽 🖥 📺 🎮 📀 📞

Sutton Court Farm Cottages

Contact: Mrs Jane Cronin, Sutton Court Farm, Little Sutton, Ludlow, Shropshire SY8 2AJ
T: (01584) 861305 **E:** enquiries@suttoncourtfarm.co.uk
W: www.suttoncourtfarm.co.uk

| Units | 6 |
| Sleeps | 2-6 |

PER UNIT PER WEEK
£265.00 - £580.00

6 comfortable cottages surrounding a peaceful, sunny courtyard, 5 miles from historic Ludlow in 'An Area of Outstanding Natural Beauty'. Ironbridge, Shrewsbury, Hereford and the Welsh borders within easy reach. Breakfast packs, cream teas and evening meals available to order. Short breaks (minimum. 2 nights) all year round. Special offer from Nov to Mar (excluding holidays), 3 nights for 2, 4 nights for 3. **Open:** All year.
Nearest Shop: 6 miles **Nearest Pub:** 3 miles

WALKERS CYCLISTS **Site:** ❀ **P Leisure:** 🚴 🏌 ▶ ∪ **Property:** 🐾 🖥 📷 🏊 **Children:** 🛝 🎱 🎿 **Unit:** 🍽 📺 🎮 📀
WALKERS CYCLISTS 🍖 BBQ 📞

The Feathers Hotel

Bull Ring, Ludlow SY8 1AA **T:** (01584) 875261 **F:** (01584) 876030
E: enquiries@feathersatludlow.co.uk
W: www.feathersatludlow.co.uk **£ BOOK ONLINE**

B&B PER ROOM PER NIGHT
S: £95.00 - £120.00
D: £130.00 - £230.00
EVENING MEAL PER PERSON
£34.50 - £42.00

At the heart of the ancient market town of Ludlow with Jacobean architecture and a medieval heritage. Recently refurbished. Award-winning restaurant. High standard of food and service.
Directions: From A49 follow signs to Ludlow town centre. We are situated on the brow of the hill, near a pedestrian crossing.
Bedrooms: 3 single, 23 double, 12 twin, 2 family.
Open: All year.

Site: ❀ **Payment:** 📧 **Leisure:** 🚴 🏌 ▶ ∪ **Property:** ⛳ 🐾 🖥 ● **Children:** 🛝 🎱 🎿 **Catering:** 🍽 🍴
Room: 🍵 ☕ 🎮 📺 📶

LUDLOW, Shropshire Map ref 4A3 S

The Silver Pear Apartments

Contact: Mr Christopher Tuffley, Director, Silver Pear Apartments, 68-69 Broad Street, Ludlow SY8 1NH **T:** (01584) 879096 **F:** (01584) 879124 **E:** sales@silverpear.co.uk
W: www.silverpearapartments.co.uk

Units 2
Sleeps 2-6

Our apartments have been restored to the highest specification, utilising all the original features of such an important building, and much of the original oak features have been saved.
Open: All year.
Nearest Shop: 0.01 miles
Nearest Pub: 0.02 miles

Payment: **Leisure:** **Property:** **Children:** **Unit:**

TELFORD, Shropshire Map ref 4A3 SatNav TF1 2HA B

The Old Orleton Inn

378 Holyhead Road, Wellington, Telford, Shropshire TF1 2HA **T:** (01952) 255011
E: info@theoldorleton.com
W: www.theoldorleton.com **£ BOOK ONLINE**

B&B PER ROOM PER NIGHT
S: £65.00 - £125.00
D: £89.00 - £145.00
EVENING MEAL PER PERSON
£12.00 - £35.00

SPECIAL PROMOTIONS
Stay & Eat offer
(DBB for £125.00 per couple).

Wrekin Weekend
(3 nights DBB plus extras £375.00).

Contemporary styled 17th century Coaching Inn facing the famous Wrekin Hill. The Old Orleton Inn, Wellington, Shropshire is a charming retreat for both work and pleasure.

Directions: 7 miles from Shrewsbury, 4 miles from Ironbridge, M54 (exit 7), 400yds on the left towards Wellington.
Bedrooms: 1 single, 7 double, 2 twin.
Open: Closed for two weeks in January.

Site: P **Payment:** **Leisure:** **Property:** **Catering:** **Room:**

Book your accommodation online

Visit our websites for detailed information, up-to-date availability and to book your accommodation online. Includes over 20,000 places to stay, all of them star rated.
www.visitor-guides.co.uk

ABBOTS BROMLEY, Staffordshire   Map ref 4B3   S

VisitEngland
★★★★
SELF CATERING

Blithfield Lakeside Barns

Contact: Mrs Maxine Brown, Blithfield Lakeside Barns, St Stephens Hill Farm, Admaston, Rugeley, Staffordshire WS15 3NQ **T:** (01889) 500234
E: blithfieldlakesidebarns@hotmail.co.uk
W: www.blithfieldlakesidebarns.co.uk **£ BOOK ONLINE**

Units   6
Sleeps   2-10

PER UNIT PER WEEK
£200.00 - £995.00

SPECIAL PROMOTIONS
Short breaks available Friday to Monday or Monday to Friday.

Superb lakeside barn conversions on organic dairy farm overlooking Blithfield Reservoir, 2 miles Abbots Bromley. Nr Peak District, Cannock Chase, National Forest, Drayton Manor and Alton Towers. Trout/carp fishing, walking, cycling. Pets welcome in 2 cottages. Excellent local pubs/restaurants.

Open: All year.
Nearest Shop: 2 miles
Nearest Pub: 2 miles

Site: ✿ P **Payment:** € **Leisure:** ♿ ♪ ↾ ∪ ♞ **Property:** ⌖ 🖵 🖿 🖳 **Children:** ⛺ 🛏 ⚤
Unit: 🖿 🖳 🖭 ⚲ TV 🎧 📀 BBQ

BURTON UPON TRENT, Staffordshire   Map ref 4B3   S

VisitEngland
★★★★
SELF CATERING

Wychnor Park Country Club

Contact: Wychnor Hall, Nr Barton-Under-Needwood, Staffordshire DE13 8BU
T: (0800) 358 6991 **E:** EuHotels@diamondresorts.com
W: www.DiamondResortsandHotels.com **£ BOOK ONLINE**

Units   44
Sleeps   1-6

PER UNIT PER WEEK
£490.00 - £1267.00

SPECIAL PROMOTIONS
Visit our website or call today for seasonal discounts and great savings.

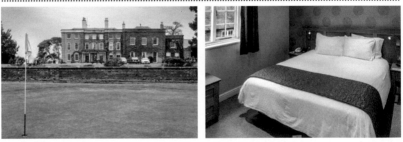

Set in a private, peaceful estate, this country club has landscaped gardens and combines the best of old and new for a relaxing environment.

All beautiful accommodation at Wychnor Park Country Club offers a high standard of luxury. Guests may be allocated rooms in the historic main building, the coach house and courtyard buildings or spacious log cabins in the grounds. The superb gardens provide a host of sporting activities. Above all, Wychnor Park Country Club is an peaceful country retreat.

Open: All year.
Nearest Shop: 3 miles
Nearest Pub: On Site

Units: A choice of one and two bedroom apartments available. All apartments boast a full kitchen, modern bathroom and Television with DVD player.

🚶 ♿ 🚲

f ✆

Site: ✿ P **Payment:** 💳 **Leisure:** ↾ ⌖ ♞ **Property:** 🖵 🖿 🖳 **Children:** ⛺ 🛏 ⚤
Unit: 🖿 🖳 🖭 ⚲ TV 📀 ✆

CHEADLE, *Staffordshire* Map ref 4B2

Rakeway House Farm B&B

Rakeway Road, Cheadle, Alton Towers Area ST10 1RA **T:** (01538) 755295
E: rakewayhousefarm@btinternet.com
W: www.rakewayhousefarm.co.uk

Charming farmhouse and gardens. Fantastic views over Cheadle and surrounding countryside. Alton Towers 15 minutes drive. Good base for Peak District and Potteries. First-class accommodation, excellent menu, superb hospitality.
Bedrooms: 1 double, 1 family.
Open: All year.

B&B PER ROOM PER NIGHT
S: £30.00
D: £60.00

Site: ❉ P Leisure: 🚴 ♪ ⚑ ∪ Property: ▤ Children: 🎋 Catering: 🍴 Room: ℞ ✦ ⓐ 📺 ⚓ 🖨

DILHORNE, *Staffordshire* Map ref 4B2
S

Little Summerhill Cottages

Contact: Mrs Beth Plant, Owner, Little Summerhill Farm, Tickhill Lane, Dilhorne, Staffordshire ST10 2PL **T:** (01782) 550967 / 07976 068560 **F:** (01782) 550967
E: info@holidaycottagesstaffordshire.com **W:** www.holidaycottagesstaffordshire.com

Units 3
Sleeps 1-5
PER UNIT PER WEEK
£200.00 - £600.00

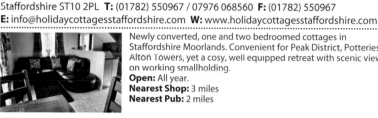

Newly converted, one and two bedroomed cottages in Staffordshire Moorlands. Convenient for Peak District, Potteries and Alton Towers, yet a cosy, well equipped retreat with scenic views, on working smallholding.
Open: All year.
Nearest Shop: 3 miles
Nearest Pub: 2 miles

Site: ❉ P Payment: € Property: ▤ Children: 🛏 Unit: 🖥 🗑 ℞ 📺 📀 BBQ

LEEK, *Staffordshire* Map ref 4B2
S

Roaches Holiday Cottages

Contact: Karen Oliver, Paddock Farm, Upper Hulme, Leek, Staffordshire Moorlands ST13 8TY **T:** (01538) 300345 **E:** karen@roachescottages.co.uk
W: www.roachescottages.co.uk **£ BOOK ONLINE**

Units 2
Sleeps 1-6

PER UNIT PER WEEK
£311.50 - £689.50

SPECIAL PROMOTIONS
Short breaks from two night's minimum available any day of the week.

Family run ETB 3 Star, Farmhouse Holiday Cottages on the south-western edge of the Peak District National Park by the Roaches. Breathtaking views stretching far over valley, reservoir and beyond. Two cosy, open plan cottages, each sleeping up to six people. Bedding, central heating and water included. The award-winning Roaches Tea Rooms is just across the courtyard open for breakfasts, lunches and afternoon teas.

Open: All year.
Nearest Shop: 3 miles
Nearest Pub: 0.5 mile

Units: Each cottage has one double bedroom and two twin bedrooms. One twin bedroom on ground floor of each cottage.

Site: P Payment: 💷 Property: 🐕 🗑 🖳 Children: 🎋 🛏 ♿ Unit: 🖥 📺 ⓐ 📀

LEEK, Staffordshire   Map ref 4B2 $\boxed{\text{S}}$

VisitEngland
★★★
SELF CATERING

Units   1
Sleeps   6
PER UNIT PER WEEK
£295.00 - £460.00

Rosewood Cottage

Contact: Lower Berkhamsytch Farm, Bottomhouse, Nr Leek, Staffordshire ST13 7QP
T: (01538) 308213 **E:** a.e.mycock@gmail.com
W: www.rosewoodcottage.co.uk

Set in picturesque Staffordshire Moorlands, bordering Peak District. Attractive three bedroomed cottage including four poster bed. Central to Alton Towers, Potteries and Peak District. Field available for pet walking and ball games. Indian restaurant and country café nearby. Free internet access.
Open: All year.
Nearest Shop: 2 miles
Nearest Pub: 2 miles

Site: ✿ P **Leisure:** ⚲ ▶ **Property:** 🐾 🖾 🖻 🖳 **Children:** 🛝 🎪 ♿ **Unit:** 🗄 🖾 🖻 🖤 📺 🎧 📀

RUGELEY, Staffordshire   Map ref 4B3   SatNav WS15 3LL $\boxed{\text{B}}$

VisitEngland
★★★★★
GUEST HOUSE

VisitEngland
Gold
AWARD

B&B PER ROOM PER NIGHT
S: £78.00 - £122.00
D: £99.00 - £218.00

Colton House

Bellamour Way, Colton, Rugeley, Staffs. WS15 3LL **T:** (01889) 578580 **F:** (01889) 578580
E: mail@coltonhouse.com
W: coltonhouse.com **£ BOOK ONLINE**

Colton House, winner of The Best B&B in England, set in 1.5 acre garden. Beautifully restored Grade II* property, in picturesque village of Colton on the edge of Cannock Chase.
Directions: M6 Toll Junction 7, A460 to Rugeley then B5013 towards Uttoxeter, after 2 miles, right into Colton. Colton House is 0.25 miles on the right.
Bedrooms: 10 double, 1 twin.
Open: All year.

🌱 🏅 **Site:** ✿ P **Payment:** 💳 **Property:** 🍷 🖾 🏛 **Catering:** 🍴 🍽 **Room:** 🖤 ♨ 📺 🧺

WATERHOUSES, Staffordshire   Map ref 4B2 $\boxed{\text{S}}$

VisitEngland
3★-4★
SELF CATERING

Units   2
Sleeps   1-6
PER UNIT PER WEEK
£240.00 - £550.00

f

Greenside Cottages

Contact: Mr & Mrs Terry & Sue Riley, Owner, Greenside Cottages, Brown End Farm, Waterhouses, Staffordshire ST10 3JR **T:** (01538) 308313 / 07779 320975 **F:** (01538) 308053
E: sriley01@gmail.com **W:** www.greenside-cottages.co.uk

2 delightful converted stone cottages in Peak District. Well equipped, very welcoming and comfortable. Ideal base for walking and cycling from doorstep. Historic houses and visitor attractions are within easy reach. Alton Towers is only 15 minutes away. Day's cycling for guests.
Open: All year.
Nearest Shop: 0.40 miles
Nearest Pub: 0.40 miles

WALKERS / CYCLISTS **Site:** ✿ P **Leisure:** ⚲ ▶ ∪ **Property:** 🖳 **Children:** 🛝 🎪 ♿ **Unit:** 🗄 🖫 🖾 ♨ 📺 🎧 📀 ⌀ BBQ

ASTON CANTLOW, Warwickshire   Map ref 2B1   SatNav B95 6JP $\boxed{\text{C}}$

VisitEngland
★★★
HOLIDAY, TOURING
& CAMPING PARK

f

🚐 (24)   £26.00
🚏 (24)   £26.00
⛺ (10)   £15.00-£22.00
🏕 (5)   £405.00-£495.00
24 touring pitches

Island Meadow Caravan Park

The Mill House, Aston Cantlow, Henley in Arden, Warwickshire B95 6JP
T: (01789) 488273 **E:** holiday@islandmeadowcaravanpark.co.uk
W: www.islandmeadowcaravanpark.co.uk

A small secluded park in rural Warwickshire, close to the historic and picturesque village of Aston Cantlow and just six miles from Stratford. Ideal for visiting Warwick, Birmingham and the Cotswolds. We hold the David Bellamy Gold Award.
Directions: Aston Cantlow village lies within the triangle formed by Stratford-upon-Avon, Henley-in-Arden and Alcester. The park is South west of the village.
Open: March to October.

Site: ▲🅿 **Payment:** 💳 € ☼ **Leisure:** ♪ **Children:** 🛝 **Catering:** 🛒 **Park:** 🐾 🖾 🐾 ♨ **Touring:** 🚰 🚽 🔌

SHIPSTON-ON-STOUR, Warwickshire   Map ref 2B1   [S]

VisitEngland ★★★★ SELF CATERING

Burmington View

Contact: Vanessa Barney, Burmington Grange Cottage, Cherington, Shipston on Stour, Warwickshire CV36 5HZ **T:** (01608) 686526 **E:** vanessa@burmington-view.co.uk
W: www.burmington-view.co.uk

Units	1
Sleeps	1-2

PER UNIT PER WEEK
£340.00 - £450.00

Situated in a lovely rural location, Burmington View is two miles from the historic Shipston-on-Stour. Bright and comfortable, fully equipped, one bedroom loft conversion with views over open countryside.
Open: All year.
Nearest Shop: 2 miles
Nearest Pub: 2 miles

Site: ✿ P Leisure: ♪ ✎ Property: ⫽ ▭ ⊡ ⊡ Unit: ⊡ ▭ ▭ ⊡ TV DVD BBQ

STRATFORD-UPON-AVON, Warwickshire   Map ref 2B1   SatNav CV37 6PB   [B]

VisitEngland ★★★★ BED & BREAKFAST   **VisitEngland Silver AWARD**

Adelphi Guest House

39 Grove Road, Stratford-upon-Avon, Warwickshire CV37 6PB **T:** (01789) 204469
E: info@adelphi-guesthouse.com
W: www.adelphi-guesthouse.com

B&B PER ROOM PER NIGHT
S: £50.00 - £75.00
D: £90.00 - £105.00

Breakfasts are popular, as are the home baked cakes. The rooms are decorated in period style. The bedding is pure cotton. The house overlooks the Fir Gardens and is minutes from the train station, town centre, Shakespeare sites, & theatre.
Directions: From the A3400 turn onto the A4390 which becomes Grove Road at the next crossroads. The Adelphi is approx. 200m on the right as is a lane to parking. **Bedrooms:** Rooms have luxury toiletries and hospitality tray. **Open:** All year.

Site: P Payment: ▦ Property: ▭ Catering: ▦ Room: ⛉ ♨ TV DVD ♨ ▥

STRATFORD-UPON-AVON, Warwickshire   Map ref 2B1   [S]

VisitEngland ★★★ SELF CATERING

As You Like It

Contact: Mr & Mrs Ian & Janet Reid, c/o Inwood House, New Road, Stratford-upon-Avon CV37 8PE **T:** (01789) 450266 / 07956 692015 **E:** ian@alderminster99.freeserve.co.uk
W: www.asyoulikeitcottage.co.uk **£ BOOK ONLINE**

Units	1
Sleeps	1-3

PER UNIT PER WEEK
£320.00 - £425.00

'As You Like It' is a character cottage in central Stratford within easy walking distance of the theatres and the town's many attractions. It is located within the 'Old Town' area close to the river and Holy Trinity Church, and ten minutes' walk from the Royal Shakespeare Theatre. There is private parking provided.
Open: All year.
Nearest Shop: 0.25 miles
Nearest Pub: 0.25 miles

Site: P Property: ☂ ▭ ⊡ Unit: ▭ ⊡ ⛉ TV ⊙ ☎

STRATFORD-UPON-AVON, *Warwickshire* Map ref 2B1   SatNav CV37 7LN   **B**

GUEST HOUSE ★★★★ VisitEngland | VisitEngland *Silver* AWARD

Avonlea

47 Shipston Road, Stratford-Upon-Avon CV37 7LN **T:** (01789) 205940
E: enquiries@avonlea-stratford.co.uk
W: www.avonlea-stratford.co.uk

B&B PER ROOM PER NIGHT
S: £55.00 - £65.00
D: £80.00 - £95.00

SPECIAL PROMOTIONS
£5 Discount on stays of
4 or more nights,
subject to availability
and T&Cs.

Avonlea is winner many awards including;
Pride of Stratford - Hospitality Business of the Year Award
Coventry & Warwickshire Tourism & Culture Awards - Best B&B
Stratford-Upon-Avon Independent Shop Awards - Best Hotel or B&B

Located south of the River Avon, just a five minute walk from the town centre and its cultural
attractions including the RSC and Shakespeare's Birthplace.

Directions: A3400 Shipston Road, 100m from Clopton Bridge.

Bedrooms: 2 single, 2 double, 2 twin/superking, 2 family (1 Double 1 Single bed).
Open: All year except Mid December till end of January.

Site: P **Payment:** ⊞ **Leisure:** ♿ ♪ ► **Property:** ▨ **Children:** ⛲ **Catering:** ⛾ **Room:** ♨ ♨ TV ♨

STRATFORD-UPON-AVON, *Warwickshire* Map ref 2B1   SatNav CV37 9SR   **C**

VisitEngland ★★★ TOURING & CAMPING PARK

Dodwell Park

Evesham Road (B439), Dodwell, Stratford-upon-Avon CV37 9SR
T: (01789) 204957 **E:** enquiries@dodwellpark.co.uk
W: www.dodwellpark.co.uk

🚐 (50)   £19.50-£27.00
🚏 (15)   £19.50-£27.00
⛺ (50)   £18.50-£25.00
50 touring pitches

Small, family-run touring park 2 miles SW of Stratford-upon-Avon.
Country walks to River Avon and Luddington village. Ideal for
visiting Warwick Castle, Shakespeare properties and Cotswolds.
Brochure on request. Rallies welcome. Over 50 years as a family
business! **Directions:** Leaving Stratford-upon-Avon take the B439
signposted 'B349 Bidford' (also signposted Racecourse) for 2 miles,
we are on left (after going over a large hill).
Open: All year.

Site: ⛺🅿 **Payment:** ⊞ ☼ **Leisure:** ♿ ♪ ► **Children:** ⛲ **Catering:** 🐾 **Park:** 🐕 ♞ **Touring:** 🚾 ♿ 🎣

WARWICK, *Warwickshire* Map ref 4B3   **S**

VisitEngland ★★★ SELF CATERING

Bianca & Whitley Elm Cottages

Contact: Katherine Russell, Case Lane, Mousley End, Warwick CV35 7JE
T: (01926) 484577 / 07929 264386 **E:** enquiries@whitleyelmcottages.co.uk
W: www.whitleyelmcottages.co.uk

Units   4
Sleeps   4-6
PER UNIT PER WEEK
£355.00 - £595.00

Four attractive cottages converted from 18th century barns, in the
grounds of a Tudor manor house set in beautiful countryside.
Open: All year.
Nearest Shop: 2 miles
Nearest Pub: 0.75 mile

Site: ⚘ P **Property:** 🐕 🚾 🔲 🍴 **Children:** ⛲ ⛾ ♿ **Unit:** 🔲 🔲 📺 ♨ TV DVD BBQ

WARWICK, Warwickshire Map ref 4B3 SatNav CV34 5QR B

VisitEngland ★★★ GUEST HOUSE

B&B PER ROOM PER NIGHT
S: £50.00 - £55.00
D: £65.00 - £70.00

Jersey Villa Guest House

69 Emscote Road, Warwick CV34 5QR **T:** (01926) 730336 / 07929 338321
E: info@jerseyvillaguesthouse.co.uk
W: www.jerseyvillaguesthouse.co.uk

Jersey Villa Guest House is located on the borders of Warwick and Royal Leamington Spa. The guest house offers quality bed and breakfast accommodation. Both towns are within walking distance, Warwick Castle is a mere 15 minute walk. **Directions:** Warwick Railway Station, come out onto Broad Street, turn left into Emscote Road, continue for 5 minutes, turn left into Jersey Villa Guest House. **Bedrooms:** Family room sleeps up to 5. Doubles, singles and twins. All rooms large, with en suite, welcome tray etc. **Open:** All year.

Site: P **Leisure:** **Property:** **Children:** 5 **Catering:** **Room:** TV DVD

MALVERN, Worcestershire Map ref 2B1 S

VisitEngland ★★★★ SELF CATERING

Units 1
Sleeps 10
PER UNIT PER WEEK
£643.00 - £1525.00

Beesoni Lodge

Contact: Laura Smith, Owner, Beesoni, Hill End, Castlemorton, Malvern WR13 6BL
T: (01684) 830016 / 07557 353600 **E:** info@beesonilodge.co.uk
W: www.beesonilodge.co.uk

Fabulous spacious Four Star detached barn conversion, exceptional standard with exposed beams throughout. Sleeps ten, four bedrooms (one four-poster), three bathrooms (one with spa bath). Large fully equipped kitchen. Heating, Linen and Towels included. Set in private grounds. Stunning views of Malvern Hills and Cotswolds. Within easy reach of Malvern, Upton upon Severn, Cheltenham and Worcester. **Open:** All year.
Nearest Shop: 3 miles **Nearest Pub:** 2.5 miles

Site: P **Property:** **Children:** **Unit:** TV DVD BBQ

MALVERN, Worcestershire Map ref 2B1 S

VisitEngland ★★★★ SELF CATERING · VisitEngland Gold AWARD

Units 1
Sleeps 1-2
PER UNIT PER WEEK
£320.00 - £440.00

Rhydd Barn

Contact: Miss Rosemary Boaz, Under Ley, Doverhay, Porlock, Somerset TA24 8LL
T: (01643) 862359 **E:** info@rhyddbarn.co.uk
W: www.rhyddbarn.co.uk

Outstanding barn conversion with spacious accommodation on three floors and wonderful views of the Malvern Hills. Tiled and wooden floors, white walls interspersed with pine beams and black iron work. Commended finalist for the Best Self Catering Award - Visit Worcestershire Awards for Excellence 2013.
Open: All year.
Nearest Shop: 2 miles
Nearest Pub: 0.25 miles

WALKERS WELCOME **Site:** P **Property:** **Unit:** TV DVD

PERSHORE, Worcestershire Map ref 2B1 S

VisitEngland ★★★★

Units 1
Sleeps 1-3
PER UNIT PER WEEK
£305.00 - £420.00

Garth Cottage

Contact: Mrs Margaret Smith, Owner, 8 Pensham Hill, Pershore, Worcestershire WR10 3HA
T: (01386) 561213 / 07759 655717 **F:** (01386) 561213 **E:** stephen.smith@homecall.co.uk
W: www.garthcottage.co.uk

Delightful detached cottage in peaceful location, 10 minutes leisurely walk from Pershore. Large airy bedroom, double bed settee in lounge. Use of owners outdoor swimming pool (seasonal May to October weather dependent), by arrangement. Short breaks from £135. Special rates for Bank Holidays, Christmas & New Year.
Open: All year.
Nearest Shop: 1 mile
Nearest Pub: 0.75 miles

WALKERS WELCOME **Site:** P **Leisure:** **Property:** **Children:** **Unit:** TV DVD BBQ

For **key to symbols** see page 6

SUTTON, Worcestershire   Map ref 4A3   S

VisitEngland ★★★★ SELF CATERING

VisitEngland Gold AWARD

Long Cover Cottage & The Coach House

Contact: Mrs Eleanor Van Straaten, Holiday Cottage, Fishpool Cottage, Kyre, Tenbury Wells WR15 8RL **T:** (01885) 410208 / 07725 972486
E: ellie_vanstraaten@yahoo.co.uk **W:** www.a-country-break.co.uk

Units	2
Sleeps	2-8

PER UNIT PER WEEK
£700.00 - £900.00

Long Cover Cottage: A retreat from the outside world with magnificent views in all directions over the Teme and Kyre Valleys. Exposed beams, oak/elm staircase, Aga, woodburning stove.

Coach House: Retire to your own private viewpoint with its picture-postcard views across open pastures to the Teme and Kyre valleys.

Open: All year.
Nearest Shop: 3 miles
Nearest Pub: 3 miles

Site: ✿ Leisure: ♪ ► ∪ ☂ Property: 🐾 ▦ 🗗 🗐 Children: 🛝 ▥ 🎋 Unit: 🗋 🗒 🖾 🖑 📺 ⓐ 📀 🍴 BBQ

TENBURY WELLS, Worcestershire   Map ref 4A3   S

VisitEngland ★★★★ SELF CATERING

VisitEngland Gold AWARD

Rochford Park Cottages

Contact: Mrs Jarka Robinson, Rochford Park, Nr Tenbury Wells, Worcestershire WR15 8SP
T: (01584) 781392 / 07582 583841 **F:** (01584) 781392 **E:** cottages@rochfordpark.co.uk
W: www.rochfordpark.co.uk

Units	2
Sleeps	3-8

PER UNIT PER WEEK
£199.00 - £762.00

Former farm outbuildings, now stylish, comfortable cottages suitable for couples, families or groups of friends, situated in beautiful Teme valley. Restful places, full of character. Woodlands, lakes nearby.
Open: All year.
Nearest Shop: 3 miles
Nearest Pub: 1.5 miles

f

Site: ✿ P Leisure: 🚴 ♪ ► ∪ 🎣 Property: 🗗 🗐 Children: 🛝 ▥ 🎋 Unit: 🗋 🗒 🖾 🗐 📺 📀 🍴 BBQ

Welcome
Pets!

Want to travel with your faithful companion? Look out for accommodation displaying the **Welcome Pets!** sign. Participants in this scheme go out of their way to meet the needs of guests bringing dogs, cats and/or small birds. In addition to providing water and food bowls, torches or nightlights, spare leads and pet washing facilities, they'll buy in food on request, and offer toys, treats and bedding. They'll also have information on pet-friendly attractions, pubs, restaurants and recreation. Of course, not everyone is able to offer suitable facilities for every pet, so do check if there are any restrictions on type, size and number of animals when you book.

Look out for the following symbol in the entry.

Don't Miss...

Castle Howard
Malton, North Yorkshire YO60 7DA
(01653) 648444
www.castlehoward.co.uk
A magnificent 18th century house situated in breathtaking parkland, dotted with temples, lakes statues and fountains; plus formal gardens, woodland garden and ornamental vegetable garden. Inside the House guides share stories of the house, family and collections, while outdoor-guided tours reveal the secrets of the architecture and landscape.

National Media Museum
Bradford, West Yorkshire BD1 1NQ
(08448) 563797
www.nationalmediamuseum.org.uk
A fabulous free museum devoted to film, photography & TV. Journey through popular photography, discover the past, present and future of television in Experience TV, watch your favourite film and TV moments in the BFI Mediatheque, play with light, lenses and colour in the Magic Factory, explore the world of animation and get gaming in the Games Lounge! The National Media Museum is also home to Yorkshire's only IMAX cinema, for an eye-opening, jaw-dropping 3D cinema experience.

National Railway Museum
York, North Yorkshire YO26 4XJ
0844 815 3139
www.nrm.org.uk
Explore giant halls full of trains, railway legends including the majestic Duchess of Hamilton and the futuristic Japanese Bullet Train and marvel at the stunning opulence of the Royal Trains. Watch engineers at work in The Workshop, uncover hidden treasures in The Warehouse and make tracks to the outdoor area where children can let off steam in the play area or take a trip on the miniature railway rides.

Royal Armouries Museum
Armouries Drive, Leeds LS10 1LT
(01132) 201999
www.royalarmouries.org/leeds
Located near to the city centre at Leeds dock and is home to the national collection of arms and armour from across the world.

The Deep
Hull, East Riding of Yorkshire HU1 4DP
(01482) 381000
www.thedeep.co.uk
Full with over 3500 fish and more than 40 sharks, The Deep tells the amazing story of the world's oceans through stunning marine life, interactives and audio-visual presentations making it a fun-filled family day out for all ages.

Yorkshire Sculpture Park
West Bretton, West Yorkshire WF4 4LG
(01924) 832631
www.ysp.co.uk
Showing work by British and international artists, including Henry Moore and Barbara Hepworth the Yorkshore Sculpture Park is an extraordinary place that sets out to challenge, inspire, inform and delight.

Yorkshire

Yorkshire, the largest county in England, is one of the most popular and boasts award-winning culture, heritage and scenery. There's cosmopolitan Leeds, stylish Harrogate and rural market towns full of charm and character. The wild moors and deserted dales of the Yorkshire Dales and North York Moors National Parks are majestic in their beauty and the county has a spectacular coastline of rugged cliffs and sandy beaches. The region also has a wealth of historic houses, ruined castles, abbeys and fortresses for visitors to discover.

Yorkshire

Explore – Yorkshire

North Yorkshire

Steeped in history, North Yorkshire boasts some of the country's most splendid scenery. Wherever you go in The Dales, you'll be faced with breathtaking views and constant reminders of a historic and changing past. In medieval days, solid fortresses like Richmond and Middleham were built to protect the area from marauding Scots. Ripley and Skipton also had their massive strongholds, while Bolton Castle in Wensleydale once imprisoned Mary, Queen of Scots. The pattern of history continues with the great abbeys, like Jervaulx Abbey, near Masham, where the monks first made Wensleydale cheese and the majestic ruins of Fountains Abbey in the grounds of Studley Royal. Between the Dales and the North York Moors, Herriot Country is named for one of the world's best loved writers, James Herriot, who made the area his home for more than 50 years and whose books have enthralled readers with tales of Yorkshire life.

Escape to the wild, deserted North York Moors National Park with its 500 square miles of hills, dales, forests and open moorland, neatly edged by a spectacular coastline. Walking, cycling and pony trekking are ideal ways to savour the scenery and there are plenty of greystone towns and villages dotted throughout the Moors that provide ideal bases from which to explore. From Helmsley, visit the ruins of Rievaulx Abbey, founded by Cistercian monks in the 12th century or discover moorland life in the Ryedale Folk Museum at Hutton-le-Hole. The Beck Isle Museum in Pickering provides an insight into the life of a country market town and just a few miles down the road you'll find Malton, once a Roman fortress, and nearby Castle Howard, the setting for Brideshead Revisited.

York

Wherever you turn within the city's medieval walls, you will find glimpses of the past. The splendours of the 600-year old Minster, the grim stronghold of Clifford's Tower, the National Railway Museum, the medieval timbers of the Merchant Adventurers' Hall and the fascinating Jorvik Viking Centre all offer an insight into the history of this charming city.

Throughout the city, statues and monuments remind the visitor that this was where Constantine was proclaimed Holy Roman Emperor, Guy Fawkes was born and Dick Turpin met his end.

Modern York has excellent shopping, a relaxed Café culture, first class restaurants and bars, museums, tours and attractions. Whether you visit for a romantic weekend or a fun-filled family holiday, there really is something for everyone.

Leeds & West Yorkshire

For centuries cloth has been spun from the wool of the sheep grazing in the Pennine uplands and the fascinating story of this industrial heritage can be seen in the numerous craft centres and folk museums throughout West Yorkshire.

Bradford was a major industrial centre and this can be seen in the number of converted wool, cotton and other textile mills in the area. Salts Mill is a Grade II Listed historic mill building built in 1853 by Sir Titus Salt along with the village to house his workers, in what is now an area of architectural and historical interest. Not far from Haworth is Bingley, where the Leeds & Liverpool canal makes its famous uphill journey, a route for the coal barges in days gone by, nowadays replaced by holidaymakers in gaily painted boats. Leeds itself is a vibrant city with its Victorian shopping arcades, Royal Armories Museum and lively arts scene.

Yorkshire Coastline

The Yorkshire coastline is one of the UK's most naturally beautiful and rugged, where pretty fishing villages cling to rocky cliffs, in turn towering over spectacular beaches and family-friendly seaside destinations.

At the northern end of the coastline, Saltburn is a sand and shingle beach popular with surfers and visitors can ride the Victorian tram from the cliff to the promenade during the summer. Whitby is full of quaint streets and bestowed with a certain Gothic charm. At Scarborough, one of Britain's oldest seaside resorts, the award-winning North Bay and South Bay sand beaches are broken by the rocky headland, home to the historic Scarborough Castle. Filey, with its endless sands, has spectacular views and a 40-mile stretch of perfect sandy beach sweeps south from the dramatic 400 ft high cliffs at Flamborough Head. Along this coastline you can find the boisterous holiday destination of Bridlington, or a gentler pace at pretty Hornsea and Withernsea.

East Yorkshire

Hull is the UK City of Culture in 2017 which makes it the perfect time to visit the city to discover its past and present. Once a great port, gateway to the Baltic and the New World, and home of Georgian statesman William Wilberforce, father of the abolition movement, the lively city is best approached across the impressive 1328m Humber Bridge. The Yorkshire Wolds, a landscape of swirling grasslands, medieval towns, manor houses and Bronze Age ruins are only a stone's throw from attractive seaside resorts. Historic places to explore include 13th century Beverley Minster in its lattice of medieval streets and the Elizabethan prodigy house of Burton Constable.

South Yorkshire

The historic market town of Doncaster was founded by the Romans and has a rich horseracing and railway heritage. The area around Sheffield - the steel city - was once dominated by the iron and steel industries and was the first city in England to pioneer free public transport. The Industrial Museum and City Museum display a wide range of Sheffield cutlery and tools. Today, Meadowhall shopping centre, with 270 stores all under one roof, a must-visit draw for shopaholics.

Visit – Yorkshire

North Yorkshire

Flamingo Land Theme Park and Zoo
Malton, North Yorkshire YO17 6UX
0800 408 8840
www.flamingoland.co.uk
One-price family funpark with over 100 attractions, 5 shows and Europe's largest privately-owned zoo.

The Forbidden Corner
Middleham, Leyburn, North Yorkshire DL8 4TJ
(01969) 640638
www.theforbiddencorner.co.uk
A unique labyrinth of tunnels, chambers, follies and surprises created within a four acre garden in the heart of Tupgill Park and the Yorkshire Dales.

Grassington Festival
June - July, Grassington, North Yorkshire
01756 752691
www.grassington-festival.org.uk
15 days of music and arts in the Yorkshire Dales.

Malton Food Lovers Festival
May, Malton, North Yorkshire
www.maltonyorkshire.co.uk/food-lovers-festival
Fill up on glorious food and discover why Malton is considered 'Yorkshire's Food Town' with mountains of fresh produce.

North Yorkshire Moors Railway
Pickering, North Yorkshire YO18 7AJ
(01751) 472508
www.nymr.co.uk
Take a classic steam train from Pickering to Grosmont on the famous North Yorkshire Moors Railway for breathaking scenery.

Ripon International Festival
September, Ripon, North Yorkshire
www.riponinternationalfestival.com
A festival packed with music events, solo dramas, intriguing theatre, magic, fantastic puppetry, literary celebrities, historical walks - and more!

Scarborough Castle
Scarborough, North Yorkshire YO11 1HY
www.english-heritage.org.uk
(01723) 372451
One of the finest tourist attractions in Yorkshire, with its 3,000 year history, stunning location and panoramic views over the dramatic Yorkshire coastline.

Scarborough Jazz Festival
September, Scarborough, North Yorkshire
www.jazz.scarboroughspa.co.uk
A variety and range of jazz acts with a balanced programme of predominantly British musicians, with the addition of a few international stars.

Scarborough Seafest

July, Scarborough, North Yorkshire
www.discoveryorkshirecoast.com
Celebrating Scarborough's maritime heritage with seafood kitchen cooking demonstrations, exhibitor displays and musical performances.

Swaledale Festival

May - June, Various locations, North Yorkshire
www.swaledale-festival.org.uk
The award-winning Festival is an annual celebration of music and arts in the beautiful landscape of the three northernmost Yorkshire Dales - Swaledale, Wensleydale and Arkengarthdale. A Varied programme of top-quality events, individually ticketed, realistically priced, and spread over two glorious weeks.

The Walled Garden at Scampston

Malton, North Yorkshire YO17 8NG
(01944) 759111
www.scampston.co.uk
Set within the 18th century walls of the original kitchen garden for Scampston Hall, an exciting 4 acre contemporary garden. Created by Piet Oudolf, with striking perennial meadow planting as well as traditional spring/autumn borders.

Whitby Abbey

Whitby, North Yorkshire, YO22 4JT
(01947) 603568
www.english-heritage.org.uk/whitbyabbey
Perched high on a cliff, it's easy to see why the haunting remains of Whitby Abbey were inspiration for Bram Stoker's gothic tale of 'Dracula'. Recently named Britain's most romantic ruin, Whitby Abbey is bursting with history just waiting to be explored.

York

Fairfax House

York, North Yorkshire, YO1 9RN
(01904) 655543
www.fairfaxhouse.co.uk
Fairfax House is one of the finest Georgian houses in England, ready to transport you straight back to Georgian England with magnificent architect designed John Carr, changing exhibitions and a range of special events.

JORVIK Viking Centre

York, North Yorkshire YO1 9WT
(01904) 615505
www.jorvik-viking-centre.co.uk
Reopening in April 2017. The Re-imagined Jorvik experience lets you travel back 1000 years on board your time machine through the backyards and houses to the bustling streets of Jorvik. JORVIK Viking Centre also offers four exciting exhibitions and the chance to actually come face to face with a 'Viking'.

York Early Music Festival

July, York, North Yorkshire
www.ncem.co.uk/yemf
Celebrating it's 40th anniversary the internationally acclaimed York Early Music Festival mixes music from 12th - 18th centuries, bringing together music-lovers from across the world.

York Boat Guided River Trips

North Yorkshire YO1 7DP
(01904) 628324
www.yorkboat.co.uk
Sit back, relax and enjoy a drink from the bar as the sights of York city and country sail by onboard a 1 hour Guided River Trip along the beautiful River Ouse with entertaining live commentary delivered by the local and knowledgeable skippers.

York Minster

York, North Yorkshire YO1 7JN
(0)1904 557201
www.yorkminster.org
Regularly voted one of the most popular things to do in York, the Minster is not only an architecturally stunning building but is a place to discover the history of York over the centuries, its artefacts and treasures.

Yorkshire Air Museum

York, North Yorkshire YO41 4AU
(01904) 608595
www.yorkshireairmuseum.org
The Yorkshire Air Museum is based on a unique WWII Bomber Command Station with fascinating exhibits and attractive award-winning Memorial Gardens. In addition to its role as a history of aviation museum, the Yorkshire Air Museum is also home to The Allied Air Forces Memorial.

Leeds & West Yorkshire

The Bronte Parsonage Museum
Haworth, West Yorkshire BD22 8DR
(01535) 642323
www.bronte.org.uk
Stop off at Haworth, home of the Bronte sisters, to visit The Bronte Parsonage museum and experience the rugged atmosphere of Wuthering Heights.

Eureka! The National Children's Museum
Halifax, West Yorkshire HX1 2NE
(01422) 330069
www.eureka.org.uk
Eureka! The National Children's Museum is a magical place where children play to learn and grown-ups learn to play.

Harewood House
Leeds, West Yorkshire LS17 9LG
(0113) 218 1010
www.harewood.org
Harewood House, Bird Garden, Grounds and Adventure Playground - The Ideal day out for all the family.

Haworth 1940's Weekend
May, Haworth, West Yorkshire
www.haworth1940sweekend.co.uk
A fabulous weekend celebrating and comemorating the 1940s.

The Henry Moore Institute
Leeds, LS1 3AH
(0113) 246 7467
www.henry-moore.org/hmi
Discover sculpture in Leeds. Feel inspired in three beautiful gallery spaces with an ever-changing programme of exhibitions accompanied by tours, talks and events which explore sculpture from ancient to modern.

Leeds City Museum
Leeds, LS2 8BH
(0113) 224 3732
www.leedsmuseum.co.uk
Leeds City Museums offers six galleries to visit and lots of fun, interactive learning for all the family.

Leeds Festival
August, Wetherby, Leeds
www.leedsfestival.com
From punk and metal, through rock, alternative and indie to dance, Leeds offers music fans a chance to see hot new acts, local bands, huge stars and exclusive performances.

Lotherton Hall & Gardens
Leeds, West Yorkshire LS25 3EB
(0113) 378 2959
www.leeds.gov.uk/lothertonhall
Lotherton is a charming Edwardian house and country estate set in beautiful grounds.

National Coal Mining Museum for England
Wakefield, West Yorkshire WF4 4RH
(01924) 848806
www.ncm.org.uk
Based at the site of Caphouse Colliery in Overton the National Coal Mining Museum offers an exciting and enjoyable insight into the working lives of miners through the ages.

Pontefract Liquorice Festival
July, Wakefield, West Yorkshire
www.experiencewakefield.co.uk
The festival celebrates this unusual plant, the many wonderful products created from it and its historic association with the town.

Royal Armouries Museum
Leeds, West Yorkshire LS10 1LT
(0133) 220 1999
www.royalarmouries.org
Over 8,000 objects displayed in five galleries - War, Tournament, Oriental, Self Defence and Hunting. Among the treasures are Henry VIII's tournament armour and the world record breaking elephant armour. Regular jousting and horse shows.

Salt's Mill
Saltaire, West Yorkshire BD18 3LA
(01274) 531163
www.saltsmill.org.uk
Shopping, dining and art in one glorious building... Salt's Mill is an art gallery, shopping and restaurant complex inside a converted former mill, built by Sir Titus Salt.

Xscape Castleford
Castleford, West Yorkshire WF10 4TA
(01977) 664 794
www.xscape.co.uk/yorkshire
The ultimate family entertainment awaits! Dine, bowl, snow, skate, climb, movies, shop, dance on ice!

York Gate Garden
Leeds LS16 8DW
0113 267 8240
www.perennial.org.uk/garden/york-gate-garden
Tucked away behind the ancient church in Adel, on the northern outskirts of Leeds, York Gate is a garden of immense style and craftsmanship, widely recognised as one of the most innovative small gardens of the period.

East Yorkshire

East Riding Rural Life Museum
Beverley, East Yorkshire HU16 5TF
(01482) 848405
www.museums.eastriding.gov.uk/skidby-mill
Working early 19th century four-sailed Skidby Windmill, the last working mill in Yorkshire, plus Museum of East Riding Rural Life.

RSPB Bempton Cliffs Reserve
Bridlington, East Riding of Yorkshire YO15 1JF
(01262) 422212
www.rspb.org.uk
A family favourite, and easily the best place in England to see, hear and smell seabirds! More than 200,000 birds (from April to August) make the towering chalk cliffs seem alive.

Skipsea Castle
Hornsea, East Riding of Yorkshire YO15 3NP
0870 333 1181
www.english-heritage.org.uk/visit/places/skipsea-castle
The remaining earthworks of a motte-and-bailey castle dating from before 1086 and among the first raised in Yorkshire.

Treasure House and Art Gallery
Beverley, East Riding of Yorkshire HU17 8HE
(01482) 392780
www.museums.eastriding.gov.uk/treasure-house-and-beverley-art-gallery
Art gallery and museum with historic exhibitions. The Treasure House tower provides splendid views over the rooftops of Beverley.

Wilberforce House
Hull, East Riding of Yorkshire HU1 1NQ
(01482) 300300
www.visithullandeastyorkshire.com
Slavery exhibits, period rooms and furniture, Hull silver, costume, Wilberforce and abolition.

South Yorkshire

Barnsley Market
Barnsley, South Yorkshire, S70 1SX
(01226) 772239
www.barnsley.gov.uk
Barnsley Markey boats over 300 stalls including local butchers, fishmongers and grocers and a huge variety of craft, cosmetics, antiques and much more. Every day except Thursdays.

Brodsworth Hall and Gardens
Doncaster, South Yorkshire DN5 7XJ
(01302) 722598
www.english-heritage.org.uk/brodsworth
*One of England's most complete surviving Victorian
houses. Inside many of the original fixtures &
fittings are still in place, although faded with time.
Outside the 15 acres of woodland & gardens have
been restored to their 1860's heyday.*

Cannon Hall Farm
Barnsley, South Yorkshire, S75 4AT
(01226) 790427
www.cannonhallfarm.co.uk
*Cannon Hall Farm is a family-run farm filled with
animal magic. Watch out for special events, new
arrivals, and one of the best farm shops around with
both local and worldwide produce.*

Doncaster Racecourse
Leger Way, Doncaster DN2 6BB
(01302) 304200
www.doncaster-racecourse.co.uk
*The St Leger at Doncaster Racecourse is the oldest
classic horse race in the world, and the town
celebrates in style with a whole festival of events.*

Magna Science Adventure Centre
Rotherham, South Yorkshire S60 1DX
(01709) 720002
www.visitmagna.co.uk
*Magna is the UK's 1st Science Adventure Centre set in
the vast Templeborough steelworks in Rotherham. Fun
is unavoidable here with giant interactives.*

RSPB Old Moor Nature Reserve
Barnsley, South Yorkshire S73 0YF
(01226) 751593
www.rspb.org.uk
*Whether you're feeling energetic or just fancy some
time out visit Old Moor to get closer to the wildlife.*

Sheffield Botanical Gardens
South Yorkshire S10 2LN
(0114) 268 6001
www.sbg.org.uk
*Extensive gardens with over 5,500 species of plants,
Grade II Listed garden pavillion.*

Sheffield: Millennium Gallery
South Yorkshire S1 2PP
(0114) 278 2600
www.museums-sheffield.org.uk
*One of modern Sheffield's landmark public spaces, the
Gallery always has something new to offer.*

Tourist Information Centres

When you arrive at your destination, visit the Tourist Information Centre for quality assured help with accommodation and information about local attractions and events, or email your request before you go.

Aysgarth Falls	Aysgarth Falls National Park Centre	01969 662910	aysgarth@yorkshiredales.org.uk
Beverley	34 Butcher Row	01482 391672	beverley.tic@vhey.co.uk
Bradford	City Hall	01274 433678	bradford.vic@bradford.gov.uk
Bridlington	25 Prince Street	01482 391634	bridlington.tic@vhey.co.uk
Brigg	The Buttercross	01652 657053	brigg.tic@northlincs.gov.uk
Cleethorpes	Cleethorpes Library	01472 323111	cleetic@nelincs.gov.uk
Danby	The Moors National Park Centre	01439 772737	moorscentre@northyorkmoors-npa.org.uk
Doncaster	1 Priory Place	01302 734309	tourist.information@doncaster.gov.uk
Filey	The Evron Centre	01723 383636	tourismbureau@scarborough.gov.uk
Grassington	National Park Centre	01756 751690	grassington@yorkshiredales.org.uk
Halifax	Central Library	01422 368725	halifax@ytbtic.co.uk
Harrogate	Royal Baths	01423 537300	tic@harrogate.gov.uk
Hawes	Yorkshire Dales National Park Centre	01969 666210	hawes@tybtic.co.uk
Haworth	2/4 West Lane	01535 642329	haworth.vic@bradford.gov.uk
Hebden Bridge	New Road	01422 843831	hebdenbridge@ytbtic.co.uk
Holmfirth	47 Huddersfield Road	01484 223200	holmfirth.tic@kirklees.gov.uk
Hornsea	Hornsea Museum	01964 536404	hornsea.tic@vhay.co.uk
Horton-in-Ribblesdale	Pen-y-ghent Cafe	01729 860333	mail@pen-y-ghentcafe.co.uk
Huddersfield	Huddersfield Library	01484 223200	huddersfield.information@kirklees.gov.uk
Hull	1 Paragon Street	01482 223559	tourist.information@hullcc.gov.uk

Humber Bridge	North Bank Viewing Area	01482 640852	humberbridge.tic@vhay.co.uk
Ilkley	Town Hall	01943 602319	ilkley.vic@bradford.gov.uk
Ingleton	The Community Centre Car Park	015242 41049	ingleton@btconnect.com
Knaresborough	9 Castle Courtyard	01423 866886	kntic@harrogate.gov.uk
Leeds	The Headrow	0113 378 6977	tourinfo@leeds.gov.uk
Leeming Bar	The Yorkshire Maid	01677 424262	thelodgeatleemingbar@btinternet.com
Leyburn	The Dales Haven	01969 623814	info@welcometoleyburn.co.uk
Malham	National Park Centre	01729 833200	malham@yorkshiredales.org.uk
Otley	Nelson Street	01943 462485	otleytic@leeds.gov.uk
Nidderdale Plus	Station Square	01423 714953	pbtic@harrogate.gov.uk
Reeth	Hudson House, The Green	01748 884059	reeth@ytbtic.co.uk
Richmond	Friary Gardens	01748 828742	hilda@richmondtouristinformation.co.uk
Ripon	Ripon Town Hall	01765 604625	ripontic@harrogate.gov.uk
Rotherham	40 Bridgegate	01709 835904	tic@rotherham.gov.uk
Scarborough (Harbourside)	Sandside	01723 383636	harboursidetic@scarborough.gov.uk
Selby	52 Micklegate	0845 034 9543	selby@ytbtic.co.uk
Settle	Town Hall	01729 825192	settle@ytbtic.co.uk
Sheffield	Unit 1 Winter Gardens	0114 275 7754	visitor@sheffield.gov.uk
Skipton	Town Hall	01756 792809	skipton@ytbtic.co.uk
Sutton Bank	Sutton Bank Visitor Centre	01845 597426	suttonbank@northyorkmoors.org.uk
Todmorden	15 Burnley Road	01706 818181	todmorden@ytbtic.co.uk
Wakefield	Wakefield Cathedral	0845 601 8353	vic@wakefield.gov.uk
Wetherby	17 Westgate	01937 582151	wetherbytic@leedslearning.net
Whitby	Langborne Road	01723 383636	whitbytic@scarborough.gov.uk
Withernsea	Withernsea Lighthouse Museum	01964 536404	withernseatic@vhay.co.uk
York	1 Museum Street	01904 550099	info@visityork.org

Regional Contacts and Information

For more information on accommodation, attractions, activities, events and holidays in Yorkshire, contact one of the following regional or local tourism organisations.

Welcome to Yorkshire
www.yorkshire.com
(0113) 322 3500

Stay – Yorkshire

Entries appear alphabetically by town name in each county. A key to symbols appears on page 6

VisitEngland
★★★★★
BED & BREAKFAST

B&B PER ROOM PER NIGHT
S: £60.00
D: £85.00 - £130.00

Newbegin B&B

Newbegin House, 10 Newbegin, Beverley, East Yorkshire HU17 8EG **T:** (01482) 888880
E: wsweeney@wsweeney.karoo.co.uk
W: www.newbeginhousebbbeverley.co.uk

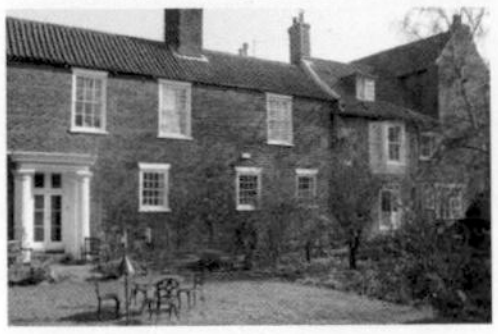

Beverley's only 5 Star B&B. Warm welcome in beautiful Georgian mansion 100 metres from Saturday Market. Three luxurious en suite guest bedrooms, including one family room, king sized beds; splendid dining room; free parking. We also appear in the latest edition of the Good Hotel Guide. **Directions:** 100 metres on foot from Saturday Market. By car, approach from Westwood Road and go down Newbegin (one way) to number 10 on left.
Bedrooms: 2 double, 1 family suite. **Open:** All year.

Site: ❀ **P** **Leisure:** ⟁ ∪ **Property:** 🖳 🗗 **Children:** 🖎 **Catering:** 🍴 **Room:** 🍴 🖐 📶 📺

VisitEngland
★★★★
HOTEL

VisitEngland
Silver
AWARD

B&B PER ROOM PER NIGHT
S: £97.00 - £160.00
D: £130.00 - £200.00
EVENING MEAL PER PERSON
£29.50 - £37.50

Tickton Grange Hotel & Restaurant

Tickton, Near Beverley, East Yorkshire HU17 9SH **T:** (01964) 543666 **F:** (01964) 542556
E: info@ticktongrange.co.uk
W: www.ticktongrange.co.uk **£ BOOK ONLINE**

Georgian Country Hotel surrounded by gardens and meadows just outside Beverley, on the edge of the Wolds and a few miles from the coast. With fabulous food in the restaurant Hide or in the more relaxed Library and 21 glorious bedrooms.

Directions: Two miles outside of Beverley on the A1035.

Bedrooms: Stylishly refurbished with all amenities and handmade flapjack.
Open: All year.

f **y**

Site: ❀ **P** **Payment:** 💳 **Property:** ♟ 🐾 🖳 ◗ ⌑ **Children:** 🖎 ⚲ **Catering:** ⟨✗ ♟ 🍴 **Room:** 🍴 🖐 ☏ 🖨 🖳

★★★
SELF CATERING

Units 1
Sleeps 1-4

PER UNIT PER WEEK
£265.00 - £445.00

SPECIAL PROMOTIONS
Short breaks available,
2 nights (excluding
Christmas, New Year,
Easter and Bank
Holidays - 4 days
minimum).

Old Cobbler's Cottage

Contact: Ms Chris Wade, Owner, Waterfront Cottages, 2 Mere Cottages, Star Row,
North Dalton, Driffield, East Yorkshire YO25 9UX **T:** (01377) 219901 / 07801 124264
F: (01377) 217754 **E:** chris.wade@adastra-music.co.uk
W: www.waterfrontcottages.co.uk **£ BOOK ONLINE**

19th century, mid-terraced, oak-beamed cottage on the edge of a picturesque pond in a peaceful
and friendly farming village, between York and Yorkshire's Heritage Coast. The cottage has a small
garden for sitting in with BBQ facilities. Dining area and main bedroom look directly over the pond -
where the local ducks can be watched from! Open fire. Ideally located for walking, visiting the coast,
historic houses, races at York and Beverley and Hockney country. Excellent pub serving meals
adjacent, which welcomes dogs and children. Up to 2 pets welcome, free of charge.
Parking at the cottage.

Open: All year.
Nearest Shop: 3 miles
Nearest Pub: 0.10 miles

Units: Double bedroom and single bedroom
(with opportunity for a Z Bed), Shower room and
toilet on ground floor. Drying area in entrance.

Site: ✿ **P Payment:** 💳 **Leisure:** ⊁ **Property:** 🐴 ⊟ 📷 💷 **Children:** ⛱ 🛏 ⩍
Unit: ⊟ 📷 💷 📺 ◉ ⊟ 🍴 DDQ 📞

[Facebook] [Twitter]

★★★★
FARMHOUSE

B&B PER ROOM PER NIGHT
S: £35.00 - £45.00
D: £70.00 - £90.00
EVENING MEAL PER PERSON
£12.00 - £20.00

[Facebook]

South Moor Farm

Dalby Forest Drive, Langdale End, Scarborough YO13 0LW **T:** (01751) 460285
E: gol@southmoorfarm.co.uk
W: southmoorfarm.co.uk **£ BOOK ONLINE**

Quiet rural location on Dalby Forest Drive between Pickering and
Scarborough. An excellent base to explore Dalby Forest, North York
moors, or coast on foot, bike or horse. A full English breakfast
included. Packed lunches and evening meals. **Directions:** GPS/SAT
NAV not Reliable in Dalby Forest. Follow Dalby Forest Drive (look
for brown tourism signs). We are 10 miles from Thornton-le-Dale,
3.5 miles from Langdale End. Grid Ref SE905905.
Bedrooms: 1 single, 1 double, 1 twin, 1 family. **Open:** All year.

Site: P Payment: 💳 **Leisure:** 🚴 U **Property:** 🐴 ⊟ **Children:** ⛱ 🛏 ⩍
Catering: (✗ 🍽 **Room:** 🍵 ♨ 📺 📻

Grassington, Yorkshire ©VisitBritain Tomo Brejc

Clitherbecks Farm

Contact: Catherine Harland, Proprietor, Clitherbecks Farm, Danby, Whitby, North Yorkshire YO21 2NT **T:** (01287) 660321 **E:** enquiries@clitherbecks.co.uk
W: www.clitherbecks.co.uk

Units   1
Sleeps   1-7

PER UNIT PER WEEK
£240.00 - £410.00

Dwelling mentioned in Doomsday Book. Present building built in 1780. Self-contained accommodation with separate entrance. Two bedrooms that can comfortably sleep 7 people. Shared bathroom.

Downstairs is one living room with central heating and coal fire adjoining a kitchen with electric cooker, microwave, and a fridge-freezer. Towels and bedding are provided. Heating and electric are included in the price with the exception of coal and wood for which there will be an additional charge. You have your own entrance through a fenced in garden. Get away from it all in this quiet working farm.

Open: All year.
Nearest Shop: 1 mile (supermarket 3 miles)
Nearest Pub: 1 mile

Units: 2 bedrooms, 1 bathroom, Living room and kitchen. You have the run of one third of an old farmhouse with your own entrance & fenced in garden.

Site: ❀ P Property: 🐾 📧 🗄 🖧 Children: ☌ Unit: 📱 📺 📺 📀 ⌀

Crows Nest Caravan Park

Crows Nest Caravan Park, Gristhorpe, Filey, North Yorkshire YO14 9PS
T: (01723) 582206 **E:** enquiries@crowsnestcaravanpark.com
W: www.crowsnestcaravanpark.com **£ BOOK ONLINE**

🚐 (50)   £22.00-£37.00
🚐 (50)   £22.00-£37.00
⛺ (200) £22.00-£37.00
🏠 (30)   £340.00-£650.00

Crows Nest Caravan Park is located on the beautiful Yorkshire coast between Scarborough and Filey, it is the ideal park to enjoy these two great seaside towns, their sandy beaches and wonderful attractions.

Crows Nest offers luxury holiday homes for short breaks and family holidays. You will find a range of facilities including indoor swimming pool and evening entertainment (high season only).

Directions: 2 miles north of Filey, 5 miles south of Scarborough. Just off A165 main road, turn off at roundabout with Jet petrol station.

Open: 1st March to 31st October.

Site: 🏕 ▲🅿 Payment: 💷 ☼ Leisure: ► ♣ ♣ Children: ☌ ⚠ Catering: ✕ 🛒 Park: 🐾 🎵 📧 🗄 🎍 🔥 Touring: 🚻 🚿 🔌

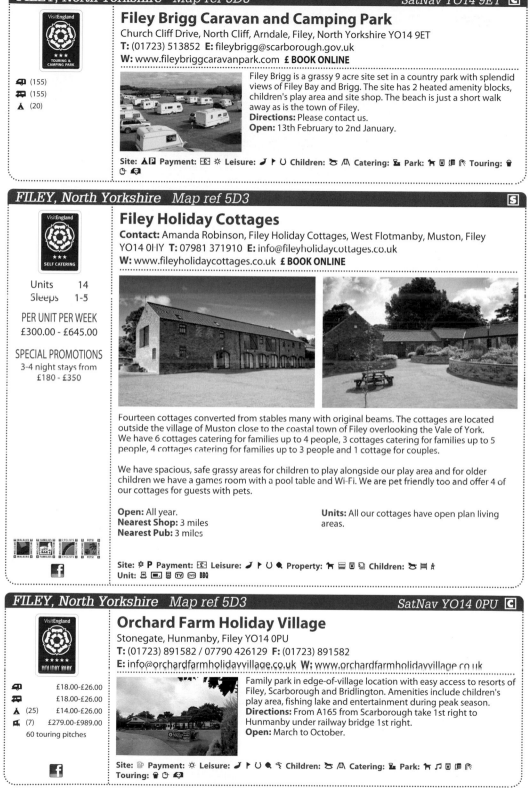

VisitEngland
★★★
TOURING & CAMPING PARK

🚐 (155)
🚏 (155)
⚑ (20)

Filey Brigg Caravan and Camping Park

Church Cliff Drive, North Cliff, Arndale, Filey, North Yorkshire YO14 9ET
T: (01723) 513852 **E:** fileybrigg@scarborough.gov.uk
W: www.fileybriggcaravanpark.com **£ BOOK ONLINE**

Filey Brigg is a grassy 9 acre site set in a country park with splendid views of Filey Bay and Brigg. The site has 2 heated amenity blocks, children's play area and site shop. The beach is just a short walk away as is the town of Filey.
Directions: Please contact us.
Open: 13th February to 2nd January.

Site: ⚑🅿 **Payment:** 💷 ☀ **Leisure:** ♪ ► ∪ **Children:** 🐾 ⚠ **Catering:** 🛒 **Park:** 🐕 🖥 🏢 🍴 **Touring:** 🚻 🚽 🚰

VisitEngland
★★★
SELF CATERING

Units   14
Sleeps   1-5

PER UNIT PER WEEK
£300.00 - £645.00

SPECIAL PROMOTIONS
3-4 night stays from
£180 - £350

Filey Holiday Cottages

Contact: Amanda Robinson, Filey Holiday Cottages, West Flotmanby, Muston, Filey YO14 0HY **T:** 07981 371910 **E:** info@fileyholidaycottages.co.uk
W: www.fileyholidaycottages.co.uk **£ BOOK ONLINE**

Fourteen cottages converted from stables many with original beams. The cottages are located outside the village of Muston close to the coastal town of Filey overlooking the Vale of York. We have 6 cottages catering for families up to 4 people, 3 cottages catering for families up to 5 people, 4 cottages catering for families up to 3 people and 1 cottage for couples.

We have spacious, safe grassy areas for children to play alongside our play area and for older children we have a games room with a pool table and Wi-Fi. We are pet friendly too and offer 4 of our cottages for guests with pets.

Open: All year.
Nearest Shop: 3 miles
Nearest Pub: 3 miles

Units: All our cottages have open plan living areas.

WALKERS   FAMILIES   CYCLISTS   PETS!
WALKERS   FAMILIES   CYCLISTS   PETS!

f

Site: ✿ P **Payment:** 💷 **Leisure:** ♪ ► ∪ ♣ **Property:** 🐕 🖥 🏢 🍴 **Children:** 🐾 🛏 ⚡
Unit: 🖥 📺 📻 📺 📀 BBQ

VisitEngland
★★★★★
HOLIDAY PARK

🚐   £18.00-£26.00
🚏   £18.00-£26.00
⚑ (25)   £14.00-£26.00
🛏 (7)   £279.00-£989.00
60 touring pitches

f

Orchard Farm Holiday Village

Stonegate, Hunmanby, Filey YO14 0PU
T: (01723) 891582 / 07790 426129 **F:** (01723) 891582
E: info@orchardfarmholidayvillage.co.uk **W:** www.orchardfarmholidayvillage.co.uk

Family park in edge-of-village location with easy access to resorts of Filey, Scarborough and Bridlington. Amenities include children's play area, fishing lake and entertainment during peak season.
Directions: From A165 from Scarborough take 1st right to Hunmanby under railway bridge 1st right.
Open: March to October.

Site: 🏕 **Payment:** ☀ **Leisure:** ♪ ► ∪ ♣ 🎣 **Children:** 🐾 ⚠ **Catering:** 🛒 **Park:** 🐕 🎵 🖥 🏢 🍴
Touring: 🚻 🚽 🚰

GIGGLESWICK, North Yorkshire Map ref 5B3

S

VisitEngland
★★★★
SELF CATERING

Ivy Cottage (Giggleswick) Limited

Contact: David & Betty Hattersley, 22 Malvern Drive, Woodford Green IG8 0JW
T: (020) 8504 8263 **E:** info@ivycottagegiggleswick.co.uk
W: www.ivycottagegiggleswick.co.uk **£ BOOK ONLINE**

Units   1
Sleeps   6

PER UNIT PER WEEK
£295.00 - £595.00

SPECIAL PROMOTIONS
Short Breaks and
Special Offers by
arrangement.

A bright and well maintained stone cottage in the centre of Giggleswick village, sleeping 6 in two doubles and one twin-bedded room. The upstairs bathroom is by Villeroy & Bosch with a separate shower unit, whilst downstairs there is a second WC and a clothes drying area. There is also central heating, an open fire, private parking and a cycle store.

For your leisure there is a flat screen TV in the kitchen and lounge, Wi-Fi, an iPod dock and a library of local books and maps.

The ancient church and two inns with restaurants are close by and a walk into Settle takes around ten minutes.

Open: All year.
Nearest Shop: 0.80 miles
Nearest Pub: 0.05 miles

Units: Ivy Cottage (Giggleswick) Limited is a family owned business established in 1987.

WALKERS · CYCLISTS
WALKERS · CYCLISTS

Site: ✿ P **Payment:** € **Leisure:** 🚶 ⛷ **Property:** 📺 🔲 🔲 **Children:** 👶5 **Unit:** 🔲 🔲 🔲 🔲 🔲 📺 📀 ⌀ 📞

GIGGLESWICK, North Yorkshire Map ref 5B3

S

VisitEngland
★★★★
SELF CATERING

Pendle View Holiday Apartment

Contact: Mrs Chris Chandler, Owner, Pendle View Holiday Apartment, 2 Pendle View, Giggleswick, Settle BD24 0AZ **T:** (01729) 822147 / 07879 643878
E: pendleview@hotmail.com **W:** www.settleholiday.co.uk

Units   1
Sleeps   2-3
PER UNIT PER WEEK
£280.00 - £350.00

Pendle View is a spacious, self-contained, garden flat with a kitchen, living room, bedroom and shower room. It is the lower ground floor of a grade II listed early Victorian semi-detached house, stone-built in the local style. It has car parking and patio.
Open: All year except Christmas and New Year.
Nearest Shop: 1 mile
Nearest Pub: 0.01 miles

f

Site: ✿ P **Property:** 📺 🔲 **Children:** 👶 🛏 ♿ **Unit:** 🔲 🔲 🔲 🔲 🔲 📺 📀

HARROGATE, North Yorkshire Map ref 4B1

S

VisitEngland
★★★★
SELF CATERING

Ashness Apartments

Contact: Hazel Spinlove, Ashness Apartments, 15 St Marys Avenue, Harrogate HG2 0LP
T: (01423) 526894 **F:** (01423) 700038 **E:** office@ashness.com
W: www.ashness.com **£ BOOK ONLINE**

Units   9
Sleeps   2
PER UNIT PER WEEK
£406.00 - £560.00

High quality apartments, superbly situated in a nice, quiet road of fine Victorian townhouses very near the town centre of Harrogate. Well equipped with high speed wired and wireless internet throughout. Excellent shops, restaurants and cafés are a short walk away through Montpellier Gardens with the Stray, Valley Gardens, Royal Hall and Conference Centre just around the corner.
Open: All year. **Nearest Shop:** 0.10 miles **Nearest Pub:** 0.10 miles

f

Site: P **Payment:** 💷 **Property:** 〃 🐾 🔲 🔲 **Children:** 👶 🛏 ♿ **Unit:** 🔲 🔲 🔲 🔲 📺 🔲 📀 📞

VisitEngland
★★★
HOTEL

Cairn Hotel

Ripon Road, Harrogate, North Yorkshire HG1 2JD **T:** (01423) 504005 **F:** (01423) 500056
E: salescairn@strathmorehotels.com
W: www.strathmorehotels.com **£ BOOK ONLINE**

B&B PER ROOM PER NIGHT
S: £50.00 - £130.00
D: £80.00 - £180.00
HB PER PERSON PER NIGHT
£60.00 - £150.00

SPECIAL PROMOTIONS
Free child places 0-4
years. Half-price 5-14
years. Christmas and
New Year breaks
available. Special last
minute breaks. See
website.

Built during Harrogate's period as a spa town, stylish and comfortable decor goes hand in hand with gracious hospitality to offer a welcome that is second to none. This charming hotel is only five minutes walk from the town centre - ideal for leisure breaks, meetings/conferences and exhibitions.

Directions: By car: 7 miles off the north/south A1 and 17 miles from the M1/M62.
By rail: Harrogate station.
By air: Leeds/Bradford airport (12 miles).

Bedrooms: 13 single, 48 double, 65 twin, 8 family, 1 suite.
Open: All year.

Site: ✿ **Payment:** 💷 **Leisure:** 🏹 **Property:** ♈ 🖿 ◐ **Children:** 🛝 🎠 🎋 **Catering:** 🍷 🍽
Room: 🖐 📞 🖭 📺 📠 🚱

VisitEngland
★★★★
SELF CATERING

Helme Pasture Lodges & Cottages

Contact: Mrs Rosemary Helme, Helme Pasture Lodges & Cottages, Hartwith Bank, Summerbridge, Harrogate HG3 4DR **T:** (01423) 780279 **E:** info@helmepasture.co.uk
W: www.helmepasture.co.uk

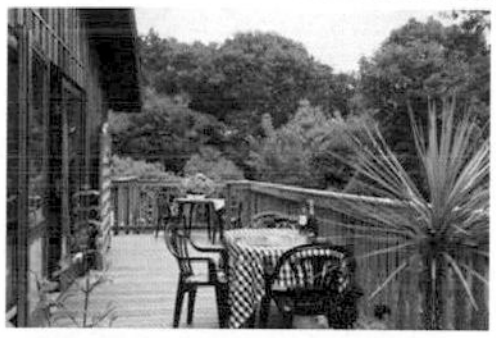

Units   4
Sleeps   2-10
PER UNIT PER WEEK
£229.00 - £799.00

Spacious and comfortable Scandinavian lodges situated within award-winning natural woodland in the heart of Nidderdale with endless possibilities for walking and cycling (with storage for up to 10 bikes). Numerous places to visit are all within a few miles travel, such as local markets, villages, abbeys and castles with the towns of Harrogate, Skipton, Ripon and Knaresborough nearby.
Open: All year. **Nearest Shop:** 0.30 miles **Nearest Pub:** 0.30 miles

Site: ✿ P **Payment:** 💷 **Leisure:** 🎵 ⚲ ♺ **Property:** ∥ 🐾 🖿 ⊡ 🔲 **Children:** 🛝 **Unit:** ⊡ ⊟ 🖵

For **key to symbols** see page 6

AA
★★★★
Inn

B&B PER ROOM PER NIGHT
S: £80.00
D: £100.00 - £120.00

The Station Hotel

Station Road, Birstwith, Harrogate, North Yorkshire HG3 3AG **T:** (01423) 770254
E: admin@station-hotel.net
W: www.station-hotel.net **£ BOOK ONLINE**

Situated in the beautiful Nidderdale village of Birstwith, just 6 miles from Harrogate. Our location provides excellent access to the Yorkshire Dales, Ripon, Knaresborough and the spa town of Harrogate.

We have five fantastic guest bedrooms which are all furnished to a very high standard with traditional oak furniture, comfortable beds and luxury en suites.

We look forward to welcoming you.

Directions: Please see our website for directions. www.station-hotel.net/contact

Bedrooms: We have 4 rooms called Merlot, Chablis, Malbec & Rioja. We also have The Coach House which is joint occupancy.
Open: All year.

Site: ❀ P Payment: 💷 Property: 🖥 ∅ Children: 🧍 Catering: ❌ 🍷 🍽 Room: 🐾 🖥 📺 ☕

VisitEngland
★★★★
SELF CATERING

Units   1
Sleeps   1-4
PER UNIT PER WEEK
£285.00 - £485.00

Townend Cottage

Contact: Mrs Margaret Begg, Owner, Townend Farmhouse, High Lane, Beadlam, Nawton, York YO62 7SY **T:** (01439) 770103 **E:** margaret.begg@ukgateway.net
W: www.townendcottage.co.uk

A very warm, comfortable, oak beamed stone cottage. Off main road 3 miles from charming market town of Helmsley. Ideal for walking/touring moors, coast and York. Cosy log fire. Special offers available for low season short breaks. Minimum stay 2 nights £130, 3 nights £200.
Open: All year.
Nearest Shop: 3 miles
Nearest Pub: 0.25 miles

Site: ❀ P Leisure: 🎣 ⚲ ∪ Property: 🐾 🖥 🖼 Children: 🛏 🏠 🧍 Unit: 🖥 📺 ∅

VisitEngland
★★★★
SELF CATERING

Units   1
Sleeps   1-4
PER UNIT PER WEEK
£395.00 - £495.00

Tykes Cottage

Contact: Mrs. Laura Barry, Proprietor, 8 Bondgate Mews, Bondgate, Helmsley, North Yorkshire YO62 5EU **T:** (0113) 286 9735 / 07879 448391 **E:** lpbarry@btinternet.com
W: www.tykescottage.co.uk

Superbly equipped modern 2 bedroom stone 'Mews' cottage, (sleeps 4) with gardens to the front and rear. BBQ, seating and sun deck. Set in a quiet location 5 mins. stroll from the picturesque market square. Private parking, all linen and electric included. An ideal base from which to explore the area.
Open: All year.
Nearest Shop: 100 yards
Nearest Pub: 400 yards

Site: ❀ P Payment: 💷 Property: 🖥 🖼 Children: 🛏 🏠 🧍 Unit: 🖥 📺 BBQ

INGLEBY GREENHOW, North Yorkshire   Map ref 5C3   Ⓢ

Units 6
Sleeps 2-6

PER UNIT PER WEEK
£350.00 - £905.00

SPECIAL PROMOTIONS
Winter breaks 4 nights
for the price of 3. 5%
discount on summer
season bookings of
one week or longer
confirmed before
Christmas. 5% discount
for 2nd and
subsequent weeks in
same summer season.

Ingleby Manor

Contact: Christine Bianco, Ingleby Manor, Ingleby Greenhow, Great Ayton,
North Yorkshire TS9 6RB **T:** (01642) 722170 **E:** christine@inglebymanor.co.uk
W: www.inglebymanor.co.uk

Ingleby Manor, once the home of a Courtier of Henry VIII, is an important 16th century Grade II*
Listed building in 50 acres of beautiful formal gardens and woodland, with a trout stream in a
peaceful hidden valley in the North York Moors National Park.

Spacious apartments and cottages individually designed with appropriate furnishings, log fires and
full central heating, fully equipped kitchens with dishwasher, clothes washer and dryer, etc. Ingleby
Manor has been awarded 5 Star Gold Award from VisitEngland for 'Exceptional quality of
accommodation and customer service'.

Open: All year.
Nearest Shop: 3 miles
Nearest Pub: 0.5 miles

Units: 4 apartments in the Manor House
(3 ground floor) and 2 cottages in the grounds.
All fully self-contained with own entrances.
Beautiful views.

Site: ✿ **P Payment:** 🏧 € **Leisure:** ♿ ♪ ♈ **Property:** ✽ 🐾 ▤ 🖥 🖼 **Children:** ⛟ 🛏 ⚲
Unit: 🗋 🖫 ▣ 🖫 ⚒ 📺 📻 ∅ BBQ ☎

KIRKBYMOORSIDE, North Yorkshire   Map ref 5C3   Ⓢ

Units 6
Sleeps 2-6
PER UNIT PER WEEK
£240.00 - £580.00

Cowldyke Farm

Contact: Mrs Janet Benton, Owner, Salton Road, Great Edstone, Kirkbymoorside, York,
North Yorkshire YO62 6PE **T:** (01751) 431242 **E:** janetbenton@btconnect.com
W: www.cowldyke-farm.co.uk

Our family cottages sleeping 2 or more, are all rated 4 star and are
very spacious. All are tastefully decorated, spotlessly clean, cosy,
and warm. Three cottages have the added attraction of an open fire
or a log burning stove in addition to the central heating. There is
plenty to see and do on the farm. Down by the river is a good place
for a bit of wildlife spotting. Bring your fly fishing rod.
Open: All year. **Nearest Shop:** 4 miles **Nearest Pub:** 4 miles

Site: ✿ **P Leisure:** ♪ **Property:** 🖥 🖼 **Children:** ⛟ **Unit:** 🗋 🖫 ▣ 🖫 ⚒ 📺 📻 ∅ BBQ

KIRKBYMOORSIDE, North Yorkshire   Map ref 5C3   [S]

Surprise View Cottage, Field Barn Cottage & Lowna Farmhouse

Contact: Mrs Ruth Wass, Surprise View Cottages, Sinnington Lodge, Sinnington, York YO62 6RB **T:** (01751) 431345 **E:** info@surpriseviewcottages.co.uk
W: www.surpriseviewcottages.co.uk **£ BOOK ONLINE**

| Units | 3 |
| Sleeps | 1-8 |

PER UNIT PER WEEK
£330.00 - £1290.00

SPECIAL PROMOTIONS
Short breaks available all year round in the farmhouse except for school holidays, 3 day breaks in the smaller cottages November, December, January & February.

Lowna Farmhouse and 2 Barn conversions; historic location, originally old mill and tannery, giving panoramic views over moorland edge and immediate access to field and woodland walks. Warm, roomy accommodation with quality furnishings and fittings. A wealth of beams and original stone and brick features. 'Comfort' is the key word. Tranquillity is assured at Surprise View Cottages; in the heart of the countryside yet central for touring, walking, cycling. Whether it's history, scenery, wildlife, pub life or farm activities - you'll find it here!

Open: All year.
Nearest Shop: 3 miles
Nearest Pub: 1 mile

Units: Three cottages, two smaller units sleeping 4, large farmhouse sleeping up to 8.

Site: ✿ **P Leisure:** 🚲 ♪ ◊ ∪ ⌖ **Property:** 🐕 ⊟ 🗗 🖵 **Children:** 🐾 🖼 ⌾
Unit: 🗗 🗄 🖵 🗗 ⌵ 📺 🔘 ⊚ ∅ BBQ ☎

LITTLE BARUGH, North Yorkshire   Map ref 5C3   [S]

Stainers Farm Cottages

Contact: Jackie Smith, Stainers Farm Cottages, Stainers Farm, Little Barugh YO17 6UY
T: (01653) 668224 / 07879 636979 **E:** info@stainersfarm.co.uk
W: www.stainersfarm.co.uk **£ BOOK ONLINE**

| Units | 5 |
| Sleeps | 4-10 |

PER UNIT PER WEEK
£295.00 - £1150.00

Renovated country cottages with individual character and charm in a peaceful rural setting with wonderful views of open countryside. 1 pet allowed by arrangement, friendly cottage, Wi-Fi available.
Open: All year.
Nearest Shop: 5 miles
Nearest Pub: 1.5 miles

Site: ✿ **Property:** ⊟ 🗗 🖵 **Children:** 🐾 🖼 ⌾ **Unit:** 🗗 🗄 🖵 📺 ⊚ ∅ BBQ

MALTON, North Yorkshire   Map ref 5D3   [S]

Home Farm Holiday Cottages

Contact: Mrs Rachel Prest, Owner, The Old Fold, Railway Street, Slingsby, York YO62 4AL
T: (01653) 628277 / 07803 186941 **E:** rachelprest@yahoo.co.uk
W: www.yorkshire-holiday-cottage.co.uk

| Units | 2 |
| Sleeps | 4-6 |

PER UNIT PER WEEK
£355.00 - £645.00

Attractive single storey, ground floor, stone barn conversions in a lovely village setting. The spacious cottages are furnished and equipped to a very high standard with the inclusion of antique and mellow pine and coordinating fabrics and furnishings. Ideally situated for moors, coast and York. Three miles from Castle Howard.
Open: All year.
Nearest Shop: 400m
Nearest Pub: 100m

Site: ✿ **P Property:** ⊟ 🗗 🖵 **Children:** 🐾 🖼 ⌾ **Unit:** 🗗 🗄 🖵 🗗 ⌵ 📺 ⊚ ∅ ☎

MALTON, *North Yorkshire* Map ref 5D3

Walnut Garth

Contact: Cas Radford, Proprietor, Walnut Garth, c/o Havendale, High Street, Swinton, Malton YO17 6SL **T:** (01653) 691293 / 07766 208348 **E:** cas@walnutgarth.co.uk
W: www.walnutgarth.co.uk

Units	1
Sleeps	1-4

PER UNIT PER WEEK
£227.00 - £449.00

SPECIAL PROMOTIONS
£25 discount for stays
of 2 weeks or longer.

Tastefully decorated, two-bedroom cottage furnished to a high standard with all modern conveniences. Set in owner's grounds at edge of Swinton village, yet only 2 miles from market town of Malton with excellent selection of local amenities and attractions. Easy access to York, coast and Moors. Gym on site. £25 discount for stays of 2 weeks or longer. Christmas cake, pudding & 'Winter Warmer' for Christmas weeks.

Open: All year.
Nearest Shop: 0.25 miles
Nearest Pub: 0.25 miles

Units: All rooms are on the ground floor - floor plan available on website for further information.

Site: ❀ P **Leisure:** ♪ ∪ **Property:** 🐾 🖥 🛁 🔌 **Children:** 🚼 🛏 ⚲ **Unit:** 🍴 🧺 🖥 ⚲ 📺 💿 📀 BBQ 📞

NUNTHORPE, *North Yorkshire* Map ref 4C1

Blackthorn Gate

Contact: Mrs Rita Corrigan, Blackthorn Gate, Eastfields Farm, Nunthorpe, Nr Stokesley, North Yorkshire TS7 0PB **T:** (01642) 324496 **E:** info@blackthorngate.co.uk
W: www.blackthorngate.co.uk **£ BOOK ONLINE**

Units	4
Sleeps	1-5

PER UNIT PER WEEK
£396.00 - £885.00

SPECIAL PROMOTIONS
Weekend and
midweek breaks
available. Friday to
Monday or Monday to
Friday.

Four Swedish designed two bedroom log Lodges set in 230 acres of beautiful open farmland with stunning views of Roseberry Topping. A tranquil haven for your holiday, perfect for spotting wildlife and bird watching. Private on site fishing with 3 fully stocked ponds. Games Room with table tennis, bar football and pool table. Ideally situated for touring and walking in North Yorkshire and the Tees Valley. Larger Lodges wheelchair friendly with downstairs bathroom with wet room style shower.

Open: All year.
Nearest Shop: 2 miles
Nearest Pub: 1.5 miles

Units: Living/dining room, fully fitted kitchen, master en suite, separate bathroom with sauna. Each Lodge has a BBQ, veranda with garden furniture.

Site: ❀ P **Payment:** 💷 € **Leisure:** ♪ ⚓ ∪ 🎣 **Property:** 🐾 🖥 🛁 🔌 **Children:** 🚼 🛏 ⚲
Unit: 🍴 🧺 🖥 ⚲ 📺 💿 BBQ

Kale Pot Cottage

Contact: Diane & Mike Steele, Kale Pot Cottage, Kale Pot Hole, Newtondale, Pickering, North Yorkshire YO18 8HU **T:** (01751) 476654 **E:** enquiries@northyorkmoorscottage.co.uk **W:** www.northyorkmoorscottage.co.uk

SELF CATERING ★★★★
Gold AWARD

Units   1
Sleeps   2-5

PER UNIT PER WEEK
£325.00 - £625.00

SPECIAL PROMOTIONS
Weekend and mid week short breaks available November to February.

Comfortable, spacious, individual cottage situated in our paddock in beautiful Newtondale. A converted 18th century barn, the cottage is well equipped and completely restored. Stunning views of forest and the North York Moors. An ideal base for walking and mountain biking or just relaxing, with the North Yorkshire Moors steam railway nearby. We are remote, but the market town of Pickering is just 10 miles away, Whitby and the coast 15 miles and historic York 35 miles. Owners living nearby.

Open: All year.
Nearest Shop: 10 miles
Nearest Pub: 3 miles

Units: Kitchen, lounge and dining areas upstairs to take advantage of the views, double bedroom en suite, twin room with space for third bed, own wetroom.

Site: ❀ P **Payment:** € **Leisure:** 🦮 ♪ ♨ **Property:** 🐴 ☕ 🖥 **Children:** 🐕 🎏 🚼
Unit: 🛏 🍴 🖥 🖥 🍳 📺 🎛 💿 🌀 ⌀ BBQ 📞

Holme Grange Farm

Galphay, Ripon, North Yorkshire HG4 3NJ **T:** (01765) 658718
E: b.c.stonard@btinternet.com
W: www.holmegrangefarm.co.uk

FARMHOUSE ★★★★

B&B PER ROOM PER NIGHT
S: £45.00
D: £90.00

Beautiful unique wheelhouse B&B accommodation on small working farm within the Nidderdale AONB. Close to Fountains Abbey and Ripon. The large circular room has exposed beams and its own access. A minute's walk away from the village pub.
Directions: Located in the centre of the village, opposite the flagpole on the village green.
Bedrooms: 2 king, 1 double, 1 x 2 bedroom cottage.
Open: All year.

Site: ❀ P **Leisure:** ⛰ **Property:** 🖥 **Children:** 🐕5 **Room:** 🍵 ♨ 📺 ♿

ROSEDALE ABBEY, North Yorkshire   Map ref 5C3   S

VisitEngland
★★★★
SELF CATERING

| Units | 5 |
| Sleeps | 2-4 |

PER UNIT PER WEEK
£251.00 - £521.00

SPECIAL PROMOTIONS
Short breaks are available, Friday to Monday or Monday to Friday. Short breaks from £183. Please visit the website or call us to check prices and availability.

Rosedale Abbey Holiday Cottages

Contact: Rosedale Abbey Caravan Park, Pickering, North Yorkshire YO18 8SA
T: (01723) 584311 **E:** info@flowerofmay.com
W: www.flowerofmay.com **£ BOOK ONLINE**

The cottages and apartment are immaculately presented, beautifully furnished and equipped to a very high standard. In a peaceful village setting nestling in the North York Moors National Park. Ideal walking country within easy reach of Yorkshire's Heritage Coast. Many guests comment that they cannot wait to return to our cosy, comfortable cottages.

Open: All year.
Nearest Shop: 0.05 miles
Nearest Pub: 0.10 miles

Site: ✿ P **Payment:** 💷 **Property:** ⊩ 🖥 🔓 🖵 **Children:** ⛱ 🛏 ☀ **Unit:** 🔓 💻 🔓 📺 📀 ☎

SALTBURN-BY-THE-SEA, North Yorkshire   Map ref 5C3   SatNav TS12 2QX   B

VisitEngland
★★★★
GUEST ACCOMMODATION

B&B PER ROOM PER NIGHT
S: £45.00 - £60.00
D: £70.00 - £80.00

SPECIAL PROMOTIONS
Check website for special offers.

The Arches Country House

Low Farm, Ings Lane, Brotton, Salturn-By-The-Sea, North Yorkshire TS12 2QX
T: (01287) 677512 **F:** (01287) 677150 **E:** sales@gorallyschool.co.uk
W: www.thearcheshotel.co.uk **£ BOOK ONLINE**

The Arches Country House is an independent, family owned and run accommodation located not far from Saltburn in North Yorkshire. We pride ourselves on our relaxed and informal atmosphere. We offer bed and breakfast. We also offer functions and a conference facility. Licenced to hold Civil Ceremony Weddings.

Directions: From North A1(M) Junction 60, A689 to A19 for Thirsk. From A19 to A174 toward Redcar, through Saltburn & Brotton. Stay on main road, 2nd left to St Margarets Way, past houses, past golf club, turn right.

Bedrooms: All rooms en suite. Flat screen TV, tea & coffee making facilities. Four poster room, family, single, double, twin rooms, ground floor available.
Open: All year except Christmas and New Year.

Site: ✿ P **Payment:** 💷 **Leisure:** ⊩ **Property:** ⊮ ⊩ 🖥 **Children:** ⛱ 🛏 ☀ **Catering:** 🍴
Room: 🔓 ♨ 📺 ☕ 🖵

SCARBOROUGH, North Yorkshire   Map ref 5D3   SatNav YO11 3NN C

VisitEngland
★★★★★
TOURING & CAMPING PARK

Cayton Village Caravan Park Ltd

Mill Lane, Cayton Bay, Scarborough YO11 3NN
T: (01723) 583171 **E:** info@caytontouring.co.uk
W: www.caytontouring.co.uk

🚐 (235) £14.00-£36.00
🚎 (20)   £16.00-£36.00
⛺ (55)   £14.00-£29.00
310 touring pitches

Playground, recreation field, dog walk, shop & bus service from park entrance. Seasonal pitches, winter storage, caravan sales. Super sites, Hardstanding & grass pitches. Beach 0.5m, Scarborough 3m. Adjoining village with fish shop & pub.
Directions: From A64 take B1261 to Filey. In Cayton turn left onto Mill Lane. From A165 turn inland at Cayton Bay roundabout onto Mill Lane. 0.5m on right hand side.
Open: 1st March to 5th November.

Site: ⅄🅿 **Payment:** 🎫 ☼ **Leisure:** ♪ ► **Children:** 🛝 ⚠ **Catering:** 🍴 **Park:** 🐾 🚾 🔋 🔥 🐕
Touring: 🚿 🕭 🚱 🛁

SCARBOROUGH, North Yorkshire   Map ref 5D3   SatNav YO11 1XX

Empire Guesthouse

39 Albemarle Crescent, Scarborough YO11 1XX **T:** (01723) 373564
E: gillian@empire1939.wanadoo.co.uk
W: www.empireguesthouse.co.uk

B&B PER ROOM PER NIGHT
S: £28.00
D: £56.00

The Empire overlooks pleasant gardens located in the centre of town, ideally situated for all Scarborough's many attractions and town centre amenities. Every effort made to make your visit enjoyable. Evening meals available from Easter until the end of September. **Directions:** The Empire is 5 minutes from bus & rail terminals. We extend a very warm welcome to all our guests.
Bedrooms: 2 single, 1 double, 1 twin, 1 family, 3 suite.
Open: All year except Christmas and New Year.

Property: 🖵 🔋 🎡 **Children:** 🛝 🎮 🚶 **Catering:** 🍴✕ 🍷 🍽 **Room:** 🍵 🚿 🎧 📺

SCARBOROUGH, North Yorkshire   Map ref 5D3   SatNav YO11 3NU C

VisitEngland
★★★★★
HOLIDAY, TOURING & CAMPING PARK

Flower of May Holiday Park

Flower of May Holiday Park, Lebberston, Scarborough, North Yorkshire YO11 3NU
T: (01723) 584311 **F:** (01723) 585716 **E:** info@flowerofmay.com
W: www.flowerofmay.com **£ BOOK ONLINE**

🚐 (300) £24.00-£30.00
🚎 (20)   £24.00-£30.00
⛺ (60)   £24.00-£30.00
🚍 (20)   £260.00-£710.00

SPECIAL PROMOTIONS
Early booking offer available please refer to be website. Short breaks also available.

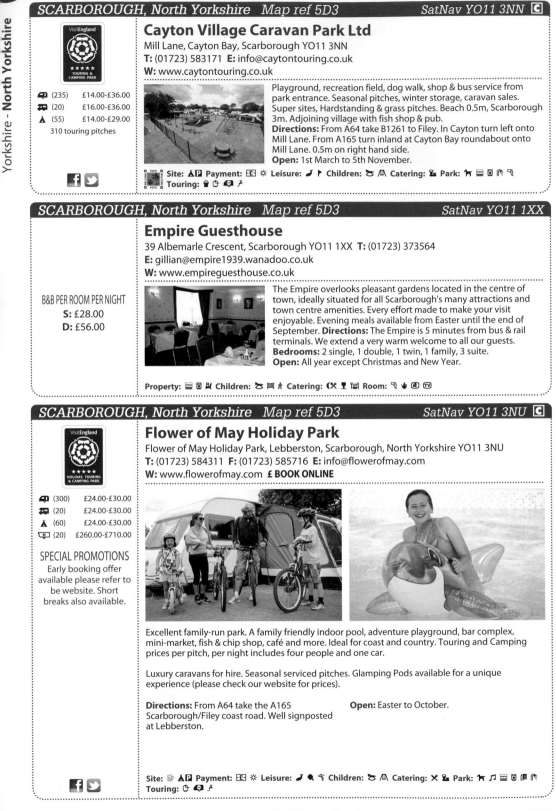

Excellent family-run park. A family friendly indoor pool, adventure playground, bar complex, mini-market, fish & chip shop, café and more. Ideal for coast and country. Touring and Camping prices per pitch, per night includes four people and one car.

Luxury caravans for hire. Seasonal serviced pitches. Glamping Pods available for a unique experience (please check our website for prices).

Directions: From A64 take the A165 Scarborough/Filey coast road. Well signposted at Lebberston.

Open: Easter to October.

Site: 📶 ⅄🅿 **Payment:** 🎫 ☼ **Leisure:** ♪ ⚓ 🎣 **Children:** 🛝 ⚠ **Catering:** ✕ 🍴 **Park:** 🐾 🎵 🚾 🔋 🛢 🔥
Touring: 🕭 🚱 🛁

VisitEngland
★★★
GUEST HOUSE

B&B PER ROOM PER NIGHT
D: £56.00 - £92.00

Howdale

121 Queen's Parade, Scarborough YO12 7HU　**T:** (01723) 372696
E: mail@howdalehotel.co.uk
W: www.howdalehotel.co.uk/ve　**£ BOOK ONLINE**

A cosy stay at the Howdale ensures your visit to Scarborough is perfect! Close to town. Stunning views over Scarborough North Bay & Castle. Fantastic delicious breakfast. Spotless, comfortable, friendly, efficient! Free parking.
Directions: At traffic lights opposite railway station turn left. Next traffic lights turn right. At 1st roundabout turn left. Property is 0.5 miles on the right.
Bedrooms: 11 double, 2 twin. **Open:** March to October.

Site: ❀ **P Payment:** 💷 **Property:** 🖥 🎬 **Children:** 🎠 🎮 🧒 **Room:** 🍵 ♨ 📺

VisitEngland
★★★★★
HOLIDAY, TOURING & CAMPING PARK

🚐 (74)　£22.00-£37.00
🚚 (74)　£22.00-£27.00
⛺ (20)　£17.00-£37.00
🏠 (30)　£450.00-£700.00
94 touring pitches

Jasmine Park

Cross Lane, Snainton, Scarborough YO13 9BE
T: (01723) 859240　**E:** enquiries@jasminepark.co.uk
W: www.jasminepark.co.uk　**£ BOOK ONLINE**

Family-owned, tranquil park in picturesque countryside setting between Scarborough (8 miles) and Pickering. Superbly maintained facilities including our fantastic children's play area. Tents and tourers welcome. Seasonal pitches and storage available.

Luxury holiday homes for hire and sale.

Directions: Turn south off the A170 in Snainton opposite the junior school at traffic lights. Signposted.

Open: March to October.

Payment: 💷 ❀ **Leisure:** ♿ 🎵 ▶ ⏱ **Children:** 🎠 ⛰ **Catering:** 🛒 **Park:** 🐕 🚍 🗄 📦 🏧
Touring: 🚰 ⚡ 🚐 ⚓

For **key to symbols** see page 6

The Whiteley

99-101 Queens Parade, Scarborough YO12 7HY **T:** (01723) 373514 **F:** (01723) 373007
E: thewhiteley@gmail.com
W: www.yorkshirecoast.co.uk/whiteley

B&B PER ROOM PER NIGHT
S: £37.50 - £39.00
D: £63.00 - £74.00

SPECIAL PROMOTIONS
October to May
inclusive (excl Bank
Holidays): reduction of
£1.50pppn when
staying 2 nights or
more.

Small, family-run, non-smoking guest accommodation located in an elevated position overlooking
the North Bay, close to the town centre and ideally situated for all amenities.

Directions: Left at traffic lights near railway
station, right at next lights, Castle Road to
roundabout. Left onto North Marine Road.
2nd right onto Queens Parade.

Bedrooms: 7 double, 3 family.
Open: Closed December & January.

Site: ✿ **P** Payment: 💳 Property: 🖥 🍴 Children: 🚼 Catering: 🍽 Room: 🔌 🕯 📺 ♿

The Coniston Hotel, Country Estate & Spa

Coniston Cold, Skipton BD23 4EA **T:** (01756) 748080 **F:** (01756) 749487
E: reservations@theconistonhotel.com
W: www.theconistonhotel.com **£ BOOK ONLINE**

B&B PER ROOM PER NIGHT
S: £89.00 - £189.00
D: £99.00 - £249.00
EVENING MEAL PER PERSON
£9.95 - £39.95

Set in 1400 acre estate with stunning views, warm friendly welcome
awaits, perfect location as a base to explore the Dales. Estate
activities include clay pigeon shooting, Kubota RTV and off road
experience, archery, falconry and state of the art spa and leisure
facilities. **Directions:** On the A65 between Skipton (7 miles) and
Settle (9 miles) at Coniston Cold. Just 8 miles from Malham.
Bedrooms: 65 double, 6 family.
Open: All year.

Site: ✿ **P** Payment: 💳 € Leisure: 🏊 🎣 ▶ ♨ ⛷ Property: 🏨 ♟ 🐾 🖥 🅿 🍴 ☾ ◐ ✎ Children: 🚼 🍴 ⚤
Catering: (✗ 🍷 🍽 Room: 🔌 🕯 🎧 📺 📀 ♿

SLINGSBY, North Yorkshire   Map ref 5C3   SatNav YO62 4AP C

VisitEngland
★★★★★
HOLIDAY, TOURING
& CAMPING PARK

🚐 (38)   £22.00-£29.00
🚙 (38)   £22.00-£29.00
🏕 (38)   £16.00-£27.00
⛺ (15)   £225.00-£565.00
38 touring pitches

Robin Hood Caravan Park

Slingsby, York YO62 4AP
T: (01653) 628391 **F:** (01653) 628392 **E:** info@robinhoodcaravanpark.co.uk
W: www.robinhoodcaravanpark.co.uk **£ BOOK ONLINE**

An award-winning, privately owned park set in the heart of picturesque Ryedale. Peaceful and tranquil, a perfect base for families and couples wishing to explore the stunning countryside of North Yorkshire. Within easy reach of York, Castle Howard, Flamingoland and the coastal resorts of Scarborough, Whitby and Filey. Seasonal Pitches available. Visit York's Caravan Park of the Year 2015 & 2016.

Directions: Situated on the edge of Slingsby with access off the B1257 Malton to Helmsley road.

Open: March to October.

Payments: 💳 ✳ Leisure: 🎣 ⛵ Children: 🛝 🎢 Catering: 🍴 Park: 🐕 🚮 📮 🎮 📶 Touring: 🚽 🚿 ♿ ⚡

STAITHES, North Yorkshire   Map ref 5C3   S

VisitEngland
★★★
SELF CATERING

Units   1
Sleeps   1-5

PER UNIT PER WEEK
£330.00 - £630.00

SPECIAL PROMOTIONS
Short breaks on request - mainly in Low Season or at short notice.

Pennysteel Cottage

Contact: Ms Chris Wade, Owner, Waterfront Cottages, 2 Mere Cottages, Star Row, North Dalton, Driffield, East Yorkshire YO25 9UX **T:** (01377) 219901 / 07801 124264
F: (01377) 217754 **E:** chris.wade@adastra-music.co.uk
W: www.waterfrontcottages.co.uk **£ BOOK ONLINE**

Old fisherman's cottage with original character and features, including beamed ceilings and wood panelled walls. All rooms and terrace overlooking the attractive harbour of Staithes and its lifeboat station. Sit and relax with the comfort of a log burning stove and watch the ships go past. Perfect for those with a romantic love of the past. Located off the main High Street in a quiet corner, just a couple of minutes from the beach, pubs, restaurant and shops. Ideal for walking (on the Cleveland Way long distance footpath) and the coast. Close to Whitby, Heartbeat Country, and the Moors.

Open: All year.
Nearest Shop: 0.10 miles
Nearest Pub: 0.10 miles

Units: Kitchen, living and dining room on ground floor. Double bedroom, single bedroom and toilet on first floor. Twin attic room, shower and bathroom on second floor.

Site: ✳ Payment: 💳 Leisure: 🎣 Property: 🐕 🚮 📮 🍴 🍽 Children: 🛝 🎮 ♿
Unit: 🚽 🚿 📺 📻 📶 📡 💿 🎵 BBQ 📞

THIRSK, North Yorkshire Map ref 5C3 SatNav YO7 1PQ [B]

The Gallery Bed & Breakfast

VisitEngland ★★★★ BED & BREAKFAST
VisitEngland Silver AWARD

18 Kirkgate, Thirsk, North Yorkshire YO7 1PQ T: (01845) 523767
E: kathryn@gallerybedandbreakfast.co.uk
W: www.gallerybedandbreakfast.co.uk £ BOOK ONLINE

B&B PER ROOM PER NIGHT
S: £50.00
D: £70.00 - £75.00

The Gallery Bed & Breakfast is Grade II Listed and full of charm, located close to Thirsk Market Square and opposite The World of James Herriot. 3 en suite rooms, serving award-winning locally sourced breakfasts.
Directions: From the Market Square turn down Kirkgate and we are 50 yards on the right.
Bedrooms: All rooms en suite, TV/DVD, Wi-Fi, tea/coffee etc.
Open: All year except Christmas and New Year.

Payment: Leisure: Property: Catering: Room:

WHITBY, North Yorkshire Map ref 5D3 [S]

Croft Farm Holiday Cottages

VisitEngland ★★★★ SELF CATERING

Contact: Emma Carpenter, Owner, Croft Farm, Ruswarp, Whitby, North Yorkshire YO21 1NY T: (01947) 825853 E: emma@croftfarm.com
W: www.croftfarm.com

Units 3
Sleeps 1-16
PER UNIT PER WEEK
£420.00 - £640.00

These superb cottages in the village of Ruswarp near Whitby are furnished to a very high standard with private parking and a friendly welcome. Short breaks are available and pets by arrangement.
Open: All year.
Nearest Shop: 50m
Nearest Pub: 150m

Site: P Payment: Property: Children: Unit:

WHITBY, North Yorkshire Map ref 5D3 [S]

Fayvan Holiday Apartments

VisitEngland ★★★★ SELF CATERING

Contact: Benita and Michael Nicholson, Owner, 43 Crescent Avenue, West Cliff, Whitby, North Yorkshire YO21 3EQ T: (01947) 604813 / 07808 340871
E: fayvan.apartments@btinternet.com W: www.fayvan.co.uk £ BOOK ONLINE

Units 3
Sleeps 5
PER UNIT PER WEEK
£520.00 - £620.00

Fayvan is a stunning Victorian residence situated on the West Cliff, in the most prestigious area of Whitby, just off the Royal Crescent on Crescent Avenue. These extremely spacious apartments are finished to a high standard and all have side sea views.
Our first-class non-smoking accommodation has been rated 4 stars by Visit England. **Open:** All year.
Nearest Shop: 400m
Nearest Pub: 400m

Payment: Leisure: Property: Children: Unit:

WHITBY, North Yorkshire Map ref 5D3 [S]

Flask Inn Holiday Home Park

VisitEngland ★★★★★ HOLIDAY PARK

Contact: Blacksmiths Hill, Robin Hood's Bay, Whitby, North Yorkshire YO22 4QH
T: (01947) 880592 F: (01947) 880592 E: info@flaskinn.com
W: www.flaskinn.com

Units 10
Sleeps 4
PER UNIT PER WEEK
£290.00 - £520.00

Small, family-run 5 star site for over 30 years, in the North York Moors. All our holiday homes have central heating and double glazing throughout. All have a double bedroom en suite, Freeview TV, DVD, full kitchen with fridge/freezer and microwave. All holiday homes have outside decking and seating. Situated in the North Yorkshire Moors on the A171, 7 miles to Whitby, 12 miles to Scarborough and 4 miles to Robin Hood's Bay.
Open: March to November.

Payment: Leisure: Property: Children:

WHITBY, North Yorkshire   Map ref 5D3

[S]

Forest Lodge Farm

Contact: Peter & Kate Stannard, Owners, Forest Lodge Cottages, Castleton, Whitby, North Yorkshire YO21 2DZ **T:** (01287) 660024 / 07980 159071 **E:** pandkstannard@aol.com **W:** www.forestlodgecottages.co.uk **£ BOOK ONLINE**

Units   3
Sleeps   2-18

PER UNIT PER WEEK
£450.00 - £1650.00

SPECIAL PROMOTIONS
Friday to Monday and Monday to Friday breaks available. For other breaks please contact us. All 3 cottages can be booked together to sleep 18 plus infants.

In the North York Moors National Park, Forest Lodge is an organic farm with three luxury 5* Gold Award, Grade 2 Listed cottages around a flagged courtyard. Each cottage has its own garden/sitting area with table/chairs/BBQ and is surrounded by our meadows and open moorland with footpaths and bridleway from the farm. There is also a 2 acre field with slide/swings/play area with goalpost and badminton net and plentiful car parking on site. Beautiful sandy beaches are a short drive away at Whitby, Robin Hoods Bay, Runswick Bay and Saltburn. NYM Railway steam trains run from Whitby to Pickering.

Open: All year.
Nearest Shop: 0.75 miles
Nearest Pub: 0.75 miles

Units: Dale House (8) 4 double, 2 and shower ground floor. North Range (6) 3 double, 1 ground floor. Coltus (4) 2 double, 1 en suite. All with underfloor heating.

Site: ✿ P **Payment:** 💷 **Leisure:** ⚑ **Property:** 🖥 📺 🖳 **Children:** 👶 🛏 🧍
Unit: 🚪 🍳 📺 🎧 📺 📀 BBQ

[f]

WHITBY, North Yorkshire   Map ref 5D3

[S]

Lemon Cottage

Contact: Andy Martin, Park Manager, Northcliffe & Seaview Holiday Parks, Bottoms Lane, High Hawsker, Whitby YO22 4LL **T:** (01947) 880477 **E:** enquiries@northcliffe-seaview.com **W:** www.northcliffe-seaview.com **£ BOOK ONLINE**

Units   1
Sleeps   1-4
PER UNIT PER WEEK
£415.00 - £750.00

Lemon Cottage is a Gold Award 4 Star Holiday Cottage situated on our 5 Star Seaview Holiday Park. Sleeping 4 with 2 en suite bedrooms, a stunning interior and private sun terrace. Ground floor accommodation. Fabulous location with easy access to the beautiful Heritage Coast & Cinder Cycle Path. 3 Night weekend breaks from £255 & 4 night mid week breaks from £285. Free Wi-Fi.
Open: 1st March to 7th November.
Nearest Shop: 1m **Nearest Pub:** 800m

[f]

Site: P **Payment:** 💷 **Leisure:** ⚑ 🔍 🔍 **Property:** 🖳 **Children:** 👶 🛏 🧍 **Unit:** 🚪 🍳 📺 🎧 📺 📀

Sign up for our newsletter

Visit our website to sign up for our e-newsletter and receive regular information on events, articles, exclusive competitions and new publications.
www.visitor-guides.co.uk

For **key to symbols** see page 6

WHITBY, North Yorkshire Map ref 5D3

S

VisitEngland ★★★★★ HOLIDAY & TOURING PARK

Units 6
Sleeps 2-4

PER UNIT PER WEEK
£220.00 - £750.00

SPECIAL PROMOTIONS
Visit our website to view our new caravans for sale, check availability & book your holiday.

Register your email address to receive our 'special offers' by email.

Northcliffe & Seaview Holiday Parks

Contact: Northcliffe & Seaview Holiday Parks, Bottoms Lane, High Hawsker, Whitby, North Yorkshire YO22 4LL **T:** (01947) 880477 **E:** enquiries@northcliffe-seaview.com
W: www.northcliffe-seaview.com **£ BOOK ONLINE**

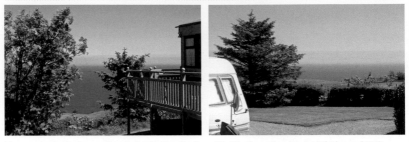

These award-winning parks are situated on the beautiful Heritage Coast twixt Whitby and RHB. Both Gold Award Conservation parks have fabulous countryside and coastal views with access to superb walks and a cycle track.

We sell and hire luxurious caravans, have a 4 Star Gold Award cottage and an exclusive seasonal only touring park. Facilities include free Wi-Fi, play parks, football pitches and lots more.

Open: 1st March to 7th November.

Payment: **Leisure:** **Property:** **Children:**

WHITBY, North Yorkshire Map ref 5D3 SatNav YO21 3QN

B

VisitEngland ★★★★ GUEST ACCOMMODATION

B&B PER ROOM PER NIGHT
S: £44.95
D: £89.90

EVENING MEAL PER PERSON
£10.00

SPECIAL PROMOTIONS
Monday to Friday from 3rd October to 13th April
2 or 4 night breaks from £80 for single occupants and £150 for 2 people sharing. See our website for full details.

Sneaton Castle Centre

Castle Road, Whitby YO21 3QN **T:** (01947) 600051 **F:** (01947) 603490
E: reception@sneatoncastle.co.uk
W: www.sneatoncastle.co.uk

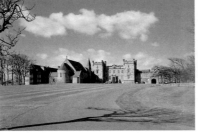

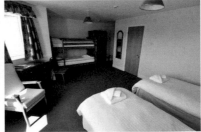

Set in the stunning grounds and gardens of Sneaton Castle, on the outskirts of Whitby and on the edge of the North York Moors and near the seashore. We offer high quality en suite accommodation and an excellent Yorkshire breakfast. Ample free and safe parking.

Directions: Please refer to website.

Bedrooms: 5 single, 1 double, 8 twin and 3 family.
Open: All year except Christmas and New Year.

Site: P **Payment:** **Leisure:** **Property:** **Children:** **Catering:**
Room:

YORK, North Yorkshire   Map ref 4C1   S

VisitEngland
★★★★
SELF CATERING

Units   1
Sleeps   1-2
PER UNIT PER WEEK
£335.00 - £460.00

44 Postern Close

Contact: Mrs Christine Turner, Booking Enquiries, 44 Postern Close, Meadowcroft, Millfield, Willingham, Cambridge CB24 5HD **E:** 44posternclose@gmail.com
W: www.yorkholidayflat.co.uk

One double bedroom apartment, within the prestigious Bishops Wharf Riverside development. Five minutes' walking distance from city centre. Sitting/dining room, kitchen, bathroom, small balcony and parking space. No smoking.
Open: All year.
Nearest Shop: 5 minute walk
Nearest Pub: 2 minute walk

Site: P Payment: 💷 **Leisure:** 🚲 ✈ ⚑ **Property:** 🖋 📺 📶 **Unit:** 🛏 🖥 🗄 ⚑ 📺 📀

YORK, North Yorkshire   Map ref 4C1   SatNav YO61 1RY   C

VisitEngland
★★★★★
TOURING & CAMPING PARK

🚐 (87)   £22.00-£26.00
🚍   £22.00-£26.00
⛺   £22.00-£26.00
🏠 (4)   £40.00-£47.00
87 touring pitches

f

Alders Caravan Park

Home Farm, Monk Green, Alne nr Easingwold, York YO61 1RY
T: (01347) 838722 **E:** enquiries@homefarmalne.co.uk
W: www.alderscaravanpark.co.uk

A working farm in historic parkland where visitors may enjoy peace and tranquillity. York (on bus route), Moors, Dales and coast nearby. Tastefully landscaped, adjoins village cricket ground. Woodland walk.
Camping pods available.
Directions: From A19 exit at Alne sign, in 1.5 miles turn left at T-junction, 0.5 miles park on left in village centre.
Open: March to October.

Site: 📶 **Payment:** 💷 ☀ **Leisure:** ♪ ⚑ ♺ **Children:** 🛝 **Catering:** 🛒 **Park:** 🐕 📺 📶 🏧 **Touring:** 🚿 🛁 🚐

YORK, North Yorkshire   Map ref 4C1   SatNav YO61 1ET   C

VisitEngland
★★★★
HOLIDAY & TOURING PARK

🚐 (90)   £24.00-£30.00
🚍 (10)   £24.00-£30.00
🏠 (5)   £369.00-£1199.00
🏡 (14)   £190.00-£840.00

SPECIAL PROMOTIONS
Early booking offer available please refer to be website. Short breaks also available.

Goosewood Holiday Park

Sutton on the Forest, York, North Yorkshire YO61 1ET
T: (01347) 810829 **F:** (01347) 811498 **E:** info@flowerofmay.com
W: www.flowerofmay.com **£ BOOK ONLINE**

A quiet, peaceful park with fishing lake, children's adventure play area and leisure complex with indoor pool, bar and games room. Luxury holiday lodges and lodge-style holiday homes, many with hot tubs available to hire. A perfect place to relax and ideal for visiting the historic city of York and surrounding beauty spots of Yorkshire. A warm welcome. For bookings please call (01723) 584311 or book online.

Directions: North of York. Follow route to Strensall.

Open: March to 2nd January.

Site: 📶 🅿 **Payment:** 💷 ☀ **Leisure:** ♪ ⚓ ♺ **Children:** 🛝 ⛰ **Catering:** ✗ 🛒 **Park:** 🐕 📺 📶 🏧
Touring: 🚿 🛁 🚐 ♪

YORK, North Yorkshire   Map ref 4C1   [S]

The Blue Rooms

Contact: Mrs Kirsty Wheeldin, Executive Manager, The Blue Rooms, 4 Franklins Yard, Fossgate, York YO1 9TN **T:** (01904) 673990 **F:** (01904) 658147 **E:** info@thebluebicycle.com
W: www.thebluebicycle.com

Units   6
Sleeps   1-4
PER UNIT PER WEEK
£875.00 - £1400.00

Beautifully decorated apartments, some with wood beam ceilings, four poster beds and views over the River Foss. Guests will be welcomed on arrival with a complimentary bottle of champagne and fruit basket. Guests also receive a breakfast platter for each morning of their stay which they prepare at their leisure in the fully fitted kitchen in each apartment. Each apartment also includes a fridge full of complimentary mixers, fruits juices, soft drinks, beers and milk. **Open:** All year.
Nearest Shop: 0.10 miles **Nearest Pub:** 0.10 miles

Site: **P** Payment: Property: Children: Unit:

YORK, North Yorkshire   Map ref 4C1   SatNav YO1 6DH   [H]

The Queens Hotel

Queens Staith Road, Skeldergate, York YO1 6DH **T:** (01904) 611321 **F:** (01904) 611388
E: sales@queenshotel-york.com
W: www.queenshotel-york.com **£ BOOK ONLINE**

B&B PER ROOM PER NIGHT
S: £90.00 - £135.00
D: £100.00 - £150.00
EVENING MEAL PER PERSON
£10.50 - £30.00

Ideally located on the banks of the river in the heart of the city of York, The Queens Hotel offers quality accommodation for leisure, families and groups. The restaurant is open daily and serves breakfast and dinner. A warm welcome awaits you.
Bedrooms: 30 double, 33 twin, 15 family.
Open: All year.

Payment: Property: Children: Catering: Room:

YORK, North Yorkshire   Map ref 4C1   [S]

The Riverside York

Contact: Patrick Lavers, 8/8a Peckitt Street, York YO1 9SF **T:** (01904) 623008 / 07734 554755 **F:** (01904) 656588 **E:** relax@riverside-york.co.uk
W: www.riverside-york.co.uk **£ BOOK ONLINE**

Units   2
Sleeps   2-8
PER UNIT PER WEEK
£590.00 - £1390.00

Situated in the heart of historic York, our beautiful 5-star Victorian riverside townhouse and apartment offers the perfect luxury self-catering base. The Riverside House offers three double bedrooms and spacious living with Digital Freeview, DVD, Wii console and free parking. The Riverside Apartment has one large kingsize bedroom, with generous ground floor living space, bathroom and kitchen.
Open: All year. **Nearest Shop:** 300 yards **Nearest Pub:** 150 yards

Site: **P** Payment: Property: Children: Unit:

YORK, North Yorkshire   Map ref 4C1   [S]

York Lakeside Lodges

Contact: Mr Neil Manasir, Booking Enquiries, Moor Lane, York YO24 2QU
T: (01904) 702346 / 07831 885824 **E:** neil@yorklakesidelodges.co.uk
W: www.yorklakesidelodges.co.uk

Units   16
Sleeps   2-7
PER UNIT PER WEEK
£260.00 - £895.00

Lodges and cottages around a large fishing lake, in parkland yet 2 miles from the city centre with Tesco and a coach service to city centre just over the road.
Open: All year.
Nearest Shop: 0.10 miles
Nearest Pub: 0.60 miles

Site: **P** Leisure: Property: Children: Unit:

DONCASTER, South Yorkshire   Map ref 4C1

SatNav DN2 6AD H

HOTEL ★★★★
VisitEngland

B&B PER ROOM PER NIGHT
S: £65.00 - £279.00
D: £75.00 - £289.00
EVENING MEAL PER PERSON
£24.95 - £29.95

SPECIAL PROMOTIONS
For the best rates and to see our special accommodation packages please book direct at www.theearl.co.uk or call (01302) 361371

The Earl of Doncaster Hotel
The Earl of Doncaster Hotel, Bennetthorpe, Doncaster, South Yorkshire DN2 6AD
T: (01302) 361371 **F:** (01302) 321858 **E:** enquiries@theearl.co.uk
W: www.theearl.co.uk **£ BOOK ONLINE**

The Earl of Doncaster Hotel is a four star art deco property brilliantly situated within walking distance of the Doncaster Racecourse and town centre. Our Wi-Fi and secure on-site car parking is complimentary to all guests. The Hotel offers 73 individually designed bedrooms, the stylish Café Bar Concerto restaurant, two spacious function suites and a 1930's style Ballroom ideal for Weddings.

Directions: Follow the signs for Doncaster Racecourse, at the roundabout take the A638 (Bennetthorpe) towards the town centre, the Hotel is located on the left and car park is situated at the rear of the Hotel.

Bedrooms: En suite, flat screen TVs, Wi-Fi, tea & coffee facilities, desk and chair, 24 hour room service, climate control, iron & ironing board.
Open: All year.

Site: P Payment: ▣ **Leisure:** ▶ ☆ **Property:** ⊛ ⚲ ☎ ▦ ♨ ◑ **Children:** ⛄ ▥ ⚲ **Catering:** (✗ ⚑ ⛄
Room: ⚲ ⚱ ☏ 📺 ⚲ ✉

HAWORTH, West Yorkshire   Map ref 4B1

SatNav BD22 9SG B

GUEST ACCOMMODATION ★★★★
VisitEngland

B&B PER ROOM PER NIGHT
S: £55.00 - £69.00
D: £79.00 - £89.00

Leeming Wells
Long Causeway, Oxenhope, Keighley, West Yorkshire BD22 9SG **T:** (01535) 646757
F: (01535) 648992 **E:** info@leemingwells.co.uk
W: www.leemingwells.co.uk

Leeming Wells offers 4* accommodation in an amazing setting in Oxenhope, near Haworth. With beautiful en suite bedrooms you can relax in our Swimming Pool with the backdrop of Yorkshire rolling countryside. Breakfast at Dog & Gun next door.
Directions: By car: Haworth 9 minutes. Skipton Market Town 30 minutes. Bradford Alhambra Theatre 20 minutes.
Bedrooms: En suite, flat screen TV, tea/coffee and biscuit tray.
Open: All year.

Site: ✿ **P Payment:** ▣ **Leisure:** ▶ ⚲ ⚲ **Property:** ⚑ ⚲ ☎ ▦ **Children:** ⛄ ▥ **Catering:** (✗ ⚑
Room: ⚲ ⚱ ☏ 📺 ⚲

Need more information?
Visit our websites for detailed information, up-to-date availability and to book your accommodation online. Includes over 20,000 places to stay, all of them star rated.
www.visitor-guides.co.uk

Don't Miss...

Blackpool Illuminations
Sept-Nov, Blackpool
www.illuminations.visitblackpool.com
This world famous display lights up Blackpool's promenade with over 1 million glittering lights that will make you oooh and aaah in wonder. Head for the big switch on or buy tickets for the Festival Weekend. There's also Blackpool Zoo, the Pleasure Beach Resort and fabulous entertainment at the Blackpool tower. Whether you're nine or 90, there are plenty of things to do in Blackpool day and night, all year round.

Chester Zoo
Cheshire CH2 1LH
(01244) 380280
www.chesterzoo.org
Over 12000 animals and 400 different species, including some of the most exotic and endangered species on the planet in 125 acres of award-winning zoological gardens. Chester Zoo is one of the world's top zoos, and the UK's number one wildlife attraction, with over the 1.4 million visitors every year.

Jodrell Bank Discovery Centre
Macclesfield, Cheshire SK11 9DL
(01477) 571766
www.jodrellbank.net
A great day out for all the family, explore the wonders of the universe and learn about the workings of the giant Lovell Telescope. Start your visit in the Planet Pavillion by exploring our place in the universe with the clockwork Orrery. Discover how Jodrell Bank scientists use radio telescopes to learn more about distant objects in space in the Space Pavilion exhibition, listen to the sound of the Big Bang, and find out about 'Big Telescopes' via a range of hands-on activities.

Muncaster Castle
Ravenglass, Cumbria CA18 1RQ
(01229) 717614
www.muncaster.co.uk
Medieval Muncaster Castle is a treasure trove of paintings, silver, embroideries and more in acres of Grade 2 woodland gardens, famous for rhododendrons and breathtaking views of the Lake District. The Great Hall, octagonal library and elegant dining room must not be missed. Elegant rooms, historic furnishings, superb works of art, yet still a lived-in home. The audio tour, narrated by the Pennington family, whose ancestors have been at Muncaster for 8 centuries, enlivens the castle, bringing the past to the present.

Tate Liverpool
Merseyside L3 4BB
(0151) 702 7400
www.tate.org.uk/liverpool
Housing the national collection of modern art in the North in beautiful light filled galleries, Tate Liverpool is one of the largest galleries of modern and contemporary art outside London. Major exhibitions in recent years have included the work of Jackson Pollock, Andy Warhol and René Magritte. Free to visit except for special exhibitions. The Tate Liverpool café offers a range of refreshments with views of the historic Albert Dock.

North West

Cheshire, Cumbria, Lancashire, Greater Manchester, Merseyside

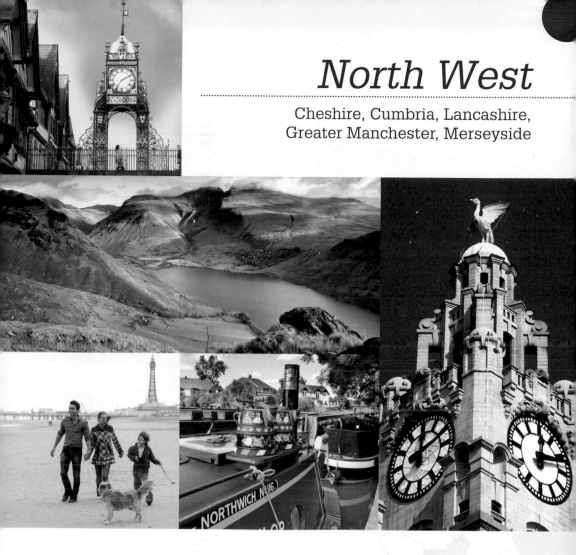

The breathtaking scenery of the Lake District captures all the attention in the North West, but urban attractions, such as cosmopolitan Manchester or Liverpool with its grand architecture and cultural credentials, have much to recommend them. Further afield, you can explore the Roman and medieval heritage of Chester, discover Lancashire's wealth of historic houses and gardens, or make a date for one of the huge variety of events that take place in this region throughout the year.

Cumbria

Lancashire

Greater Manchester

Merseyside

Cheshire

Explore – North West

Cheshire

The charms of the old walled city of Chester and the picturesque villages that dot Cheshire's countryside contrast sharply with the industrial towns of Runcorn and Warrington. Iron age forts, Roman ruins, Medieval churches, Tudor cottages and elegant Georgian and Victorian stately homes are among the many attractive sights of the county. South Cheshire, like Cumbria to the north, has long been the home of the wealthy from Manchester and Liverpool and boasts a huge selection of of excellent eateries. It also has peaceful, pretty countryside, and is within easy reach of the wilder terrain of the Peak District and North Wales.

Cumbria

In this lovely corner of England, there is beauty in breathtaking variety. The area is loved by many who come back time and again to its inspirational magic, brilliant blue lakes and craggy mountain tops. The central Lake District with its mountains, lakes and woods is so well known that there is a tendency to forget that the rest of Cumbria contains some of the most varied and attractive landscape in Britain. In the east of the county, the peaceful Eden Valley is sheltered by the towering hills of the Pennines, with charming little red sandstone villages and reminders of the Roman occupation everywhere. Alston, with its cobbled streets is the highest town in England, and has been used for numerous TV location sets.

Cumbria's long coastline is full of variety with rocky cliffs, sea birds, sandy estuaries, miles of sun-trap sand dunes and friendly harbours. In Autumn the deciduous woodlands and bracken coloured hillsides glow with colour. In Winter, the snow covered mountain tops dazzle magnificently against blue skies. In Spring, you can discover the delights of the magical, constantly changing light and the joy of finding carpets of wild flowers.

The English Lakes

The Lake District is an outdoor enthusiasts paradise offering everything from walking and climbing to orienteering, potholing, cycling, riding, golf, sailing, sailboarding, canoeing, fishing and waterskiing. A great way to take in the beauty of this unique area is to plan your own personal route on foot, or cycle one of the many formal trails such as the Cumbria Cycle Way.

The Cumbrian climate is ideal for gardens and the area is famous for the rhododendrons and azaleas which grow here in abundance.

If you fancy a break from the great outdoors there is a wealth of historic houses, from small cottages where famous writers have lived to stately homes, that have seen centuries of gracious living and architectural importance.

Lancashire

Lancashire's Forest of Bowland is an 'Area Of Outstanding Natural Beauty' with wild crags, superb walks, streams, valleys and fells.

Blackpool on the coast has been the playground of the North West for many years and still draws millions of holiday makers every year, attracted to its seven miles of beach, illuminations, Pleasure Beach Amusement Park and golf. Morecambe, Southport, Lytham St Annes and Fleetwood also offer wide beaches, golf and bracing walks.

Lancaster, a city since Roman times, has fine museums, a castle and an imitation of the Taj Mahal, the Ashton Memorial.

Manchester

Manchester's prosperity can be traced back to the 14th century when Flemish weavers arrived to transform a market town into a thriving boom city at the forefront of the Industrial Revolution.

Now known as The Capital of the North, the city is rich in culture with plenty of galleries, museums, libraries and theatres. The City Art Gallery displays its famous pre-Raphaelite collection while the Halle Orchestra regularly fills the Bridgewater Hall.

At Granada Studios you can still tour the set of Coronation Street and you can find quality shopping locations and sporting (particularly football) traditions. Cosmopolitan Manchester makes a great place to stay for a spot of retail therapy too!

Merseyside

Liverpool was an important city long before The Beatles emerged from their Cavern in the Swinging Sixties. It grew from a village into a prosperous port, where emigrants sailed for the New World and immigrants arrived from Ireland. Today the ocean going liners are fewer, but the revitalised dock complex ensures that the city is as vibrant as ever. Liverpool's waterfront regeneration flagship is the Albert Dock Village, which includes the Maritime Museum and Tate Gallery Liverpool. The city has two modern cathedrals, a symphony orchestra, plenty of museums and Britain's oldest repertory theatre The Playhouse.

In recent years, Liverpool has seen the opening of an extensive range of cafés, restaurants and accommodation to suit all tastes and budgets, as well as becoming a mecca for serious shoppers with locations such as the Metquarter and Liverpool ONE, the huge open-air shopping district that is home to more than 160 famous high street shops, cool independent boutiques, cafés and restaurants in the heart of the city centre.

Visit – North West

Cheshire

Anson Engine Museum
Macclesfield, Cheshire SK12 1TD
(01625) 874426
www.enginemuseum.org
*Recognised as one of the Country's leading
specialist museums; see exhibitions of
engines of all sizes, as well as craft demonstrations,
working machinery and local history exhibitions. A
must-see for both enthusiasts and non-enthusiasts.*

Arley Hall & Gardens
Northwich, Cheshire CW9 6NA
(01565) 777353
www.arleyhallandgardens.com
*The Gardens are outstanding for their vitality, variety
and historical interest and are particularly celebrated
for the magnificent double herbaceous border. The
Hall is an impressive example of a Victorian country
house built in the Elizabethan style.*

Catalyst Science Discovery Centre
Widnes, Cheshire WA8 0DF
(0151) 420 1121
www.catalyst.org.uk
*Interactive science centre whose aim is to make
science exciting and accessible to people of all ages.*

Chester Cathedral
Cheshire CH1 2HU
(01244) 324756
www.chestercathedral.com
*A must-see for Chester, a beautiful cathedral with a
fascinating history.*

Cholmondeley Castle Gardens
Malpas, Cheshire SY14 8AH
(01829) 720383
www.cholmondeleycastle.com
*Visitors can enjoy the tranquil Temple Water
Garden, Ruin Water Garden, memorial mosaic, Rose
garden & many mixed borders.*

Forest Live
June - July, Delamere Forest Cheshire, CW8 2JD
www.forestry.gov.uk/music
*Hosted in seven different forest venues with some
of the biggest names in the music industry.*

Go Ape! Hire Wire Forest Adventure - Delamere
Northwich, Cheshire CW8 2JD
(0333) 331 5995
www.goape.co.uk/days-out/delamere
*Take to the trees and experience an exhilarating
course of rope bridges, tarzan swings and zip slides.*

Grosvenor Park Open Air Theatre
July-August, Grosvenor Park, Chester, Cheshire
www.grosvenorparkopenairtheatre.co.uk
*The award-winning theatre is the greatest open air
theatre experience outside of London.*

Hare Hill Gardens
Macclesfield, Cheshire SK10 4PY
(01625) 584412
www.nationaltrust.org.uk/harehill
*A small but perfectly formed and tranquil woodland
garden, surrounded by parkland.*

National Waterways Museum
Ellesmere Port, Cheshire CH65 4FW
(0151) 335 5017
www.canalrivertrust.org.uk
*Unlock the wonders of our waterways, a fun and
informative day out for all ages.*

RHS Flower Show Tatton Park
July, Tatton Park, Knutsford, Cheshire WA16 6QN
www.rhs.org.uk/shows-events/rhs-flower-show-tatton-park
*A fantastic display of flora and fauna and all things
garden related in stunning Cheshire countryside.*

Wirral Folk on the Coast Festival
Whitby, Cheshire CH65 6QF
www.wirralfolkonthecoast.com
*All-on-one-site friendly festival at Whitby Sports &
Social Club, with fine music real ale and good food.*

Cumbria

Great North Swim
June, Windermere, Cumbria
www.greatswim.org
Europe's biggest open water swim series comes to the Lake District.

Grizedale Forest Visitor Centre
Hawkshead, Cumbria LA22 0QJ
(0300) 067 4495
www.forestry.gov.uk/grizedale
Grizedale Forest offers a range of activities for all ages through the year, from mountain biking to relaxing walks, Go-Ape to the sculpture trails.

Holker Hall & Gardens
Grange-over-Sands, Cumbria LA11 7PL
(01539) 558328
www.holker.co.uk
Home to Lord and Lady Cavendish, Victorian wing, glorious gardens, parkland and woodlands.

Hutton-in-the-Forest
Penrith, Cumbria CA11 9TH
(017684) 84449
www.hutton-in-the-forest.co.uk
A beautiful house surrounded by magnificent woodland of the medieval forest of Inglewood. Both the interior and exterior show a wide variety of architectural and decorative styles from the 17th century to the present day.

Museum of Lakeland Life
Kendal, Cumbria LA9 5AL
(01539) 722464
www.lakelandmuseum.org.uk
This award-winning museum takes you and your family back through time to tell the story of the Lake District and its inhabitants.

Penrith Castle
Cumbria CA11 7EA
0870 333 1181
www.english-heritage.org.uk/visit/places/penrith-castle/
The mainly 15th century remains of a castle begun by Bishop Strickland of Carlisle and developed by the Nevilles and Richard III.

Ravenglass & Eskdale Railway
Cumbria CA18 1SW
(01229) 717171
www.ravenglass-railway.co.uk
Heritage steam engines haul open-top and covered carriages from the Lake District coastal village of Ravenglass to the foot of England's highest mountains.

South Lakes Safari Zoo
Lindal-in-Furness, Cumbria LA12 0LU
(01229) 466086
www.southlakessafarizoo.com
The ultimate interactive animal experience. Get close to wildlife at Cumbria's top tourist attraction.

Ullswater Steamers
Cumbria CA11 0US
(01768) 482229
www.ullswater-steamers.co.uk
The 'Steamers' create the opportunity to combine a cruise with some of the spectacular walks in the lake District.

Windermere Lake Cruises, Lakeside
Newby Bridge, Cumbria LA12 8AS
(01539) 443360
www.windermere-lakecruises.co.uk
Steamers and launches sail daily between Ambleside, Bowness and Lakeside.

The World of Beatrix Potter
Bowness, Cumbria LA23 3BX
0844 504 1233
www.hop-skip-jump.com
A magical indoor attraction that brings to life all 23 Beatrix Potter's Peter Rabbit tales.

Lancashire

Blackpool Dance Festival
May - June, Blackpool, Lancashire
www.blackpooldancefestival.com
The world's first and foremost festival of dancing.

Blackpool Pleasure Beach
Blackpool, Lancashire FY4 1EZ
(0871) 222 1234
www.blackpoolpleasurebeach.com
The UK's most ride intensive theme park and home to the legendary Big One and Valhalla.

The Blackpool Tower
Blackpool, Lancashire FY1 4BJ
(0871) 222 9929
www.theblackpooltower.com
Built in 1894, The Blackpool Tower is one of Britain's best loved landmarks. There are plenty of experiences on offer to ensure you have an unparalleled experience.

Clitheroe Food Festival
August, Clitheroe, Lancashire
www.clitheroefoodfestival.com
Celebrating the very finest Lancashire food and drink produces. Includes chef demos, tastings and cookery workshops.

Farmer Ted's Farm Park
Ormskirk, Lancashire L39 7HW
(0151) 526 0002
www.farmerteds.com
An interactive children's activity park, sited on a working farm within the beautiful Lancashire countryside.

Garstang Walking Festival
May, Garstang, Lancashire
www.garstang.net/garstang-walking-festival
A celebration of springtime in the stunning countryside of Garstang and the surrounding area. Guided walks and activities for all the family.

Lytham Proms Festival
August, Lytham & St Annes, Lancashire
0844 888 0200
www.lytham Proms Festival
Summer proms spectacular with shows from leading performers.

Ribchester Roman Museum
Preston, Lancashire PR3 3XS
(01254) 878261
www.ribchesterromanmuseum.org
Lancashire's only specialist Roman museum, located on the North bank of the beautiful River Ribble.

Sandcastle Waterpark
Blackpool, Lancashire FY4 1BB
(01253) 343602
www.sandcastle-waterpark.co.uk
The UK's Largest Indoor Waterpark and with 18 slides and attractions.

Thornton Hall Farm Country Park
Lancashire BD23 3TS
(01282) 841148
www.thorntonhallcountrypark.co.uk
Come rain or shine, a fun filled family day out is always guaranteed at Thornton Hall Farm. Get involved with hands-on activities, make friends with the farm animals and visit the new Tearoom while the little ones burn off the remainder of their energy in the huge fun filled Wizzick Play Barn.

Wyre Estuary Country Park
Thornton Lancashire FY5 5LR
(01253) 863100
www.wyre.gov.uk
The award-winning Wyre Estuary Country Park offers year-round activities and events for all the family including ranger-led walks, environmentally themed activities and annual events like the Family Sculpture Day.

Manchester

East Lancashire Railway
Bury, Greater Manchester BL9 0EY
(0161) 764 7790
www.eastlancsrailway.org.uk
The beautifully restored East Lancashire Railway takes you on a captivating journey to discover the region's rich transport heritage.

Greater Manchester Marathon in Trafford
April, Trafford, Manchester
www.greatermanchestermarathon.com
The UK's flattest, fastest and friendliest Marathon with a superfast course, great entertainment, outstanding crowd support and glorious finish at Manchester United Football Club.

The Lowry
Pier 8, Salford Quays M50 3AZ
(0843) 208 6000
www.thelowry.com
Set in a stunning waterside location at the heart of the redeveloped Salford Quays in Greater Manchester, The Lowry is an architectural gem that brings together a wide variety of performing and visual arts, including the works of LS Lowry and contemporary exhibitions.

Manchester Art Gallery
Greater Manchester M2 3JL
(0161) 235 8888
www.manchestergalleries.org
Houses one of the country's finest art collections in spectacular Victorian and Contemporary surroundings. With changing exhibitions and a programme of events and a host of free family friendly resources.

Manchester Histories Festival
Various city centre locations
www.manchesterhistoriesfestival.org.uk
The ten-day MHF celebrates the heritage and history of Manchester across numerous city centre venues. The festival offers a fantastic opportunity to explore and learn this great city and is a great event for old and young alike.

Manchester Museum
Greater Manchester M13 9PL
(0161) 275 2648
www.manchester.ac.uk/museum
Found on Oxford Road, on The University of Manchester campus (in a very impressive gothic-style building). Highlights include Stan the T.rex, mummies, live animals such as frogs and snakes, object handling and a varied programme of events.

Manchester United Museum & Tour Centre
Greater Manchester M16 0RA
(0161) 868 8000
www.manutd.com/museum
The story of Manchester United is unlike any other club in the world. Beginning more than a century ago, it combines eras of total English and European domination. The official museum and tour offers every football fan a unique insight into Manchester United Football Club and a fantastic day out.

National Football Museum
Urbis Building, Manchester M4 3BG
0161 605 8200
www.nationalfootballmuseum.com
The world's biggest and best football museum. Drama, History, Skill, Art, Faith, Style, Passion is what we're all about at the National Football Museum. More than 140,000 football-related items plus a kids' discovery zone and skills-testing simulators.

People's History Museum
Greater Manchester M3 3ER
(0161) 838 9190
www.phm.org.uk
National centre for the collection, conservation, interpretation and study of material relating to the history of working people in Britain.

Ramsbottom Chocolate Festival
Ramsbottom, Greater Manchester
www.visitramsbottom.org/chocolatefestival.html
Two-day chocolate market, with interactive workshops, activities for adults and children, music, competitions, Giant Easter Egg display, and much more.

Saddleworth and District Whit Friday Brass Band Contest
June, Oldham, Greater Manchester
www.whitfriday.brassbands.saddleworth.org
Brass bands compete in contests at venues scattered around the moorland villages and towns on the western edge of the Pennines.

Whitworth Art Gallery
Manchester M15 6ER
(0161) 275 7450
www.manchester.ac.uk/whitworth
Home to an famous collection of British watercolours, textiles and wallpapers.

Merseyside

'Another Place' by Antony Gormley
Crosby Beach, Liverpool L23 6SX
www.antonygormley.com
100 cast-iron, life-size figures spread out along three kilometres of the foreshore on Crosby beach in Liverpool, stretching almost one kilometre out to sea. The spectacular sculptures - each one weighing 650 kilos - are made from casts of the artist's own body standing on the beach, all of them looking out to sea, staring at the horizon in silent expectation.

Beatles Story
Liverpool, Merseyside L3 4AD
(0151) 709 1963
www.beatlesstory.com
A unique visitor attraction that transports you on an enlightening and atmospheric journey into the life, times, culture and music of the Beatles.

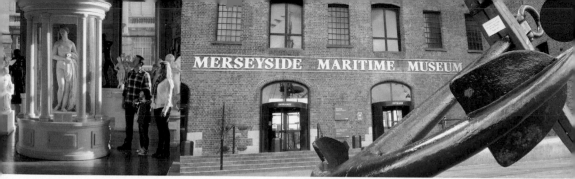

Birkenhead Festival of Transport
Birkenhead, Merseyside
www.bheadtransportfest.com
The Birkenhead Festival of Transport offers a
fantastic week-end of activities for all the family.
Featuring classic cars, steam engines and other
modes of vintage transport.

Croxteth Hall & Country Park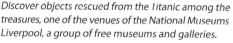
Liverpool, Merseyside L12 0HB
(0151) 233 3020
www.liverpoolcityhalls.co.uk/croxteth-hall/
Situated in a beautiful Country Park setting and one
of Liverpool's most important heritage sites. The
Country Park is also home to a real working Home
Farm, a Victorian Walled Garden and a 500 acre
nature reserve - all open to the public.

The Gallery Liverpool
Merseyside L8 5RE
(0151) 709 2442
www.thegalleryliverpool.co.uk
Set in the heart of Liverpool's Independent Cultural
District, the gallery occupies the entire upper floor of
the industrial premises of John O'Keeffe and Son Ltd.

Grand National
April, Aintree, Merseyside
www.aintree.co.uk
The most famous horse race over jumps takes place
over the challenging Aintree fences.

Knowsley Safari Park
Merseyside L34 4AN
(0151) 430 9009
www. knowsleysafariexperience.co.uk
Enjoy a 5 mile safari through 450 acres of parkland.
Find out more about the world we live in and the
role our amazing animals have to play in it

Liverpool Football Club
Merseyside L4 0TH
(0151) 260 6677
www.liverpoolfc.com
Meet an LFC Legend; get your photograph with one
of our many trophies or indulge yourself in one of our
award-winning Experience Days.

Liverpool Sound City
May, Clarence Dock, Liverpool
www.liverpoolsoundcity.co.uk
A 2-day festival of incredible live music and arts.

Mersey Ferries
Woodside Ferry Terminal, Merseyside, CH41 6DU
(0151) 330 1444
www.merseyferries.co.uk
Step aboard to see Liverpool's stunning waterfront.
The decks of the Mersey Ferry offer the best way
to see the city's world-famous skyline. Our River
Explorer Cruise takes you on a 50 minute trip where
you'll be captivated by Liverpool's fascinating history.

Merseyside Maritime Museum
Liverpool Waterfront, Liverpool L3 4AQ
www.liverpoolmuseums.org.uk/maritime
(0151) 478 4499
Discover objects rescued from the Titanic among the
treasures, one of the venues of the National Museums
Liverpool, a group of free museums and galleries.

Speke Hall, Gardens & Estate
Liverpool, Merseyside L24 1XD
(0151) 427 7231
www.nationaltrust.org.uk/spokehall
One of the most famous half timbered houses in
Britain. The Great Hall and priest hole date from Tudor
times, while the Oak Parlour and smaller rooms,
some with William Morris wallpapers, illustrates the
Victorian desire for privacy and comfort.

Walker Art Gallery
Liverpool, Merseyside L3 8EL
(0151) 478 4199
www.liverpoolmuseums.org.uk/walker
Home to outstanding works by Rubens, Rembrandt,
Poussin, Gainsborough and Hogarth, the Walker Art
Gallery is one of the finest art galleries in Europe

World Museum Liverpool
Merseyside L3 8EN
(0151) 478 4393
www.liverpoolmuseums.org.uk/wml
Extensive collections from the Amazonian Rain
Forest to the mysteries of outer space.

Tourist Information Centres

When you arrive at your destination, visit the Tourist Information Centre for quality assured help with accommodation and information about local attractions and events, or email your request before you go.

Accrington	Town Hall	01254 380293	information@leisureinhyndburn.co.uk
Alston Moor	Town Hall	01434 382244	alston.tic@eden.gov.uk
Altrincham	20 Stamford New Road	0161 912 5931	tourist.information@trafford.gov.uk
Ambleside	Central Buildings	0844 225 0544	tic@thehubofambleside.com
Appleby-in-Westmorland	Moot Hall	017683 51177	tic@applebytown.org.uk
Barnoldswick	Post Office Buildings	01282 666704 / 661661	tourist.info@pendle.gov.uk
Barrow-in-Furness	Forum 28	01229 876505	touristinfo@barrowbc.gov.uk
Blackburn	Blackburn Market	01254 688040	visit@blackburn.gov.uk
Blackpool	Festival House, Promenade	01253 478222	information@vistitblackpool.com
Bolton	Central Library Foyer	01204 334321	tourist.info@bolton.gov.uk
Bowness	Glebe Road	0845 9010 845	bownesstic@lakedistrict.gov.uk
Brampton	Moot Hall	016977 3433	bramptontic@gmail.co.uk
Broughton-in-Furness	Old Town Hall	01229 716115	broughtontic@btconnect.com
Burnley	Burnley Bus Station	01282 454086	tic@burnley.gov.uk
Bury	The Fusilier Museum	0161 253 5111	touristinformation@bury.gov.uk
Carlisle	Old Town Hall	01228 598596	tourism@carlisle.gov.uk
Chester (Town Hall)	Town Hall	01244 405340	welcome@chestervic.co.uk
Clitheroe	Platform Gallery & VIC	01200 425566	tourism@ribblevalley.gov.uk
Cockermouth	4 Old Kings Arms Lane	01900 822634	cockermouthtouristinformationcentre@btconnect.com
Congleton	Town Hall	01260 271095	congletontic@cheshireeast.gov.uk
Coniston	Ruskin Avenue	015394 41533	mail@conistontic.org
Egremont	12 Main Street	01946 820693	lowescourt@btconnect.com
Ellesmere Port	McArthur Glen Outlet Village	0151 356 5562	visitorinformation@cheshireoakdesigneroutlet.com

Garstang	1 Cherestanc Square	01995 602125	garstangtic@wyre.gov.uk
Glennridding Ullswater	Bekside Car Park	017684 82414	ullswatertic@lakedistrict.gov.uk
Grange-Over-Sands	Victoria Hall	015395 34026	informationcentre@grangeoversands.net
Kendal	Made in Cumbria	01539 735891	info@kendaltic.com
Keswick	Market Square	0845 901 0845	keswicktic@lakedistrict.gov.uk
Kirkby Stephen	Market Street	017683 71199	ks.tic@eden.gov.uk
Lancaster	The Storey	01524 582394	lancastervic@lancaster.gov.uk
Liverpool Albert Dock	Anchor Courtyard	0151 233 2008	liverpoolvisitorcentre@liverpool.gov.uk
Liverpool John Lennon Airport	Information Desk	0151 233 2008	liverpoolvisitorcentre@liverpool.gov.uk
Lytham St Annes	c/o Town Hall	01253 658443	touristinformation@fylde.gov.uk
Macclesfield	Town Hall	01625 378123	macclesfieldtic@cheshireeast.gov.uk
Manchester	1 Piccadilly Gardens	0871 222 8223	touristinformation@visitmanchester.com
Maryport	The Wave Centre	01900 811450	info@thewavemaryport.co.uk
Millom	Station Building	01229 774819	millomtic@copelandbc.gov.uk
Morecambe	Old Station Buildings	01524 582808	morecambevic@lancaster.gov.uk
Nantwich	Civic Hall	01270 628633	tourist.information @nantwichtowncouncil.gov.uk
Northwich	Information Centre	0300 123 8123	infocentrenorthwich@ cheshirewestandchester.gov.uk
Oldham	Oldham Library	0161 770 8035	tourist@oldham.gov.uk
Pendle	Boundary Mill Stores	01282 856186	discoverpendle@pendle.gov.uk
Pendle	Park Hill	01282 677150	heritage.centre@pendle.gov.uk
Penrith	Middlegate	01768 867466	pen.tic@eden.gov.uk
Preston	Town Hall	01772 253731	tourism@preston.gov.uk
Rheged	Redhills	01768 868000	tic@rheged.com
Rochdale	Touchstones	01706 924928	tic@link4life.org
Rossendale	Rawtenstall Queens Square	01706 217777	tourism@rossendalebc.gov.uk
Saddleworth	Saddleworth Museum	01457 870336	ecs.saddleworthtic@oldham.gov.uk
Sedbergh	72 Main Street	015396 20125	tic@sedbergh.org.uk
Silloth-on-Solway	Solway Coast Discovery Centre	016973 31944	sillothtic@allerdale.gov.uk
Southport	112 Lord Street	01704 533333	info@visitsouthport.com
Stockport	Staircase House	0161 474 4444	tourist.information@stockport.gov.uk
Ulverston	Coronation Hall	0845 642 6480	info@visitulverston.com
Windermere	Victoria Street	015394 46499	Info@windermereinfo.co.uk

Regional Contacts and Information

For more information on accommodation, attractions, activities, events and holidays in North West England, contact one of the following regional or local tourism organisations. Their websites have a wealth of information and many produce free publications to help you get the most out of your visit.

Visit Chester
www.visitchester.com

Cumbria Tourism
T (01539) 822 222
E info@cumbriatourism.org
www.cumbriatourism.org

Visit Lancashire
T (01772) 426450
E info@visitlancashire.com
www.visitlancashire.com

Visit Manchester
T (0871) 222 8223
E touristinformation@visitmanchester.com
www.visitmanchester.com

Visit Liverpool
T (0151) 233 2008
E liverpoolvisitorcentre@liverpool.gov.uk
www.visitliverpool.com

Stay – North West

Entries appear alphabetically by town name in each county. A key to symbols appears on page 6

CHESTER, Cheshire Map ref 4A2
SatNav 28CH4 8JQ **B**

VisitEngland ★★★★★ GUEST HOUSE
VisitEngland Gold AWARD

Mitchell's of Chester Guest House

28 Hough Green, Chester CH4 8JQ **T:** (01244) 679004
E: welcome@mitchellsofchester.com
W: www.mitchellsofchester.com **£ BOOK ONLINE**

B&B PER ROOM PER NIGHT
S: £70.00 - £110.00
D: £94.00 - £110.00

Highly recommended by good guides. Relax in this tastefully restored Victorian residence with rooms having hospitality tray, clock/radio, TV, free Wi-Fi, hairdryer and many other comforts. Easy 20 minutes walking to city. Off-road car park. **Directions:** Leave south side of Chester on A483, turn right on to A5104 (Saltney). This is Hough Green. We are 300m along on the right.
Bedrooms: 3 doubles en suite. Can be let as singles.
Open: All year except Christmas and New Year.

Site: P Payment: Leisure: Property: Catering: Room:

MACCLESFIELD, Cheshire Map ref 4B2
S

VisitEngland ★★★★ SELF CATERING

Cheshire Hunt Holiday Cottages

Contact: Mrs Anne Gregory, Owner, Cheshire Hunt Holiday Cottages, Hedge Row, Off Spuley Lane, Rainow, Macclesfield, Cheshire SK10 5DA **T:** (01625) 572034 / 07506 825480 **E:** enquiries@cheshirehuntholidaycottages.co.uk
W: www.cheshirehuntholidaycottages.co.uk

Units   2
Sleeps   2-11
PER UNIT PER WEEK
£595.00 - £890.00

Situated on a small track which winds through a valley, each cottage has its own unique character and both enjoy wonderful views over open countryside but are within walking distance of the local village and amenities. Both cottages have separate facilities and share the use of a games room. There is also the flexibility of hiring both properties for extended family holidays and weddings.
Open: All year. **Nearest Shop:** 1 mile **Nearest Pub:** 0.5 miles

Site: P Leisure: Property: Children: Unit:

MACCLESFIELD, Cheshire Map ref 4B2
S

VisitEngland ★★★ SELF CATERING

Mill House Farm Cottage

Contact: Mrs Lynne Whittaker, Mill House Farm Cottage, Mill House Farm, Bosley, Macclesfield, Cheshire SK11 0NZ **T:** (01260) 226265 / 07773 451448
E: lynne_whittaker@yahoo.co.uk **W:** www.millhousebosley.co.uk

Units   1
Sleeps   6
PER UNIT PER WEEK
£190.00 - £320.00

A spacious, comfortable cottage on the edge of the Peak District ideally situated for Manchester Airport, Jodrell Bank, The Potteries, Alton Towers, and numerous National Trust properties. It is attached to the farmhouse which is category 2 listed. There is ample parking, a large front garden, and wild garden with pond where ducks and chucks wander freely. We have approximately 50 cattle of all ages. **Open:** All year except Christmas and New Year.
Nearest Shop: 5 miles **Nearest Pub:** 0.5 miles

Site: P Property: Children: Unit: BBQ

AMBLESIDE, Cumbria *Map ref 5A3* — SatNav LA22 0BH **B**

Churchill Inn

33 Lake Road, Ambleside, Cumbria LA22 0BH **T:** (01539) 433192 **F:** (01539) 434900
E: info@churchillinn.co.uk
W: www.churchillinn.co.uk **£ BOOK ONLINE**

SPECIAL PROMOTIONS
Book by telephone for
best rates.

The Churchill Inn is situated at the heart of the picturesque South Lakeland town of Ambleside. Charming shops, cafés and galleries are nestled around the Inn. Come and enjoy walking the local fells, sailing on Windermere or just relax and soak up the atmosphere of Ambleside and the surrounding area. To make your stay as comfortable as possible, all of our rooms have en suite bathroom, tea/coffee making facilities, LCD television with multiple channels and free Wi-Fi. We welcome all visitors equally; however, we do not accept bookings from Hen or Stag parties. Parking in Ambleside or any town centre is of a premium and the Churchill Inn is unique in that regard, having its own car park. Parking is available on a first come first served basis; there are numerous car parks within a 5 minute walk of the inn.

Directions: Leave the M6 at J36, Ambleside approx 18 miles. Go past Market Place on to Lake Road. The Churchill Inn is on the right immediately after Church Street.

Bedrooms: 16 rooms, all recently refurbished to a high standard, many with wonderful scenic views of the local fells.
Open: Please contact for details.

Site: P Property: ▦ Children: ❧ Catering: ⟨✗ ⟡ Room: ♨ 📺 ⚲

AMBLESIDE, Cumbria *Map ref 5A3* **S**

The Lakelands

Contact: Janine Wagstaff, Site Coordinator, Lower Gale, Ambleside, Cumbria LA22 0BD
T: (015394) 33777 **E:** admin@resort-solutions.co.uk
W: www.the-lakelands.com

Sleeps   2-8

PER UNIT PER WEEK
£270.00 - £1500.00

The Lakelands is a prestigious development offering a variety of self-catering holiday accommodation in the heart of the Lake District. The 1 & 2 bedroom apartments and two 4 bedroom detached houses are situated in a unique position overlooking the popular town of Ambleside offering superb, unspoilt views of the town, Lakeland countryside and the fells beyond.

Ambleside offers an excellent selection of shops, restaurants and friendly inns. Walkers are spoilt for choice with a number of pathways directly accessed from the town.
To make reservations call (01858) 431160 and quote VBLAK17.

Open: All year.

Units: Designed and furnished to a high standard, 1 and 2 bedroom apartments and 2 four bedroom houses, all self contained and fully-equipped.

Site: ✿ P Payment: 🖭 Leisure: ⚶ Property: ▦ 🖲 🖫 Children: ❧ ♨ ⚹ Unit: 🖫 ▣ ⚲ 📺 📼

The Hollies

Roman Road, Appleby in Westmorland, Cumbria CA16 6JH T: (01768) 352553
E: stay@theholliesappleby.co.uk
W: www.TheHolliesAppleby.co.uk £ BOOK ONLINE

B&B PER ROOM PER NIGHT
S: £45.00 - £58.00
D: £75.00 - £88.00

SPECIAL PROMOTIONS
10% discount to
walkers & cyclists.

Blending homely Victorian elegance with modern facilities and 'green' credentials. Situated in the historic county town of Appleby between The Lakes & The Dales we provide the perfect base to explore by foot cycle or car. A relaxing base within 3 acres of woodland & wild flowers. Start your day with our locally sourced Westmorland breakfast.

1 dog per room welcome. Boot room & secure cycle store.

Directions: M6J40 - A66 - Appleby exit keep right at T-Junction. Roman Road, turn right. We are 1/2 mile on left. A66 East or M6 Junction 38 - From Appleby centre, turn right past station, at T-Junction. Turn left under A66. We are 1/4 mile on right.

Bedrooms: Large en suite with power shower. Free-view TV. Hospitality tray with tea, filter coffee & fresh milk. Pocket sprung beds, quality linen & towels.
Open: All year.

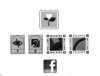

Site: ❀ P Leisure: ⚐ Property: 🐕 🚃 Children: 🧍 Catering: 🍴 Room: 🕾 ♿ 📺

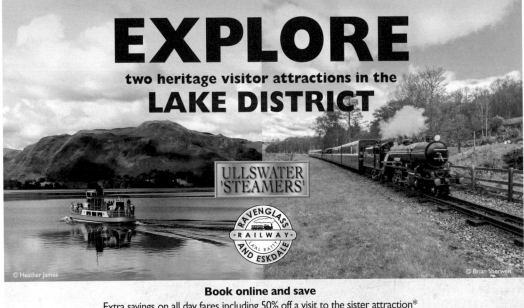

APPLEBY-IN-WESTMORLAND, *Cumbria*   *Map ref 5B3*   *SatNav CA16 6EJ* C

Wild Rose Park

VisitEngland ★★★★★ HOLIDAY, TOURING & CAMPING PARK

Ormside, Appleby-in-Westmorland CA16 6EJ
T: (017683) 51077 **F:** (017683) 52551 **E:** reception@wildrose.co.uk
W: www.harrisonholidays.com **£ BOOK ONLINE**

£15.00-£40.00
£15.00-£40.00
(25) £199.00-£619.00
250 touring pitches

Friendly, family park in the lovely, unspoilt Eden Valley with mountain views. Within easy reach of the Lakes and the Dales. Five star touring and motorhome pitches. This park also offers luxury static accommodation and glamping pods.
Directions: Please contact us for Directions.
Open: All year.

Site: **Payment:** **Leisure:** **Children:** **Catering:** **Park:** **Touring:**

BORROWDALE, *Cumbria*   *Map ref 5A3*   S

Over Brandelhow

VisitEngland ★★★★ SELF CATERING
VisitEngland Gold AWARD

Contact: Kath Manners, T manners & Sons Ltd, 2 Dovecote Hill, South Church Enterprise Park, Bishop Auckland, Co. Durham DL14 6XW **T:** 07711 592156
E: info@overbrandelhow.com **W:** www.overbrandelhow.com

Units 1
Sleeps 6
PER UNIT PER WEEK
£550.00 - £1065.00

The views down the Borrowdale valley from the cottage must be some of the best in the area. The location is so peaceful and has great walks from the doorstep. The cottage benefits from a very social open plan living area and the use of natural materials. There is a terrace for alfresco dining and from there is a view of the lake.
Open: All year.
Nearest Shop: 4 miles
Nearest Pub: 2 miles

Site: **P Property:** **Children:** **Unit:** **BBQ**

BOWNESS-ON-WINDERMERE, *Cumbria*   *Map ref 5A3*   S

Burnside Park

VisitEngland ★★★★ SELF CATERING

Contact: Lisa Holden, Resort Manager, Hapimag Resorts & Residences UK Ltd, The Lodge, Burnside Park, Kendal Road, Bowness-on-Windermere LA23 3EW
T: (01539) 446624 **F:** (01539) 447754 **E:** bowness@hapimag.com
W: www.burnsidepark.co.uk **£ BOOK ONLINE**

Units 46
Sleeps 2-6

PER UNIT PER WEEK
£460.00 - £1180.00

SPECIAL PROMOTIONS
Short breaks are available throughout the year starting from £240 for minimum 2 nights in a sleep 4.

Luxury self catering apartments 300m from Lake Windermere and Bowness centre. Sleeping 2-6 guests. Your stay here includes use of the leisure facilities at the Burnside Hotel Spa. Complimentary Wi-Fi. Our apartments are let on a weekly basis Saturday to Saturday, short breaks available on a minimum 2 night stay.

Open: All year.
Nearest Shop: 0.5 miles
Nearest Pub: 0.5 miles

Units: 2 room apartments have a double bedroom en suite & a twin bedroom with a separate shower room & the 1 room apartments have a double room & bathroom.

Site: **P Payment:** **Leisure:** **Property:** **Children:** **Unit:**

CARLISLE, Cumbria Map ref 5A2   **S**

3★ - 5★ SELF CATERING

Gold AWARD

Units 2
Sleeps 2-16
PER UNIT PER WEEK
£721.00 - £3090.00

Brackenhill Tower & Jacobean Cottage

Contact: Mrs Jan Ritchie, Manageress, Brackenhill Estates, Brackenhill, Longtown, Carlisle, Cumbria CA6 5TU **T:** (01461) 800285 / 07779 138 694
E: enquiries@brackenhilltower.co.uk **W:** www.brackenhilltower.co.uk **£ BOOK ONLINE**

A 16th century castle with the wow factor! Stated luxury and comfort in a real historic landmark of character and authentic clan Graham Reiver stronghold.
Now with a Jacuzzi with in the grounds.
Nearest Shop: Longtown
Nearest Pub: Longtown

Site: ❀ P Payment: 💳 Property: 📺 📶 🛁 Children: 👶 🛏 👶 Unit: 🛏 🍴 💻 🧺 📶 📺 📀 BBQ 📞

CARLISLE, Cumbria Map ref 5A2   SatNav CA1 1HR   **B**

VisitEngland

★★★★ GUEST HOUSE

Langleigh House

6 Howard Place, Carlisle, Cumbria CA1 1HR **T:** (01228) 530440 **E:** langleighhouse@aol.com
W: www.langleighhouse.co.uk **£ BOOK ONLINE**

Situated in a quiet conservation area with private car park, just five minutes' walk from the city centre. The city offers excellent road, rail and bus services. This delightful period property dressed tastefully in Victorian style has been awarded the prestigious TripAdvisor 2016 "Certificate of Excellence". Be assured of a warm and friendly welcome. We look forward to greeting you.

Directions: Junction 43 off the M6. Drive along Warwick Road and we are the third turning on the right after St. Aidans church.

Bedrooms: Free Wi-Fi, Flat screen TV's, welcome tray.
Open: All year except Christmas and New Year.

Site: ❀ P Payment: 💳 Leisure: 🚲 ⛳ Property: 📺 🛁 Children: 👶 🛏 👶 Catering: ⊘✗ 🍴
Room: 📶 🛁 📺 🍴

CARLISLE, Cumbria Map ref 5A2   **S**

★★★★★ SELF CATERING

Gold AWARD

Units 8
Sleeps 2-6
PER UNIT PER WEEK
£659.00 - £1400.00

The Tranquil Otter

Contact: Nick & Tazeem, The Tranquil Otter, The Lough, Thurstonfield, Carlisle, Cumbria CA5 6HB **T:** (01228) 576661 **E:** info@thetranquilotter.co.uk
W: www.thetranquilotter.co.uk **£ BOOK ONLINE**

Experience the tranquillity of living next to a lake in rural Cumbria. Our five star lodges are perfect for couples, families & friends. Each lodge is beautifully equipped with log fire, hot tub, boat & Wi-Fi. Close to the Lake District and Hadrian's Wall. Explore the surrounding woodlands or enjoy the lake by boat. Pets welcome by arrangement. Early booking is recommended.
Open: All year except two weeks in January.
Nearest Shop: 2 Miles **Nearest Pub:** 2 Miles

Site: ❀ P Payment: 💳 Leisure: 🚲 ⛳ Property: 🐾 📺 🛁 Children: 👶 🛏 👶 Unit: 🛏 🍴 💻
📶 📺 📀 🍴 BBQ

CLIFTON, Cumbria   Map ref 5B2   SatNav CA10 2ER B

**** INN

B&B PER ROOM PER NIGHT
S: £85.00 - £119.00
D: £95.00 - £160.00
EVENING MEAL PER PERSON
£13.50 - £25.00

George and Dragon

Clifton, Penrith, Cumbria CA10 2ER **T:** (01768) 865381
E: enquiries@georgeanddragonclifton.co.uk
W: www.georgeanddragonclifton.co.uk **£ BOOK ONLINE**

The George and Dragon is a stylish and welcoming country inn with a lovely restaurant, cosy bar and 11 elegant yet comfortable en suite bedrooms. A great foodie destination where the menu changes seasonally and the specials daily. **Directions:** Just a few miles from Penrith and junction 40 of the M6 in Clifton village. By direct train, Penrith is just three hours from London.
Bedrooms: En suite, flat screen TV, bath or shower.
Open: All year (closed on Boxing Day).

Site: ❀ P Payment: 🖃 Leisure: ♪ Property: 🐾 🖨 🏠 Children: 🧸 🛏 🚶
Catering: (✗ 🍽 🍴 Room: 🍵 🔌 📺 📀

GRANGE-OVER-SANDS, Cumbria   Map ref 5A3   SatNav LA11 7HQ H

★★ HOTEL   Gold AWARD

B&B PER ROOM PER NIGHT
S: £74.50 - £82.00
D: £149.00 - £164.00
EVENING MEAL PER PERSON
£20.00 - £40.00

SPECIAL PROMOTIONS
Early-season terms
avialable in Spring.
Special 3 and 4-day
breaks available all
season.

Clare House

Park Road, Grange-over-Sands, Cumbria LA11 7HQ **T:** (015395) 33026
E: info@clarehousehotel.co.uk
W: www.clarehousehotel.co.uk

Charming hotel in its own grounds, with well-appointed bedrooms, pleasant lounges and superb bay views, offering peaceful holidays to those who wish to relax and be looked after. Delightful meals, prepared with care and pride from fresh local produce, will add greatly to the enjoyment of your stay.

AA 2 RED STAR, AA ROSETTE FOR MEALS AND INSPECTORS CHOICE HOTEL.

Directions: From M6 junction 36 follow A590 through Grange, keep alongside sea. Clare House is on Park Road next to bandstand, between sea and road.

Bedrooms: 3 single rooms, 4 double rooms and 11 twin rooms all en suite with flat screen TV and tea and coffee making facilities.
Open: Mid-March to Mid-December.

Site: ❀ P Payment: 🖃 Property: 🖨 🏠 ⌀ Children: 🧸 Catering: (✗ 🍽 🍴 Room: 🍵 ♨ 🔌 📺 🛗

For **key to symbols** see page 6

Cumbria Grand Hotel

Lindale Road, Grange-over-Sands, Cumbria LA11 6EN **T:** (01539) 532331
F: (01539) 534534 **E:** salescumbria@strathmorehotels.com
W: www.strathmorehotels.com **£ BOOK ONLINE**

B&B PER ROOM PER NIGHT
S: £40.00 - £100.00
D: £60.00 - £150.00

HB PER PERSON PER NIGHT
£50.00 - £120.00

SPECIAL PROMOTIONS
Free child places 0-4 years. Half-price 5-14 years. Christmas and New Year breaks available. Special last minute breaks. See website.

Set in 20 acres of private gardens and woodlands, overlooking the stunning Morecambe Bay; you will receive a warm & friendly welcome at this charming Victorian hotel. Only a short drive from Lake Windermere, there is much to see and do in the beautiful surrounding area.

Directions: By car: 15 minutes from the M6. By train: connections to Grange-over-Sands station from London, Birmingham, Leeds, Glasgow and Edinburgh.

Bedrooms: 14 single, 31 double, 66 twin, 10 family, 3 suite. Bay view room upgrades available.
Open: All year.

Site: ❀ **Payment:** 🖼 **Leisure:** ♪ ► ∪ ✎ **Property:** 🐕 🐾 🖵 ◐ **Children:** 🧺 🎠 🎎 **Catering:** ♟ 🍴
Room: 🛁 📞 🕒 📺 ⚙ ✂

Greaves Farm Caravan Park

c/o Nether Edge, Field Broughton, Grange-over-Sands, Cumbria LA11 6HR
T: (01539) 536587 **E:** info@greavesfarmcaravanpark.co.uk
W: www.greavesfarmcaravanpark.co.uk

🚐 (10)	£18.00-£22.00
🚚 (10)	£18.00-£22.00
⚊ (10)	£16.00-£20.00
🏠 (2)	£250.00-£480.00

20 touring pitches

Small quiet park in pleasant rural location 2.8m north of Cartmel. Family owned and supervised. Ideal base for exploring the South Lakes within easy reach of Windermere, Kendal, Furness Peninsula and Morecambe Bay. Conveniently situated for many places of interest and easy walks on the lower fells. Two well-equipped 4 berth luxury holiday caravans for hire. Spacious touring and camping park, level grass tent pitches in 4 acre meadow, hard standings and electric hook ups (6amp) available, indoor washing up facilities.

Directions: Exit 36 off M6. Follow A590 signed Barrow. After Meathop roundabout continue on A590 for further 4.5miles, just after end of dual carriageway take left hand road signed Cartmel and Holker. Continue 1.5m. Site is signed.

Open: Early March to End October.

Payment: ☀ **Leisure:** ♪ ► ∪ **Children:** 🧺 **Park:** 🐾 🎈 🏠 **Touring:** 🚐 🅿 🚙

HIGH LORTON, *Cumbria* Map ref 5A3 [S]

VisitEngland ★★★★★ SELF CATERING

Holemire Barn Cottage

Contact: Mrs Angela Fearfield, Holemire Barn, c/o Holemire House, High Lorton, Cockermouth CA13 9TX **T:** (01900) 85225 **E:** enquiries@lakelandbarn.co.uk
W: www.lakelandbarn.co.uk **£ BOOK ONLINE**

Traditional Lakeland barn with exposed beams, converted to high quality accommodation. Close to Keswick. Warm, light and sunny. In superb walking country. Ospreys nesting close by. Red squirrels in garden.
Open: All year.
Nearest Shop: 0.25 miles
Nearest Pub: 0.25 miles

Units 1
Sleeps 2
PER UNIT PER WEEK
£400.00 - £500.00

Site: ✿ P Leisure: ⚘ ♪ ▶ ♾ Property: 🖥 🖨 Unit: 🗄 🖳 🗄 🗄 📺 🎦 📀

KENDAL, *Cumbria* Map ref 5B3 SatNav LA9 4JW [B]

VisitEngland ★★★★ GUEST ACCOMMODATION

Hillside Bed & Breakfast

4 Beast Banks, Kendal, Cumbria LA9 4JW **T:** (01539) 722836 **E:** info@hillside-kendal.co.uk
W: www.hillside-kendal.co.uk **£ BOOK ONLINE**

A warm welcome awaits you at this 4 Star B&B, just 2 minutes walk to town centre. Located in a quiet conservation area, close to golf course, Brewery Arts Centre, museums, restaurants and shops. Ideally placed to explore the Lakes and Dales.
Directions: 10 minutes drive from M6 motorway, within easy walking distance to Kendal train and bus stations.
Bedrooms: En suite, LCD TV, free Wi-Fi and hospitality tray.
Open: All year.

B&B PER ROOM PER NIGHT
S: £38.00 - £45.00
D: £66.00 - £85.00

[f]

Site: P Payment: 💳 Leisure: ▶ Property: ⌂ Catering: 🍽 Room: ☎ ♨ 📺

KENDAL, *Cumbria* Map ref 5B3 [S]

VisitEngland ★★★★ SELF CATERING

Shaw End Mansion

Contact: Mr & Mrs Edward & Karlyn Robinson, Shaw End Holidays, Haveriggs Farm, Whinfell, Kendal LA8 9EF **T:** (01539) 824220 / 07778 596863 **F:** (01539) 824220
E: info@shawend.co.uk **W:** www.shawend.co.uk **£ BOOK ONLINE**

Shaw End Mansion is set on 200 acres of farm and woodland in a beautiful location. A restored Georgian house that contains spacious and elegant apartments with fantastic views and walks from the doorstep. Why not rent the whole house, which is ideal for weddings and parties.
Open: All year.
Nearest Shop: 3 miles
Nearest Pub: 3 miles

Units 4
Sleeps 2-18
PER UNIT PER WEEK
£285.00 - £510.00

[f] [t]

Site: ✿ P Payment: 💳 Leisure: ♪ ♾ Property: ⌂ 🖥 🖨 Children: ⛰ 🍽 ⚘ Unit: 🗄 🖳 🖳 🗄 📺 🎦 📀 ✎

KENDAL, *Cumbria* Map ref 5B3 SatNav LA7 7NN [C]

VisitEngland ★★★★ HOLIDAY, TOURING & CAMPING PARK

Waters Edge Caravan Park

Crooklands, Kendal, Cumbria LA7 7NN
T: (01539) 567708 **E:** stay@watersedgecaravanpark.co.uk
W: www.watersedgecaravanpark.co.uk

🚐 (26) £17.90-£25.90
🚍 (26) £17.90-£25.90
⛺ (6) £10.00-£27.50
26 touring pitches

Friendly site in open countryside. Lake District, Morecambe and Yorkshire Dales nearby. All hardstanding pitches. Lounge, bar, pool room and patio area. Shower block with laundry. Local pub/restaurant within 300 yards. Overnight holding area available.
Directions: Leave M6 at junction 36, take A65 toward Kirkby Lonsdale for approx. 100 yards, then left on A65 toward Crooklands. Site approx 1 mile on the right.
Open: 1st March to 14th November.

Site: 📷 A🅿 Payment: 💳 ☼ Leisure: ♪ ▶ ♾ ⚲ Children: ⛰ Catering: 🍽 Park: 🐾 ⌂ 🖨 🅿 Touring: 🚰 ⟳ 🚐

KESWICK, Cumbria   Map ref 5A3 | SatNav CA12 4DH   **B**

VisitEngland
★★★★
GUEST HOUSE

B&B PER ROOM PER NIGHT
S: £45.00
D: £35.00 - £40.00

Charnwood Guest House

6 Eskin Street, Keswick CA12 4DH **T:** (01768) 774111 **E:** sue.banister@gmail.com
W: www.charnwoodkeswick.co.uk

Elegant listed building. Close to lake and fells and in a quiet street.
A warm welcome and really good food can be found at Charnwood.
We cater for vegetarians.
Directions: From A66 join the A591 to town centre and before the
traffic lights turn left into Greta Street which leads to Eskin Street.
Bedrooms: 2 double, 3 family.
Open: All year except Christmas.

Payment: 📧 Property: 🛏 Children: 👶5 Catering: 🍴 Room: 🔌 🚿 📶 📺 🛁 🛏 ✎

KESWICK, Cumbria   Map ref 5A3 | **S**

VisitEngland
★★★★
SELF CATERING

Units   2
Sleeps   2-5

PER UNIT PER WEEK
£385.00 - £495.00

SPECIAL PROMOTIONS
Short breaks available.
Minimum stay 3 nights.
Please contact for
information.

Peter House Cottages

Contact: Cerita Trafford, Owners, Peter House Farm, Bassenthwaite, Keswick, Cumbria
CA12 4QX **T:** (01768) 776018 / 07743 898729 **E:** info@peterhousecottages.co.uk
W: www.peterhousecottages.co.uk **£ BOOK ONLINE**

Peterhouse cottage and Pembroke cottage are situated on a lakeland hill farm with wonderful
scenery. Situated in a peaceful location at the foot of Skiddaw, with Dash Falls, Ullock Pike and
Binsey literally on the doorstep.

Close by is the village of Bassenthwaite and the market town of Keswick. The cottages are spacious,
comfortable and well equipped and are an ideal base for either walking, cycling or relaxing.
Private off road parking.

Open: March to December.
Nearest Shop: 2 mile
Nearest Pub: 2 mile

Units: Both cottages have two bedrooms
sleeping 5 and 4, electric hob/ovens, microwave,
kettle, toaster, fridge/freezer. Linen, towels &
heating inclusive. Electric showers over bath,
toilet & wash basin. TV/DVD player and electric
storage heating.

Site: ✿ P Leisure: ▶ Property: 🐾 🚭 🖼 Children: 🚼 🏢 ⚲ Unit: 🎱 🔲 🖥 🔌 📺 📀 ∅

KIRKBY LONSDALE, Cumbria   Map ref 5B3 | SatNav LA6 2AU   **B**

VisitEngland
★★
GUEST
ACCOMMODATION

B&B PER ROOM PER NIGHT
S: £35.00 - £40.00
D: £57.00 - £67.00
EVENING MEAL PER PERSON
£10.00 - £12.00

Copper Kettle Restaurant & Guest House

3-5 Market Street, Kirkby Lonsdale LA6 2AU **T:** (015242) 71714 **F:** (015242) 71714
E: gamble_p@btconnect.com

Building was built in 1610-1640. Lovely restaurant on site. In town
there is Ruskin's View with the river and Devil's Bridge. Lots of good
walking and plenty of shops and pubs in the nearby town. Prices
include breakfast.
Directions: M6, exit 36, follow road for 5 miles. Turn into Kirkby
Lonsdale on Market Street.
Bedrooms: 2 single, 3 double, 3 twin, 2 family.
Open: All year.

Site: P Payment: 📧 € Leisure: 🎵 ▶ Property: 🐾 Children: 🚼 🏢 ⚲ Catering: 🍷 🍴 Room: 🚿 📶 📺

KIRKBY LONSDALE, Cumbria   Map ref 5B3

VisitEngland ★★★★★ HOLIDAY, TOURING & CAMPING PARK

Woodclose Park
Chapel House Lane, High Casterton, Kirkby Lonsdale LA6 2SE
T: (01524) 271597 **F:** (01524) 272301 **E:** info@woodclosepark.com
W: www.woodclosepark.com **£ BOOK ONLINE**

🚐 (33)
🚛 (33)
⛺ (10)
54 touring pitches

Award-winning park within the Yorkshire Dales National Park and easy distance to the Lake District. Ten minutes walk to award winning Kirkby Lonsdale with its array of award winning pubs/tearooms. Touring, Wigwams, S/C Flats & Holiday Homes
Directions: M6 junction 36, follow A65 for approx 6 miles.
The park entrance can be found just past Kirkby Lonsdale on the left-hand side, up the hill.
Open: 1st March to 31st October. Holiday Homes until 1st January.

Site: ✿ ▲🔲 Payment: 💷 ☼ Leisure: 🚴 ♪ ▶ Children: 🐾 🎢 Catering: 🍴 Park: 🐕 🚃 🗃 📶 ⟲ 🏌
Touring: 🚰 🕐 🚐

LONGSLEDDALE, Cumbria   Map ref 5B3

VisitEngland ★★★ SELF CATERING

The Coach House
Contact: Jenny Farmer, The Coach House, c/o Capplebarrow House, Kendal, Longsleddale, Cumbria LA8 9BB **T:** (01539) 823686 **E:** jenyfarmer@aol.com
W: www.capplebarrowcoachhouse.co.uk **£ BOOK ONLINE**

Units   1
Sleeps   1 2
PER UNIT PER WEEK
£160.00 - £300.00

Stone-built, converted coach house with ground-floor shower room, bedroom and open staircase to first-floor kitchen and lounge. Excellent views. Located in peaceful, picturesque valley. Log burner and super-king bed. Pets welcome.
Open: All year.
Nearest Shop: 6 miles
Nearest Pub: 7 miles

Site: ✿ P Property: 🐾 🚃 🗃 🗝 Children: 🐾 ‖‖ 🧍 Unit: 🖥 📺 📶 📀 ⟲ BBQ

NEWBY BRIDGE, Cumbria   Map ref 5A3

VisitEngland ★★★★★ HOLIDAY PARK

Newby Bridge Country Caravan Park
Contact: Canny Hill, Newby Bridge, Windermere, Cumbria LA12 8NF **T:** (015395) 31030
E: newbybridge@lakedistrictestates.co.uk
W: www.newbybridgepark.co.uk **£ BOOK ONLINE**

Units   8
Sleeps   2-6
PER UNIT PER WEEK
£275.00 - £675.00

The Park is surrounded by woodland with excellent facilities and easy access to a variety of walking and cycling areas. Water based activities, restaurants, inns and local visitor attractions nearby. Located near the Southern shore of Windermere in the Lake District National Park and the ancient village of Cartmel. Self catering units for short and weekly lets. Fully accessible unit available.
Open: 1st March to Mid November.
Nearest Shop: 0.1 **Nearest Pub:** 1

Site: P Payment: 💷 € Leisure: ♪ ▶ ⟲ Property: ⫻ 🐕 🗃 🗝 🍴 Children: 🐾 ‖‖ 🧍 Unit: 🗃 🖥 📺 📀

PENRITH, Cumbria   Map ref 5B2

VisitEngland ★★★★★ HOLIDAY &

Flusco Wood
Flusco, Penrith CA11 0JB
T: (01768) 480020 **E:** info@fluscowood.co.uk
W: www.fluscowood.co.uk

🚐 (26)   £21.00-£24.00
🚛 (10)   £21.00-£24.00
36 touring pitches

A high-standard, quiet woodland touring caravan park with fully serviced pitches and centrally heated amenity building. Short drive to many attractions and places of interest in the Lake District. Overnight holding area available.
Directions: M6 junction 40, travel west on A66 towards Keswick. After about 4 miles turn right (signposted Flusco). Entrance along lane on the left.
Open: Easter to November.

Payment: 💷 ☼ Leisure: 🚴 ♪ ⟲ Children: 🐾 🎢 Catering: 🍴 Park: 🐕 🗃 📶 Touring: 🚰 🕐 🚐

ROSTHWAITE, Cumbria *Map ref 5A3* SatNav CA12 5XB

Scafell Hotel

Rosthwaite, Borrowdale, Keswick CA12 5XB **T:** (01768) 777208 **F:** (01768) 777280
E: info@scafell.co.uk
W: www.scafell.co.uk

B&B PER ROOM PER NIGHT
S: £60.00 - £115.00
D: £120.00 - £230.00
EVENING MEAL PER PERSON
£9.95 - £45.00

SPECIAL PROMOTIONS
Spring, summer, autumn and winter breaks available throughout the year. Please call or check the website for details.

The Scafell Hotel is in the heart of Borrowdale Valley, considered by many to be England's finest valley. Situated almost at the foot of Great Gable and Scafell Massif, the hotel is an excellent centre for walking. The Scafell boasts great rooms, great food, great service and a great atmosphere. AA Rosette, Dining Award, Gold Award and Breakfast Award. Individual and Independent for 46 years.

Directions: From junction 40 (Penrith) of the M6 follow A46 to Keswick. From Keswick follow the B5298 for Borrowdale. Travel 6.5 miles to Rosthwaite.

Bedrooms: 3 single, 9 double, 7 twin, 3 family, 1 suite. All en suite, Flat Screen TV's, tea & coffee, H2K bathroom products & mountain views.
Open: All year.

Site: **Payment:** **Leisure:** **Property:** **Children:** **Catering:**
Room:

SILLOTH, Cumbria *Map ref 5A2*

Stanwix Park Holiday Centre

Contact: Greenrow, Silloth, Wigton, Cumbria CA7 4HH **T:** (01697) 332666
E: enquiries@stanwix.com
W: www.stanwix.com

Units 103
Sleeps 6
PER UNIT PER WEEK
£179.00 - £613.00

At Stanwix Park the emphasis is on comfort and value. Whether you choose a stylish caravan, one of our modern apartments or one of our various camping options, you'll discover all the comforts of home.
Open: All year.

Site: P **Payment:** **Leisure:** **Property:**

ULLSWATER, Cumbria *Map ref 5A3*

Elm How, Cruck Barn & Eagle Cottage

Contact: Patterdale, Glenridding, Ullswater, Cumbria CA11 0PU **T:** (01539) 445756
E: info@matsonground.co.uk
W: www.matsonground.co.uk

Units 3
Sleeps 2-8
PER UNIT PER WEEK
£345.00 - £1450.00

Near Patterdale and Glenridding, we have 3 self-catering holiday cottages all offering quiet, comfortable accommodation.
Elm How, sleeps 8 and Cruck Barn, sleeps 2 are in the Grisedale Valley above Patterdale, near Ullswater.
Eagle Cottage sleeps 4 is in the village of Patterdale.
Open: All year.
Nearest Shop: 2 miles
Nearest Pub: 2 miles

Site: P **Payment:** **Leisure:** **Property:** **Children:** **Unit:**
BBQ

ULLSWATER, Cumbria Map ref 5A3 [S]

Hartsop Fold Holiday Lodges

Contact: Peter Sewell, Manager, Lyon Leisure, Crossgate Lane, Hartsop, Patterdale, Cumbria CA11 0NZ **T:** 07917 784977 **E:** info@hartsop-fold.co.uk
W: www.hartsop-fold.co.uk **£ BOOK ONLINE**

Units	12
Sleeps	2-6

PER UNIT PER WEEK
£509.00 - £795.00

Between Ullswater and Windermere. Scandanavian style lodges on a secluded site, in a quiet corner of the Lakes. Sleep up to six in all Lodges. Week, mid-week & weekend breaks available. Equipped with fitted kitchen, colour TV and free Wi-Fi.
Open: All year.
Nearest Shop: 3 miles
Nearest Pub: 1 mile

Site: P **Leisure:** **Property:** **Children:** **Unit:**

ULLSWATER, Cumbria Map ref 5A3 SatNav CA10 2LT [C]

Hillcroft Holiday Park

Roe Head Lane, Pooley Bridge, Penrith, Cumbria CA10 2LT
T: (017684) 86363 **E:** info@hillcroftpark.co.uk
W: www.hillcroftpark.co.uk

(14)	£20.00-£33.00
(14)	£20.00-£33.00
(64)	£15.00-£27.00
(16)	£40.00-£60.00
(14)	£305.00-£599.00
(5)	£249.00-£465.00

A warm and friendly welcome awaits you when you visit Hillcroft Park, Ullswater in the northern part of the Lake District. Hillcroft Park is the perfect holiday retreat, especially for those who love the outdoor life. Various pitches, lodges & caravans available, Some with Hot Tubs! Please see website for further details.
Directions: Please see website.
Open: Camping & Pods: 1st March to 15th November.
Static Caravans & lodges: 1st March to 6th January.

Site: **Payment:** **Leisure:** **Children:** **Catering:** **Park:** **Touring:**

ULLSWATER, Cumbria Map ref 5A3 SatNav CA11 0JF [C]

Waterfoot Caravan Park

Pooley Bridge, Penrith, Ullswater CA11 0JF
T: (017684) 86302 **F:** (017684) 86728 **E:** bookings@waterfootpark.co.uk
W: www.waterfootpark.co.uk **£ BOOK ONLINE**

(34)	
(4)	

34 touring pitches

Set in the grounds of a Georgian Mansion overlooking Ullswater on the Ullswater Way path. 10 minute walk from Pooley Bridge and Steamer Pier. Excellent facilities including electric car hire. Touring, self-catering wigwam & cottage holidays.
Directions: M6 junction 40, follow signs marked Ullswater Steamers. West on A66 1 mile. Left at roundabout A592 (Ullswater). Park located on right. Sat Nav not compatible.
Open: 1st March to 14th November.

Site: **Payment:** **Leisure:** **Children:** **Catering:** **Park:** **Touring:**

ULVERSTON, Cumbria Map ref 5A3 SatNav LA12 7HD [B]

St Marys Mount

Belmont, Ulverston LA12 7HD **T:** (01229) 583372 **E:** gerry.bobbett@virgin.net
W: www.stmarysmount.co.uk

B&B PER ROOM PER NIGHT
S: £50.00
D: £80.00
EVENING MEAL PER PERSON
£25.00

Guest house overlooking Morecambe Bay in own grounds. 5 minutes' walk to Ulverston town centre at the foot of the Hoad Monument. Peaceful surroundings and guests can enjoy homecooked food. Evening meals by request.
Directions: Follow the A590 into Ulverston, pass Booths. At next major roundabout take the 3rd exit onto Fountain Street. At mini roundabout take a sharp right.
Bedrooms: 4 double, 2 twin. **Open:** All year.

Site: P **Payment:** **Leisure:** **Property:** **Children:** **Catering:** **Room:**

WIGTON, Cumbria Map ref 5A2 S

Foxgloves

Contact: Mrs Janice Kerr, Foxgloves, Greenrigg Farm, Westward, Wigton, Cumbria CA7 8AH **T:** (01697) 342676 **E:** kerr_greenrigg@hotmail.com
W: NEW WEBSITE COMING SOON! Please contact for details.

Units 1
Sleeps 1-8

PER UNIT PER WEEK
£295.00 - £625.00

SPECIAL PROMOTIONS
Please contact for
short breaks
information.

Spacious, extremely well-equipped, comfortable cottage with Aga, offering a high standard of accommodation. Superlative setting and views. Large, safe garden. Guests are welcome to explore the farm and fields where a variety of wildlife can be seen. Within easy reach of Lake District, Scottish Borders and Roman Wall. Children and Pets very welcome.

Open: All year.
Nearest Shop: 1 mile
Nearest Pub: 1 mile

Site: ❀ P Leisure: ♨ ♪ ⌖ ∪ Property: ⌘ ▦ ☐ Children: ⚲ ⨿ ⚹ Unit: ☐ ☐ ▣ ☐ ⚲ TV ⚫ ⊚ ∅ BBQ

WINDERMERE, Cumbria Map ref 5A3 SatNav LA23 3JY B

Bowfell Cottage

Middle Entrance Drive, Storrs Park, Bowness-on-Windermere, Cumbria LA23 3JY
T: (01539) 444835 **E:** annetomlinson45@btinternet.com
W: www.bowfell-cottage.co.uk

B&B PER ROOM PER NIGHT
S: £32.00 - £35.00
D: £60.00 - £70.00

Cottage in a delightful setting, about 1mile south of Bowness off A5074, offering traditional Lakeland hospitality with comfortable accommodation and good home-cooking. Secluded parking in own grounds surrounding the property. **Directions:** From Bowness opposite church, take A5074 Kendal Road for 1.2 miles. Turn right into Middle Entrance Drive, entrance 100 yards down Lane on left. **Bedrooms:** 1 double, en-suite 1 twin, 1 family\ flat screen tv. **Open:** All year except Christmas.

Site: ❀ P Leisure: ♨ ♪ ⌖ ∪ Property: ⌘ ▦ ☐ Children: ⚲ Catering: (✕ ⊞ Room: ⚲ ♨ ✆ TV

WINDERMERE, Cumbria Map ref 5A3 SatNav LA12 8NR C

Hill of Oaks Park

Tower Wood, Windermere LA12 8NR
T: (015395) 31578 **F:** (015395) 30431 **E:** enquiries@hillofoaks.co.uk
W: www.hillofoaks.co.uk **£ BOOK ONLINE**

🚐 (54)
🚎 (54)
🚍 (3)
54 touring pitches

A 5 star award-winning park located on the shores of Windermere. Excellent facilities for touring, boat launching and jetties, water bus in high season and woodland walks. Self catering weekly lets and Holiday Homes & Lodges for sale. **Directions:** M6 junction 36, west on A590 towards Barrow and Newby Bridge. At roundabout turn right, onto A592. Park is approx 3 miles on left-hand side. **Open:** 1st March to Mid November.

Site: ❀ ▲▣ Payment: ▦ ☼ Leisure: ♪ ⌖ Children: ⚲ ♨ ⛰ Catering: ⚲ Park: ⌘ ▦ ☐ ☐ ⊙ ⚲ Touring: ⚲ ⚲ 🚐

WINDERMERE, Cumbria Map ref 5A3
SatNav LA23 3PG **C**

Park Cliffe Camping & Caravan Estate

Birks Road, Windermere LA23 3PG
T: (015395) 31344 **F:** (015395) 31971 **E:** info@parkcliffe.co.uk
W: www.parkcliffe.co.uk **£ BOOK ONLINE**

🚐 (60)	£27.00-£35.00
🚐 (60)	£27.00-£35.00
⛺ (80)	£21.00-£35.00
🛖 (3)	£200.00-£660.00

60 touring pitches

The winner of many top-quality awards, Park Cliffe is set in 25 acres of picture-postcard countryside above the eastern shores of Windermere with sweeping views across the lake. Tourer & camping pitches, caravans & camping pods for hire.
Camping pods £44-£63. **Directions:** Do not follow SatNav - M6 jct 36, follow A590 towards Barrow. At Newby Bridge take A592 towards Windermere. After 3.6 miles turn right into Birks Road.
Open: 1st March to mid November.

Site: Payment: Leisure: Children: Catering: Park: Touring:

OLDHAM, Greater Manchester Map ref 4B1
SatNav OL3 5UN **C**

Moorlands Caravan Park

Ripponden Road, Denshaw, Oldham OL3 5UN
T: (01457) 874348 **E:** themoorlandssaddleworth@gmail.com
W: www.moorlandscp.co.uk

🚐 (40)	£18.00-£24.00
🚐 (18)	£18.00-£24.00
⛺ (20)	£8.00
🛖 (2)	£25.00-£48.00

40 touring pitches

Newly refurbished, 4 star park on the moors of Saddleworth. Ideal for walkers, horse riders, or just a family stay. Half a mile from the Pennine Way and Pennine Bridal Way. Short walk to pub and stunning views for tents, caravans and camping pods.
Limited winter availability.
Directions: Junction 22 of the M62, 2 miles in the direction of Saddleworth.
Open: All year.

Site: Payment: Leisure: Children: Park: Touring:

ROCHDALE, Greater Manchester Map ref 4B1
SatNav OL15 0AS **C**

Hollingworth Lake Caravan Park

Roundhouse Farm, Hollingworth Lake, Littleborough OL15 0AT
T: (01706) 378661 **E:** info@hollingworthlakecaravanpark.com
W: www.hollingworthlakecaravanpark.com

🚐 (30)	
🚐 (10)	
⛺ (10)	

50 touring pitches

A popular, five-acre park adjacent to Hollingworth Lake. At the foot of the Pennines, within easy reach of many local attractions. Backpackers walking the Pennine Way are welcome at this family-run park. Hardstanding and grass areas. Excellent train service into Manchester Victoria. 20 minutes from Littleborough/Smithybridge. Overnight holding area available. Restaurant/café within 1m of site. Please contact for 2017 rates. **Directions:** From M62. Junction 21 Milnrow. Follow Hollingworth signs to Fishermans Inn/The Wine Press. Take Rakewood Road then 2nd on right. **Open:** All year.

Payment: Leisure: Catering: Park: Touring:

SALE, Greater Manchester Map ref 4A2
SatNav M33 2AE **B**

Belforte House

7-9 Broad Road, Sale, Manchester M33 2AE **T:** (01619) 738779 **F:** (01619) 738779
E: belfortehousehotel@aol.co.uk
W: www.belfortehousehotel.co.uk **£ BOOK ONLINE**

B&B PER ROOM PER NIGHT
S: £38.00 - £49.95
D: £65.00 - £69.95
EVENING MEAL PER PERSON
£6.95 - £13.95

Privately owned hotel with a personal, friendly approach. Ideally located for Manchester Airport, the Metrolink and the city centre. Situated directly opposite Sale Leisure Centre.
Directions: 1 mile from Junction 6 M60.
200 metres from Tram Station.
Bedrooms: 13 single, 4 double, 2 twin, 3 family.
Open: All year except Christmas and New Year.

Site: P Payment: Leisure: Property: Children: Catering: Room:

BLACKBURN, Lancashire   Map ref 4A1   SatNav BB2 7NP   H

Stanley House Hotel & Spa

Further Lane, Mellor, Blackburn, Ribble Valley BB2 7NP   **T:** (01254) 769200
F: (01254) 769206   **E:** info@stanleyhouse.co.uk
W: www.stanleyhouse.co.uk   **£ BOOK ONLINE**

B&B PER ROOM PER NIGHT
S: £155.00 - £205.00
D: £185.00 - £285.00
HB PER PERSON PER NIGHT
£135.00 - £150.00

Stanley House is an award-winning hotel, with 30 first-class bedrooms, unrivalled wedding and conference facilities, the stylish Grill on the Hill restaurant, the hugely popular Mr Fred's and a world-class spa, truly a hotel like no other.
Directions: Located on the A677, 4 miles from the M6/M65. Preston station 6 miles. Blackpool International Airport 25 miles. Manchester International Airport 40 miles.
Open: All year.

Site: ❀ P Payment: 💷 Leisure: ♪ ⚑ ✗ ⚔ ♨ Property: ⊛ 🛡 💻 🛏 🚪 ◑ Children: 🍼 🛏 🎄 Catering: 🍴✗ 🍷 🍽 Room: 📶 💧 📞 🕙 📺 🔌 🖥

BLACKPOOL, Lancashire   Map ref 4A1   SatNav FY1 6BP   B

4 Star Phildene Blackpool

5-7 St. Chads Road, Blackpool, Lancashire FY1 6BP   **T:** (01253) 346141   **F:** (01253) 345243
E: info@4starblackpool.co.uk
W: www.4starblackpool.co.uk   **£ BOOK ONLINE**

B&B PER ROOM PER NIGHT
S: £45.00 - £65.00
D: £85.00 - £125.00
EVENING MEAL PER PERSON
£15.00 - £25.00

We are ideally located 25 metres from Blackpool seafront, opposite St Chad's Headland. Just a short walk from the centre of Blackpool and all major attractions. Perfectly suited for both business and leisure guests. Child free property 18+. **Directions:** The easiest directions to give you are to make your way on to the Promenade Blackpool. St Chads Road is halfway between Central Pier and South Pier. **Bedrooms:** 5 Single, 6 Doubles, 2 premiers & 1 superior suite. **Open:** All year Except Christmas & New Year.

Site: ❀ Payment: 💷 € Leisure: ♿ ♪ ⚑ ♨ Property: 💻 🛏 Catering: 🍷 🍽 Room: 📶 💧 📞 📺 🔌

BLACKPOOL, Lancashire   Map ref 4A1   SatNav FY1 4PR   B

Arabella

102 Albert Road, Blackpool, Lancashire FY1 4PR   **T:** (01253) 623189
E: g.waters3@yahoo.com
W: www.thearabella.co.uk

SPECIAL PROMOTIONS
We charge per person not per room. Price starts at £25 per person and all prices are based on two adults sharing.

B&B: 4 night stay for two people £152.
BB&EM: 4 night stay for two people £208.

We provide clean and comfortable accommodation within a family friendly atmosphere. Home cooking, dietary needs catered for, rooms are serviced daily, few minutes walk from the winter gardens, 10 minutes from the Tower and sea front. We do not take stag or hen parties. Specials available Monday to Friday. Prices on application. We also have a licensed bar, free car park & Wi-Fi.

Directions: Contact our website for google map directions.

Bedrooms: All rooms have en suites, central heating, tea & coffee facilities and flat screen TV. **Open:** All year.

Site: ❀ P Payment: 💷 Property: 💻 Children: 🍼 🛏 🎄 Catering: 🍷 🍽 Room: 📶 💧 🕙 📺

BLACKPOOL, Lancashire   Map ref 4A1

SatNav FY2 9RP [H]

VisitEngland
★★★
HOTEL

B&B PER ROOM PER NIGHT
S: £32.00 - £55.00
D: £64.00 - £125.00
HB PER PERSON PER NIGHT
£34.00 - £60.00

Doric Hotel

48-52 Queens Promenade, Blackpool FY2 9RP **T:** (01253) 352640 **F:** (01253) 596842
E: info@dorichotel.co.uk
W: www.dorichotel.co.uk

Situated on Queens Promenade with breathtaking views over the Irish Sea. The Doric has become popular offering a wide range of facilities and good-value holidays for all.
Directions: Exit M55 signposted Fleetwood A585 onto Promenade B5265 approximately 0.5miles on the right hand side.
Bedrooms: 10 single, 20 double, 13 twin, 47 family, 13 suite.
Open: All year.

Site: ✿ Payment: £ € Leisure: ↘ ↗ Property: ♟ ▭ ◑ Children: ⌒ ⊨ ⚶ Catering: ♟ ᵜ Room: ⌐ ⚲ ☎ TV ⌇

BLACKPOOL, Lancashire   Map ref 4A1

SatNav FY1 6AN [H]

VisitEngland
★★
HOTEL

B&B PER ROOM PER NIGHT
S: £28.00 - £122.00
D: £35.00 - £128.00
HB PER PERSON PER NIGHT
£39.00 - £64.00

SPECIAL PROMOTIONS
Big Reductions Early Season.

Lyndene Hotel

305-315 Promenade, Blackpool FY1 6AN **T:** (01253) 346779 **F:** (01253) 346466
E: enquiries@lyndenehotel.com
W: www.lyndenehotel.com **£ BOOK ONLINE**

Situated between Tower/Pleasure Beach, the Lyndene is an ideal location from which to enjoy all the resort has to offer. 140 comfortable bedrooms makes us the right choice for your stay in Blackpool. Three lifts access all floors inc. ground floor rooms. Three bars, two air conditioned sea-view Cabaret lounges (entertainment nightly). Two restaurants with choice of cuisine. Bar snacks served daily.

Directions: See web page for directions.

Bedrooms: 1 single, 52 double, 21 twin and 66 family.
Open: All year.

Site: ✿ Payment: £ Leisure: ✦ Property: ▭ ▣ ⋈ ◑ Children: ⌒5 Catering: (✗ ♟ ᵜ Room: ⌐ ⚲ ☎ ⌀ TV ⌔ ⌇

For **key to symbols** see page 6

Lynton Apartments

Contact: Iggy or Koko, Lynton Apartments, 227 Promenade, Blackpool FY1 5DL
T: (01253) 624296 **E:** info@lyntonapartments.co.uk
W: www.lyntonapartments.co.uk **£ BOOK ONLINE**

Units 10
Sleeps 2-6

PER UNIT PER WEEK
£150.00 - £450.00

SPECIAL PROMOTIONS
Massive savings of up to 50% off high season rates! Low/mid season early bird discounts. (Terms & Conditions apply).

Lynton Apartments offer spacious, self-catering holiday flats at the heart of the Promenade located halfway between Blackpool Tower and the Pleasure Beach with stunning sea views, fully equipped kitchens & private bathrooms. Our units are refurbished annually to very high standards, have flat screen colour TV's with Freeview in all lounges & free Wi-Fi throughout the building.

Open: All year.
Nearest Shop: 0.10 miles
Nearest Pub: 0.10 miles

Payment: 💷 **Property:** 🛏 🍴 **Children:** 👶 🛏 🚶 **Unit:** 🛏 📺 📺

Park House Hotel

308 North Promenade, Blackpool FY1 2HA **T:** (01253) 620081 **F:** (01253) 290181
E: enquiries@blackpoolparkhousehotel.com
W: www.blackpoolparkhousehotel.com **£ BOOK ONLINE**

B&B PER ROOM PER NIGHT
S: £32.00 - £55.00
D: £64.00 - £120.00
EVENING MEAL PER PERSON
£14.95

Ideally situated on north promenade within walking distance of town centre and all major attractions. Fabulous cuisine. Entertainment seven nights a week in our ballroom or bar lounge. **Directions:** End of M55 along Yeadon Way onto Promenade from A584 heading north approximately 1 mile.
Bedrooms: 12 single, 34 double, 33 twin, 20 family, 4 suites.
Open: All year.

Site: ❀ **Payment:** 💷 **Property:** 🍷 🛏 🌙 **Children:** 👶 🛏 🚶 **Catering:** 🍴 🍽 **Room:** 🛏 ♨ 📞 📺

Ruskin Hotel

55-61 Albert Road, Blackpool, Lancashire FY1 4PW **T:** (01253) 624063 **F:** (01253) 623571
E: reception@ruskinhotel.com
W: www.ruskinhotel.com **£ BOOK ONLINE**

B&B PER ROOM PER NIGHT
S: £35.00 - £72.00
D: £60.00 - £92.00
HB PER PERSON PER NIGHT
£35.00 - £74.00

Centrally located. Conference facilities, fabulous food and nightly entertainment (in season). Four bars, three dance floors, public bar and bistro. Cabaret weekends available.
Bedrooms: 5 single, 29 double, 24 twin, 13 family.
Open: All year.

Site: ❀ **Payment:** 💷 **Leisure:** ♿ 🎵 🏃 **Property:** 🍷 🐾 🛏 📅 🌙 **Children:** 👶 🛏 🚶 **Catering:** 🍴 🍽
Room: 🛏 ♨ 📞 📺 🛗

CARNFORTH, *Lancashire* Map ref 5B3 [S]

Brackenthwaite Farm Holiday Cottages

Contact: Matthew, Brackenthwaite Farm, Yealand Redmayne, Near Carnforth, Lancashire
LA5 9TE **T:** (01539) 563276 **E:** info@brackenthwaite.com
W: www.brackenthwaite.com

VisitEngland
3★ - 4★
SELF CATERING

Units   4
Sleeps   4-6

PER UNIT PER WEEK
£290.00 - £650.00

SPECIAL PROMOTIONS
70% of the weekly
booking charge;
minimum charge of
3 nights.

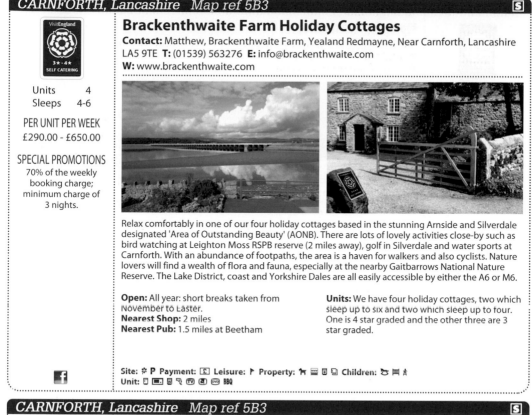

Relax comfortably in one of our four holiday cottages based in the stunning Arnside and Silverdale designated 'Area of Outstanding Beauty' (AONB). There are lots of lovely activities close-by such as bird watching at Leighton Moss RSPB reserve (2 miles away), golf in Silverdale and water sports at Carnforth. With an abundance of footpaths, the area is a haven for walkers and also cyclists. Nature lovers will find a wealth of flora and fauna, especially at the nearby Gaitbarrows National Nature Reserve. The Lake District, coast and Yorkshire Dales are all easily accessible by either the A6 or M6.

Open: All year: short breaks taken from November to Easter.
Nearest Shop: 2 miles
Nearest Pub: 1.5 miles at Beetham

Units: We have four holiday cottages, two which sleep up to six and two which sleep up to four. One is 4 star graded and the other three are 3 star graded.

f

Site: ✿ P **Payment:** 🖃 **Leisure:** ⊁ **Property:** 🐾 🖾 🖺 🖳 **Children:** 🌣 🛏 🕴
Unit: 🍽 🖾 🖭 🖳 📺 🎛 🕸 BBQ

CARNFORTH, *Lancashire* Map ref 5B3 [S]

Pine Lake Resort

Contact: Dock Acres, Carnforth, Lancashire LA6 1JZ **T:** (0800) 358 6991
E: EuHotels@diamondresorts.com
W: www.DiamondResortsandHotels.com **£ BOOK ONLINE**

VisitEngland
★★★★
SELF CATERING

Units   124
Sleeps   1-6

PER UNIT PER WEEK
£419.00 - £1267.00

SPECIAL PROMOTIONS
Visit our website or call
today for seasonal
discounts and great
savings.

These unique Scandinavian-style Lodges lie in a tranquil location by Pine Lake near Carnforth. Guests can enjoy water skiing, sailing and canoeing and there is also an indoor swimming pool, fitness centre and spa. The on site restaurant provides a varied menu including children's options and evening entertainment is available in the bar area.

Each 2 bedroom lodge or studio comes with a fully equipped kitchen and some have lake views. Complimentary toiletries, a flat-screen TV and a DVD player are all included, Wi-Fi can be purchased as extra.

Open: All year.
Nearest Shop: On site
Nearest Pub: On site

Units: A choice of Studios and two bedroom apartments available. All apartments boast a modern bathroom, kitchen and Television with DVD player.

f t

Site: ✿ P **Payment:** 🖃 **Leisure:** ⊁ 🔍 🐟 🦢 **Property:** 🖾 🖺 🖳 **Children:** 🌣 🛏 🕴 **Unit:** 🖾 🖳 📺 🕸 📞

New Parkside Farm Caravan Park

Denny Beck, Caton Road, Lancaster LA2 9HH
T: (01524) 770723 **E:** enquiries@newparksidefarm.co.uk
W: www.newparksidefarm.co.uk **£ BOOK ONLINE**

(36)	£16.00-£19.00
(4)	£16.00-£19.00
(8)	£9.00-£19.00

40 touring pitches

Peaceful, family-run park on a working farm on the edge of the Forest of Bowland. Extensive views of the Lune Valley and Ingleborough. Excellent base for exploring the Lakes, Dales and unspoilt coast and countryside of North Lancashire.
Directions: Leave M6 at junction 34, A683 east towards Caton/Kirkby Lonsdale, caravan park entrance 1 mile from motorway junction on the right (signposted).
Open: 1st March to 31st October.

Site: 👤📶 Payment: ☼ Children: 🐷 Park: 🐴 🐾 🦌 Touring: 🚽 🚰 ⚡

Thurnham Hall

Contact: Thurnham, Nr Lancaster, Lancashire LA2 0DT **T:** (0800) 358 6991
E: EuHotels@diamondresorts.com
W: www.DiamondResortsandHotels.com **£ BOOK ONLINE**

Units	60
Sleeps	1-6

PER UNIT PER WEEK
£280.00 - £1267.00

SPECIAL PROMOTIONS
Visit our website or call today for seasonal discounts and great savings.

With an elegant Jacobean Great Hall, this resort a features a leisure centre and traditional restaurant. Thurnham Hall is a 12th century country estate, set in nearly 30 acres of grounds in scenic Lancashire. The stylish, self-catering accommodation is set in either the historic main house or in modern courtyard buildings. All apartments and studios have a satellite TV and a private bathroom.

The leisure centre at Thurnham Hall has a large indoor swimming pool and a state-of-the-art fitness suite. Guests can relax in the sauna and spa bath, or enjoy treatments in the beauty salon.

Open: All year.
Nearest Shop: 2 miles
Nearest Pub: 2 miles

Units: A choice of Studio, one and two bedroom apartments available. All apartments boast a full kitchen, modern bathroom and Television with DVD player.

Site: ♿ P Payment: 💳 Leisure: 🎵 ▶ 🎯 Property: 🛏 📶 🛗 Children: 🐷 🎪 🎏 Unit: 🔲 🔳 📺 🎞 📞

LYTHAM ST. ANNES, Lancashire   Map ref 4A1   SatNav FY8 1HN H

Clifton Park Hotel

299-301 Clifton Drive South, St Annes-on-Sea, Lytham St Annes, Lancashire FY8 1HN
T: (01253) 725801 **F:** (01253) 721735 **E:** info@cliftonpark.co.uk
W: www.cliftonpark.co.uk **£ BOOK ONLINE**

B&B PER ROOM PER NIGHT
S: £40.00 - £80.00
D: £79.00 - £160.00
EVENING MEAL PER PERSON
£17.50 - £24.95

SPECIAL PROMOTIONS
Look out for our Winter Warmers, Spring Savers and Summertime Sizzlers throughout the year. We also offer themed breaks such as our Cruise weeks and our famous Turkey & Tinsel breaks.

Just 10 minutes from Blackpool's bustling centre the adult only Clifton Park Hotel is situated in the popular seaside resort of Lytham St Annes.

The hotel boasts excellent facilities and a warm friendly atmosphere, a tranquil leisure centre which boasts a luxurious heated indoor swimming pool and spa area.We welcome corporate guests, functions, group bookings and weddings and exclusive hire.

Directions: From the end of the M55, follow signs for Lytham St. Annes. We are situated 150 yards on your left after St. Annes Square.

Bedrooms: All our rooms vary in shapes, sizes and styles.
Open: All year.

Site: ❋ P **Payment:** 💷 **Leisure:** ↾ ⚔ ☌ **Property:** ⚓ 🖥 🛢 ◖ ◐ **Catering:** ⟨✕ ⟡ 🍲
Room: 🝙 🕯 ☏ 📺 ⚒

LYTHAM ST. ANNES, Lancashire   Map ref 4A1   SatNav FY8 4LR C

Eastham Hall Caravan Park

Saltcotes Road, Lytham St Annes, Lancashire FY8 4LS
T: (01253) 737907 **E:** info@easthamhall.co.uk
W: www.easthamhall.co.uk **£ BOOK ONLINE**

🚐 (140)   £20.00-£35.00
🚛   £20.00-£35.00
🚃 (150)   £2625.00
140 touring pitches

SPECIAL PROMOTIONS
Please see website for discounts throughout the year.

Eastham Hall Caravan Park has been owned and managed by the Kirkham family for 50 years. Whether you buy a holiday home on the park or visit with your touring caravan, you can share our lovely rural retreat in a highly sought after location. The park has an on-site shop which is open seven days a week selling essential items including bread, milk, ice cream and newspapers (a newspaper ordering service is provided).

We have a children's adventure playground, extensive playing fields and a dedicated dog exercise area and a dog walk. Touring Pitches: 100 Seasonal, 40 nightly.

Directions: Please see website.

Open: Touring: 1st March to 1st December
Holiday Homes: 20th February to 3rd January.

Site: ⚠🅿 **Payment:** 💷 ☼ **Children:** 🛝 ⚠ **Catering:** 🛒 **Park:** ▤ **Touring:** ♨ 🚐 ⚡

ORMSKIRK, Lancashire   Map ref 4A1

Units 4
Sleeps 1-6

PER UNIT PER WEEK
£315.00 - £630.00

Martin Lane Farm Holiday Cottages

Contact: Owner, 5 Martin Lane, Burscough, Ormskirk, Lancashire L40 8JH
T: (01704) 893527 / 07803 049128 **E:** cottages@btinternet.com
W: www.martinlanefarm-holidaycottages.co.uk **£ BOOK ONLINE**

Four beautiful, award-winning country cottages, one fully accessible for guests with disabilities. Nestling in the peaceful, arable farmland of West Lancashire, a haven of rest and tranquillity. For those who don't want a 'quiet life' we are just 4 miles from Southport's seaside attractions and the quaint market town of Ormskirk. Martin Mere Wildfowl Trust and Rufford Old Hall, just 2 miles away. **Open:** All year.
Nearest Shop: 0.5 miles **Nearest Pub:** 0.75 miles

Site: ❀ P **Payment:** 💷 € **Leisure:** ♪ ♪ ∪ **Property:** 📺 📶 📖 **Children:** ⛱ 🎠 ⚘
Unit: 📺 🔲 💻 📶 📺 📀 BBQ

PRESTON, Lancashire   Map ref 4A1

Units 4
Sleeps 2-6

PER UNIT PER WEEK
£700.00 - £1200.00

Crabtree Narrowboat Hire

Contact: Robert Foulkes, Owner, Crabtree Farm, Hagg Lane, St Michael's On Wyre, Preston, Lancashire PR3 0UJ **T:** (01995) 671712 / 07572 664949
E: info@crabtreenarrowboathire.com **W:** www.crabtreenarrowboathire.com

Crabtree Narrowboat Hire is a friendly, family run narrowboat hire company based on the beautiful, lock-free Lancaster Canal.

We operate 4 luxury boats from our base at Barton Grange Marina – "Willow" (44ft), "Linden" (44ft), "Cedar" (45ft) and "Mulberry" (57ft). All our boats have been assessed and awarded 5 Stars by VisitEngland and we are the only hire company in England to have been awarded a 2015 VisitEngland ROSE Award in Recognition Of Service Excellence.

For a family holiday, short break or a romantic, relaxing getaway you will find a warm welcome with Crabtree Narrowboat Hire.

Open: March to November.
Nearest Shop: 25 yards
Nearest Pub: 1 mile

Site: P **Payment:** 💷 **Property:** 🐾 📖 **Children:** ⛱ **Unit:** 📶 📺 📀

WORSTON, Lancashire   Map ref 4A1

Units 3
Sleeps 1-6

Angram Green Holiday Cottages

Contact: John Haworth, Angram Green Holiday Cottages, Angram Green Cottage, Worston, Clitheroe, Lancashire BB7 1QB **T:** (01200) 441455 / 07782 215984
E: info@angramgreen.co.uk **W:** www.angramgreen.co.uk

Farm-based cottages in rural Lancashire. Stunning views across open countryside. Ideal base for walkers and cyclists. One double bedroom, one pair of child-size bunks in smaller units. Two double bedrooms and one twin room in the larger unit. Also dishwasher and washing machine in larger unit. Pets in Pendleside only. Restaurant and bar within walking distance.
Please contact for up-to-date pricing.
Open: All year. **Nearest Shop:** 2 miles **Nearest Pub:** 0.5 miles

Site: ❀ P **Leisure:** ♪ ♪ **Property:** 🐾 📖 **Children:** ⛱ 🎠 ⚘ **Unit:** 💻 📶 📺 📀 📀

AINSDALE, Merseyside   Map ref 4A1

SatNav PR8 3ST **C**

Willowbank Holiday Home and Touring Park

Coastal Road, Ainsdale, Southport PR8 3ST
T: (01704) 571566 **E:** info@willowbankcp.co.uk
W: www.willowbankcp.co.uk

VisitEngland
★★★★★
HOLIDAY &
TOURING PARK

🚐 (87)   £16.00-£21.20
🚙 (87)   £16.00-£21.20
🏕 (228)
87 touring pitches

SPECIAL PROMOTIONS
Please see our website
for offers.

Willowbank Holiday Home & Touring Park offers an easily accessible location, convenient for Southport & Liverpool with modern facilities in a quiet and relaxed atmosphere. The park is open from 14th February to 31st January for holiday homes, touring caravans, motor homes and trailer tents. Last check in 9.00pm. Check out 12.00pm. No vans or Commercial vehicles. Please note we do not rent out vans.

Directions: From M6 junction 26 for M58, from the M62 junction for M57. A5036 & A5207 leading to A565 towards Southport, RAF Woodvale, Coastal Road.

Open: 14th February to 31st January.

Payment: 💳 ☼ Leisure: ↑ ♿ Children: 👶 Park: 🐾 ♿ 🅿 ⛽ 🛒 🎣 Touring: 🚿 🔌 ⚡ ♿

LIVERPOOL, Merseyside   Map ref 4A2

SatNav L20 3AW **B**

Breeze Guest House

237 Hawthorne Road, Bootle L20 3AW **T:** (0151) 933 2576 **E:** breezegh@googlemail.co.uk
W: www.breezeguesthouse.co.uk **£ BOOK ONLINE**

VisitEngland
★★★
GUEST HOUSE

B&B PER ROOM PER NIGHT
S: £40.00 - £70.00
D: £70.00 - £80.00

The Breeze Guesthouse is a luxury townhouse located in Bootle Village, 3 miles away from vibrant city of Liverpool home of the Beatles, Liverpool & Everton stadia & Aintree Race Course.
Directions: Conveniently located for all modes of transport to/from Liverpool city centre, Crosby or Southport including bus, train and motorway.
Bedrooms: 1 single, 2 doubles, 6 twins & 1 family room.
Open: All year except Christmas.

Site: **P** Payment: 💳 Property: 🐾 ♿ Children: 👶 🍽 ♿ Catering: 🍴 Room: 🛁 ☕ 📺 📀 🔌 📞

For **key to symbols** see page 6

LIVERPOOL, Merseyside Map ref 4A2 SatNav L1 9DA H

★★★★
HOTEL

Hope Street Hotel

40 Hope Street, Liverpool, Merseyside L1 9DA **T:** (01517) 093000 **F:** (01517) 092454
E: sleep@hopestreethotel.co.uk
W: www.hopestreethotel.co.uk **£ BOOK ONLINE**

B&B PER ROOM PER NIGHT
S: £102.00 - £507.00
D: £114.00 - £519.00
EVENING MEAL PER PERSON
£25.00 - £55.00

SPECIAL PROMOTIONS
Lazy Sunday Package - from £149 for two. Stay Sunday, enjoy a two course dinner in The London Carriage Works followed by a full Liverpool breakfast and a late check out of 12 noon on the Monday.

Liverpool's original boutique hotel, in the centre of the city's Georgian quarter, is surrounded by cathedrals, theatres, an international concert hall, a National Trust house, and several infamous hostelries. The style is chic with original warehouse features. The hotel's restaurant, The London Carriage Works, is a destination in its own right and a consistent 2 AA Rosette holder.

Directions: From M62, continue to end of motorway, follow signs for cathedrals (approx 3 miles). Hope Street links the two cathedrals and Hope Street Hotel is in the middle opposite the Philharmonic Hall.

Bedrooms: Oversized beds with white Egyptian cotton, solid birch and oak floors, bespoke furniture, original beams and brickwork, REN toiletries and free Wi-Fi.
Open: All year.

Site: P Payment: ⊞ **Leisure:** ⚲ **Property:** ⊛ 🍷 🐕 🖼 🛗 📺 ◑ **Children:** 🧸 🛏 🚼 **Catering:** 🍴 🍷 🎛
Room: 🛎 ♨ 📞 🎧 📺 🛗

LIVERPOOL, Merseyside Map ref 4A2 SatNav L1 9JG B

★★★
HOSTEL

International Inn

4 South Hunter Street, Liverpool L1 9JG **T:** (0151) 709 8135 **E:** info@internationalinn.co.uk
W: www.internationalinn.co.uk **£ BOOK ONLINE**

BED ONLY PER NIGHT
£17.00 - £24.00

Tourist hostel, located in the heart of the city centre, near to theatres, cathedrals and nightlife. With a variety of dormitory sizes, Free tea/coffee, toast. No curfew, bedding provided. Free Wi-Fi.
Directions: Check out our website for full directions. We have great connections from all transport links.
Bedrooms: 3 double, 4 twin & dormitories from 4 to 10 beds.
Open: All year except Christmas.

Payment: ⊞ **Leisure:** ⚲ **Property:** ⊛ 🍷 🖼 🎧 📺 📀 🛗 **Children:** 🧸 🛏 🚼 **Room:** ♨ 🔚 **Bedroom:** 🛎 🖥

SOUTHPORT, Merseyside Map ref 4A1 SatNav PR9 8DF C

★★★
HOLIDAY, TOURING
& CAMPING PARK

Riverside Holiday Park

Southport New Road, Banks, Southport, Merseyside PR9 8DF
T: (01704) 228886 **F:** (01704) 505886 **E:** stacey@harrisonleisureuk.com
W: www.harrisonholidays.com **£ BOOK ONLINE**

🚐 (150) £10.00-£40.00
🚙 (150) £10.00-£40.00
🏠 (60)   £199.00-£635.00
150 touring pitches

Riverside Holiday Park, located in Banks, Southport is an award winning Holiday Park. A warm welcome awaits you, with luxury self catering holiday homes and touring areas with standard and fully serviced pitches.
Open: All year.

Site: 🏕 🅿 **Payment:** ⊞ ☀ **Leisure:** ♪ ⚑ 🎣 **Children:** 🧸 🛝 **Catering:** ✗ 🛒 **Park:** 🐕 🎵 🛗 🔦
Touring: 🚰 🚐 ⚒

VisitEngland
★★★
SELF CATERING

Units 5
Sleeps 2-6

PER UNIT PER WEEK
£215.00 - £415.00

SPECIAL PROMOTIONS
Last minute short
breaks available.
Please ring for details.

Sandy Brook Farm

Contact: Mrs W Core, Sandy Brook Farm, 52 Wyke Cop Road, Scarisbrick, Southport
PR8 5LR **T:** (01704) 880337 / 07719 468712 **E:** sandybrookfarm@gmail.com
W: www.sandybrookfarm.co.uk **£ BOOK ONLINE**

Our converted barn stands in peaceful countryside, offering five superbly equipped and
traditionally furnished self-catering holiday apartments. The comfortable apartments sleep 2/4/6
and 'The Dairy' is equipped for disabled guests.

The seaside town of Southport is 3.5 miles away and the historic town of Ormskirk is 5 miles away.
Liverpool, Manchester, and Blackpool are all within easy reach. Rufford Old Hall and Martin Mere
Wildfowl Trust plus many other places of interest are also close by.

Open: All year.
Nearest Shop: 2 miles
Nearest Pub: 1 mile

Units: Fully equipped apartments, with one or
two bedrooms and sofa beds in the lounge.
Sleeps 2/4/6.

Site: ❀ P Leisure: ♪ ▶ ∪ Property: ▦ ▣ ▨ Children: ☡ ▥ ⋏ Unit: ▭ ▤ ⋧ ▣

Wasdale Valley, Cumbria ©VisitBritain Rod Edwards

Don't Miss...

The Alnwick Garden
Alnwick, Northumberland NE66 1YU
(01665) 511350
www.alnwickgarden.com
Be inspired by the most exciting contemporary garden developed in
the last century, The Alnwick Garden. The inspiration of the Duchess
of Northumberland, this fascinating garden features the Grand Cascade
as its centrepiece to create spellbinding water displays. Explore the Rose
Garden, Ornamental Garden, Serpent Garden with eight water sculptures
nestling in the coils of a topiary serpent, Bamboo Labyrinth and don't miss
the Poison Garden which holds dangerous plants and their stories. The
garden is also home to the and one of the world's largest tree houses,
with rope bridges, walkways in the sky and a fantastic place to eat.

BALTIC Centre for Contemporary Art
Gateshead, Tyne and Wear NE8 3BA
(01914) 781810
www.balticmill.com
Housed in a landmark industrial building on the south bank of the River
Tyne in Gateshead, BALTIC is a major international centre for contemporary
art and is the biggest gallery of its kind in the world. It presents a
dynamic, diverse and international programme of contemporary visual
art, ranging from blockbuster exhibitions to innovative new work and
projects created by artists working within the local community.

Beamish Museum
County Durham DH9 0RG
(01913) 704000
www.beamish.org.uk
Beamish - The Living Museum of the North, is a world-famous open air
museum vividly recreating life in the North East in the early 1800's and 1900's.
It tells the story of the people of North East England during the Georgian,
Victorian, and Edwardian periods through a costumed cast, engaging
exhibits and an exciting programme of events including The Great North
Festival of Transport, a Georgian Fair, The Great North Festival of Agriculture.

Durham Cathedral
County Durham DH1 3EH
(0191) 3864266
www.durhamcathedral.co.uk
Durham Cathedral is perhaps the finest example of Norman church
architecture in England or even Europe. Set grandly on a rocky
promontory next to the Castle with the medieval city huddled
below and the river sweeping round, it is a World Heritage Site and
houses the tombs of St Cuthbert and The Venerable Bede.

Lindisfarne Priory
Holy Island, Northumberland TD15 2RX
(01289) 389200
www.english-heritage.org.uk/lindisfarnepriory
Lying just a few miles off the beautiful Northumberland coast, Holy Island
contains a wealth of history and is home to one of the region's most revered
treasures, Lindisfarne Priory. The epicentre of Christianity in Anglo Saxon
times and once the home of St Oswald, it was the birthplace of the Lindisfarne
Gospels, one of the world's most precious books and remains a place of
pilgrimage today. NB: watch the tides as the causeway is only open at low tide.

North East

County Durham, Northumberland,
Tees Valley, Tyne & Wear

The North East contains two 'Areas of Outstanding Natural Beauty', a National Park, Hadrian's Wall, the dynamic city of Newcastle, and Durham, with its fine cathedral and castle. This region is awash with dramatic hills, sweeping valleys, vast expanses of dune-fringed beaches and ragged cliffs with spectacular views. Littered with dramatic castles, ruins and historic houses, there are plenty of exciting family attractions and walking routes galore.

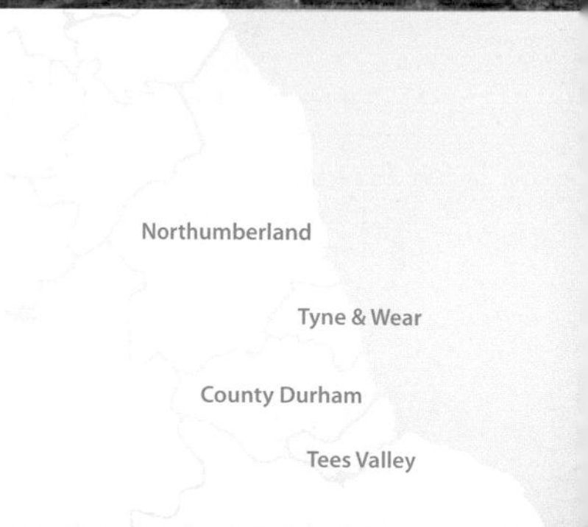

Northumberland

Tyne & Wear

County Durham

Tees Valley

Explore – North East

County Durham & Tees Valley

Durham Cathedral, the greatest Norman building in England, was once a prison and soars grandly above the Medieval city and surrounding plain. Famed for its location as much as for its architecture, it is the burial place of both St Cuthbert, a great northern saint, and the Venerable Bede, author of the first English history.

The Vale of Durham is packed full of award-winning attractions including Locomotion: The National Railway Museum at Shildon and Beamish – The Living Museum of the North, the country's largest open air museum. Part of the North Pennines 'Area of Outstanding Natural Beauty', the Durham Dales including Teesdale and Weardale, is a beautiful landscape of hills, moors, valleys and rivers, with numerous picturesque villages and market towns.

Comprising miles of stunning coastline and acres of ancient woodland, Tees Valley covers the lower, flatter area of the valley of the River Tees. This unique part of the UK, split between County Durham and Yorkshire, has nearly a hundred visitor attractions, including Preston Hall and Saltholme Nature Reserve, which can both be found in Stockton-on-Tees.

The Durham Heritage Coast, from Sunderland to Hartlepool, is one of the finest in England. The coastal path that runs along much of its length takes you on a spectacular journey of natural, historical and geological interest, with dramatic views along the shore and out over the North Sea. The historic port city of Hartlepool has award-winning attractions, a fantastic marina, beaches and countryside.

Newcastle & Tyne and Wear

Newcastle-upon-Tyne, once a shipbuilding centre, is a rejuvenated city of proud civic tradition with fine restaurants, theatres, and one of the liveliest arts scenes outside London. As well as the landmark Baltic Contemporary Art Gallery, there's the Laing Art Gallery, the Great North Museum and The Sage concert venue. The Theatre Royal is the third home of the Royal Shakespeare Company and a venue for major touring companies. The Metro Centre in neighbouring Gateshead attracts shoppers from all over the country with more than 300 outlets and 11 cinema screens.

Northumberland

Northumberland is an under visited holiday paradise where the scenery is wild and beautiful, the beaches golden and unspoiled, and the natives friendly. The region is edged by the North Sea, four national parks and the vast Border Forest Park. It includes Europe's largest Dark Sky zone best viewed from the Kielder Observatory while nearby Kielder Lake offers watersports, walking and cycling. Its eastern sea boundary makes a stunning coastline, stretching 100 miles from Staithes on the Cleveland boundary, to Berwick-on-Tweed, England's most northerly town, frequently fought over and with the finest preserved example of Elizabethan town walls in the country. In between you'll find as many holiday opportunities as changes of scenery.

Step back in time 2,000 years along Hadrian's Wall, explore the hills, forests and waterfalls of the National Parks, and discover historic castles, splendid churches and quaint towns. Visitors can trace man's occupation of the region from prehistoric times through rock carvings, ancient hill forts, Saxon churches, Norman priories, medieval castles, and a wealth of industrial archaeology. Housesteads Roman Fort at Haydon Bridge is the most complete example of a British Roman fort. It features magnificent ruins and stunning views of the countryside surrounding Hadrian's Wall.

The region has a rich maritime heritage too. Ruined coastal fortifications such as Dunstanburgh and fairy-tale Lindisfarne are relics of a turbulent past. Agriculture is also one of the region's most important industries. Take a trip on the Heatherslaw Light Railway, a narrow gauge line operating from Etal Village to Heatherslaw Mill, a restored waterdriven corn mill and agricultural museum near the delightful model village of Ford.

Visit – North East

 Attractions with this sign participate in the Visitor Attraction Quality Assurance Scheme.

County Durham & Tees Valley

Adventure Valley
Durham, County Durham DH1 5SG
(01913) 868291
www.adventurevalley.co.uk
Split into six Play Zones (with three under cover), you'll find the very best in family fun come rain or shine.

Billingham International Folklore Festival
Billingham, County Durham
www.billinghamfestival.co.uk
A festival of traditional and contemporary world dance, music and arts.

Bishop Auckland Food Festival
April, Bishop Auckland, County Durham
www.bishopaucklandfoodfestival.co.uk
Be inspired by cookery demonstrations and entertained by performers.

The Bowes Museum
Barnard Castle, County Durham DL12 8NP
(01833) 690606
www.thebowesmuseum.org.uk
A collection of outstanding European fine and decorative arts offering an acclaimed exhibition programme, special events and children's activities.

Durham Book Festival
Durham, County Durham
www.durhambookfestival.com
With writers covering everything from politics to poetry, and fiction to feminism, there's something for everyone at the Durham Book Festival. See website for dates and full programme.

Durham Castle
County Durham DH1 3RW
(01913) 343800
www.dur.ac.uk/durham.castle
Durham Castle is part of the Durham City World Heritage Site and has enjoyed a long history of

continuous use. Along with Durham Cathedral, it is among the greatest monuments of the Norman Conquest of Britain and is now home to students of University College, Durham. Entrance is by guided tour only, please telephone opening and tour times.

East Durham Heritage and Lifeboat Centre
County Durham, SR7 7EE
(0191) 581 8904
www.eastdurhamheritagegroup.co.uk
Take a look at exhibitions with themed displays on the area's maritime, industrial and social heritage dating back from before the 8th century.

Hall Hill Farm
Durham, County Durham DH7 0TA
(01388) 731333
www.hallhillfarm.co.uk
Award-winning farm attraction set in attractive countryside, see and touch the animals at close quarters.

Hamsterley Forest
Bishop Auckland, County Durham DL13 3NL
(01388) 488312
www.forestry.gov.uk/hamsterleyforest
A 5,000 acre mixed woodland open to the public all year.

Hartlepool Art Gallery
Hartlepool, Tees Valley TS24 7EQ
(01429) 869706
www.hartlepoolartgallery.co.uk
Former church building also includes the TIC and a bell tower viewing platform looking over Hartlepool.

Hartlepool's Maritime Experience
Tees Valley TS24 0XZ
(01429) 860077
www.hartlepoolsmaritimeexperience.com
A superb re-creation of an 18th century seaport and a fantastic place to visit. It brings to life the time of Nelson, Napoleon and the Battle of Trafalgar.

Hartlepool Museum
Maritime Avenue, Hartlepool TS24 0XZ
(01429) 860077
www.hartlepoolsmaritimeexperience.com
*Situated beside Hartlepool Historic Quay, includes
local historical exhibits, PSS Wingfield Castle and
the original lighthouse light.*

Head of Steam
Tees Valley DL3 6ST
(01325) 405060
www.darlington.gov.uk/leisure-and-culture/head-of-steam
*Restored 1842 station housing a collection of
exhibits relating to railways in the North East of
England, including Stephenson's Locomotion, call
for details of events.*

High Force Waterfall
Forest-in-Teesdale, County Durham DL12 0XH
(01833) 622209
www.highforcewaterfall.com
*Discover the force of nature at High Force, one of the
most spectacular waterfalls in England. Enjoy a picnic
or take a walk along many way marked routes.*

HMS Trincomalee
Hartlepool, Tees Valley TS24 0XZ
(01429) 223193
www.hms-trincomalee.co.uk
*HMS Trincomalee, built in 1817, is one of the oldest
ship afloat in Europe. Come aboard for a unique
experience of Navy life two centuries ago.*

Killhope, The North of England
Lead Mining Museum
Bishop Auckland, County Durham DL13 1AR
(01388) 537505
www.killhope.org.uk
*Fully restored Victorian lead mine and the most
complete lead mining site in Great Britain.*

Locomotion: The National Railway
Museum at Shildon
Shildon, County Durham DL4 2RE
(01904) 685780
www.nrm.org.uk/locomotion
*The first National Museum in the North East. Free
admission. View over 60 vehicles, children's play
area and interactive displays.*

mima

Middlesbrough, Tees Valley TS1 2AZ
(01642) 931232
www.visitmima.com
*mima, Middlesbrough Institute of Modern Art,
is a £14.2m landmark gallery in the heart of
Middlesbrough. mima showcases an international
programme of fine art and applied art from the
1900s to the present day.*

Preston Hall Museum and Park
Stockton-on-Tees, Tees Valley TS18 3RH
(01642) 527375
www.prestonparkmuseum.co.uk
*A Georgian country house set in beautiful parkland
overlooking the River Tees. A Museum of social
history with a recreated Victorian street and
working craftsmen.*

Raby Castle
Staindrop, County Durham DL2 3AH
(01833) 660202
www.rabycastle.com
*Home of Lord Barnard's family since 1626, includes
a 200 acre deer park, gardens, carriage collection,
adventure playground, shop and tearoom.*

Saltburn Smugglers Heritage Centre
Saltburn-by-the-Sea, Tees Valley TS12 1HF
(01287) 625252
www.thisisredcar.co.uk/visit/saltburn-smugglers-
heritage-centre.asp
*Step back into Saltburn's past and experience the
authentic sights, sounds and smells.*

Saltholme Wildlife Reserve
Middlesbrough, Tees Valley TS2 1TU
(01642) 546625
www.rspb.org.uk/reserves/guide/s/saltholme
An amazing wildlife experience in the Tees Valley.

Weardale Railway
County Durham, DL13 2YS
(01388) 526203
www.weardale-railway.org.uk
*The Weardale Railway follows the path of the River
Wear and passes through spectacular scenery. A
good time is to be had by all on these heritage
locomotives.*

Newcastle & Tyne And Wear

Arbeia Roman Fort and Museum
South Shields, Tyne and Wear NE33 2BB
(01912) 771410
www.arbeiaromanfort.org.uk
Arbeia is the best reconstruction of a Roman fort in Britain and offers visitors a unique insight into the every day life of the Roman army, from the soldier in his barrack room to the commander in his luxurious house.

BBC Tours Newcastle
Newcastle upon Tyne, NE2 4NS
www.bbc.co.uk/showsandtours/tours/newcastle
Take a tour of the broadcasting house for an in depth behind the scenes look into what it's like to be a director and presenter for the BBC. Take a seat in the director's chair, or ask questions that have always been a mystery.

Centre for Life
Newcastle-upon-Tyne, Tyne and Wear NE1 4EP
(01912) 438210
www.life.org.uk
The Centre for Life is an award-winning science centre where imaginative exhibitions, interactive displays and special events promote greater understanding of science and provoke curiosity in the world around us.

Discovery Museum
Newcastle-upon-Tyne, Tyne and Wear NE1 4JA
(01912) 326789
www.twmuseums.org.uk/discovery
A wide variety of experiences for all the family to enjoy.

Evolution Emerging
May, Newcastle, Tyne and Wear
www.evolutionemerging.com
The North East's premier music event, taking place over a Bank Holiday.

Great North Museum: Hancock
Newcastle-upon-Tyne, Tyne and Wear NE2 4PT
(0191) 208 6765
www.greatnorthmuseum.org.uk
See major new displays showing the wonder of the animal and plant kingdoms, objects from the Ancient Greeks and a planetarium and a life-size T-Rex.

Hatton Gallery
Newcastle-upon-Tyne, Tyne and Wear NE1 7RU
(0191) 208 6059
www.hattongallery.org.uk
Temporary exhibitions of contemporary and historical art. Permanent display of Kurt Schwitters' Merzbarn.

Laing Art Gallery
Newcastle-upon-Tyne, Tyne and Wear NE1 8AG
(0191) 278 1611
www.laingartgallery.org.uk
Home to an important collection of 18th and 19th century painting, which is shown alongside temporary exhibitions of historic and contemporary art.

Namco Funscape
Gateshead, Tyne and Wear, NE11 9XY
(0191) 406 1066
www.namcofunscape.com/location/metrocentre-gateshead
Find fun in 38, 000 sq ft of state-of-the-art arcade games, tenpin bowling, fantastic bars and the fastest dodgem track in Europe.

National Glass Museum
Liberty Way, Sunderland, SR6 0GL
(01915) 155555
www.nationalglasscentre.com
Overlooking the River Wear, enjoy an ever-changing programme of exhibitions, live glass blowing, and banqueting and a stunning restaurant.

Newcastle Theatre Royal
Newcastle upon Tyne NE1 6BR
(0844) 811 2121
www.theatreroyal.co.uk
The Theatre Royal is a Grade I listed building situated on historic Grey Street in Newcastle-upon-Tyne. It hosts a variety of shows, including ballet, contemporary dance, drama, musicals and opera in a restored 1901 Frank Matcham Edwardian interior.

Sage Gateshead
Gateshead Quays, Gateshead NE8 2JR
(0191) 443 4661
www.sagegateshead.com
A concert venue and centre for musical education on the south bank of the River Tyne. It stages a varied and eclectic programme in state-of-the-art halls.

Segedunum Roman Fort, Baths & Museum 🌹
Wallsend, Tyne and Wear NE28 6HR
(0191) 278 4217
www.segedunumromanfort.org.uk
*Segedunum Roman Fort is the gateway to
Hadrian's Wall. Explore the excavated fort site, visit
reconstructions of a Roman bath house, learn about
the history of the area in the museum and enjoy the
view from the 35 metre viewing tower.*

Tyneside Cinema
Newcastle upon Tyne, Tyne and Wear NE1 6QG
(0191) 227 5500
www.tynesidecinema.co.uk
*Showing the best films in beautiful art deco
surroundings, Tyneside Cinema's programme ranges
from mainstream to arthouse and world cinema. As
the last surviving Newsreel theatre still operating
full-time in the UK, this Grade II-listed building is a
must-visit piece of lovingly restored heritage.*

WWT Washington Wetland Centre 🌹
Washington, Tyne and Wear NE38 8LE
(01914) 165454
www.wwt.org.uk/visit/washington
*45 hectares of wetland, woodland and wildlife reserve.
Home to wildfowl, insects and flora with lake-side hides,
wild bird feeding station, waterside café, picnic areas,
sustainable garden, playground and events calendar.*

Northumberland

Alnwick Beer Festival
September, Alnwick, Northumberland
www.alnwickbeerfestival.co.uk
*If you enjoy real ale, or simply want to enjoy a
fantastic social event, then make sure you pay this
festival a visit.*

Alnwick Castle
Northumberland NE66 1NQ
(01665) 511100
www.alnwickcastle.com
*A significant visitor attraction with lavish State
Rooms and superb art collections, as well as
engaging activities and events for all ages, and all
set in beautiful landscape by Northumberland-
born 'Capability' Brown. Potter fans will recognise
Alnwick as Hogwarts from the Harry Potter films.*

Bailiffgate Museum
Alnwick, Northumberland NE66 1LX
(01665) 605847
www.bailiffgatemuseum.co.uk
*Bailiffgate Museum brings to life the people and places
of North Northumberland in exciting interactive style.*

Bamburgh Castle 🌹
Northumberland NE69 7DF
(01668) 214515
www.bamburghcastle.com
*A spectacular castle with fantastic coastal views.
The stunning Kings Hall and Keep house collections
of armour, artwork, porcelain and furniture.*

Belsay Hall, Castle & Gardens
Nr Morpeth, Northumberland NE20 0DX
(01661) 881636
www.english-heritage.org.uk
*Lose yourself at Belsay with its unique combination
of Grecian architecture, medieval ruins, formal
terraces and lush jungle-esque Quarry Garden. Enjoy
wonderful views from the top of the castle tower and
a tasty treat at the tempting Victorian tearoom.*

Chillingham Castle
Northumberland, NE66 5NJ
01668 215359
www.chillingham-castle.com
*A remarkable Medieval fortress with Tudor additions,
torture chamber, shop, dungeon, tearoom, woodland
walks, furnished rooms and topiary garden.*

Cragside House, Gardens & Estate

Morpeth, Northumberland NE65 7PX
(01669) 620333
www.nationaltrust.org.uk/cragside/
*Built on a rocky crag high above Debdon Burn,
the house is crammed with ingenious gadgets
and was the first in the world to be lit electrically.
The gardens are breathtaking with 5 lakes, one of
Europe's largest rock gardens, and over 7 million
trees and shrubs.*

Haydon Bridge Festival

June, Haydon Bridge, Northumberland NE47 6AE
www.haydonbridgefestival.co.uk
Annual celebration of the finest real ales and wines.

Hexham Abbey Festival

September, Hexham, Northumberland
www.hexhamabbeyfestival.org.uk
*An exciting array of events to capture the
imagination, bringing the very best world-class
musicians and artists to Hexham.*

Hexham Old Gaol

Northumberland NE46 1XD
(01670) 624523
www.hexhamoldgaol.org.uk
Step into the oldest purpose-built prison in
England. *Tour the Old Gaol, 1330AD, by glass lift.
Meet the gaoler to learn about the treatment of
criminals then put yourself in the prisoners' shoes
and try on costumes.*

Kielder Castle Forest Park Centre

Northumberland NE48 1ER
(01434) 250209
www.forestry.gov.uk/kielder
*Features include forest shop, information centre,
Tearoom and exhibitions. Bike hire available.*

Lindisfarne Castle

Northumberland TD15 2SH
(01289) 389244
www.nationaltrust.org.uk/lindisfarne-castle/
*Rising from the sheer rock face at the tip of Holy
Island off the Northumberland coast, Lindisfarne
Castle was built to defend a harbour sheltering
English ships during skirmishes with Scotland.*

Northumberland National Park

Northumberland, NE46 1BS
(01434) 605555
www.northumberlandnationalpark.org.uk
*Covering 405 acres of breathtaking landscape rich
in wildlife, heritage and picturesque valleys.*

RNLI Grace Darling Museum

Bamburgh, Northumberland NE69 7AE
(01668) 214910
www.rnli.org.uk/gracedarling
*A museum dedicated to Grace Darling and her
family, as well as all those who Save Lives at Sea.*

Warkworth Castle

Warkworth, Northumberland NE65 0UJ
(01665) 711423
www.english-heritage.org.uk/warkworthcastle
*This hill-top fortress and hermitage offers a
fantastic family day out. The magnificent cross-
shaped keep was once home to 'Harry Hotspur',
immortalised as a rebel lord by Shakespeares.*

Whalton Manor Gardens

Northumberland, NE61 3UT
(01670) 775205
www.whaltonmanor.co.uk
*Experience a first-hand insight into nature's true
beauty with a guided tour from the owner. Why not
stay for home-cooked lunch and a cream tea as well?*

Tourist Information Centres

When you arrive at your destination, visit the Tourist Information Centre for quality assured help with accommodation and information about local attractions and events, or email your request before you go.

Alnwick	2 The Shambles	01670 622152	alnwick.tic@northumberland.gov.uk
Amble	Queen Street Car Park	01665 712313	amble.tic@northumberland.gov.uk
Bellingham	The Heritage Centre	01434 220616	bellinghamtic@btconnect.com
Berwick-Upon-Tweed	Walker Gate	01670 622155 /	berwick.tic@northumberland.gov.uk
Bishop Auckland	Town Hall	01388 602610	bishopauckland.touristinfo@durham.gov.uk
Corbridge	Hill Street	01434 632815	corbridge.tic@northumberland.gov.uk
Craster	Craster Car Park	01665 576007	craster.tic@northumberland.gov.uk
Darlington	13 Hoursemarket	01325 388666	tic@darlinton.gov.uk
Durham	3-4 Millenium Place	03000 262626	visitor@thisisdurham.com
Gateshead	Central Library	0191 433 8420	libraries@gateshead.gov.uk
Guisborough	Priory Grounds	01287 633801	guisborough_tic@redcar-cleveland.gov.uk
Haltwhistle	Westgate	01434 321863	haltwhistle.tic@northumberland.gov.uk
Hartlepool	Hartlepool Art Gallery	01429 869706	hpooltic@hartlepool.gov.uk
Hexham	Hexham Library	01670 620450	hexham.tic@northumberland.gov.uk
Middlesbrough	Middlesbrough Info. Centre & Box Office	01642 729900	tic@middlesbrough.gov.uk
Middleton-in-Teesdale	10 Market Place	01833 641001	middletonplus@compuserve.com
Morpeth	The Chantry	01670 623455	morpeth.tic@northumberland.gov.uk
North Shields	Unit 18	0191 2005895	ticns@northtyneside.gov.uk
Once Brewed	National Park Centre	01434 344396	tic.oncebrewed@nnpa.org.uk
Otterburn	Otterburn Mill	01830 520093	tic@otterburnmill.co.uk
Saltburn by Sea	Saltburn Library	01287 623584	saltburn_library@redcar-cleveland.gov.uk
Seahouses	Seafield Car Park	01670 625593	seahouses.tic@northumberland.gov.uk
South Shields	The Word	0191 424 7788	tourism@southtyneside.gov.uk
Stockton-On-Tees	High Street	01642 528130	visitorinformation@stockton.gov.uk
Whitley Bay	York Road	0191 6435395	ticwb@northtyneside.gov.uk
Wooler	The Cheviot Centre	01668 282123	wooler.tic@northumberland.gov.uk

Regional Contacts and Information

For more information on accommodation, attractions, activities, events and holidays in North East England, contact one of the regional or local tourism organisations. Their websites have a wealth of information and many produce free publications to help you get the most out of your visit.

www.visitnortheastengland.com

www.thisisdurham.com
www.newcastlegateshead.com
www.visitnorthumberland.com
www.visithadrianswall.co.uk
www.visitnorthtyneside.com
www.visitsouthtyneside.co.uk
www.seeitdoitsunderland.co.uk

Stay – North East

Entries appear alphabetically by town name in each county. A key to symbols appears on page 6

BISHOP AUCKLAND, Co Durham Map ref 5C2 Ⓢ

VisitEngland
★★★★
SELF CATERING

New Cottage

Contact: Margaret Partridge, Owner, Hollymoor Farm, Cockfield DL13 5HF
T: (01388) 718567 **E:** margandpatpartridge@tiscali.co.uk
W: www.hollymoorfarm.co.uk

Units	1
Sleeps	2

PER UNIT PER WEEK
£280.00

New Cottage is on a working farm in County Durham, on the borders of the beautiful Durham Dales, Teesdale and Weardale. With its elevated position it is surrounded by beautiful views. The panoramic views from the lounge are a never-ending source of delight - they are stunning. The sunsets are truly magnificent.
Open: All year.
Nearest Shop: 1 Mile
Nearest Pub: 1 Mile

Site: ✿ P Property: 🖧 🖵 Unit: 🗐 ▣ 🔧 📺 BBQ

BOWES, Co Durham Map ref 5B3 Ⓢ

VisitEngland
★★★★
SELF CATERING

VisitEngland
Gold
AWARD

Mellwaters Barn

Contact: Mr Andrew Tavener, Mellwaters Barn, East Mellwaters Farm, Stainmore Road, Bowes, Barnard Castle DL12 9RH **T:** (01833) 628181 **E:** mellwatersbarn@aol.com
W: www.mellwatersbarn.co.uk **£ BOOK ONLINE**

Units	4
Sleeps	2-4

PER UNIT PER WEEK
£294.00 - £525.00

SPECIAL PROMOTIONS
3 nights short breaks from £136, small cottage, £240 large cottage.

We would like to welcome you to Mellwaters Barn Cottages in beautiful Teesdale centrally placed in Northern England within easy reach of the Lake District, Yorkshire Dales, Durham and York. Auckland Castle, Beamish and Bowes Museum are all places of interest and are easy to reach. Mellwaters Barn is an ideal visitor centre in beautiful countryside with clean air; these award-winning spacious luxury cottages are designed for a perfect relaxing holiday. All cottages are fully equipped and prices include all accommodation costs. Open all year. Arrival / departure any day of the week.

Open: All year, short breaks available.
Nearest Shop: Barnard Castle
Nearest Pub: Bowes

Units: Two cottages fully wheelchair accessible, sleep four people, bedrooms on the ground floor. Two smaller cottages sleep 2 people bedrooms upstairs.

f

Site: P Property: 🖳 🖧 🖵 Unit: 🗐 🖾 ▣ 🔧 ◎ 📀

CORNRIGGS, Co Durham Map ref 5B2 Ⓢ

VisitEngland
★★★★★
SELF CATERING

Cornriggs Cottages

Contact: Mrs Janet Elliott, Low Cornriggs Farm, Cowshill in Weardale, Bishop Auckland, Durham DL13 1AQ **T:** (01388) 537600 / 07760 766794 **E:** cornriggsfarm@btconnect.com
W: www.cornriggsfarm.co.uk **£ BOOK ONLINE**

Units	2
Sleeps	2-6

PER UNIT PER WEEK
£399.00 - £550.00

Both luxury cottages have spectacular views. Easy access to Durham, Beamish and The Lakes. Three large accessible bedrooms, two WC's with shower and bathroom. Dining kitchen very well equipped, large lounge with fire and big comfy sofas, Satellite TV & Garden. Wi-Fi & internet access. Working farm with Hereford cattle and beautiful wild flower meadows/birds. Breakfast is available. Near to the village of Cowshill. **Open:** All year.
Nearest Shop: 4 miles **Nearest Pub:** 1 mile

Site: ✿ P Payment: € Leisure: 🚲 ♪ ▶ Property: 🖳 🖧 🖵 Children: 🐴 🛏 🎎
Unit: 🗐 🖾 ▣ 🔧 📺 ◎ 📀

DURHAM, Co Durham Map ref 5C2
SatNav DH1 4PS **B**

VisitEngland ★★★★ GUEST ACCOMMODATION
VisitEngland *Silver* AWARD

B&B PER ROOM PER NIGHT
D: £100.00 - £130.00

Castle View Guest House
4 Crossgate, Durham DH1 4PS **T:** (0191) 386 8852 **E:** castle_view@hotmail.com
W: www.castle-view.co.uk

Two hundred and fifty year old listed building in the heart of the old city, with woodland and riverside walks and magnificent views of the cathedral and castle. Complimentary parking.
Directions: From A1(M) take junction 62, follow signs A690 Crook until river crossing. At traffic lights turn left into Crossgate, next to St Margarets Church.
Bedrooms: 3 double, 2 twin.
Open: All year except Christmas and New Year.

Site: ✿ Payment: 💷 Property: 🖥 Children: 😊² Catering: 🍴 Room: 🔌 ✋ 📺 🛁

DURHAM, Co Durham Map ref 5C2
SatNav DH1 3RH **B**

VisitEngland ★★★ GUEST ACCOMMODATION

B&B PER ROOM PER NIGHT
S: £35.00 - £40.00
D: £60.00 - £75.00
EVENING MEAL PER PERSON
£15.00 - £35.00

St Chad's College
18 North Bailey, Durham DH1 3RH **T:** (01913) 343358 **F:** (01913) 343371
E: chads.admin@durham.ac.uk
W: www.dur.ac.uk/chads/

In the heart of historic Durham, adjacent to the World Heritage Site and next to the Cathedral, St Chad's provides comfortable modern accommodation, supported by friendly service, in its range of listed buildings - a spectacular location. Group bookings welcome.

Directions: Follow the A1(M) until the A690, direct to Durham, towards Cathedral. The college lies opposite of Durham Cathedral.

Bedrooms: Over 150 en suite and standard bedrooms. Evening meals pre book only.
Open: Easter/Summer student vacations.

Site: ✿ Payment: 💷 Leisure: 🎵 ▶ Property: 🅱 Children: 😊 🍴 ♿ Catering: 🍷 🍴 Room: ✋ 🛁

DURHAM, Co Durham Map ref 5C2
SatNav DH1 3RJ **B**

VisitEngland ★★★ GUEST ACCOMMODATION

B&B PER ROOM PER NIGHT
S: £36.00 - £48.00
D: £64.00 - £80.00

St John's College
3 South Bailey, Durham DH1 3RJ **T:** (0191) 334 3877 **E:** s.l.hobson@durham.ac.uk
W: www.durham.ac.uk/st-johns.college

Located in the heart of Durham City alongside the cathedral, St John's offers accommodation in distinctive, historic buildings with riverside gardens.
Directions: Take A1(M) motorway junction 62, dual carriageway A690 Gilesgate roundabout. Take third exit, second left exit, then left to Market Square, 200 yards to College.
Bedrooms: Double and single en suites, single, double and twin standard. **Open:** Summer vacations only.

Site: ✿ Payment: 💷 Property: 🖥 🅱 Children: 😊 ♿ Catering: 🍴 Room: ✋ 🛁

MIDDLETON-IN-TEESDALE, Co Durham   Map ref 5B3   Ⓢ

Firethorn Cottage

Contact: Mrs Clare Long, Firethorn Cottage, c/o 53 Union Street, Fairview, Cheltenham, Gloucestershire GL52 2JN **T:** (01242) 700308 / 07780 951162
E: Firethorncottage@hotmail.co.uk

Units   1
Sleeps   2
PER UNIT PER WEEK
£225.00 - £275.00

A delightful Grade II listed, detached stone-built lead miner's cottage. One up/one down with flagstone floor, lounge diner, open fire, traditional rag rugs and beamed ceiling. Modern bathroom upstairs with bath and shower over and heated towel rail. Double bedroom with storage. Outside a small cottage garden with views. Night storage heaters throughout. Superb walking and fishing close by. **Open:** All year.
Nearest Shop: 200 yards **Nearest Pub:** 300 yards

Site: ✿ Property: 🐕 🖳 Unit: 🖥 🍳 📺 📀 ⌁

ALNWICK, Northumberland   Map ref 5C1   SatNav NE66 2HJ   Ⓑ

Alnwick Lodge

West Cawledge Park, Alnwick NE66 2HJ
T: (01665) 604363 / (01665) 603377 / 07392 848 036 **E:** bookings@alnwicklodge.com
W: www.alnwicklodge.com **£ BOOK ONLINE**

B&B PER ROOM PER NIGHT
S: £45.00 - £55.00
D: £62.00 - £130.00
EVENING MEAL PER PERSON
£15.00 - £30.00

SPECIAL PROMOTIONS
Stay Monday to Thursday get Thursday half price.
Stay Friday & Saturday get Sunday half price, Ex Bank Holidays and July & August.
Adaptable family rooms.

Lonely Planet recommended and Trip Advisor 4* rated accommodation in beautiful Northumberland. A unique creation AD1650-2012. Alnwick Lodge, West Cawledge Park is a combination of history and rural charm with an air of sophistication, whilst linked to technology. Fascinating, incomparable accommodation for business, pleasure, conferences, film crews and parties. Antique galleries, reclamation and log fires.

Directions: 1 mile south of Alnwick. Direct access from A1 (trunk road) highway signposted to West Cawledge Park (chair on the roof).

Bedrooms: 4 single, 4 double, 3 twin and 4 family. Glamping - Foresters Wagon, Shepherds Hut, Gypsy Caravans. Camping.
Open: All year.

Site: ✿ P Payment: 💳 Leisure: ⚤ 🎣 ⚑ ∪ Property: 🐕 🖵 Children: 🐾 🛏 ♣ Catering: 🍴
Room: 🍳 ☕ 📺 🛁 ♨ ⌁

BAMBURGH, Northumberland   Map ref 5C1   Ⓢ

Breaks For 2

Contact: Gabrielle McAleaney, Property Manager, Bradford House, Bradford Farm, Belford, Northumberland NE70 7JT **T:** (01668) 213432 / 07712 159134 **E:** info@breaksfor2.co.uk
W: www.breaksfor2.co.uk **£ BOOK ONLINE**

Units   4
Sleeps   2
PER UNIT PER WEEK
£200.00 - £600.00

🇫 🐦

Our cottages are located in the north of England, in the beautiful and often referred to as, The Norths best kept secret. We are well placed on the edge of historic Bamburgh.
Breaks for 2 gives you the choice of four cottages – Rose Cottage, Poppy Cottage Tulip Cottage and Daisy Cottage and with all year availability, you can experience the stunning views of Northumberland whenever you desire. **Open:** All year.
Nearest Shop: 2 miles **Nearest Pub:** 2 miles

Site: P Leisure: 🎣 ⚑ Property: 🖵 📶 🖳 Unit: 🖥 🍳 📺

BAMBURGH, *Northumberland* *Map ref 5C1* **S**

Outchester & Ross Farm Cottages

Contact: John and Heather Sutherland, Outchester & Ross Farm Cottages, The Farmhouse, Ross, Belford, Northumberland NE70 7EN **T:** (01668) 213336 **E:** stay@rosscottages.co.uk
W: www.rosscottages.co.uk **£ BOOK ONLINE**

Units	17
Sleeps	2-6

PER UNIT PER WEEK
£320.00 - £1055.00

SPECIAL PROMOTIONS
Special offers from time to time. Discounts for under occupancy. Please look on the website.

Enjoy a peaceful break in spacious, warm 4 and 5 star cottages, close to beaches, cycle and walking routes. Our cottages sleep 2 to 6 and are comfortable and well-equipped with Wi-Fi and private gardens. Three cottages are dog friendly. Star gazing observatory, extra telescopes, canoe, bird-hide and barbecue available at no extra charge.

Cottages at Ross are walking distance to spectacular, unspoilt Ross Sands, overlooking Holy Island. Or enjoy a romantic 5 star retreat in our beautiful Ducket, an 18th century stone tower, now restored with 21st century facilities.

Open: All year.
Nearest Shop: 3 miles
Nearest Pub: 3 miles

Site: ✿ P **Payment:** 💳 **Leisure:** ♿ ▶ ♉ **Property:** 🏠 🗄 📶 **Children:** 👶 🛏 🏃
Unit: 🖥 📞 📺 🎬 🌐 📞

BAMBURGH, *Northumberland* *Map ref 5C1* **S**

Point Cottages

Contact: Mrs Elizabeth Sanderson, Point Cottages, 30 The Oval, Benton, Newcastle-upon-Tyne NE12 9PP **T:** (01912) 662800 **F:** (01912) 151630 **E:** info@bamburgh-cottages.co.uk
W: www.bamburgh-cottages.co.uk **£ BOOK ONLINE**

Units	5
Sleeps	2-6

PER UNIT PER WEEK
£335.00 - £1400.00

SPECIAL PROMOTIONS
3 night winter breaks from £245. Please contact for details.

A cluster of one, two and three bedroom cottages in a superb location next to a beautiful links golf course at the edge of historic Bamburgh overlooking magnificent sandy beaches. Large shared garden. Views to Farne Islands, Lindisfarne & Bamburgh Castle. Ten car parking spaces, two per cottage. Guest comments: really cosy - beautiful - comfortable - peaceful - very enjoyable - great beds - will return. Free - Wi-Fi.

Open: All year.
Nearest Shop: 1 mile
Nearest Pub: 1 mile

Units: All ground floor except Aiden. Cuthbert/Bede interconnectable (10 person), shared laundry at rear of cottages.

Site: ✿ P **Leisure:** ♿ ♪ ▶ ♉ **Property:** 🐾 🏠 🗄 📶 **Children:** 👶 🛏 🏃 **Unit:** 📺 🌐 🎬 BBQ

BELFORD, Northumberland   Map ref 5B1   SatNav NE70 7DP C

Dunham Leisure Limited

South Meadows Caravan Park, South Road, Belford, Northumberland NE70 7DP
T: (01668) 213326 **E:** info@southmeadows.co.uk
W: www.southmeadows.co.uk **£ BOOK ONLINE**

VisitEngland
★★★★★
HOLIDAY, TOURING
& CAMPING PARK

🚐 (45)   £22.00-£26.00
🚌 (45)   £22.00-£26.00
⛺ (34)   £19.00-£23.00
🏠 (1)   £450.00-£750.00
79 touring pitches

Friendly rural site, near the coast and close to the Cheviots and Lindisfarne. Excellent washroom facilities. Full hook-up connections, free Wi-Fi. Within walking distance of Belford village. 10 minutes' drive to Bamburgh Castle and beach and 15 minutes' drive to the famous Alnwick Castle renowned for the Harry Potter films also Alnwick Gardens which is a must see. Local bus service in the village.

Directions: Heading North 15 miles south of Berwick turn right off A1 onto B6349 Heading South 15 miles north of Alnwick turn left off A1 onto B6349 turn left after 500 yards following signs to South Meadows.

Open: All year.

Site: ▲🄿 **Payment:** 🏧 ☼ **Leisure:** ▶ **Children:** ⛹ 🎢 **Park:** 🐶 🚐 🛢 🍴 🎣 **Touring:** 🔌 🕭 🔌 ⚡

BELSAY, Northumberland   Map ref 5B2   S

Shortflatt Farm Cottage

Contact: Victoria Dodd, Owner, West Belsay Farm, Belsay, Northumberland NE20 0JN
T: (01661) 881318 / 07500 958905 **E:** gwdodd@westbelsay.co.uk
W: www.shortflattfarm.co.uk **£ BOOK ONLINE**

VisitEngland
★★★★
SELF CATERING

Units   1
Sleeps   1-4
PER UNIT PER WEEK
£425.00 - £650.00

Cosy and inviting detached Northumbrian property, a former farmhouse in a picturesque and secluded rural location with a private lake and summerhouse. Centrally located for all Northumberland has to offer. Fully refurbished and modernised in 2016. Log burner, open pastoral views in all directions. Large enclosed walled garden. Sleeps 4 in 2 rooms. Great for cyclists, walkers and dog lovers. **Open:** All year.
Nearest Shop: 3 miles **Nearest Pub:** 5 miles

WALKERS FAMILIES CYCLISTS PETS
WALKERS FAMILIES CYCLISTS PETS

Site: ❀ **P** **Property:** 🐾 **Children:** ⛹ **Unit:** 🛢 🛢 📺 🛢 ♿

BERWICK-UPON-TWEED, Northumberland   Map ref 5B1   SatNav TD15 1DU B

Alannah House

84 Church Street, Berwick-upon-Tweed, Northumberland TD15 1DU **T:** (01289) 307252
E: info@alannahhouse.com
W: www.alannahhouse.com

VisitEngland
★★★★
BED & BREAKFAST

VisitEngland
Silver
AWARD

B&B PER ROOM PER NIGHT
S: £50.00 - £60.00
D: £75.00 - £80.00

Georgian town house, situated in town centre within the famous Elizabethan town walls. We have a well maintained walled garden and patio area for guests' use. Parking permits available. All rooms en suite and have digital TV.
Directions: Enter Berwick town centre, head for town hall turn immediately left behind the hall, 400 yards on the right past the police station. **Bedrooms:** 1 double, 1 triple, 1 family. All en suite.
Open: All year.

WALKERS CYCLISTS
WALKERS CYCLISTS

Site: ❀ **Leisure:** ♪ ▶ **Property:** 🚐 🛢 **Children:** ⛹ 🛏 🚶 **Catering:** 🍴 **Room:** 📶 ♨ ♿ 📺

BERWICK-UPON-TWEED, Northumberland   Map ref 5B1   S

Broadstone Cottage - Norham

Contact: Mr Edward Chantler, Broadstone Farm, Grafty Green, Maidstone ME17 2AT
T: (01622) 850207   **E:** davidchantler@btconnect.com

VisitEngland ★★★ SELF CATERING

Units 1
Sleeps 1-5
PER UNIT PER WEEK
£175.00 - £375.00

Village cottage. Ideal centre for touring, walking and fishing holidays. 20 minutes to beach. Shops and pubs nearby. Full central heating. Bathroom with shower. One double, one twin. Good sized secure garden.
Open: All year.
Nearest Shop: 0.05 miles
Nearest Pub: 0.05 miles

Site: ✿ P Property: 🐕 🖳 Children: 🛏 🍴 Unit: 🗐 🖵 📷 🔌 📺

BERWICK-UPON-TWEED, Northumberland   Map ref 5B1   SatNav TD15 2PL   B

Fenham Farm Coastal Bed & Breakfast

Beal, Berwick-upon-Tweed TD15 2PL **T:** (01289) 381245 **E:** stay@fenhamfarm.co.uk
W: www.fenhamfarm.co.uk **£ BOOK ONLINE**

VisitEngland ★★★★ GUEST ACCOMMODATION
VisitEngland Gold AWARD

B&B PER ROOM PER NIGHT
S: £75.00 - £85.00
D: £95.00 - £105.00

Quality Bed & Breakfast accommodation in converted farm outbuildings on a beautiful coastal spot overlooking the Holy Island of Lindisfarne. 7 warm & comfortable en suite bedrooms. Lounge with sea view. Delicious locally sourced breakfasts.
Directions: Fenham Farm is on the coast approximately 1.5 miles off the A1, 10 miles south of Berwick upon Tweed and 6 miles north of Belford.
Bedrooms: 6 double/ twin, 1 family.
Open: Easter until November.

f 𝕐

Site: P Payment: 💳 Leisure: ▶ Property: 🏊 🖳 🅿 ⊘ Children: 🛏 🍴 ♿
Catering: 🍴 Room: 🔌 ♨ 📺 🕎

BERWICK-UPON-TWEED, Northumberland   Map ref 5B1   S

Marlborough Cottage

Contact: Mr Peter Adamson, Proprietor, Marlborough House, 133 Main Street, Spittal, Berwick-upon-Tweed TD15 1RP **T:** (01289) 305293 / 07443 953857
E: marlboroughcottage@live.co.uk **W:** www.marlboroughcottage.info

VisitEngland ★★★★ SELF CATERING

Units 1
Sleeps 1-5
PER UNIT PER WEEK
£300.00 - £600.00

Superior two-bedroom cottage, enviable seafront location, comfortable fully-furnished sea-facing lounge, fully equipped kitchen, shower-room with double-sized cubicle provided with grips & anti-slip mats. Ramp access to Cottage, all on one level, wheelchair-accessible, off-road private parking. Freshly-laundered bedding & towels provided Sheltered furnished patio area for guests' use. **Open:** All year, including Festive Season.
Nearest Shop: 0.25 miles **Nearest Pub:** 0.25 miles

Site: ✿ P Leisure: ⚓ 🎣 ▶ ∪ Property: 🖳 🗐 🖳 Children: 🛏 Unit: 🗐 🖳 🖵 🔌 📺 🕎 📀

CHATHILL, Northumberland   Map ref 5C1   S

The Joiners Arms

Contact: Newton By The Sea NE66 3EA **T:** 01665 576 239 **E:** accommodation@newton-hall.com
W: www.joiners-arms.com **£ BOOK ONLINE**

VisitEngland ★★★★★ INN

Units 5
Sleeps 1-10

Our 5 Gorgeous boutique bedrooms are individually designed to put the luxe into luxury, with irresistible charms like four-poster beds, roll top baths and lots of room for love.
Expect antler chandeliers, low-slung French beds, double-ended baths in the corner of most rooms. Some have Juliet balconies with a panoramic rural vista, others exposed brickwork, all have rich colours & flat-screen TVs.
Open: 365 days.

f 𝕐

Site: P Payment: 💳 Property: 🐕 🖳 🖳 Children: 🛏 🍴 ♿ Unit: 🔌 📺 📀

CRASTER, *Northumberland*   *Map ref 5C1*   S

VisitEngland ★★★★★ SELF CATERING   VisitEngland Gold AWARD

Craster Tower Penthouse Apartment

Contact: Mrs Fiona Craster, Craster Tower Penthouse Apartment, Craster Tower, Alnwick, Northumberland NE66 3SS **T:** (01665) 576674 **E:** stay@crastertower.co.uk
W: www.crastertower.co.uk **£ BOOK ONLINE**

Units	1
Sleeps	1-8

PER UNIT PER WEEK
£650.00 - £1840.00

Spacious comfortable apartment encompassing the whole top floor of historic Craster Tower, beside picturesque fishing village producing world famous kippers. Elegantly furnished, with spectacular sea views. Ideal for beaches, walkers, golfers and history lovers. Comprehensively equipped kitchen, comfortable sitting room with flat screen TV, log burner and Wi-Fi, 18th century drawing room and tennis. **Open:** All year including Christmas and New Year. **Nearest Shop:** 0.10 miles **Nearest Pub:** 0.5 miles

Site: ✿ **P Payment:** 💳 € **Leisure:** 🚴 🏊 🏌 ↻ ◔ **Property:** 🐾 🖥 🖬 🗒 **Children:** 👶 🛏 🔥 **Unit:** 📺 🍴 📷 📼 🎮 📀 🌊 BBQ 📞

HALTWHISTLE, *Northumberland*   *Map ref 5B2*   S

VisitEngland ★★★★ SELF CATERING

Lambley Farm Cottages

Contact: Lambley Farm Cottages, Lambley CA8 7LQ **T:** 07967 274286
E: stay@lambleycottages.co.uk
W: www.lambleycottages.co.uk **£ BOOK ONLINE**

Units	5
Sleeps	3-28

PER UNIT PER WEEK
£299.00 - £845.00

This cluster of barn conversions are set within 90 acres. Close to the South Tyne River. Outside space is not in short supply here, as our guests are welcome to explore all of the 100 acre Lambley Country Estate. From the cottages, there are spectacular views along the salmon-rich River South Tyne and down the valley towards Lambley Viaduct. Sauna facilities now available and indoor games room. **Open:** All year.
Nearest Shop: 4 miles **Nearest Pub:** 1.5 miles

Site: ✿ **P Payment:** 💳 € **Leisure:** 🚴 🏊 🏌 ↻ ◔ **Property:** 🐾 🖥 🖬 🗒 **Children:** 👶 🛏 🔥 **Unit:** 📺 🍴 📷 📼 🎮 📀 BBQ

HEXHAM, *Northumberland*   *Map ref 5B2*   S

VisitEngland ★★★★ SELF CATERING

Braemar

Contact: Mrs Cynthia Bradley, Owner, Edenholme, John Martin Street, Haydon Bridge, Northumberland NE47 6AA **T:** (01434) 684622 / 07949 369222
E: edenholme@btinternet.com **W:** www.edenholme.co.uk **£ BOOK ONLINE**

Units	1
Sleeps	1-5

PER UNIT PER WEEK
£245.00 - £450.00

Delightful two bedroom bungalow with large garden to front and back. Sleeping 4/5 it is located in a small village with shops, pub and restaurant 100 yards away. Ideal location for visiting Hadrian's Wall, Northumberland, Kielder Water, Metro Centre, Durham, Carlisle, Lakes and Scotland.
Open: All year.
Nearest Shop: 100 yards
Nearest Pub: 100 yards

WALKERS WELCOME   **Site:** ✿ **P Leisure:** 🏊 🏌 **Property:** 🐾 🖥 🗒 **Children:** 👶 🛏 🔥 **Unit:** 📺 📷 📼 🎮 📀 BBQ

HEXHAM, *Northumberland*   *Map ref 5B2*   *SatNav NE46 2JP*   C

VisitEngland ★★ TOURING & CAMPING PARK

Hexham Racecourse Caravan Site

High Yarridge, Yarridge Road, Hexham NE46 2JP
T: (01434) 606847 **F:** (01434) 605814 **E:** hexrace.caravan@btconnect.com
W: www.hexham-racecourse.co.uk

🚐	(50)	£15.00-£18.00
🚍	(30)	£15.00-£18.00
⛺	(10)	£11.00
50 touring pitches		

Grass area, sloping in parts. Most pitches with electrical hook-up points. Separate area for tents.
Directions: From Hexham take the B6305 Allendale Road for 3 miles turn left at T Junction, site 1.5 miles on the right.
Open: May to September.

Site: ⛺🅿 **Payment:** 💳 ☀ **Leisure:** 🏌 ◔ **Children:** 👶 🛝 **Park:** 🐾 🖥 🗒 🚿 🚻 **Touring:** 🚰 🔌 ♿

HEXHAM, Northumberland   Map ref 5B2
SatNav NE46 1RS B

VisitEngland
★★★★
GUEST ACCOMMODATION

B&B PER ROOM PER NIGHT
S: £50.00 - £60.00
D: £110.00 - £150.00
HB PER PERSON PER NIGHT
£80.00 - £100.00

Loughbrow House
Dipton Mill Road NE46 1RS T: (01434) 603351 E: patriciaclark351@btinternet.com
W: www.loughbrow.fsnet.co.uk

A mansion house built in 1780 set in 9 acres of garden, surrounded by own farm land looking up the North Tyne valley. Situated 1 mile from Hexham. Ample parking.
Directions: From Hexham take B6306. After 0.25 miles take right-hand fork, Dipton Mill Road, for further 0.25 miles. Turn into drive gates, house is 0.5 miles.
Bedrooms: 2 single, 1 double, 2 twin with en suite £100 - £140 prpn, with private bathroom £95 - £120 prpn.
Open: All year except Christmas and New Year.

Site: ✿ P Leisure: ▶ Property: ▦ Children: ☌5 Catering: ⛾ Room: ☖ 💧 📺

MORPETH, Northumberland   Map ref 5C2
SatNav NE65 9QH C

VisitEngland
★★★★
HOLIDAY PARK

🚐 (22) £500.00-£980.00
🚍 (10) £500.00-£650.00
🚏 (5) £150.00-£480.00

Felmoor Park
Eshottheugh, Felton, Morpeth, Northumberland NE65 9QH
T: (01670) 787790 E: info@felmoorpark.com
W: www.felmoorpark.com **£ BOOK ONLINE**

Felmoor Holiday Park is set in 40 acres of Northumbrian woodland. We have luxury log cabins, lodges and static caravans to rent, most with hot tubs. Park facilities include Gym, Sauna and Steam room. Felmoor Park is centrally located for all of Northumberland's historical and natural attractions. We also have new and pre-loved homes available for sale.

Directions: 6 miles North of Morpeth or 9 miles South of Alnwick on the East side of the A1.

Open: All year.

f y

Site: ⌂ ▲🄿 Payment: 💳 ☼ Leisure: 🚲 ▶ 🎣 Children: ☌ ⚠ Park: 🐾 🚍 ▯

NEWTON-BY-THE-SEA, Northumberland   Map ref 5C1
S

VisitEngland
★★★★
SELF CATERING

VisitEngland
Gold AWARD

Units   13
Sleeps   2-8
PER UNIT PER WEEK
£165.00 - £1600.00

Link House Farm Holiday Cottages
Contact: Mrs Kathleen Thompson, Owner, Link House Farm, Newton-by-the-Sea, Alnwick, Northumberland NE66 3ED T: (01665) 576820 E: stay@linkhousefarm.co.uk
W: www.linkhousefarm.com

Northumbrian Luxury coastal cottages, located on our farm between the fishing villages of Craster & Beadnell. Each property is completely self contained and equipped to a high standard with their own garden area and seating. Also, a large adventure play ground and football area. Ideal for families, couples, walkers, cyclists and bird watchers or for those who deserve and crave a peaceful holiday on our beautiful picturesque coastline. No pets.
Open: All year. **Nearest Shop:** 2.5 Miles **Nearest Pub:** 0.5 Miles

Site: P Payment: 💳 Leisure: 🎵 ▶ ∪ Property: ▯ 🄳 Children: ☌ Unit: 🔲 ☖ 📺 📀

NEWTON-BY-THE-SEA, Northumberland   Map ref 5C1

S

Sea Winds

Contact: Mrs Jo Leiper, Sea Winds, Bygate, Black Heddon, Newcastle-upon-Tyne NE20 0JJ
T: (01661) 881506 / 07720 051201 **E:** stay@seawinds-lownewton.co.uk
W: www.seawinds-lownewton.co.uk

Units   1
Sleeps   2-6
PER UNIT PER WEEK
£425.00 - £950.00

Situated within the picturesque village of Low Newton-by-the-Sea, this former fisherman's cottage is just 200m from a beautiful sandy beach which is part of Northumberland's Heritage Coast. High-quality and offering many home comforts make it an exceptional family base to discover the secrets of the surrounding area.
Open: All year.
Nearest Shop: 3 miles
Nearest Pub: 0.25 miles

Site: ✿ P Leisure: ✦ Property: 🐾 🗄 🖬 Children: 🚼 🛏 ⚥ Unit: 🗄 🖬 🖥 🍴 📺 📀 DVD BBQ ☎

SEAHOUSES, Northumberland   Map ref 5C1

S

1, 2 & 3 The Old Bakery

Contact: Susan Parker, Owner, No's 1, 2 & 3 The Old Bakery, Crown Street, Seahouses, Northumberland NE68 7TQ **T:** (01484) 665633 / 07833 357974
E: susanparker400@btinternet.com **W:** www.oldbakeryseahouses.co.uk

Units   3
Sleeps   2

PER UNIT PER WEEK
£265.00 - £430.00

SPECIAL PROMOTIONS
Short break information available upon request.

Numbers 1, 2 & 3 The Old Bakery are 3 separate one double-bedroom properties converted from the old bakery in Seahouses. Each cottage is individually and tastefully furnished and offers excellent accommodation with private parking for a couple wishing to be based on the Northumbria Coast. The harbour and village amenities are a few minutes walk away, with another 10 minute walk to the beach. No2 The Old Bakery is a member of Seahouses Ocean Club.

Open: All year.
Nearest Shop: 2 minute walk
Nearest Pub: 4 minute walk

Units: 3 x 1 double-bedroomed cottages with bath & over bath shower, lounge, kitchen/diner and private parking.

Site: P Leisure: 🚲 🏌 ↟ ∪ Property: ⚓ 🗄 🖬 📺 🖥 Unit: 🗄 🖬 🖥 🍴 📺 DVD

BEAMISH, Tyne and Wear   Map ref 5C2

S

Riding Farm Cottages

Contact: Ms Louise Johnson, Owners, Riding Farm Cottages, Riding Farm, Riding Lane, Beamish, Durham, Gateshead NE11 0JA **T:** (01913) 701868 **E:** ridingfarm@btconnect.com
W: ridingfarmcottages.co.uk **£ BOOK ONLINE**

Units   8
Sleeps   2-6
PER UNIT PER WEEK
£255.00 - £750.00

Cottages with a relaxed spacious country style combined with modern luxuries sleeping 2 - 6. Surrounded by quiet & peaceful countryside but close to everything perfect for Durham & Newcastle. Beamish Museum only 3 miles. A range of cottages to suit your needs from single storey cottages - large barns. Open all year round perfect for family holidays short breaks or business accommodation. We also provide Bed & Breakfast.
Open: All year. **Nearest Shop:** 2 miles **Nearest Pub:** 2 miles

Site: ✿ P Payment: 💷 Leisure: 🚲 🏌 ∪ Property: 🐾 🛏 🗄 🖬 Children: 🚼 🛏 ⚥ Unit: 🗄 🖬 🖥 🍴 📺 📀 DVD BBQ

NEWCASTLE UPON TYNE, Tyne and Wear   Map ref 5C2   S

VisitEngland ★★★ SELF CATERING

135 Audley Road Self Catering Flat

Contact: Miss Linda Wright, 137 Audley Road, South Gosforth, Newcastle-upon-Tyne NE3 1QH **T:** (01912) 856374 / 07733 617784
W: www.audleyroad.co.uk

Self-contained flat, accommodates four people, close to shops and Metro, with easy access to city centre. All amenities. Short lets accepted, price on enquiry. Approximately 2.5 miles from city centre and 6.5 miles from Newcastle Airport. Ideal as a base to visit the North East for leisure or work-related trips.
Open: All year.
Nearest Shop: 0.20 miles
Nearest Pub: 0.20 miles

| Units | 1 |
| Sleeps | 1-4 |

PER UNIT PER WEEK
£280.00 - £350.00

Property: 🖥 📶 **Children:** 🧸 🚶 **Unit:** 🛏 🚭 📺 🗓 📺 📀 📞

SOUTH SHIELDS, Tyne And Wear   Map ref 5C2   S

VisitEngland ★★★★ SELF CATERING

Embla

Contact: Jon & Sue, Westoe Crown Village, South Shields, Tyne and Wear NE33 3ND
T: 07958 176622 / 07480 300228 **E:** embla@fastmail.co.uk
W: www.selfcateringapartmentnortheast.co.uk

| Units | 1 |
| Sleeps | 1-4 |

PER UNIT PER WEEK
£380.00 - £540.00

SPECIAL PROMOTIONS
Short breaks are available please see our website

A unique 2 bedroom luxury apartment, free Wi-Fi. Just a few metres from the parks & beaches of South Shields. Perfect for anyone wanting to relax, walk, enjoy culture, shopping, history etc. We are unique in that there is no one below and no one above, so guests don't have to suffer noise from people below or above them. Private covered parking. Beautifully decorated throughout to a very high standard, ideal for anyone who demands comfort and modern surroundings. Strictly no smoking & no pets.

Open: All year.
Nearest Shop: 500 metres
Nearest Pub: 500 metres

Units: Unique 2 bedroom apartment with private entrance and sunny terrace.

Site: ✿ **P Payment:** 💳 **Leisure:** 🎵 ▶ ∪ **Property:** 🖥 📶 **Unit:** 🛏 🚭 📺 🗓 📺 📀

SOUTH SHIELDS, Tyne And Wear   Map ref 5C2   S

VisitEngland ★★★★ SELF CATERING

Hill Head Farm

Contact: William & Margaret Stewart, Owners, Lizard Lane, South Shields, Tyne and Wear SR6 7NN **T:** (01915) 295248 / (01915) 292076 / Tearoom: 07786 534250
E: hillheadm@aol.com **W:** www.hillheadfarm.co.uk

2 bedroom farm bungalow, newly decorated to very high standard, in beautiful countryside overlooking the sea. Weekly price is based on couple sharing. Extra £50 charge per person per week for parties over 2. Onsite Tearoom is closed 22nd December to 5th January.
Open: All year.
Nearest Shop: 0.25 miles
Nearest Pub: 0.25 miles

| Units | 1 |
| Sleeps | 2-5 |

PER UNIT PER WEEK
£500.00

Site: ✿ **P Property:** 🖥 📶 **Children:** 🧸 🚼 🚶 **Unit:** 🛏 📺 🗓 📺 📀

VisitEngland
★★★
HOTEL

B&B PER ROOM PER NIGHT
S: £84.00 - £231.00
D: £84.00 - £231.00

SPECIAL PROMOTIONS
Please visit our website
for special offers and
forthcoming events.
Book online for
advance purchase
rates.

Little Haven Hotel

River Drive, South Shields NE33 1LH **T:** (01914) 554455 **F:** (01914) 554466
E: info@littlehavenhotel.com
W: www.littlehavenhotel.com **£ BOOK ONLINE**

Uniquely situated at the gateway of the River Tyne, Little Haven Hotel boasts extensive views of the river and Little Haven Beach. Within 15 minutes of both Newcastle and Sunderland. Enjoy a varied and exciting wining and dining experience in the Boardwalk restaurant, fashionably set in the conservatory overlooking the historical River Tyne with a view to Little Haven Beach and the lively waterfront.

Directions: Please contact us for directions.

Bedrooms: 33 double, 14 twin, 4 family, 8 executive & 3 penthouse suites.
Open: All year.

Site: ❀ **Payment:** 💷 **Leisure:** 🚲 🎵 🏌 ♻ **Property:** 🐕 🐎 📺 📶 ◑ **Children:** 🛏 🚶 **Catering:** 🍷 🍽
Room: 🍵 💧 📞 💻 📺

Hadrian's Wall, Northumberland ©VisitBritain Andrew Pickett

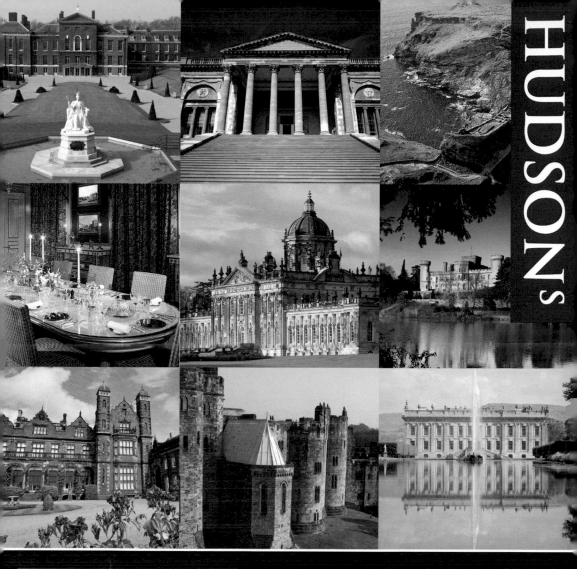

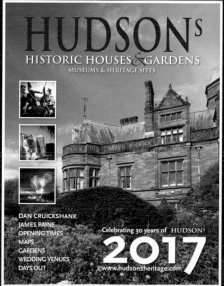

Map 1

Location
Maps

Every place name featured in the regional accommodation sections of this guide has a map reference to help you locate it on the maps which follow. For example, to find Colchester, Essex, which has 'Map ref 3B2', turn to Map 3 and refer to grid square B2.

All place names appearing in the regional sections are shown with orange circles on the maps. This enables you to find other places in your chosen area which may have suitable accommodation – the place index (at the back of this guide) gives page numbers.

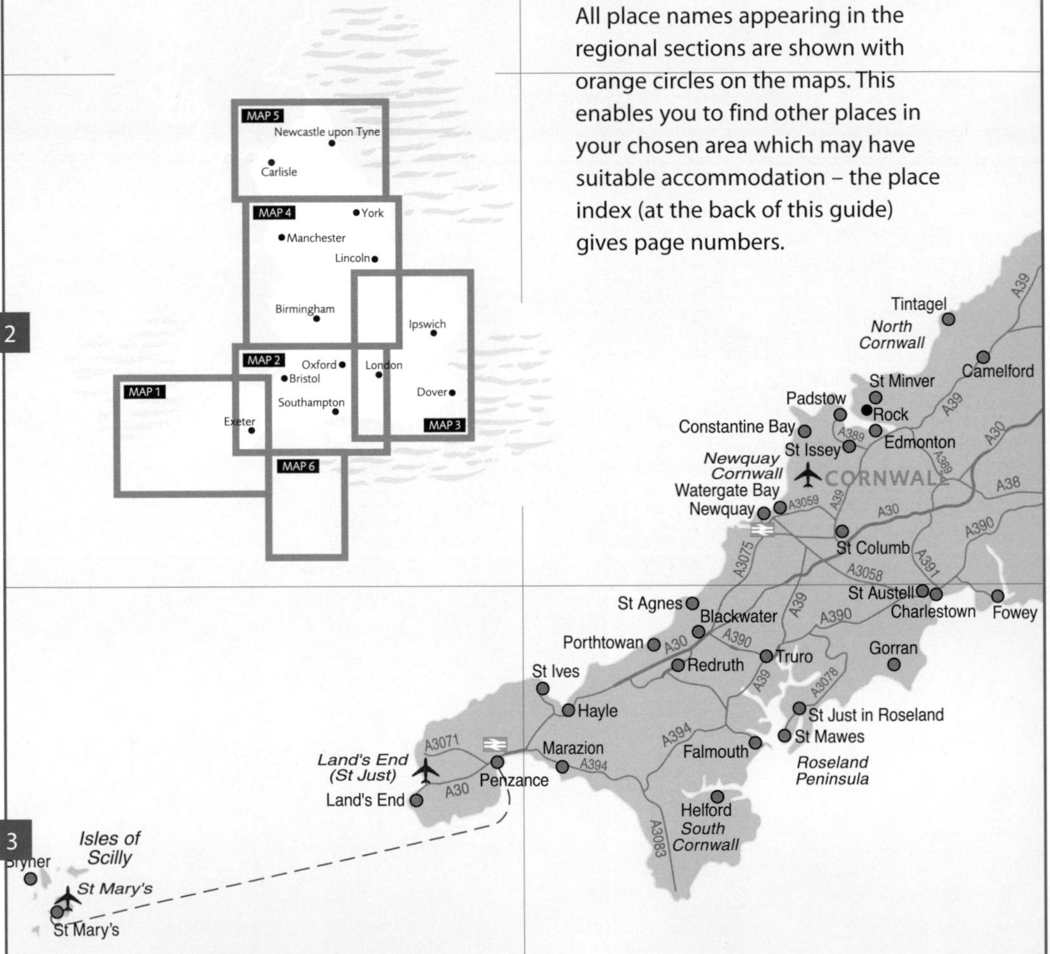

A   **B**

1

2

3

MAP 5
Newcastle upon Tyne
Carlisle

MAP 4   York
Manchester
Lincoln

Birmingham   Ipswich

MAP 2   Oxford   London
Bristol
MAP 1   Southampton   Dover
Exeter   MAP 3
MAP 6

Tintagel
North Cornwall
Camelford
St Minver
Padstow   Rock
Constantine Bay   A389   Edmonton
St Issey
Newquay Cornwall   CORNWALL
Watergate Bay
Newquay   A3059
St Columb
A3075
A3058
St Austell
St Agnes   Charlestown   Fowey
Blackwater
Porthtowan   A390   Gorran
St Ives   Redruth   Truro
Hayle   St Just in Roseland
St Mawes
Marazion   Roseland Peninsula
Land's End (St Just)   Falmouth
Penzance
Land's End   A30   Helford
South Cornwall
Isles of Scilly
Bryher
St Mary's
St Mary's

Map 1

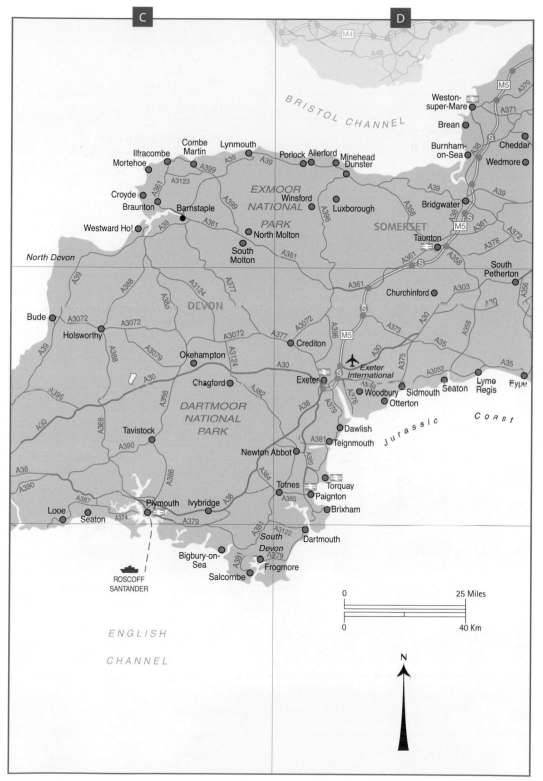

Orange circles indicate accommodation within the regional sections of this guide

Map 2

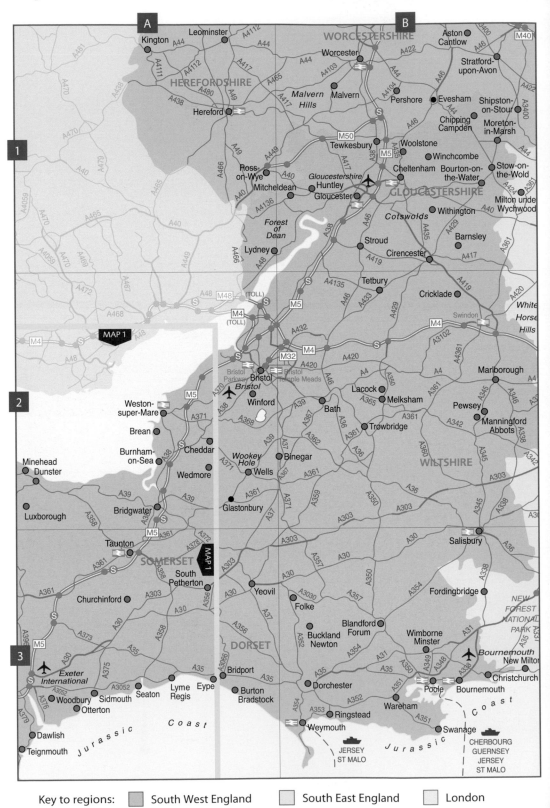

Key to regions: ■ South West England   ■ South East England   ■ London

Map 2

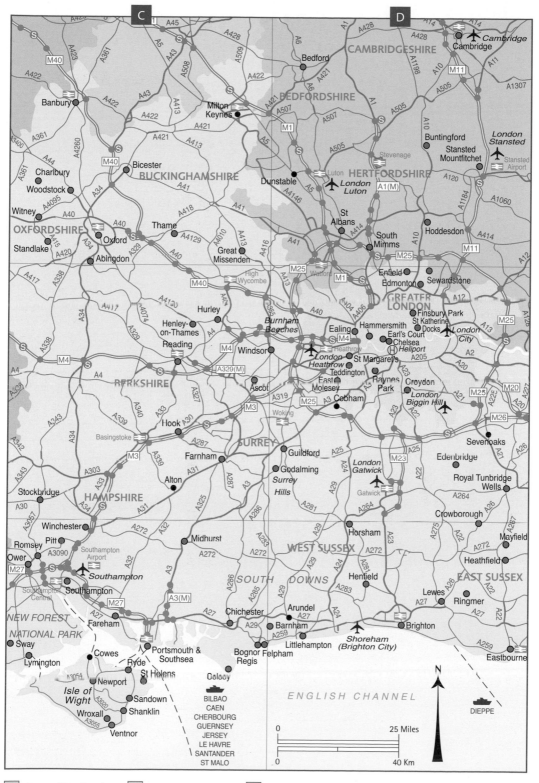

East of England   East Midlands   Heart of England
Orange circles indicate accommodation within the regional sections of this guide

Map 3

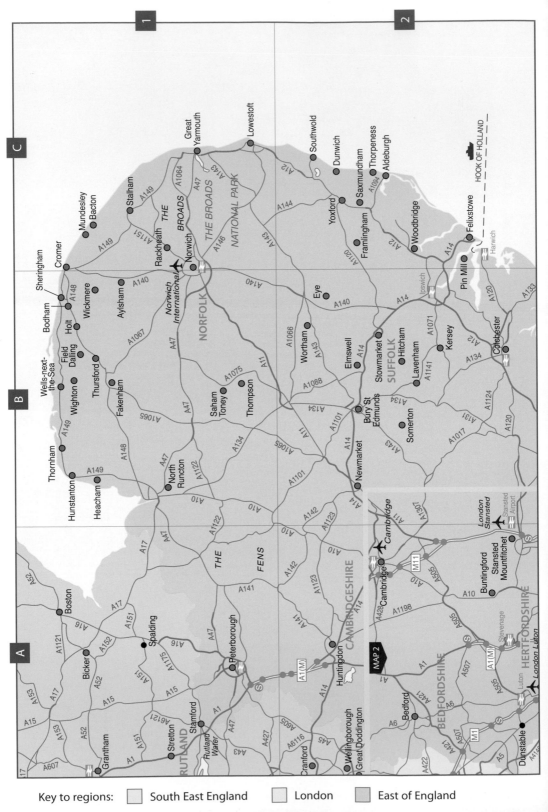

Key to regions: ▢ South East England ▢ London ▢ East of England

354

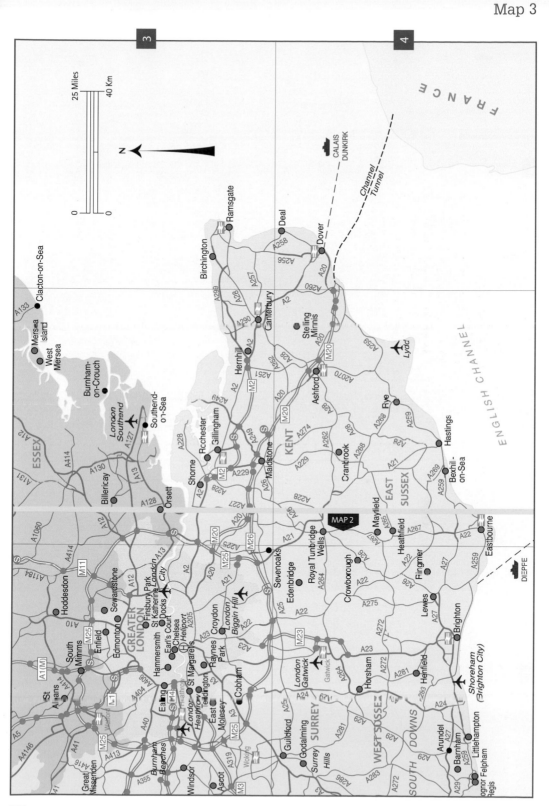

Map 3

East Midlands

Orange circles indicate accommodation within the regional sections of this guide

Map 4

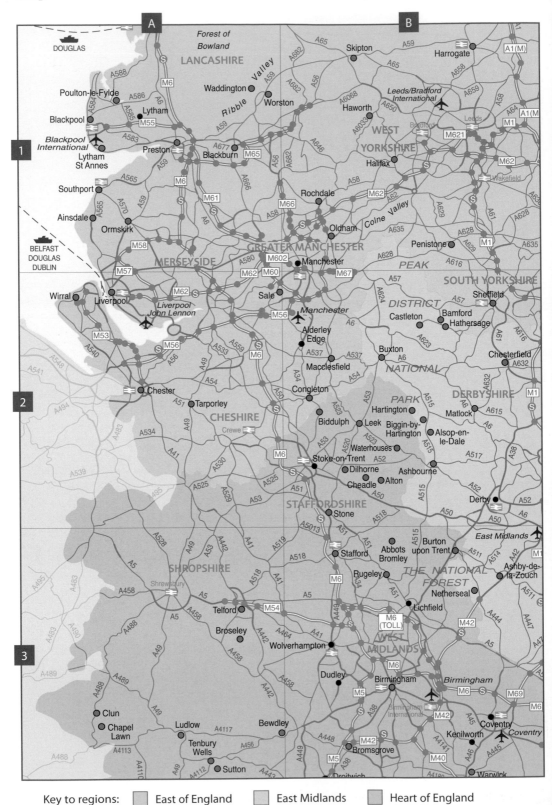

Key to regions: ☐ East of England ☐ East Midlands ☐ Heart of England

Map 4

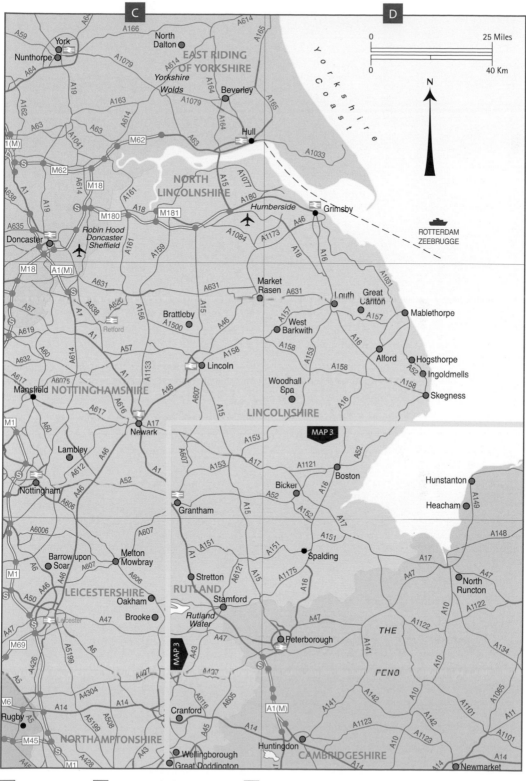

C   D

0 ——— 25 Miles
0 ——— 40 Km

N

York
Nunthorpe
North Dalton
A59
A166
A614
A614
A165
EAST RIDING OF YORKSHIRE
A64
A19
A1079
Yorkshire Wolds
A163
A164
Beverley
A1079
A165
A162
A63
A614
A1041
M62
A63
A164
A63
Hull
Yorkshire Coast
A1033
1(M)
M62
M62
M18
A638
A19
A161
NORTH LINCOLNSHIRE
A18
A180
A1077
A635
M180
M181
A18
Humberside
A46
Grimsby
ROTTERDAM ZEEBRUGGE
Doncaster
Robin Hood Doncaster Sheffield
A161
A159
A1084
A1173
A18
A16
M18
A1(M)
A631
A631
A631
A16
A1031
A57
A638
A156
Market Rasen
Louth
Great Carlton
Retford
A57
A1500
Brattleby
A15
A46
A157
West Barkwith
A157
Mablethorpe
A619
A60
A614
A632
A158
A158
A153
Alford
Hogsthorpe
A52
Ingoldmells
A617
A6075
Mansfield
NOTTINGHAMSHIRE
A1153
Lincoln
A158
Woodhall Spa
A158
A16
Skegness
A617
A616
A46
A607
A15
LINCOLNSHIRE
M1
A17
Newark
A153
MAP 3
A52
Lambley
A612
A1
A153
A17
A1121
Boston
Hunstanton
A60
A52
A152
A149
Nottingham
A606
Bicker
A16
Heacham
A6006
A607
Grantham
A15
A151
A148
A607
A151
Spalding
A151
A17
M1
Barrow upon Soar
Melton Mowbray
A607
A1
A151
A17
A47
A47
North Runcton
A6
A46
A606
Stretton
A6121
A15
A1175
A16
A10
A1122
M1
A50
LEICESTERSHIRE
Oakham
RUTLAND
Stamford
A47
THE FENS
A1122
A134
A47
Leicester
A47
Brooke
Rutland Water
A47
A141
A10
M69
A6
A43
Peterborough
A10
A5199
A607
A47
A10
A1065
A5
A4304
A407
A43
A605
A1(M)
A141
A142
A10
A1101
M6
A14
A14
Cranford
A45
A14
A1123
A10
A1123
A11
Rugby
A5
A6116
A605
Huntingdon
A141
A142
A1101
M45
NORTHAMPTONSHIRE
Wellingborough
Great Doddington
A14
CAMBRIDGESHIRE
A14
Newmarket
M1
A428
A43
A45

☐ Yorkshire   ☐ North West England   ☐ North East England
Orange circles indicate accommodation within the regional sections of this guide

Map 5

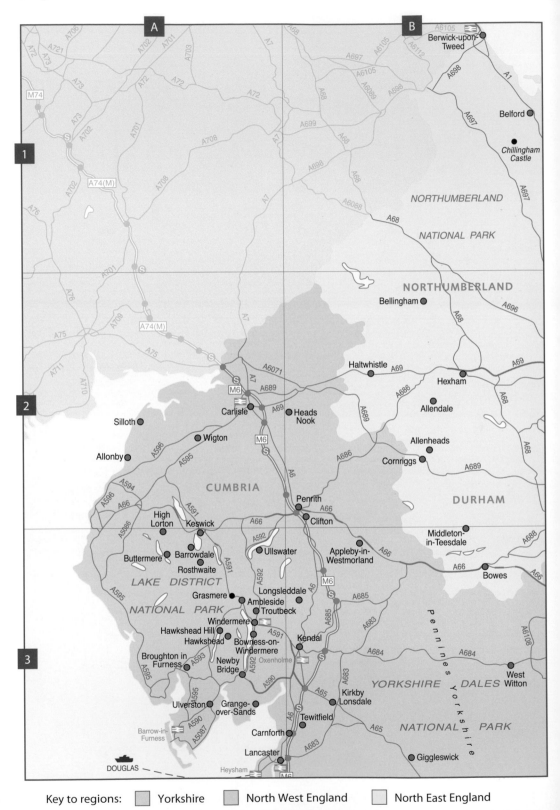

Key to regions: □ Yorkshire □ North West England □ North East England

Map 5

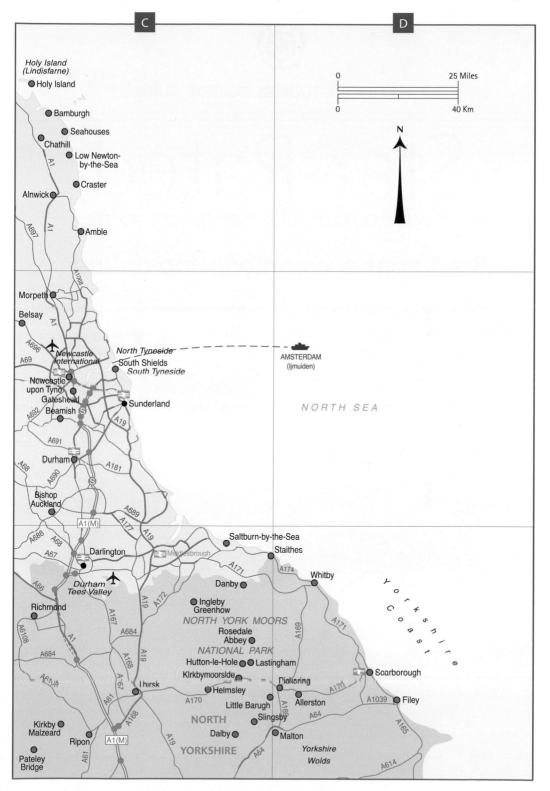

Map 6
London

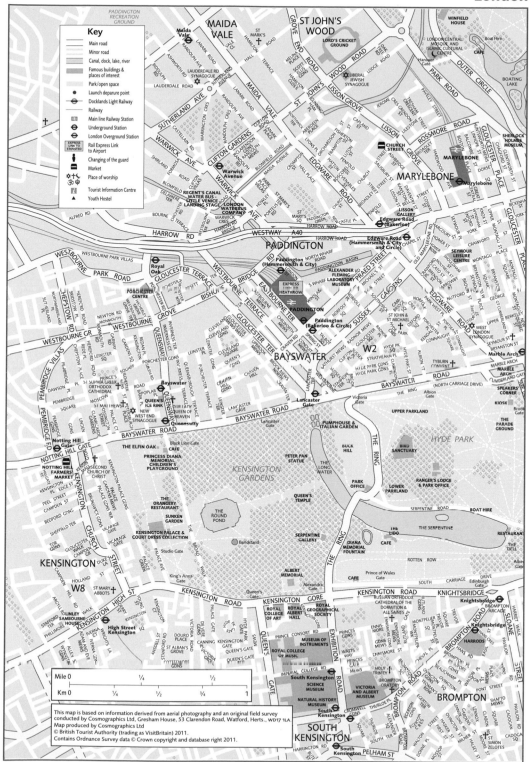

Map 7
London

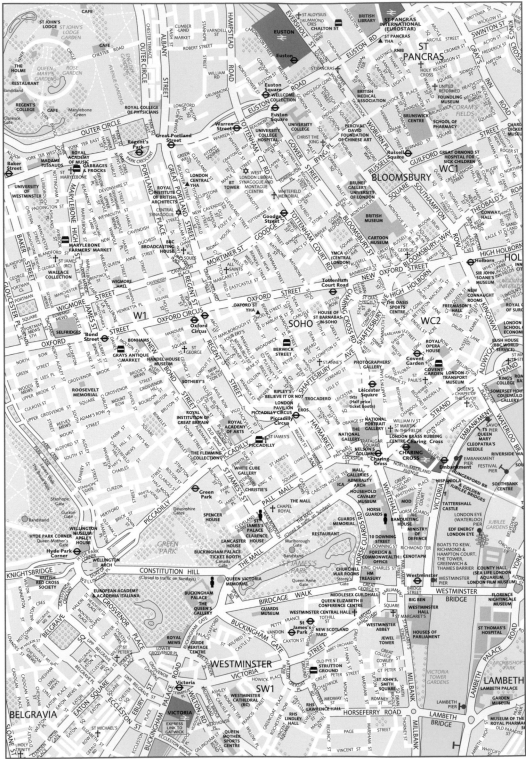

Map 7
London

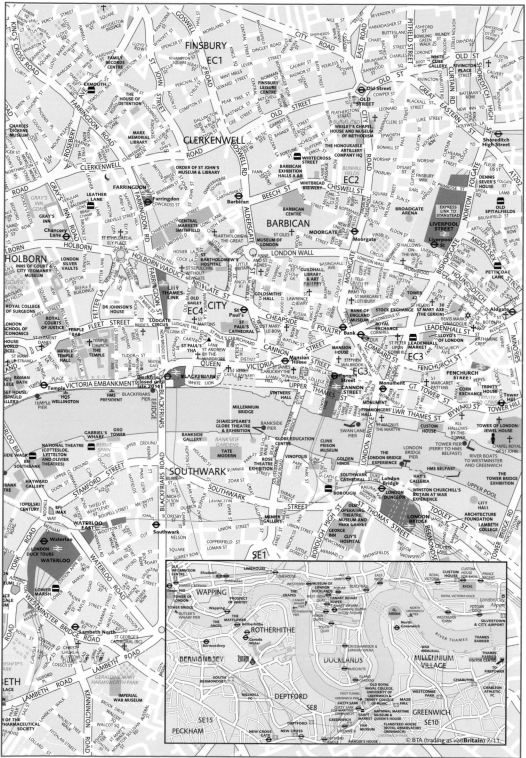

Motorway Service Area Assessment Scheme

Something we all use and take for granted but how good are they?

The star ratings cover over 250 different aspects of each operation, including cleanliness, the quality and range of catering and also the quality of the physical aspects, as well as the service. It does not cover prices or value for money.

OPERATOR: EXTRA	
Baldock	★★★★
Beaconsfield	★★★★★
Blackburn	★★★★★
Cambridge	★★★★
Cobham	★★★★★
Cullompton	★★★★
Peterborough	★★★★

OPERATOR: MOTO	
Birch E	★★★
Birch W	★★★
Bridgwater	★★★
Burton in Kendal	★★★
Cherwell Valley	★★★★
Chieveley	★★★★
Doncaster N	★★★★
Donington Park	★★★★
Exeter	★★★
Ferrybridge	★★★★
Frankley N	★★★
Frankley S	★★★★
Heston E	★★★
Heston W	★★★
Hilton Park N	★★★
Hilton Park S	★★★
Knutsford N	★★★★
Knutsford S	★★★★
Lancaster N	★★★★
Lancaster S	★★★★
Leigh Delamere E	★★★
Leigh Delamere W	★★★★
Medway	★★★
Pease Pottage	★★★
Reading E	★★★★
Reading W	★★★
Severn View	★★★
Southwaite N	★★★
Southwaite S	★★★
Stafford N	★★★★
Tamworth	★★★
Thurrock	★★★★
Toddington N	★★★★
Toddington S	★★★★
Trowell N	★★★
Trowell S	★★★
Washington N	★★★
Washington S	★★★
Wetherby	★★★★
Winchester N	★★★★
Winchester S	★★★★
Woolley Edge N	★★★★
Woolley Edge S	★★★★

OPERATOR: ROADCHEF	
Chester	★★★★
Clacket Lane E	★★★★
Clacket Lane W	★★★★
Durham	★★★
Killington Lake	★★★★
Maidstone	★★★★
Northampton N	★★★
Northampton S	★★★
Norton Canes	★★★★
Rownhams N	★★★
Rownhams S	★★★
Sandbach N	★★★★
Sandbach S	★★★★
Sedgemoor S	★★★
Stafford S	★★★★
Strensham N	★★★
Strensham S	★★★
Taunton Deane N	★★★
Taunton Deane S	★★★
Tibshelf N	★★★
Tibshelf S	★★★

Watford Gap N	★★★
Watford Gap S	★★★

OPERATOR: WELCOME BREAK	
Birchanger Green	★★★★
Burtonwood	★★★
Charnock Richard N	★★★★
Charnock Richard S	★★★
Corley E	★★★
Corley W	★★★
Fleet N	★★★★
Fleet S	★★★★
Gordano	★★★★
Hartshead Moor E	★★★
Hartshead Moor W	★★★
Hopwood Park	★★★★
Keele N	★★★
Keele S	★★★★
Leicester Forest East N	★★★★
Leicester Forest East S	★★★
London Gateway	★★★★
Membury E	★★★
Membury W	★★★★
Michaelwood N	★★★★
Michaelwood S	★★★★
Newport Pagnell S	★★★
Newport Pagnell N	★★★★
Oxford	★★★★
Sedgemoor N	★★★
South Mimms	★★★★
Telford	★★★
Warwick N	★★★★
Warwick S	★★★★
Woodall N	★★★
Woodall S	★★★

OPERATOR: WESTMORLAND	
Tebay N	★★★★★
Tebay S	★★★★★
Gloucester N	★★★★★
Gloucester S	★★★★★

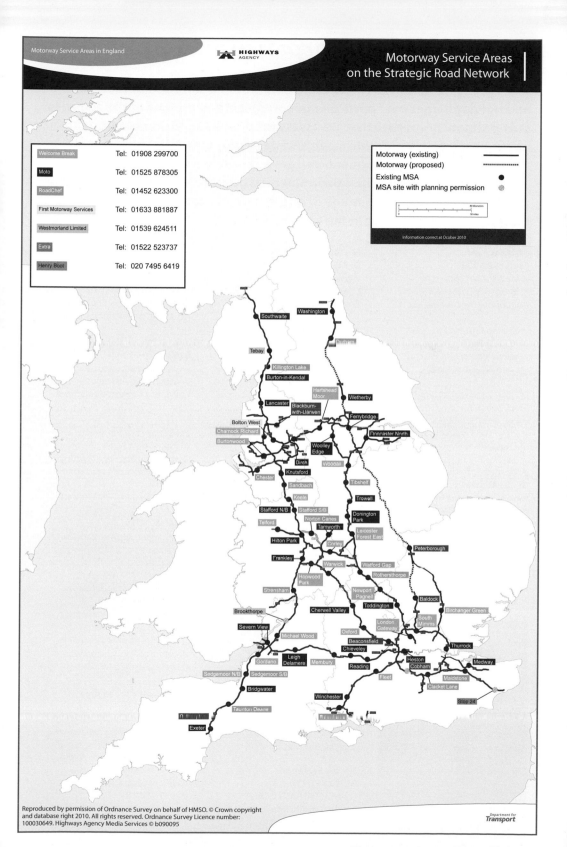

Motorway Service Areas in England

HIGHWAYS AGENCY

Motorway Service Areas
on the Strategic Road Network

Welcome Break	Tel: 01908 299700
Moto	Tel: 01525 878305
RoadChef	Tel: 01452 623300
First Motorway Services	Tel: 01633 881887
Westmorland Limited	Tel: 01539 624511
Extra	Tel: 01522 523737
Henry Boot	Tel: 020 7495 6419

Motorway (existing)
Motorway (proposed)
Existing MSA
MSA site with planning permission

Information correct at October 2010

Reproduced by permission of Ordnance Survey on behalf of HMSO. © Crown copyright
and database right 2010. All rights reserved. Ordnance Survey Licence number:
100030649. Highways Agency Media Services © b090095

Department for
Transport

Self-catering agencies

All of the self-catering agencies listed below offer a selection of cottages and holiday homes over particular geographical areas. Many of the agencies only promote properties that are assessed annually by VisitEngland, however some only promote a percentage of properties that have a star rating. To avoid disappointment, you are advised to check if your desired accommodation has a VisitEngland star rating before booking. Agencies that promote the highest percentage of quality assessed accommodation at the time of publishing feature at the top of the list.

cottages.com
0345 498 6900
www.cottages.com
Self-catering properties throughout the country.

Welcome Cottages
0345 268 0816
www.welcomecottages.com
Properties across the UK.

English Country Cottages
0345 268 0788
www.english-country-cottages.co.uk
Hand-picked holiday cottages in England.

Yorkshire Cottages
01228 406 701
www.yorkshire-cottages.info
Properties across the whole county of Yorkshire.

Cumbrian Cottages
01228 599 960
www.cumbrian-cottages.co.uk
A collection of holiday properties in Cumbria and the Lake District.

Northumbrian Cottages
01228 406 721
www.northumbrian-cottages.info
Coastal and country properties throughout Northumberland.

Cornish Horizons
01841 533 331
www.cornishhorizons.co.uk
cottages@cornishhorizons.co.uk
Providing a large portfolio of properties in Cornwall.

Lakelovers
01539 488 855
www.lakelovers.co.uk
bookings@lakelovers.co.uk
Individual properties in the heart of the Lake District.

Norfolk Country Cottages
01263 715 779
www.norfolkcottages.co.uk
info@norfolkcottages.co.uk
Over 400 properties in hand-picked locations throughout Norfolk.

Ingrid Flute's Yorkshire Holiday Cottages
01947 600 700
www.yorkshireholidaycottages.co.uk
info@yorkshireholidaycottages.co.uk
Holiday homes across Yorkshire and Northumberland.

Coast & Country Cottages
01548 843 773
www.coastandcountry.co.uk
Properties in Salcombe, Dartmouth and South Devon.

Suffolk Secrets
01502 722 717
www.suffolk-secrets.co.uk
holidays@suffolk-secrets.co.uk
Family-owned, with over 400 properties across Suffolk.

Marsdens Devon Cottages
01271 813 777
www.marsdens.co.uk
devon@marsdens.co.uk
Over 350 holiday cottages in North Devon and Exmoor.

Kent & Sussex Holiday Cottages
01580 720 770
www.kentandsussexcottages.co.uk
info@kentandsussexcottages.co.uk
Over 300 cottages throughout Kent and Sussex.

Peak District & Derbyshire Cottages
01228 406 741
www.derbyshire-cottages.info
Properties in the Peak District & Derbyshire.

Dorset Coastal Cottages
0800 980 4070
www.dorsetcoastalcottages.com
hols@dorsetcoastalcottages.com
Self-catering on the Dorset coast.

Harbour Holidays, Padstow
01841 533 402
www.padstow-self-catering.co.uk
contact@harbourholidays.co.uk
A wide range of self-catering accommodation in and around Padstow and the Seven Bays Cornwall.

Island Cottage Holidays
01929 481 555
www.islandcottageholidays.com
mail@islandcottageholidays.com
Providing a wide collection of cottages on the Isle of Wight.

Lakeland Cottage Company
01539 538 180
www.lakeland-cottage-company.co.uk
A large range of cottages in the Lake District.

Norfolk Holiday Homes
01485 534 267
www.norfolkholidayhomes.agency
info@norfolkholidayhomes.agency
Self-catering accommodation along the North West Norfolk coast and countryside.

The Good Life Cottage Company
01539 437 417
www.thegoodlifecottageco.co.uk
stay@thegoodlifecottageco.co.uk
Holiday cottages in the heart of the Lake District.

Porthleven Harbour Cottages
01326 563 198
www.cornishhideaways.co.uk
info@cornishhideaways.com
Self-catering holiday accommodation in the Porthleven and Rinsey area of West Cornwall.

Linstone Chine Holiday Services
01983 755 933
www.linstone-chine.co.uk
enquiries@linstone-chine.co.uk
Offering accommodation on the Isle of Wight.

Askrigg Cottage Holidays
01969 650 022
www.askrigg.com
stay@askrigg.com
Holiday cottages in the Yorkshire Dales National Park.

Dream Cottages
01305 789 000
www.dream-cottages.co.uk
admin@dream-cottages.co.uk
Providing cottages across Dorset, Devon and Cornwall.

Carbis Bay Holidays
01736 630 015
www.carbisbayholidays.co.uk
enquiries@carbisbayholidays.co.uk
Self-catering accommodation in Carbis Bay and St Ives, Cornwall.

Portscatho Holidays
01326 270 900
www.portscathoholidays.co.uk
info@portscathoholidays.co.uk
Offering accommodation in the Roseland Peninsula, including St Mawes and Portscatho in South Cornwall.

Cornish Collection
01503 262 736
www.cornishcollection.co.uk
enquiries@cornishcollection.co.uk
A selection of properties in Looe and across South East Cornwall.

Coquet Cottages
01665 710 700
www.coquetcottages.co.uk
info@coquetcottages.co.uk
Self-catering accommodation based in Northumberland.

Bath Holiday Rentals
01225 482 225
www.bathholidayrentals.com
alexa@bathholidayrentals.com
Self-catering apartments and cottages in and around Bath.

Keswick Cottages
01768 780 088
www.keswickcottages.co.uk
info@keswickcottages.co.uk
Cottages in and around Keswick, the Lake District.

The Coppermines Lakes Cottages
01539 441 765
www.coppermines.co.uk
info@coppermines.co.uk
A wide range of cottages set in the Lake District.

Roseland Holiday Cottages
01872 580 480
www.roselandholidaycottages.co.uk
enquiries@roselandholidaycottages.co.uk
A selection of cottages in St Mawes and Portscatho, Cornwall.

Milkbere Holiday Cottages
01297 20729
www.milkberehols.com
info@milkberehols.com
Accommodation in Devon and Dorset.

Dorset Cottage Holidays
01929 481 547
www.dhcottages.co.uk
enq@dhcottages.co.uk
A collection of cottages and apartments in Dorset.

Holiday Homes and Cottages SW
01803 299 677
www.swcottages.co.uk
info@swcottages.co.uk
Holiday cottages and apartments across Devon and Cornwall.

Natural Retreats
01625 416 430
www.naturalretreats.com
Holiday cottages and apartments across Devon and Cornwall.

Whitby Holiday Cottages
01947 603 010
www.whitby-cottages.net
enquiries@whitby-cottages.net
Offering a large collection of cottages in and around Whitby.

Holiday Cottages Cornwall
01525 272 320
www.holidaycottagescornwall.com
Cottages and apartments in the coastal resorts of South Cornwall.

Campden Cottages
01386 852 462
www.campdencottages.co.uk
admin@campdencottages.co.uk
Self-catering accommodation throughout the Cotswolds.

Wight Locations
01983 617 322
www.wightlocations.co.uk
enquiries@wightlocations.co.uk
Cottages on the Isle of Wight.

Home from Home Holidays
01983 532 385
www.homefromhomeiow.co.uk
A selection of self-catering properties on the Isle of Wight.

Country Hideaways
01969 663 559
www.countryhideaways.co.uk
info@countryhideaways.co.uk
Cottages and apartments throughout the Yorkshire Dales.

Lakeland Cottage Holidays
01768 776 065
www.lakelandcottages.co.uk
info@lakelandcottages.co.uk
Self-catering accommodation in the Lake District.

 The following agencies have been accredited by VisitEngland following an annual assessment of their policies and procedures. Individual accommodation that these agencies promote may not be part of the VisitEngland Quality Assessment Scheme. However, if the agency is part of the VisitEngland Quality Accredited Agency Scheme the agency should have their own programme of inspections in place, ensuring the accommodation they promote is rated to a comparable standard.

Aspects Holidays
01736 754 242
www.aspects-holidays.co.uk
hello@aspects-holidays.co.uk
Over 400 holiday cottages in West Cornwall, St Ives and Carbis Bay.

Beach Retreats
01637 861 005
www.beachretreats.co.uk
Self-catering holidays on the Cornish coast.

Blue Chip Holidays
0333 3315 758
www.bluechipholidays.co.uk
Accommodation available in Cornwall, Devon, Dorset, the Isle of Wight, and Yorkshire.

Classic Cottages
01326 555 555
www.classic.co.uk
Self-catering accommodation in The South West.

Coast & Country Cottages
01548 843 773
www.coastandcountry.co.uk
salcombe@coastandcountry.co.uk
Self-catering Holiday Homes in Salcombe, Dartmouth and South Devon.

Cornish Collection
01503 262 736
www.cornishcollection.co.uk
enquiries@ cornishcollection.co.uk
Self-catering properties in and around Looe, Cornwall.

Cornish Cottage Holidays
01326 573 808
www.cornishcottageholidays.co.uk
Holiday cottages in Cornwall.

Cornish Horizons Holiday Cottages
01841 533 331
www.cornishhorizons.co.uk
cottages@cornishhorizons.co.uk
Cottages throughout Cornwall.

Cornish Traditional Cottages
01208 895 354
www.corncott.com
bookings@corncott.com
Coastal and countryside self-catering holiday cottages in Cornwall.

cottages.com
0345 498 6900
www.cottages.com
Self-catering properties throughout the country.

Cumbrian Cottages
01228 599 960
www.cumbrian-cottages.co.uk
Properties in the most popular towns in the Lake District.

Dorset Coastal Cottages
0800 980 4070
www.dorsetcoastalcottages.com
hols@dorsetcoastalcottages.com
Self-catering on the Dorset coast.

Dream Cottages
01305 789 000
www.dream-cottages.co.uk
admin@dream-cottages.co.uk
Providing cottages across Dorset, Devon and Cornwall.

English Country Cottages
0345 268 0788
www.english-country-cottages.co.uk
Hand-picked holiday cottages.

Heart of the Lakes
01539 432 321
www.heartofthelakes.co.uk
Over 300 hand-picked cottages in the Lake District National Park.

holidaycottages.co.uk
01237 459 999
www.holidaycottages.co.uk
Over 2,000 holiday cottages in popular destinations across the UK.

**Ingrid Flute's
Yorkshire Holiday Cottages**
01947 600 700
www.yorkshireholidaycottages.co.uk
info@yorkshireholidaycottages.co.uk
Holiday homes across Yorkshire and Northumberland.

John Bray Cornish Holidays
01208 863 206
www.johnbraycornishholidays.co.uk
lettings@johnbray.co.uk
Cornish holiday cottages in Rock, Daymer Bay, Polzeath and Port Isaac.

Kent & Sussex Holiday Cottages
01580 720 770
www.kentandsussexcottages.co.uk
info@kentandsussexcottages.co.uk
Over 300 cottages in Kent and Sussex.

Lakelovers
01539 488 855
www.lakelovers.co.uk
bookings@lakelovers.co.uk
Properties to suit every occasion in the heart of the Lake District.

Lyme Bay Holidays
01297 443 363
www.lymebayholidays.co.uk
email@lymebayholidays.co.uk
Holiday homes in Lyme Regis and the surrounding coast and countryside areas.

Marsdens Devon Cottages
01271 813 777
www.marsdens.co.uk
devon@marsdens.co.uk
Over 350 cottages throughout North Devon and Exmoor.

Milkbere Holiday Cottages
01297 20729
www.milkberehols.com
info@milkberehols.com
Accommodation in Devon and Dorset.

New Forest Cottages
01590 679 655
www.newforestcottages.co.uk
Self-catering holiday cottages in the New Forest area.

Norfolk Country Cottages
01263 715 779
www.norfolkcottages.co.uk
info@norfolkcottages.co.uk
Over 400 properties in hand-picked locations throughout Norfolk.

Northumbrian Cottages
01228 406 721
www.northumbrian-cottages.info
Coastal and country properties throughout Northumberland.

Peak District & Derbyshire Cottages
01228 406 741
www.derbyshire-cottages.info
Properties in the Peak District & Derbyshire.

Rumsey Holiday Homes
01202 707 357
www.sandbanksbeachholidays.co.uk
office@sandbanksbeachholidays.co.uk
Self-catering flats, appartments, cottages and houses around Poole and Sandbanks

**Salcombe & Dartmouth
Holiday Homes**
01548 843 485
www.salcombe.com
shh@salcombe.com
Properties within Salcombe and Dartmouth.

Suffolk Secrets
01502 722 717
www.suffolk-secrets.co.uk
holidays@suffolk-secrets.co.uk
Family-owned, with over 400 properties across Suffolk.

Toad Hall Cottages
01548 202 020
www.toadhallcottages.co.uk
thc@toadhallcottages.co.uk
Rural and waterside cottages in the South West.

VIP Cottages
0800 148 8228
www.vipcottages.com
info@vipcottages.com
Self-catering accommodation on the Isle of Wight

Welcome Cottages
0345 268 0816
www.welcomecottages.com
Properties across the UK.

Wight Locations
01983 617 322
www.wightlocations.co.uk
enquiries@wightlocations.co.uk
Self-catering accommodation on the Isle of Wight.

Yorkshire Cottages
01228 406 701
www.yorkshire-cottages.info
Properties across the whole county of Yorkshire.

So much to see, so little time – how do you choose?

Make the most of your leisure time; look for attractions with the Quality Marque.

VisitEngland operates the Visitor Attraction Quality Assurance Scheme.

Annual assessments by trained impartial assessors test all aspects of the customer experience so you can visit with confidence.

For ideas and inspiration go to www.visitengland.com

Further Information

Advice and information

Making a booking

When enquiring about accommodation, make sure you check prices, the quality rating and other important details. You will also need to state your requirements clearly and precisely, for example:

- Arrival and departure dates, with acceptable alternatives if appropriate
- The type of accommodation you need – for example, a room with twin beds, an en suite bathroom or electric hook-up
- The terms you want – for example, bed and breakfast only; dinner and breakfast (where provided); minimum booking nights
- The number of people in your party and age of any children with you, whether you want them to share your room or be next door, and any other special requirements, such as a cot
- Any particular requirements you may have, such as a special diet or a ground-floor bathroom.

Confirmation

Misunderstandings can easily happen over the telephone, so do request a written confirmation, together with details of any terms and conditions that apply to your booking.

Deposits

If you make your reservation weeks or months in advance or book a self-catering holiday, you will probably be asked for a deposit, which will then be deducted from the final bill when you leave. The amount will vary from establishment to establishment and could be payment in full at peak times.

The reason for asking you to pay in advance is to safeguard the proprietor in case you decide to cancel at a late stage, or simple do not turn up. They may have turned down other bookings on the strength of yours, and may result in the accommodation not being at full capacity if you cancel.

In the case of caravan, camping and touring parks and holiday villages, the full charge often has to be paid in advance. This may be in two instalments – a deposit at the time of booking and the balance by say, two weeks before the start of the booked period.

Payment on arrival

Some establishments ask you to pay for your accommodation on arrival if you have not booked it in advance. This is especially likely to happen if you arrive late and have little or no luggage. If you are asked to pay on arrival, it is a good idea to see your accommodation first, to make sure it meets your requirements.

Cancellations

Legal contract

When you accept accommodation that is offered to you, by telephone or in writing, you enter into a legally binding contract with the proprietor. This means that if you cancel your booking, fail

delayed on your way, a telephone call to say that you will be late is often appreciated.

It is particularly important to liaise with the proprietor about key collection as he or she may not be on site.

Finding a park

Tourist signs similar to the one shown here are designed to help visitors find their park. They clearly show whether the park is for tents or caravans or both.

Tourist information centres throughout Britain are able to give campers and caravanners information about parks in their areas. Some tourist information centres have camping and caravanning advisory services that provide details of park availability and often assist with park booking.

Other caravan and camping places

If you enjoy making your own route through Britain's countryside, it may interest you to know that the Forestry Commission operates campsites in Britain's Forest Parks as well as in the New Forest. Some offer reduced charges for youth organisations on organised camping trips and all enquiries about them should be made well in advance of your intended stay to the Forestry Commission.

Electric hook-up points

Most parks now have electric hook-up points for caravans and tents. Voltage is generally 240v AC, 50 cycles. Parks may charge extra for this facility, and it is advisable to check rates when making a booking.

Avoiding peak season

In the summer months of June to September, parks in popular areas such as North Wales, Cumbria, the West Country or the New Forest in Hampshire may become full. Campers should aim to arrive at parks early in the day or, where possible, should book in advance. Some parks have overnight holding areas for visitors who arrive late. This helps to prevent disturbing other campers and caravanners late at night and means that fewer visitors are turned away. Caravans or tents are directed to a pitch the following morning.

Service charges and tipping

These days many places levy service charges automatically. If they do, they must clearly say so in their offer of accommodation, at the time of booking. The service charge then becomes part of the legal contract when you accept the offer of accommodation.

If a service charge is levied automatically, there is no need to tip the staff, unless they provide some exceptional service. The usual tip for meals is 10% of the total bill.

to take up the accommodation or leave early, you will probably forfeit your deposit and may expect to be charged the balance at the end of the period booked if the place cannot be re-let. You should be advised at the time of the booking of what charges would be made in the event of cancelling the accommodation or leaving early, which is usually written into the property's terms and conditions. If this is not mentioned, you should ask the proprietor for any cancellation terms that apply before booking your accommodation to ensure any disputes are avoided. Where you have already paid the full amount before cancelling, the proprietor is likely to retain the money. However if the accommodation is re-let, the proprietor will make a refund to you which normally excludes the amount of the deposit.

Remember, if you book by telephone and are asked for your credit card number, you should check whether the proprietor intends to charge your credit card account, should you later cancel your reservation. A proprietor should not be able to charge your credit card account with a cancellation fee without your consent unless you agreed to this at the time of your booking. However, to avoid later disputes, we suggest you check whether this is the intention before providing your details

Insurance

There are so many reasons why you might have to cancel your holiday, which is why we strongly advise people to take out a cancellation insurance policy.

Arrival time

If you know you will be arriving late in the evening, it is a good idea to say so when you book. If you are

Telephone charges

Establishments can set their own charges for telephone calls made through their switchboard or from direct-dial telephones in bedrooms. These charges are often much higher than telephone companies' standard charges (to defray the cost of providing the service).

Comparing costs

It is a condition of the quality assessment schemes that an establishment's unit charges are on display by the telephones or with the room information. It is not always easy to compare these charges with standard rates, so before using a telephone for long-distance calls, you may decide to ask how the charges compare.

Security of valuables

You can deposit your valuables with the proprietor or manager during your stay, and we recommend you do this as a sensible precaution. Make sure you obtain a receipt for them. Some places do not accept articles for safe custody, and in that case it is wisest to keep your valuables with you.

Disclaimer

Some proprietors put up a notice that disclaims liability for property brought on to their premises by a guest. In fact, they can only restrict their liability. By law, a proprietor is liable for the value of the loss or damage to any property (except a car or its contents) of a guest who has engaged overnight accommodation, but if the proprietor has the notice on display, liability is limited to £50 for one article and a total of £100 for any one guest. The notice must be prominently displayed in the reception area or main entrance. These limits do not apply to valuables you have deposited with the proprietor for safekeeping, or to property lost through the default, neglect or wilful act of the proprietor or his staff.

Travelling with pets

Dogs, cats, ferrets and some other pets can be brought into the UK from certain countries without having to undertake six months' quarantine on arrival, provided they meet the requirements of the Pet Travel Scheme (PETS).

For full details, visit the PETS website at
w www.gov.uk/take-pet-abroad
or contact the PETS Helpline
t +44 (0)370 241 1710
e pettravel@ahvla.gsi.gov.uk
Ask for fact sheets which cover dogs and cats, ferrets or domestic rabbits and rodents.

There are no requirements for pets travelling directly between the UK and the Channel Islands. Pets entering Jersey or Guernsey from other countries need to be Pet Travel Scheme compliant and have a valid EU Pet Passport. For more information see
www.jersey.com or www.visitguernsey.com.

What to expect

The proprietor/management is required to undertake the following:

Prior to booking

- To describe accurately in any advertisement, brochure, or other printed or electronic media, the facilities and services provided;
- To make clear to guests in print, electronic media and on the telephone exactly what is included in all prices quoted for accommodation, including taxes and any other surcharges. Details of charges for additional services/facilities should also be made clear, for example breakfast, leisure etc;
- To provide information on the suitability of the premises for guests of various ages, particularly for the elderly and the very young;
- To allow guests to view the accommodation prior to booking if requested.

At the time of booking

- To clearly describe the cancellation policy to guests i.e. by telephone, fax, internet/email as well as in any printed information given to guests;
- To adhere to and not to exceed prices quoted at the time of booking for accommodation and other services;
- To make clear to guests if the accommodation offered is in an unconnected annexe or similar, and to indicate the location of such accommodation and any difference in comfort and/or amenities from accommodation at the property.

On arrival

- To welcome all guests courteously and without discrimination in relation to gender, sexual orientation, disability, race, religion or belief.

During the stay

- To maintain standards of guest care, cleanliness, and service appropriate to the type of establishment;
- To deal promptly and courteously with all enquiries, requests, bookings and correspondence from guests;
- To ensure complaints received are investigated promptly and courteously to an outcome that is communicated to the guest.

On departure

- To give each guest, on request, details of payments due and a receipt, if required/requested.

General

- To give due consideration to the requirements of guests with special needs, and make suitable provision where applicable;
- To ensure the accommodation, when advertised as open, is prepared for the arrival of guests at all times;
- To advise guests, at any time prior to their stay, of any changes made to their booking;
- To have a complaints handling procedure in place to deal promptly and fairly with all guest complaints;
- To hold current public liability insurance and to comply with all relevant statuory obligations including legislation applicable to fire, health and safety, planning and food safety;
- To allow, on request, VisitEngland representatives reasonable access to the establishment, to confirm that the Code of Conduct is being observed or in order to investigate any complaint of a serious nature;

Comments and complaints

Information

Other than rating information, the proprietors themselves supply descriptions of their properties and other information for the entries in this book. They have all signed a declaration to confirm that their information accurately describes their accommodation business. The publishers cannot guarantee the accuracy of information in this guide, and accept no responsibility for any error or misrepresentation. All liability for loss, disappointment, negligence or other damage caused by reliance on the information contained in this guide, or in the event of bankruptcy or liquidation or cessation of trade of any company, individual or firm mentioned, is hereby excluded. We strongly recommend that you carefully check prices and other details before you book your accommodation.

Quality signage

All establishments displaying a quality sign have to hold current membership of VisitEngland's Quality Assessment Scheme.

When an establishment is sold, the new owner has to re-apply and be re-assessed. In certain circumstances the rating may be carried forward before the property is re-assessed.

Problems

Of course, we hope you will not have cause for complaint, but problems do occur from time to time. If you are dissatisfied with anything, make your complaint to the management immediately. Then the management can take action by investigating the matter in attempts to put things right. The longer you leave a complaint, the harder it is to deal with it effectively.

In certain circumstances, the national tourist board may look into your complaint. However, they have no statutory control over establishments or their methods of operating and cannot become involved in legal or contractual matters such as financial compensation.

If you do have problems that have not been resolved by the proprietor and which you would like to bring to their attention, please write to: Quality in Tourism, New Challenge House, International Dr, Tewkesbury Business Park, Tewkesbury GL20 8UQ

About the accommodation entries

Entries

All accommodation featured in this guide has been assessed or has applied for assessment under a quality assessment scheme.

Start your search for a place to stay by looking in the 'Stay' sections of this guide, where proprietors have paid to have their establishment featured in either a standard entry (includes photograph, description, facilities and prices) or an enhanced entry (photograph(s) and extended details).

Locations

Places to stay are listed by town, city or village. If a property is located in a small village, you may find it listed under a nearby town (providing it is within a seven-mile radius).

Within each region, counties run in alphabetical order. Place names are listed alphabetically within each county, and include interesting county information and a map reference.

Complete address for self-catering rental properties are not given and the town(s) listed may be a distance from the actual property. Please check the precise location before booking.

Map references

These refer to the colour location maps at the back of the guide. The first figure shown is the map number, the following letter and figure indicate the grid reference on the map. Place names that have a standard or enhanced entry appear on the maps. Some standard or enhanced entries were added at the last minute, therefore they do not appear on the maps.

Telephone numbers

Booking telephone numbers are listed below the contact address for each entry. Area codes are shown in brackets.

Prices

The prices printed are to be used as a guide only; they were supplied to us by proprietors in summer 2016.

Remember, changes may occur after the guide goes to press, therefore we strongly advise you to check prices before booking your accommodation. Prices are shown in pounds sterling, including VAT where applicable. There are many different ways of quoting prices for accommodation. We use a standardised method in the guide to allow you to compare prices. For example, when we show:

Self-catering: The prices shown are per unit per week. Touring pitch prices are based on the minimum and maximum charges for one night for two persons, car and caravan or tent. (Some parks may charge separately for a car, caravan or tent and

for each person and there may be an extra charge for caravan awnings.) Minimum and maximum prices for caravan holiday homes are given per week.

Bed and breakfast: the prices shown are per room for overnight accommodation with breakfast. The double room price is for two people. (If a double room is occupied by one person, there is sometimes a reduction in price.) Some places only provide a continental breakfast in the set price, and you may have to pay extra if you want a full English breakfast.

Evening meal: the prices shown are per person per night.

Half board: the prices shown are per person per night for room, evening meal and breakfast. These prices are usually based on two people sharing a room.

Checking prices

There is no specific regulatory requirement for establishments to display prices in the reception, but it is recommended in order to fulfil their obligations under the consumer protection from unfair Trading Regulations 2008.

In your own interests, do make sure you check prices and what they include.

Children's rates

You will find that many places charge a reduced rate for children, especially if they share a room with their parents. Some places charge the full rate, however, when a child occupies a room which might otherwise have been let to an adult. The upper age limit for reductions for children varies from one accommodation to another, so check this when you book.

Seasonal packages and special promotions

Prices often vary through the year and may be significantly lower outside peak holiday weeks. Many places offer special package rates – fully inclusive weekend breaks, for example – in the autumn, winter and spring. A number of establishments taking an enhanced entry have included any special offers, themed breaks, etc. that are available.

You can get details of other bargain packages that may be available from the establishments themselves, regional tourism organisations or your local Tourist Information Centre (TIC). Your local travel agent may also have information and can help you make reservations.

Bathrooms

En suite bathroom means the bath or shower and wc are contained behind the main door of the bedroom. Private bathroom means a bath or shower and wc solely for the occupants of one bedroom, on the same floor, reasonably close and with a key provided. If the availability of a bath, rather than a shower, is important to you, remember to check when you book.

Meals

It is advisable to check the availability of meals and set times when making your reservation. Some smaller places may ask you at breakfast whether you want an evening meal. The prices shown in each entry are for bed and breakfast or half board, but many places also offer lunch.

Open period

If an entry does not indicate an opening period, please check directly with the establishment.

Symbols

The at-a-glance symbols included at the end of each entry show many of the services and facilities available at each establishment. You will find the key to these symbols on page 6.

Smoking

In the UK and the Channel Islands, it is illegal to smoke in enclosed public spaces and places of work. Some establishments may choose to provide designated smoking bedrooms, and may allow smoking in private areas that are not used by any staff. If you wish to smoke, it is advisable to check whether it is allowed when you book.

Alcoholic drinks

Many places listed in the guide are licensed to serve alcohol. The licence may be restricted – to diners only, for example – so you may want to check this when you book. If they have a bar this is shown by the ♈ symbol

Payment accepted

The types of payment accepted by an establishment are listed in the payment accepted section. If you plan to pay by card, check that the establishment will accept the particular type of card you own before booking. Some proprietors will charge you a higher rate if you pay by credit card rather than cash or cheque. The difference is to cover the charges paid by the proprietor to the credit card company. When you book by telephone, you may be asked for your credit card number as confirmation. Remember, the proprietor may then charge your credit card account if you cancel your booking. See details of this under Cancellations on page 372.

Pets

Many places accept guests with dogs, but we advise that you check this with the proprietor before booking, remembering to ask if there are any extra charges or rules about exactly where your pet is allowed. The acceptance of dogs is not always extended to cats and it is strongly advised that cat owners contact the property well in advance of their stay.

Some establishments do not accept pets at all. Pets are welcome by arrangement where you see this symbol ♆. The quarantine laws have changed and now dogs, cats and ferrets are able to come into Britain and the Channel Islands from over 50 countries. For details of the Pet Travel Scheme (PETS) please turn to page 374.

Conferences and groups

Places which cater for conferences and meetings are marked with the symbol ♉. Rates are often negotiable, depending on the time of year, number of people involved and any special requirements you may have.

> **Awaiting confirmation of rating**
> At the time of going to press some properties featured in this guide had not yet been assessed therefore their rating for this year could not be included. The term 'Rating Applied For' indicates this throughout your guide.

Getting around

Travelling in London

London transport

Each London Underground line has its own unique colour, so you can easily follow them on the Underground map. Most lines run through central London, and many serve parts of Greater London. Tube services run every day from around 5.30am to around 1am and some services will run all night on Fridays and Saturdays. Buses are a quick, convenient way to travel around London, providing plenty of sightseeing opportunities along the way. There are over 8,000 buses in London operating 700 routes every day. You will need to buy a ticket or Travel Pass before you board the bus.

London's National Rail system stretches all over London. Many lines start at the main London railway stations (Paddington, Victoria, Waterloo, Kings Cross) with links to the tube. Trains mainly serve areas outside central London, and travel overground.

Children usually travel free, or at reduced fare, on all public transport in London.

Oyster cards

The Visitor Oyster Card is a pay-as-you-go smartcard. It's a quick and easy way to pay for journeys on bus, Tube, tram, DLR, London Overground, TfL Rail and most National Rail services in London.

A Visitor Oyster card costs £5 (plus postage) and is pre-loaded with pay as you go credit for you to spend on travel. You can choose how much credit to add to your card: £5, £10, £15, £20, £25, £30, £35, £40, or £50. As a guide a £20 card will usually cover a return journey from Heathrow plus travel around Central London for one 1 or 2 days. If you are visiting for 3-4 days, get a £30 card or if you are here for a week and you will be travelling lots every day, then a £50 card is a good option. The credit on your card never expires - it stays there until you use it. If you run out of credit on your card, it's easy to top it up and use it again.

Children with a Zip Oyster photocard that are 5-10 years can travel free on all TfL and most National Rail services in London. Children 11-15 year olds can travel free on buses and trams and travel at half adult-rate on all other TfL services. Children 16-17 year olds can travel at half adult-rate on all TfL services and most National Rail services in London.

For further information or to buy cards visit
www.visitbritainshop.com/world/london-visitor-oyster-card
www.tfl.gov.uk/travel-information/visiting-london/visitor-oyster-card
www.tfl.gov.uk/fares-and-payments/travel-for-under-18s

London congestion charge

The congestion charge is £11.50 daily charge to drive in central London at certain times. Check if the congestion charge is included in the cost of your car before booking. If your car's pick up point is in the congestion-charging zone, the company may pay the charge for the first day of your hire.

Low Emission Zone

The Low Emission Zone is an area covering most of Greater London, within which the most polluting diesel-engine vehicles are required to meet specific emissions standards. If your vehicle does not, you will be required to pay a daily charge. Vehicles affected by the Low Emission Zone are older diesel-engine Lorries, buses, coaches, large vans, minibuses and other heavy vehicles such as motor caravans and motorised horse boxes. This also includes vehicles registered outside of Great Britain. Cars and motorcycles are not affected by this scheme. For more information visit www.tfl.gov.uk/modes/driving/low-emission-zone

Vehicles affected by the Low Emission Zone are older diesel-engine lorries, buses, coaches, large vans, minibuses and other heavy vehicles such as motor caravans and motorised horse boxes. This also includes vehicles registered outside of Great Britain. Cars and motorcycles are not affected by this scheme. For more information visit www.tfl.gov.uk

Rail and train travel

Britain's rail network covers all main cities and smaller regional towns. Trains on the network are operated by a few large companies running routes from London to stations all over Britain. Therefore smaller companies that run routes in regional areas. You can find up-to-the-minute information about routes, fares and train times on the National Rail Enquiries website (www.nationalrail.co.uk). For detailed information about routes and services, refer to the train operators' websites (see page 293).

Railway passes

BritRail offer a wide selection of passes and tickets giving you the freedom to travel on all National Rail services. Passes can also include sleeper services, city and attraction passes and boat tours. Passes can usually be purchased from travel agents outside Britain or by visiting the BritRail website www.britrail.com.

Bus and coach travel

Public buses

Every city and town in Britain has a local bus service. These services are privatised and managed by separate companies. The largest bus companies in Britain are First (www.firstgroup.com/ukbus), Stagecoach (www.stagecoachbus.com) and Arriva (www.arrivabus.co.uk), and run buses in most UK towns. Outside London, buses usually travel to and from the town centre or to the busiest part of town. Most towns have a bus station, where you'll be able to find maps and information about routes. Bus route information may also be posted at bus stops.

Tickets and fares

The cost of a bus ticket normally depends on how far you're travelling. Return fares may be available on some buses, but you would usually need to buy a 'single' ticket for each individual journey.

You can also buy your ticket when boarding a bus by telling the driver where you are going. One-day and weekly travel cards are available in some towns, and these can be purchased from either the driver or from an information centre at the bus station. Tickets are valid for each separate journey rather than for a period of time, so if you get off the bus you'll need to buy a new ticket when getting on another.

Domestic flights

Flying is a time-saving alternative to road or rail when it comes to travelling around Britain. Domestic flights are fast and frequent and there are 33 airports across Britain that operate domestic routes. You will find airports marked on the maps at the front of this guide.

Domestic flight advice

Photo ID is required to travel on domestic flights. However it is advisable to bring your passport as not all airlines will accept other forms of photo identification. Please be aware of the high security measures at all airports in Britain which include include restrictions on items that may be carried in hand luggage. It is important that you check the restrictions in place with your airline prior to travel, as these can vary over time and don't forget to allow adequate time for check-in and boarding on arrival.

Cycling

Cycling is a great way to see some of England's iconic scenery and there are many networks of cycling routes available across England. The National Cycle Network offers over 10,000 miles of walking and cycling routes details for connecting towns and villages, countryside and coast across England. For more information and view these routes see page 289 or visit Sustrans at www.sustrans.org.uk

Think green

If you'd rather leave your car behind and travel by 'green transport' to some of the attractions highlighted in this guide you'll be helping to reduce congestion and pollution as well as supporting conservation charities in their commitment to green travel.

Here are just some of the most popular long distance routes on the 12,000 mile Sustrans National Cycle Network. To see the Network in it's entirety and to find routes near you, visit **www.sustrans.org.uk**

Sustrans is the UK's leading sustainable transport charity working on practical projects to enable people to choose to travel in ways which benefit their health and the environment.

68 National Cycle Network Route Number

Long Distance Routes

(1) Coast & Castles Cycle Route
(2) Pennine Cycleway - North Pennines
(3) Hadrian's Cycleway
(4) Sea to Sea
(5) Pennine Cycleway - South Pennines & the Dales
(6) Derby to York
(7) Hull to Fakenham
(8) East of England
(9) South Midlands Cycle Route
(10) Thames Valley Cycle Route
(11) Garden of England
(12) Downs & Weald Cycle Route
(13) Devon Coast to Coast
(14) The Cornish Way
(15) The West Country Way
(16) The Severn & Thames

Map reproduced from Ordnance Survey material with the permission of Ordnance Survey on behalf of the Controller of Her Majesty's Stationery Office © Crown copyright. Unauthorised reproduction infringes Crown copyright and may lead to prosecution or civil proceedings.
Licence number 100020852 (2009)

By car and by train

Distance chart

The distances between towns on the chart below are given to the nearest mile, and are measured along routes based on the quickest travelling time, making maximum use of motorways or dual-carriageway roads. The chart is based upon information supplied by the Automobile Association.

To calculate the distance in kilometres multiply the mileage by 1.6
For example: Brighton to Dover
82 miles x 1.6 =131.2 kilometres

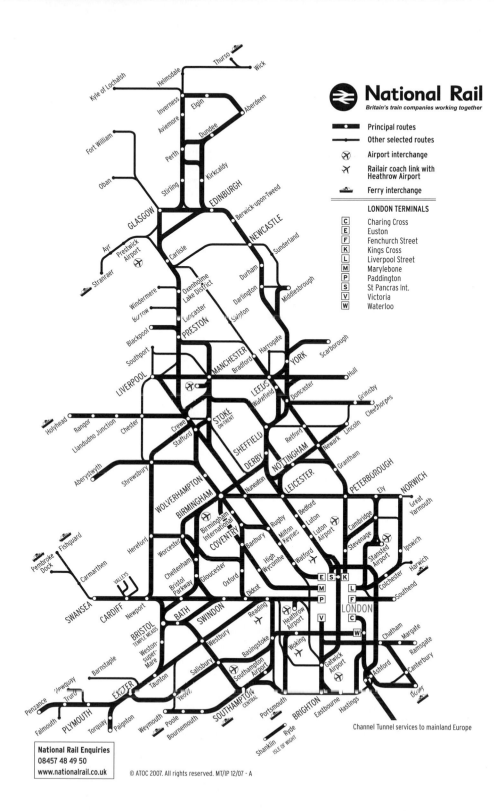

National Rail
Britain's train companies working together

	Principal routes
	Other selected routes
⊗	**Airport interchange**
✈	**Railair coach link with Heathrow Airport**
⛴	**Ferry interchange**

LONDON TERMINALS

C Charing Cross
E Euston
F Fenchurch Street
K Kings Cross
L Liverpool Street
M Marylebone
P Paddington
S St Pancras Int.
V Victoria
W Waterloo

Channel Tunnel services to mainland Europe

National Rail Enquiries
08457 48 49 50
www.nationalrail.co.uk

© ATOC 2007. All rights reserved. MT/IP 12/07 - A

Travel information

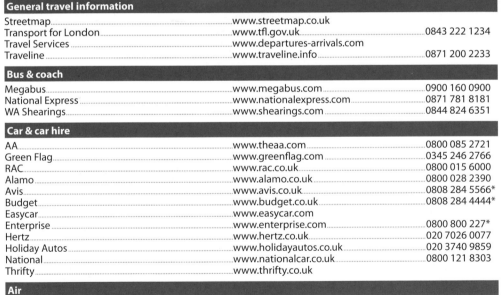

General travel information

Streetmap	www.streetmap.co.uk	
Transport for London	www.tfl.gov.uk	0843 222 1234
Travel Services	www.departures-arrivals.com	
Traveline	www.traveline.info	0871 200 2233

Bus & coach

Megabus	www.megabus.com	0900 160 0900
National Express	www.nationalexpress.com	0871 781 8181
WA Shearings	www.shearings.com	0844 824 6351

Car & car hire

AA	www.theaa.com	0800 085 2721
Green Flag	www.greenflag.com	0345 246 2766
RAC	www.rac.co.uk	0800 015 6000
Alamo	www.alamo.co.uk	0800 028 2390
Avis	www.avis.co.uk	0808 284 5566*
Budget	www.budget.co.uk	0808 284 4444*
Easycar	www.easycar.com	
Enterprise	www.enterprise.com	0800 800 227*
Hertz	www.hertz.co.uk	020 7026 0077
Holiday Autos	www.holidayautos.co.uk	020 3740 9859
National	www.nationalcar.co.uk	0800 121 8303
Thrifty	www.thrifty.co.uk	

Air

Aurigny	www.aurigny.com	0148 182 2886*
Blue Islands (Channel Islands)	www.blueislands.com	01234 589 200
BMI	www.bmiregional.com	0330 333 7998
British Airways	www.ba.com	0844 493 0787
British International Helicopters	www.britishinternationalhelicopters.com	0845 356 3007
CityJet	www.cityjet.com	020 3481 1259*
Eastern Airways	www.easternairways.com	08703 669100
Easyjet	www.easyjet.com	0843 104 5000
Flybe	www.flybe.com	0871 700 2000*
Jet2.com	www.jet2.com	0333 300 0042
Monarch Airlines	www.monarch.co.uk	0333 003 0700
Ryanair	www.ryanair.com	0871 246 0000
Skybus (Isles of Scilly)	www.islesofscilly-travel.co.uk	0173 633 4220
Thomsonfly	www.thomsonfly.com	020 3451 2688
Virgin Atlantic	www.virginatlantic.com	0344 209 7777*

Train

National Rail Enquiries	www.nationalrail.co.uk	03457 48 49 50
Trainline	www.trainline.co.uk	0871 244 1545
UK train operating companies	www.rail.co.uk	
Arriva Trains	www.arrlva.co.uk	0344 800 4411
c2c	www.c2c-online.co.uk	0345 744 422
Chiltern Railways	www.chilternrailways.co.uk	0845 600 5165
CrossCountry	www.crosscountrytrains.co.uk	0844 811 0124
East Midlands Trains	www.eastmidlandstrains.co.uk	0345 712 5678
Eurostar	www.eurostar.com	08432 186 186*
First Great Western	www.gwr.com	0845 700 0125
Gatwick Express	www.gatwickexpress.com	0845 850 1530
Greater Anglia	www.greateranglia.co.uk	0345 600 7245
Heathrow Connect	www.heathrowconnect.com	0345 604 1515
Heathrow Express	www.heathrowexpress.com	0845 600 1515
Thames Link Railway	www.thameslinkrailway.com	0845 026 4700
Hull Trains	www.hulltrains.co.uk	0345 026 4077
London Midlands	www.londonmidland.com	0121 634 2040
Merseyrail	www.merseyrail.org	0151 555 1111
Northern Rail	www.northernrailway.co.uk	0800 200 6060
ScotRail	www.scotrail.co.uk	0344 811 0141
South Eastern Trains	www.southeasternrailway.co.uk	0345 322 7021
South West Trains	www.southwesttrains.co.uk	0345 6000 650
Southern	www.southernrailway.com	0845 127 2920
Stansted Express	www.stanstedexpress.com	0345 600 7245
Translink	www.translink.co.uk	028 9066 6630
Transpennine Express	www.tpexpress.co.uk	0345 600 1671
Virgin Trains	www.virgintrains.co.uk	0344 556 5650

Ferry

Ferry Information	www.discoverferries.com	0207 436 2449
Condor Ferries	www.condorferries.co.uk	0845 609 1024*
Steam Packet Company	www.steam-packet.com	08722 992 992*
Isles of Scilly Travel	www.islesofscilly-travel.co.uk	0845 710 5555
Red Funnel	www.redfunnel.co.uk	0844 844 9988
Wight Link	www.wightlink.co.uk	0871 376 1000

Phone numbers listed are for general enquiries unless otherwise stated.
* Booking line only

David Bellamy
Conservation Award

BRONZE · SILVER · GOLD

Parks wishing to enter for a David Bellamy Conservation Award must complete a detailed questionnaire covering different aspects of their environmental policies, and describe what positive conservation steps they have taken. The park must also undergo an independent audit from a local wildlife or conservation body which is familiar with the area. Final assessments and the appropriate level of any award are then made personally by Professor Bellamy.

Parks with a current 2016/17 Bellamy Award offer a variety of accommodation from pitches for touring caravans, motor homes and tents, to caravan holiday homes, holiday lodges and cottages for rent or to buy. Holiday parks with these awards are not just those in quiet corners of the countryside. Amongst the winners are much larger centres in popular holiday areas that offer a wide range of entertainments and attractions.

The parks listed on the following pages all have a detailed entry in this guide and have received a Gold, Silver or Bronze David Bellamy Conservation Award. Use the Index by Property Name starting on page 407 to find the page number.

A full list of award-winning parks is available at www.bellamyparks.co.uk or www.ukparks.com

Wooda Farm Holiday Park	Gold	Bude	South West
Ladram Bay Holiday Park	Gold	Budleigh Salterton	South West
Harrow Wood Farm Caravan Park	Gold	Christchurch	South West
Cofton Country Holidays	Gold	Dawlish	South West
Castle Brake Holiday Park	Silver	Exeter	South West
Halse Farm Caravan & Tent Park	Silver	Exmoor	South West
Porlock Caravan Park	Gold	Minehead	South West
Watergate Bay Touring Park	Gold	Newquay	South West
Tehidy Holiday Park	Gold	Redruth	South West
Langstone Manor Holiday Park	Gold	Tavistock	South West
Trethem Mill Touring Park	Gold	Truro	South West

Trevarth Holiday Park	Silver	Truro	South West
Hurley Riverside Park	Gold	Maidenhead	South East
Whitefield Forest Touring Park	Gold	Ryde	South East
Appuldurcombe Gardens Holiday Park	Gold	Ventnor	South East
Clippesby Hall	Gold	Clippesby	East of England
Peewit Caravan Park	Gold	Felixstowe	East of England
Vauxhall Holiday Park	Gold	Great Yarmouth	East of England
Searles Leisure Resort	Gold	Hunstanton	East of England
Rivendale Caravan & Leisure Park	Gold	Ashbourne	East Midlands
Beech Croft Farm Caravan & Camping Park	Gold	Buxton	East Midlands
Darwin Forest Country Park	Gold	Matlock	East Midlands
Skegness Water Leisure Park	Gold	Skegness	East Midlands
Island Meadow Caravan Park	Gold	Isle of Sheppey	Heart of England
Cayton Village Caravan Park Ltd	Gold	Scarborough	Yorkshire
Northcliffe & Seaview Holiday Parks	Gold	Whitby	Yorkshire
Eastham Hall Caravan Park	Gold	Lytham St Annes	North West
Newby Bridge Country Caravan Park	Silver	Newby Bridge	North West
Moorlands Caravan Park	Silver	Oldham	North West
Waterfoot Caravan Park	Gold	Penrith	North West
Park Cliffe Camping & Caravan Estate	Gold	Windermere	North West

If you have
access needs…

Guests with hearing, visual or mobility needs can feel confident about booking accommodation that participates in the National Accessible Scheme (NAS).

Look out for the NAS symbols which are included throughout the accommodation directory. Using the NAS could help make the difference between a good holiday and a perfect one!

For more information on the NAS and tips & ideas on holiday travel in England, go to: www.visitengland.com/accessforall

National Accessible Scheme Index

Establishments with a detailed entry in this guide who participate in the National Accessible Scheme are listed below. At the front of the guide you can find information about the scheme. Establishments are listed alphabetically by place name.

Mobility level 1

Abingdon-on-Thames, South East	**Abbey Guest House ★★★★ Gold**	124
Ainsdale, North West	**Willowbank Holiday Home and Touring Park ★★★★★**	323
Ashbourne, East Midlands	**Rivendale Caravan & Leisure Park ★★★★ Silver**	209
Ashbourne, East Midlands	**Peak District Spa ★★★★ Silver**	208
Bamburgh, North East	**Outchester & Ross Farm Cottages ★★★★ Gold**	341
Berwick-upon-Tweed, North East	**Fenham Farm Coastal Bed & Breakfast ★★★ Gold**	343
Bicker, East Midlands	**Supreme Inns ★★★**	216
Bowes, North East	**Mellwaters Barn ★★★★ Gold**	338
Burton Upon Trent, Heart of England	**Wychnor Park Country Club ★★★★**	244
Cambridge, East of England	**The Bull Pen ★★★★**	172
Canterbury, South East	**Broome Park Golf and Country Club ★★★★**	119
Carlisle, North West	**The Tranquil Otter ★★★★ Gold**	306
Carnforth, North West	**Pine Lake Resort ★★★★**	319
Chichester, South East	**4 Canon Lane ★★★ Silver**	131
Cornriggs, North East	**Cornriggs Cottages ★★★★★**	338
Cromer, East of England	**Cromer Country Club ★★★★**	178
Dilhorne, Heart of England	**Little Summerhill Cottages ★★★★**	245
Falmouth, South West	**Mylor Harbourside Holidays ★★★★**	49
Harrogate, Yorkshire	**Helme Pasture Lodges & Cottages ★★★★**	271
Hereford, Heart of England	**Monnington House Monnington on Wye ★★★★ Gold**	240
Hogsthorpe, East Midlands	**Helsey House Holiday Cottages ★★★★**	217
Holsworthy, South West	**Woodford Bridge Country Club ★★★★ Gold**	65
Lancaster, North West	**Thurnham Hall ★★★★**	320
Maidstone, South East	**Coldblow Farm ★★★★**	122
Malton, Yorkshire	**Walnut Garth ★★★★ Gold**	275
Ormskirk, North West	**Martin Lane Farm Holiday Cottages ★★★ Gold**	322
Porthtowan, South West	**Rosehill Lodges ★★★★ Gold**	55
Portsmouth, South East	**Royal Maritime Club ★★★**	116
Southport, North West	**Sandy Brook Farm ★★★**	325
Woodhall Spa, East Midlands	**Village Limits Country Pub, Restaurant & Motel ★★★ Silver**	221

Mobility level 2

Abingdon-on-Thames, South East	**Abbey Guest House ★★★★ Gold**	124
Ainsdale, North West	**Willowbank Holiday Home and Touring Park ★★★★★**	323
Ashbourne, East Midlands	**Rivendale Caravan & Leisure Park ★★★ Silver**	209
Ashbourne, East Midlands	**Peak District Spa ★★★★ Silver**	208
Bowes, North East	**Mellwaters Barn ★★★★ Gold**	338

Mobility level 3

Visual impairment level 1

Hearing impairment level 1

Hearing impairment level 2

Gold and Silver Award Winners

Establishments with a detailed entry in this guide that have achieved recognition of exceptional quality are listed below. Establishments are listed alphabetically by place name.

South West

GOLD AWARD

Barnsley, **Barnsley House** ★★★★	81
Bath, **Marlborough House Guest House** ★★★★	86
Binegar, **Spindle Cottage Holidays** ★★★★	88
Bude, **Tamar Valley Cottages** ★★★★	46
Bude, **Whalesborough Cottages & Spa** ★★★★★	47
Bude, **Wooda Farm Holiday Park** ★★★★★	47
Cirencester, **The Stables** ★★★★★	82
Dartmouth, **Cladda House B&B and**	
Self Catering Apartments ★★★★	61
Dawlish, **Cofton Country Holidays** ★★★★	62
Holsworthy, **Woodford Bridge Country Club** ★★★★	65
Lacock, **Piccadilly Caravan Park Ltd** ★★★★	93
Mitcheldean, **Holme House Barn** ★★★★	84
Newquay, **Forty Eight The Penthouse** ★★★★★	52
Okehampton, **Knole Farm** ★★★★	67
Okehampton, **Peartree Cottage** ★★★★	67
Padstow, **Sunday & School Cottages** ★★★★	53
Porthtowan, **Rosehill Lodges** ★★★★★	55
Ringstead, **Upton Grange Holiday Cottages** ★★★★	78
Sidmouth,	
The Barn & Pinn Cottage Guest House ★★★★	70
St. Just in Roseland,	
Trethem Mill Touring Park ★★★★★	57
Stow-on-the-Wold, **Broad Oak Cottages** ★★★★★	84
Stroud, **The Close B&B** ★★★★	85

Tetbury, **Calcot Manor Hotel & Spa** ★★★★	85
Torquay, **Long Barn Luxury Holiday Cottages** ★★★★	73
Torquay, **The Downs, Babbacombe** ★★★★	73
Wareham, **Durdle Door Holiday Cottages** ★★★★	78
Wedmore, **Pear Tree Cottages** ★★★★	92

SILVER AWARD

Bath, **Pulteney House** ★★★★	87
Blandford Forum, **The Crown Hotel** ★★★★	75
Bridgwater, **Gurney Manor Mill** ★★★★	88
Charlestown, **The Pier House Hotel** ★★★	48
Lands End, **Bosavern House** ★★★★	50
St. Minver, **Tredower Barton** ★★★	57
Teignmouth, **Ness House** ★★★★	71
Truro, **Spring Cottage B&B** ★★★★	58
Wareham, **Lulworth Cove Inn** ★★★★	80
Weymouth, **Smugglers Inn** ★★★★	80
Wimborne, **1777 Bedrooms and**	
Breakfast at The Albion ★★★★	81

South East

GOLD AWARD

Abingdon-on-Thames, **Abbey Guest House** ★★★★	124
Chichester, **Laneside** ★★★★	132
Crowborough, **Hodges** ★★★★★	133
Edenbridge,	
Hever Castle Luxury Bed & Breakfast ★★★★★	120

LONDON

EAST OF ENGLAND

EAST MIDLANDS

HEART OF ENGLAND

GOLD AWARD

Hereford, **Monnington House Monnington on Wye** ★★★★	240
Kington, **White Heron Properties** ★★★★★	240
Ludlow, **Castle House Lodgings** ★★★★★	242
Ludlow, **Sutton Court Farm Cottages** ★★★	242
Ludlow, **The Silver Pear Apartments** ★★★★	243
Malvern, **Rhydd Barn** ★★★	249
Rugeley, **Colton House** ★★★★★	246
Sutton, **Long Cover Cottage & The Coach House** ★★★★	250
Tenbury Wells, **Rochford Park Cottages** ★★★★	250

SILVER AWARD

Broseley, **Broseley House** ★★★★	241
Stratford-upon-Avon, **Adelphi Guest House** ★★★★	247
Stratford-upon-Avon, **Avonlea** ★★★★	248

Yorkshire

GOLD AWARD

Ingleby Greenhow, **Ingleby Manor** ★★★★★	273
Kirkbymoorside, **Cowldyke Farm** ★★★★	273
Kirkbymoorside, **Surprise View Cottage, Field Barn Cottage & Lowna Farmhouse** ★★★★	274
Malton, **Home Farm Holiday Cottages** ★★★★	274
Malton, **Walnut Garth** ★★★★	275
Nunthorpe, **Blackthorn Gate** ★★★★	275
Pickering, **Kale Pot Cottage** ★★★★	276
Whitby, **Forest Lodge Farm** ★★★★★	283
Whitby, **Lemon Cottage** ★★★★	283
York, **The Blue Rooms** ★★★★★	286
York, **York Lakeside Lodges** ★★★★★	286

SILVER AWARD

Beverley, **Tickton Grange Hotel & Restaurant** ★★★★	266
Skipton, **The Coniston Hotel, Country Estate & Spa** ★★★★	280
Thirsk, **The Gallery Bed & Breakfast** ★★★★	282

North West

GOLD AWARD

Blackburn, **Stanley House Hotel & Spa** ★★★★	316
Borrowdale, **Over Brandelhow** ★★★★	305
Carlisle, **Brackenhill Tower & Jacobean Cottage** ★★★★★	306
Carlisle, **The Tranquil Otter** ★★★★★	306
Chester, **Mitchell's of Chester Guest House** ★★★★★	302
Grange-over-Sands, **Clare House** ★★	307
Ormskirk, **Martin Lane Farm Holiday Cottages** ★★★★	322
Rosthwaite, **Scafell Hotel** ★★	312
Ullswater, **Hartsop Fold Holiday Lodges** ★★★	313
Ullswater, **Hillcroft Holiday Park** ★★★★	313
Windermere, **Park Cliffe Camping & Caravan Estate** ★★★★★	315

SILVER AWARD

Blackpool, **4 Star Phildene Blackpool** ★★★★	316

North East

GOLD AWARD

Bamburgh, **Outchester & Ross Farm Cottages** ★★★★	341
Beamish, **Riding Farm Cottages** ★★★★	346
Berwick-upon-Tweed, **Fenham Farm Coastal Bed & Breakfast** ★★★★	343
Bowes, **Mellwaters Barn** ★★★★	338
Craster, **Craster Tower Penthouse Apartment** ★★★★	344
Newton-by-the-Sea, **Link House Farm Holiday Cottages** ★★★★	345
Newton-by-the-Sea, **Sea Winds** ★★★★	346

SILVER AWARD

Berwick-upon-Tweed, **Alannah House** ★★★★	342
Durham, **Castle View Guest House** ★★★★	339

Walkers and cyclists welcome

Look out for quality-assessed accommodation displaying the Walkers Welcome and Cyclists Welcome signs.

Participants in these schemes actively encourage and support walking and cycling. In addition to special meal arrangements and helpful information, they'll provide a water supply to wash off the mud, an area for drying wet clothing and footwear, maps and books to look up cycling and walking routes and even an emergency puncture-repair kit! Bikes can also be locked up securely undercover.

The standards for these schemes have been developed in partnership with the tourist boards in Northern Ireland, Scotland and Wales, so wherever you're travelling in the UK you'll receive the same welcome.

Walkers Welcome & Cyclists Welcome

Establishments participating in the Walkers Welcome and Cyclists Welcome schemes provide special facilities and actively encourage these recreations. Accommodation with a detailed entry in this guide is listed below. Place names are listed Alphabetically.

▶️🚲 Walkers Welcome & Cyclists Welcome

Place	Establishment	Page
Abingdon-on-Thames, South East	**Abbey Guest House ★★★★Gold**	124
Alford, East Midlands	**Woodthorpe Leisure Park ★★★★★**	216
Appleby-in-Westmorland, North West	**The Hollies ★★★★**	304
Ashbourne, East Midlands	**Rivendale Caravan & Leisure Park ★★★★Silver**	209
Ashbourne, East Midlands	**Peak District Spa ★★★★Silver**	208
Ashby-de-la-Zouch, East Midlands	**Forest Lodge ★★★★**	214
Bamford, East Midlands	**Yorkshire Bridge Inn ★★★★Silver**	210
Belsay, North East	**Shortflatt Farm Cottage ★★★★**	342
Berwick-upon-Tweed, North East	**Alannah House ★★★★Silver**	342
Berwick-upon-Tweed, North East	**Fenham Farm Coastal Bed & Breakfast ★★★★Gold**	343
Bicker, East Midlands	**Supreme Inns ★★★**	216
Bodham, East of England	**Rookery Farm Norfolk ★★★★Gold**	177
Bognor Regis, South East	**White Horses Bed & Breakfast ★★★★**	130
Brooke, East Midlands	**America Lodge ★★★**	224
Buxton, East Midlands	**Pyegreave Cottage ★★★★Gold**	212
Cambridge, East of England	**The Bull Pen ★★★★**	172
Canterbury, South East	**Kipps Independent Hostel ★★★**	119
Castleton, East Midlands	**Riding House Farm Cottages ★★★★★Gold**	212
Cirencester, South West	**Riverside House ★★★★**	82
Clifton, North West	**George and Dragon ★★★★**	307
Clun, Heart of England	**The White Horse Inn ★★★**	241
Dalby, Yorkshire	**South Moor Farm ★★★★**	267
Dawlish, South West	**Lady's Mile Touring and Camping Park ★★★★**	63
Dawlish, South West	**Cofton Country Holidays ★★★★**	62
Dawlish, South West	**Oakcliff Holiday Park ★★★★**	64
Dunster, South West	**Yarn Market Hotel ★★★**	90
Fareham, South East	**Cowes View Coastguard Cottage ★★★★**	113
Field Dalling, East of England	**Hard Farm Barns ★★★★Gold**	179
Filey, Yorkshire	**Filey Holiday Cottages ★★★**	269
Giggleswick, Yorkshire	**Ivy Cottage (Giggleswick) Limited ★★★★**	270
Grange-over-Sands, North West	**Cumbria Grand Hotel ★★★**	308
Great Yarmouth, East of England	**Clippesby Hall ★★★★★**	180
Great Yarmouth, East of England	**Clippesby Hall Holiday Park ★★★★★**	181
Hereford, Heart of England	**Monnington House Monnington on Wye ★★★★Gold**	240
Hitcham, East of England	**Stanstead Hall ★★★★**	190
Kersey, East of England	**Wheelwrights Cottage ★★★★★**	191

Louth, East Midlands	**Louth Barn ★★★★ Gold**	219
Ludlow, Heart of England	**Sutton Court Farm Cottages ★★★★ Gold**	242
Ludlow, Heart of England	**The Silver Pear Apartments ★★★★ Gold**	243
Lyme Regis, South West	**Cecilia's Cottage ★★★★★**	77
Maidstone, South East	**Coldblow Farm ★★★★**	122
Midhurst, South East	**Long Meadow ★★★★**	135
Mitcheldean, South West	**Holme House Barn ★★★★ Gold**	84
Mundesley, East of England	**Overcliff Lodge ★★★★ Silver**	183
North Dalton, Yorkshire	**Old Cobbler's Cottage ★★★**	267
Nunthorpe, Yorkshire	**Blackthorn Gate ★★★★ Gold**	275
Okehampton, South West	**Peartree Cottage ★★★★ Gold**	67
Pickering, Yorkshire	**Kale Pot Cottage ★★★★ Gold**	276
Plymouth, South West	**Caraneal ★★★★**	69
Ringstead, South West	**Upton Grange Holiday Cottages ★★★★ Gold**	78
Rosthwaite, North West	**Scafell Hotel ★★★ Gold**	312
Saltburn-by-the-Sea, Yorkshire	**The Arches Country House ★★★★**	277
Seahouses, North East	**1, 2 & 3 The Old Bakery ★★★**	346
Stroud, South West	**The Close B&B ★★★★ Gold**	85
Tavistock, South West	**Langstone Manor Holiday Park ★★★★★**	70
Tewkesbury, South West	**9 Mill Bank, Accredited**	85
Thirsk, Yorkshire	**The Gallery Bed & Breakfast ★★★★ Silver**	282
Wareham, South West	**Durdle Door Holiday Cottages ★★★★ Gold**	78
Waterhouses, Heart of England	**Greenside Cottages ★★★★**	246
Whitby, Yorkshire	**Forest Lodge Farm ★★★★★ Gold**	283
Worston, North West	**Angram Green Holiday Cottages ★★★★**	322

Walkers Welcome

Buxton, East Midlands	**Old Hall Hotel ★★★**	211
Eype, South West	**Eype's Mouth Country Hotel ★★★**	77
Haworth, Yorkshire	**Leeming Wells ★★★★**	287
Hexham, North East	**Braemar ★★★★**	344
Kersey, East of England	**Cressland ★★★★ Gold**	190
Malvern, Heart of England	**Rhydd Barn ★★★★ Gold**	249
Pershore, Heart of England	**Garth Cottage ★★★★**	249
Ullswater, North West	**Hillcroft Holiday Park ★★★★ Gold**	313
Wedmore, South West	**Pear Tree Cottages ★★★★ Gold**	92

Welcome Pets!

Want to travel with your faithful companion? Look out for accommodation displaying the **Welcome Pets!** sign. Participants in this scheme go out of their way to meet the needs of guests bringing dogs, cats and/or small birds. In addition to providing water and food bowls, torches or nightlights, spare leads and pet washing facilities, they'll buy in food on request, and offer toys, treats and bedding. They'll also have information on pet friendly attractions, pubs, restaurants and recreation. Of course, not everyone is able to offer suitable facilities for every pet, so do check if there are any restrictions on type, size and number of animals when you book.

Look out for the following symbol in the entry.

Families and Pets Welcome

Establishments participating in the Families Welcome or Welcome Pets! schemes provide special facilities and actively encourage families or guests with pets. Accommodation with a detailed entry in this guide is listed below. Place names are listed alphabetically.

🏠 🐾 Families and Pets Welcome

Ashby-de-la-Zouch, East Midlands	**Forest Lodge ★★★★**	214
Belsay, North East	**Shortflatt Farm Cottage ★★★★**	342
Bodham, East of England	**Rookery Farm Norfolk ★★★★ Gold**	177
Brooke, East Midlands	**America Lodge ★★★**	224
Clifton, North West	**George and Dragon ★★★★**	307
Dalby, Yorkshire	**South Moor Farm ★★★★**	267
Dawlish, South West	**Lady's Mile Touring and Camping Park ★★★★**	63
Filey, Yorkshire	**Filey Holiday Cottages ★★★**	269
Macclesfield, North West	**Cheshire Hunt Holiday Cottages ★★★★**	302
Maidstone, South East	**Coldblow Farm ★★★★**	122
Mitcheldean, South West	**Holme House Barn ★★★★ Gold**	84
Nunthorpe, Yorkshire	**Blackthorn Gate ★★★★ Gold**	275
Okehampton, South West	**Peartree Cottage ★★★ Gold**	67
Ullswater, North West	**Hillcroft Holiday Park ★★★★ Gold**	313
Windermere, North West	**Park Cliffe Camping & Caravan Estate ★★★★★ Gold**	315

Families Welcome

Abingdon-on-Thames, South East	**Abbey Guest House ★★★★Gold**	124
Bicker, East Midlands	**Supreme Inns ★★★**	216
Binegar, South West	**Spindle Cottage Holidays ★★★★Gold**	88
Carlisle, North West	**Brackenhill Tower & Jacobean Cottage ★★★★★Gold**	306
Dawlish, South West	**Oakcliff Holiday Park ★★★★**	64
Edenbridge, South East	**Medley Court - Hever Castle ★★★★Gold**	121
Fakenham, East of England	**2 Westgate Barns ★★★★Gold**	178
Grange-over-Sands, North West	**Cumbria Grand Hotel ★★★**	308
Leek, Heart of England	**Roaches Holiday Cottages ★★★**	245
London SW20, London	**Thalia Holiday Home ★★★★**	154
Louth, East Midlands	**Louth Barn ★★★★Gold**	219
Midhurst, South East	**Long Meadow ★★★★**	135
Otterton, South West	**Ladram Bay Holiday Park ★★★★★**	68
Pin Mill, East of England	**Alma Cottage ★★**	192
Slingsby, Yorkshire	**Robin Hood Caravan Park ★★★★★**	281
St. Austell, South West	**The Old Inn, Pentewan ★★★**	56
Torquay, South West	**Long Barn Luxury Holiday Cottages ★★★★Gold**	73
Wareham, South West	**Durdle Door Holiday Cottages ★★★★Gold**	78
Whitby, Yorkshire	**Forest Lodge Farm ★★★★★Gold**	283

Pets Welcome

Alford, East Midlands	**Woodthorpe Leisure Park ★★★★★**	216
Clun, Heart of England	**The White Horse Inn ★★★**	241
Dunster, South West	**Yarn Market Hotel ★★★**	90
Felixstowe, East of England	**Peewit Caravan Park ★★★★**	190
Field Dalling, East of England	**Hard Farm Barns ★★★★Gold**	179
Harrogate, Yorkshire	**Helme Pasture Lodges & Cottages ★★★★**	271
Kirkby Lonsdale, North West	**Copper Kettle Restaurant & Guest House ★★**	310
North Dalton, Yorkshire	**Old Cobbler's Cottage ★★★**	267
Oakham, East Midlands	**Barnsdale Lodge Hotel ★★★**	224
Scarborough, Yorkshire	**Cayton Village Caravan Park Ltd ★★★★★**	278
Skegness, East Midlands	**Skegness Water Leisure Park ★★★**	219
Staithes, Yorkshire	**Pennysteel Cottage ★★★**	281
Truro, South West	**The Valley ★★★★★**	58

Swimming Pools Index

If you're looking for accommodation with swimming facilities use this index to see at a glance detailed accommodation entries that match your requirement. Establishments are listed alphabetically by place name.

⤳ Outdoor pool

Appleby-in-Westmorland, North West	**Wild Rose Park ★★★★★**	305
Blackpool, North West	**Doric Hotel ★★★**	317
Bude, South West	**Whalesborough Cottages & Spa ★★★★★ Gold**	47
Chipping Campden, South West	**Walnut Tree ★★★★**	82
Crowborough, South East	**Hodges ★★★★★ Gold**	133
Dawlish, South West	**Lady's Mile Touring and Camping Park ★★★★**	63
Dawlish, South West	**Cofton Country Holidays ★★★★**	62
Dawlish, South West	**Cofton Country Holidays ★★★★ Gold**	62
Dawlish, South West	**Oakcliff Holiday Park ★★★★**	64
Great Yarmouth, East of England	**Clippesby Hall ★★★★★**	180
Great Yarmouth, East of England	**Clippesby Hall Holiday Park ★★★★★**	181
Hathersage, East Midlands	**Pat's Cottage ★★★**	213
Hayle, South West	**Beachside Holiday Park ★★★★**	50
Hogsthorpe, East Midlands	**Helsey House Holiday Cottages ★★★★**	217
Hunstanton, East of England	**Searles Leisure Resort ★★★★★**	183
Kington, Heart of England	**White Heron Properties ★★★★★ Gold**	240
Mayfield, South East	**Hoopers Farm Cottage ★★★★**	135
Mersea Island, East of England	**Away Resorts Mersea Island ★★★★★**	174
Moreton-In-Marsh, South West	**Forget Me Not ★★★★**	84
New Milton, New Forest, South East	**Chewton Glen ★★★★★ Gold**	115
Newton Abbot, South West	**Twelve Oaks Farm Caravan Park ★★★★★**	66
Pershore, Heart of England	**Garth Cottage ★★★★**	249
Pewsey, South West	**Huntly's Farmhouse ★★★★**	94
Selsey, South East	**Warner Farm Camping & Touring Park ★★★★★**	138
Selsey, South East	**West Sands Holiday Park (Bunn Leisure) ★★★★**	138
Selsey, South East	**White Horse Holiday Park (Bunn Leisure) ★★★★**	139
Selsey, South East	**Green Lawns Holiday Park (Bunn Leisure) ★★★★★**	137
Tetbury, South West	**Calcot Manor Hotel & Spa ★★★★ Gold**	85
Torquay, South West	**The Osborne Hotel ★★★★**	74
Torquay, South West	**Corbyn Head Hotel ★★★**	72
Torquay, South West	**Livermead House Hotel ★★★**	72
Truro, South West	**The Valley ★★★★★**	58
Wareham, South West	**Durdle Door Holiday Cottages ★★★★ Gold**	78
Watergate Bay, South West	**Watergate Bay Touring Park ★★★★**	58
Weston-super-Mare, South West	**Country View Holiday Park ★★★★**	93
Wroxall, South East	**Appuldurcombe Gardens Holiday Park ★★★★★**	118

Evening Meal Index

The following establishments offer evening meals and all have a detailed entry in this guide.

Index by Property Name

Accommodation with a detailed entry in this guide is listed below.

Index by Place Name

The following places all have detailed accommodation entries in this guide. If the place where you wish to stay is not shown the location maps (starting on page 350) will help you to find somewhere to stay in the area.

Index to Display Advertisers

HUDSON'S MEDIA LIMITED

Published by: Hudson's Media Ltd
35 Thorpe Road, Peterborough, PE3 6AG
Tel: 01733 296910 Fax: 01733 209292

On behalf of: VisitBritain, Sanctuary Buildings, 20 Great Smith Street, London SW1P 3BT

Editorial Contributors: Sarah Greenwood, Kylie Woolgar
Production: Kylie Woolgar
Production Contributors: Kylie Woolgar, Sarah Phillips, Kirsten McInroy, James O'Rawe

Creative: Jamieson Eley
Advertising team: James O'Rawe, Kirsten McInroy
Email: VEguides@hudsons-media.co.uk Tel: 01733 296913
Production System: NVG – leaders in Tourism Technology. www.nvg.net
Printer: Stephens & George, Merthyr Tydfil
Maps: ESR Cartography Ltd
Retail Sales: Compass – Tel: 020 8996 5764

Please note that all references to places to visit, products, services or experiences referred to in the editorial content are suggestions only and are not intended as endorsements of any destination, product, service or experience.

Important note: The information contained in this guide has been published in good faith on the basis of information submitted to VisitBritain by the proprietors of the premises listed, who have paid for their entries to appear. VisitBritian cannot guarantee the accuracy of the information in this guide and accepts no responsibility for any error or misrepresentations. All liability for loss, disappointment, negligence or other damage caused by reliance on the information contained in this guide, or in the event of bankruptcy, or liquidation, or cessation of trading of any company, individual, or firm mentioned is hereby excluded to the fullest extent permitted by law. Please check carefully all prices, ratings and other details before confirming a reservation.